The Contemplative Brain

Meditation, Phenomenology and Self-Discovery
from a Neuroanthropological Point of View

by

Charles D. Laughlin, Ph.D.

Daily Grail Publishing

The Contemplative Brain: Meditation, Phenomenology and Self-Discovery
from a Neuroanthropological Point of View

ISBN: 978-0-9946176-9-9

Daily Grail Publishing
Brisbane, Australia
publications@dailygrail.com
www.dailygrail.com

CONTENTS

PART FOUR: THE MYSTICAL BRAIN

ACKNOWLEDGEMENTS

There are so many folks who have helped me along the way, yet none may be blamed for my failure to understand or for facts I've misspoken. I do want to thank these friends and teachers, for they have been influential in my development, and in forming the perspective I try to express in this book. Considerable thanks go to Patricia Kolarik who taught me hatha yoga and thus triggered so many subsequent adventures. Many thanks to my meditation teachers, Tarchin Hearn, Lama Sherab (Paul Curtis), the late Professor LeRoy Johnson, the late Karma Tenzin Dorje Namgyal Rinpoche, a Canadian meditation master *par excellence*, the late Chogye Trichen Rinpoche, Sakya meditation master of Nepal who was my preceptor and friend, and by way of their writings, philosophers Edmund Husserl and Alfred North Whitehead. I have been blessed with friends and colleagues who have fed my questing brain over the years. To the late Rodney Malham, landscaper, artist and contemplative supreme, and to his lady, Margaret Stephens, master psychotherapist, who has helped me understand the full costs of childhood trauma and the pervasive problem of dissociation in our civilization, go my eternal gratitude. I am deeply indebted to my friend and consummate physicist Harold E. Puthoff who patiently nurtured what little understanding of quantum physics that I employ. My blessing on Robert G. "Bob" Jahn, Brenda Dunn, Stanley Krippner, Adam Rock and Dean Radin for teaching me so much about parapsychology and the "spooky" abilities of the human mind. Fellow anthropologists, Ivan A. Brady, Jason Throop, Mimi George, Robert A. Rubinstein, Melanie Takahashi, Robin Rodd, Robert Tonkinson, Robbie E. Davis-Floyd, Tracey Prentice, Michael Winkelman and his lady, Cindy Winkelman, Lisa Mertz, Paul Devereux and his lady Charla Devereux, Jean-Guy Goulet, the late Barbara W. Lex, have all aided in my growth of understanding about human consciousness, alternative states of consciousness, rituals, and the brain. And of course, as always, I am so grateful for the years I could work with my late friends and original biogenetic structuralist teammates, John McManus and Eugene G. d'Aquili.

Everybody Has One

Early in this book, Charles Laughlin recalls that his impetus to write had dried up and he went on to enjoy painting and kayaking. But his muse was simply taking a vacation. Readers of this book can be grateful to that muse because *The Contemplative Brain* is a unique contribution to the study of human consciousness. Indeed, Laughlin reminds his readers that "everybody has one," even though they may not know how to utilize its potential. Laughlin devotes an entire chapter to his personal odyssey with lucid dreaming, mind-altering drugs, and—most importantly—meditation that, in his experience, is a major route to contemplation.

This book provides a road map for those who want to study their own conscious processes, namely a map of contemplation and self-awareness, and the brain that mediates both. Not everyone will choose to follow that map, but the road map is there should they ever want to use it. The map's matrices are neurophenomenology (a term used to describe what happens when phenomenology is linked to the brain) and neuroanthropology (a term used when anthropology forms a similar link). Phenomenology (the study of conscious experiences on their own terms) is not popular in contemporary discourse and is even derided as "non-scientific" by major players in the scientific establishment.

Numerous other readers will take offense when they turn the pages of this book. It took decades for mainstream science to acknowledge consciousness as a topic worthy of study, and only then if it could be quantified and examined under laboratory conditions. Instead, Laughlin confesses that what he has learned about consciousness comes from meditation, contemplation, neurophenomenology, neuroanthropology and direct ethnographic fieldwork. Even worse, he admits to studying his own processes, a method that was relegated to the scrap heap of psychology early in the 20th century when "introspection" was deemed unreliable.

Social constructivists, who hold that society imposes identity and personality on a "blank slate" brain will be offended when Laughlin writes that enculturation is an adaptive process by which the organism whose brain is already structured by inheritance learns by active interactions with its social environment. Indeed, he insists that there is no such thing as a totally plastic neural structure. Simply put, humans never leave their biological nature behind.

All of these objections to his approach are marks of what Laughlin calls a "monophasic culture," one that privileges information that results from rational, logical, linear cognition and the ensuing educational institutions. But Laughlin sees merit in polyphasic cultures, those that give credence to insights gained by such resources as intuition, dreams, myths, fantasy, rapture, shamanic journeying, ritual drama, psychedelic visions, and—dare the terms be used—mystical experiences and the primordial mind. All these ways of knowing may be evoked by ritual techniques, most of which are thousands of years old. Rituals commonly incorporate "drivers" that evoke changes in brains states and lead to extraordinary experiences. I often refer to the five major "d" drivers – dreams, drumming, dancing, drugs, and deprivation.

Those who regard Jung as an on-again/off-again psychotic who spawned a cult will be displeased by Laughlin's statement that his own concept of "neurognosis" is a direct reflection of Jung's description of the way that humans process information. Jungians will be pleased at Laughlin's employment of Jung's "animus" and "anima" terms but may not be happy with his statement that Jung's hermeneutic is "culturally loaded." (Indeed, I think that the "animus" and "anima" vary from culture to culture.) In Laughlin's words, we are born to be enculturated and "archetypes" are no exception to this principle.

Theoreticians of consciousness studies may well be miffed by Laughlin's utilization of such terms as "energy centers," "sensorium," "pixels," "monad entanglement," and "implicate nature," all of which he finds essential to a clear understanding of consciousness. Laughlin describes what I see as a "dance" between "objective" and "subjective" accounts of consciousness. Conscious acts can be triggered by physiological events, which in turn can be evoked by conscious acts.

Laughlin is an equal opportunity offender and at least two other themes are bound to provoke some readers to shut the book and stubbornly refuse to read any further. Laughlin is unapologetic when he discusses parapsychology and such manifestations as "remote viewing" and "telepathy." And when he ties these topics to quantum physics, he will lose a few more readers. Of the readers who are left, some will drop out when Laughlin advocates love and compassion as counter-forces to anxiety, greed, hatred, and other of humankind's ills. However, Charles Darwin did not like the term "the survival of the fittest," but emphasized the role of moral sensitivity in evolution. He frequently used such terms as "love" and "cooperation," especially in his later writings. So, if Laughlin is accused of solipsism in using the same terms, he is in good company!

Stanley Krippner, Ph.D.
March, 2018
Saybrook University

INTRODUCTION

An Imperfection of Duty

You cannot hope to build a better world without improving the individuals. To that end, each of us must work for his own improvement and, at the same time, share a general responsibility for all humanity, our particular duty being to aid those to whom we think we can be most useful.

– Marie Curie (2012[1923]: 83)

As a child I felt myself to be alone, and I am still, because I know things and must hint at things which others apparently know nothing of, and for the most part do not want to know.

– C. G. Jung, *Memories, Dreams, Reflections*

My family, my society, my fellow human beings, made it possible for me to pursue the study of brain, consciousness and culture. Like every other scientist with a sense of social responsibility, I have felt this debt keenly, and have tried in various ways to share the results of my quest as a kind of imperfect payback. I thought I had done with that duty a few years ago when the impetus to write dried up and I went on to more introverted passions like painting and kayaking. But the muse was not through with me and seems to have only been taking a vacation. I understand now that there is more to say, to share, if only I have the wit to find the words to communicate more than I have already done.

I consider this urge to be an imperfect duty, for I know that the medium of the written word is very limiting, for language operates upon metaphors, and when the metaphors one uses are imperfectly shared with others, the potential for misunderstanding is great. Language evolved among hominins to augment potentially shareable experiences. Yet, if the experiences I am trying to describe have little context in the experience of the reader, communication fails, and worse, can create a presumed understanding when none exists. I fully realize the truth of what Wittgenstein meant when he penned, "What we cannot speak about we must pass over in silence." It is always thus of course. Language never evolved to communicate experience *in toto*, and it is simply incapable of doing so. Language is designed to augment experience, not replace it. Language works as a medium for both sharing information between conscious beings who share considerable experience in common, and to get things done in a social world (Austin 1975). Talking appeals to the imagination of the listener who then may or may not be able to reconstruct a quasi-memory of the experience being described. The trouble with language is that if the experience behind the speaker's description and the quasi-memory of the listener vary too much, the listener may now feel he has understood the speaker when in fact he has sorely missed the mark. Throughout most of the prehistory of our species, this was likely not a huge problem because primitive humans shared most of the experiences upon which accurate communication depended. This would have also applied, as it does today, in societies that credence experiences had in *alternative states of consciousness* (ASC) such as dreaming, visions, trances, drug trips and so forth.

Yet if we take Wittgenstein's dictum too far, it becomes an invitation to esotericism of the sort that is so rife in New Age accounts of mysticism. This is where wit and perspective come in. Where straightforward description ends, synecdoche, metaphor, metonymy, symbolism and other linguistic devices must suffice. Criticism that these literary tools are "unscientific" are in my opinion cop-outs to effective communication. This is especially true in the case of the science of consciousness which is populated by many researchers who reject with great disdain approaches to the study of the mind outside the laboratory. I once took a founder of modern cultural neuroscience to task for not including anthropology within the new field's interdisciplinary framework. He replied in all seriousness that they only include "empirical" sciences (read disciplines that carry out research in laboratories and perform "controlled" experiments) and that anthropology isn't "empirical." I was utterly gob-smacked. He spoke as if naturalistic disciplines are beyond the pale, outside the scope of modern science. By his reckoning, Charles Darwin would be shown the door. This cultural neuroscientist's view, representative of many in experimental science, is silly when it comes to studying consciousness, or any other naturally occurring experiential focus for that matter. When it comes to studying consciousness, everybody has one, and with the requisite intention and skill, can observe consciousness from the inside out, so to speak. That activity is what's called phenomenology—which is, as we shall see, a special case of contemplation. When linked to the study of the brain this activity becomes neurophenomenology (see Laughlin, McManus and d'Aquili 1990; Varela 1996; Gordon 2014), and when linked to anthropology becomes phenomenological anthropology (Jackson 1996; Desjarlais and Throop 2011). I will have more to say about the role of language, and especially the phenomenology of language, in the Conclusion of the book.

Contemplation and Meditation

One of the most remarkable facts about our brain is that it is designed to know itself. The brain did not evolve to do this, but rather to create and process an experienced reality to adapt to the outer world. In other words, we have evolved a brain that "hallucinates" an experienced world that is remarkably accurate from the point of view of adaptation (Seth 2017). Yet, by way of an exaptation, the very same facilities that allow the brain to perceive and come to know the outer world allow it to do the same for the inner world—the internal world of being. This book takes a close look at how our brain can study its own processes. When we study how our brain creates our world of experience by interoception, we call this "contemplation" utilizing self-awareness. Contemplation is often used as though it is synonymous with the term "meditation," but this is not true. Contemplation does not require meditation, and meditation can be carried out with little or no contemplation. An online etymological dictionary traces the origins of the word "contemplate" to:

> c. 1200, "religious musing," from Old French *contemplation* or directly from Latin *contemplationem* (nominative *contemplatio*) "act of looking at," from *contemplat-*, past participle stem of *contemplari* "to gaze attentively, observe," originally "to mark out

a space for observation" (as an augur does). From *com-*, intensive prefix ..., + *templum* "area for the taking of auguries"[1]

An "augur" is a seer who predicts the future, and a "temple" is a holy place. So "contemplation" in the present sense implies a watcher in a sacred mind-space, or sacred state of consciousness, in which self-observation may occur. Now, if we look up the etymology of the word "meditate" we will begin with a very similar history, but by the 14th century, the term can be used to mean "an act of continuous calm thought upon some subject," the implication being that to meditate, one must learn to chill-out, and focus one's mind on an object and ignore everything else. One may do this to facilitate better contemplation, or for some other benefit; i.e., stress reduction, anger management, healing, blissing-out, etc. In this book, *contemplation* refers to the intentional self-awareness of one's own mental processes and acts, while *meditation* refers to the ritualized exercise of concentration toward one object of consciousness to the exclusion of all other distractions. Meditation is often the ritual preparation for contemplation.

I am writing about the contemplative brain from the vantage point of an academically trained (University of Oregon) and ethnographically seasoned anthropologist who was also trained in neuroscience at the Institute of Neurological Sciences at the University of Pennsylvania. I am also writing as a *mature contemplative* (Laughlin, 2011; Laughlin, McManus, and d'Aquili, 1990, 1993). Much of what I have come to know about consciousness I am unable to communicate in any complete or straightforward way to those who do not share the same or similar experiences. Neurophenomenology for me is a "state-specific science" (Tart 1972, 1998). In a state-specific science, "...we would have a group of highly skilled, dedicated, and trained practitioners able to achieve certain [states of consciousness], and able to agree with one another that they have attained a common state. While in that [state of consciousness], they might then investigate other areas of interest, whether these be totally internal phenomena of that given state, the interaction of that state with external, physical reality, or people in other [states of consciousness]" (Tart 1972: 1207).

---

[1] http://www.etymonline.com/index.php?term=contemplation; retrieved on July 29, 2017.

In this book I will communicate what I have come to know about consciousness by way of meditation and contemplation, about the anthropology of consciousness and the neurophenomenological grounding of consciousness using any and every scrap of information I can glean from psychology, anthropology and neuroscience. But I will not stop there. Why hinder my project by accepting the blinders imposed by the culture of laboratory-oriented experimental empiricism? There is a story that is germane to this issue, and that I love telling anyone who will listen. An acquaintance of mine, the late Emil W. Menzel (1967), a renowned comparative psychologist who worked on primate intelligence, curiosity and creativity, had an epiphany about the relation of experimental research to the real world. He tells of spending a lot of lab time early in his career testing the intelligence of olive baboons (*Papio anubis*) and reaching the conclusion that they were very stupid animals. Later, circumstances took him to Kenya for a conference and while there he took the opportunity to visit his beloved baboons in the wild. To make a short story even shorter, he stood among the baboon troops aghast at how intelligent they appeared to be on their own home turf. He learned there and then an important lesson which he urged upon his fellow researchers—namely, make sure your laboratory questions make sense relative to the *natural state* of the animal in the wild (see Jerome Kagan's 2013: Chap. 1 discussion of the relationship between lab reality and real-world complexity).

In this respect I am a solid believer in the great psychologist William James' *radical empiricism*; to wit, *no experience is beyond the scope of scientific scrutiny, and all experiences must be included within the purview of science* (see James 1976 [1912]; Taylor 1994). By implication, science cannot exclude experiences had by people outside laboratories. To do so would be ludicrous in the extreme. It would be like science ignoring olive baboons in the wild. Moreover, as experience is the only direct route to knowledge of the real world, scientific exploration must be systematically grounded in experience. Empirical theories are like bridges with their supports buried deeply in direct experience (i.e., observation). No matter what kind of bridge—truss, arch, suspension, etc.—the footings must be lodged in bedrock. There are no sky-hooks available. Experience can disconfirm theories, but theories cannot disconfirm experience—theories can only inform experiences already had, and perhaps point toward new experiences.

Constructivism: A Persistent Hindrance

In the background of this book is a resistance I have always felt toward extreme "cultural relativism"—or as it is now termed "cultural constructionism." Constructivists offer accounts of mental acts, cultural knowledge and behavior, and social institutions that recognize no cross-cultural universals, or damn few. In short, given what we know about how the brain works, constructivism won't carry us very far for the simple reason that there is no such thing as a neural structure or process that is totally plastic, which it would have to be for cultures to be totally relative. It is interesting that a form of constructivist neuroanthropology only arose after research showed that neural systems are somewhat plastic in transforming to task (e.g., Lende and Downey 2012)—a popular view of neural processing riddled with neoliberal political attitudes about the malleability of brain and self (Pitts-Taylor 2010).

For those readers unfamiliar with the terminology and the history of anthropological theory, *constructivism* in its extreme form holds that cultures vary freely in their form, and that everyone's consciousness is totally conditioned by cultural influences—that is, the culture "constructs" and conditions consciousness during childhood. The processes by which a society influences and guides the development of a wee baby into adulthood is called *enculturation*. But enculturation does not happen by opening a baby's head and pouring in doses of "culture." Rather, enculturation is an adaptive process by which the young learn by active interaction with their social environment—it is a process of molding an already genetically structured brain (Piaget 1977, 1980; Laughlin 1991; Donald 2003; Keating, Lerner and Steinberg 2004; Kagan 2013). To understand enculturation relative to brain development, keep in mind that *there is no such thing as a totally plastic neural structure.* All neural development involves interaction between inherent neurophysiological structuration and stimuli in the environment, both physical and social (Varela 1979; Kagan 2013). For instance, during the adolescent years, three processes are going on that culture may influence: (1) major development and growth in the prefrontal cortex, (2) increased connectivity as detected by growth of myelin, especially in the prefrontal areas, and (3) there is at first an overabundance of synaptic growth followed by synaptic pruning as skills and other learning vector neural development (see Lerner and Steinberg 2004: 70-71). There is in other words tremendous plasticity in which neuronal networks are culled during adolescence, but none of these systems are totally plastic—it is a process of selecting among a field of networks that are already in place. There are numerous examples of "cultural universals"—for example, the cross-cultural study of death reveals such universal aspects (see Nahm 2017)—but this is not the topic we are discussing here. When I use the term "enculturation," I am implying this "autopoietic" process of interaction between genetically guided structuration and re-organization in response to stimuli (Varela 1979).

Anthropologists vary in how much they believe in constructivism. Obviously, cultures differ from each other. For instance, the Navajo of the American southwest have a culture distinctly different in its language, mythology, family structure, rituals, child rearing practices, daily subsistence patterns, etc. from, say, the Tikopians living in the Solomon Islands of Melanesia. And both the Navajo and Tikopians differ markedly from the culture of, say, the San people living in southern Africa. Studying those differences is what ethnology and its ethnographic research is all about—has been about since the mid-19th century. Peoples differ in what they think about, feel about and do about events in their lives. Each society enculturates its future adult members in different ways. But think about this: if peoples differed entirely from each other—if their brains were totally plastic at birth and molded by their physical and social environments, anthropologists wouldn't have a snowball's chance in hell of ever coming to understand another society's way of life. Yet we anthropologists, not to mention millions of tourists, do come to discover how other people think, feel and do. We learn their language, we participate in their daily lives, and gradually come to understand their point of view about things. Not only that, but in over a century and a half of serious ethnography, we have learned that nearly all peoples have some form of marriage and family, have a worldview expressed in myths, have healing and initiation rituals, have languages based more or less upon the same mental properties, use metaphors and other narrative tricks to communicate experiences through story-telling, have dreams they share to one extent or another, have a sense of justice, use fermented and psychotropic substances to alter their states of consciousness, and on-and-on.

The problem with Western anthropology, especially American anthropology, is that it was founded by people who *fervently believed in the free will of mankind*. To believe this ideology in extreme form requires a separation of body and mind—a separation of soul and physical being. While the early anthropologists came to acknowledge the fact of biological evolution, most either explicitly or tacitly believed that human kind had passed some unspecified Rubicon before which their natures were determined by their genetics, as was presumably the case with other animals, but after which their "natures" became determined by their "nurture." In other words, humanity passed from a pre-cultural state of being into a cultural state of being that somehow transcended mere biological and evolutionary conditioning. This view has, in one form or another, persisted in anthropology to the present day. Somehow or other, we humans have left our biological natures behind. NOT! We "nearly hairless apes" have left nothing of our biological natures behind. That is very fortunate for it makes not only ethnology possible, but it also allows both a neurophenomenology and a neuroanthropology possible. With the inclusion of modern neuroscience and evolutionary biology into issues of interest to anthropologists we can appreciate that there is a biological ground for virtually all aspects of human nature, including moral development (Wilson 1997; Kagan 2013), spirituality (Walach, Schmidt and Jonas 2011), cognitive skills (Kagan 2013; Pinker 2003), epistemology (Callebaut and Pinxten 2012), personality (McCrae and Costa 2003); language (Pinxten 1976), and emotion (Damasio 1999; Laughlin and Throop 1999; Ekman 1980).

Arguments over this issue impinge upon many of the topics we will be discussing in this book. For instance, there are arguments over whether "asceticism" is essentially the same across cultures and religions or are various asceticisms constructed differently by each religious institution (Wimbush and Valantasis 1998b). With specific reference to the constructivist take on mysticism (Chapter 9), philosopher Steven T. Katz (1978a, 1978b), arguing against the universalist position of Mircea Eliade (1964), Stace (1960) and others, essentially denied the existence of universal structures mediating mystical experiences, preferring instead to claim that culture determines the characteristic of mystical experiences, and thus all such experiences are totally different with no unifying properties. Robert Forman (1997, 1998, 1999) countered Katz's view by showing that the constructivist account cannot possibly explain the manifest commonalities in mystical experiences had all over the world. Forman hit upon the prime failure of all constructivist accounts of human consciousness, culture and behavior; namely, that no theory is possible if there are no universal qualities to observed reality. This is a problem that has plagued anthropology, and especially ethnology since its inception. Valid theories can only be built upon reproducible observations of real patterns. If Darwin had not noticed that turtles, monkeys, dolphins, people and other seemingly different species all had five metacarpal bones, and other such patterns, the *Origin of Species* would never have been written, and modern evolutionary biology would not exist. If the Russian chemist Dmitri Mendeleev (among others) had not published the periodic table based upon the perceived similarities among families of elements, modern chemistry would not exist. Anthropology was born in the mid-19th century as a kind of structuralist project in the work of Adolf Bastian (Koepping 1983; Laughlin 2011: 38), but later developments in anthropological methods gave precedence to the variations in cultural ways of life and have strenuously resisted the construction of scientific theories that might explain human mental acts and behaviors. All of this is because to believe in free will, there cannot be a genetically determined body mediating will. To believe, as most Christians do, that after death the soul leaves the body and wafts-off to the happy hunting ground, the soul (and its will) must be independent of the body which dies and decomposes away.

Effort After Truth vs. Effort After Meaning

This book will largely ignore constructivist polemics, for they are productive of neither in-depth understanding of contemplation, nor theoretical explanations of regularities in meditation and contemplative experiences. What I will take seriously is the way cultures incubate, ritualize and interpret spiritual experiences. Traditional cosmologies tend to be conservative of meaning. They resist change in knowledge, for the principle function of a society's worldview is to assure both a complementarity of experience for society's members, as well as reflect the authenticity of experience. The traditional interpretive frame for

ASC is the product of an inherent *effort after meaning*, as opposed to an *effort after truth*. That is, the cognitive processes of the human brain operate to associate what is arising in the sensorium now with patterns stored in memory—in Bartlett's (1932: 44) terms, "an effort to connect what is given with something else." The effort after truth shifts the orientation from attributing meaning to the given to discovering what is novel in the given and then evaluating meaning models by comparison with the given's experienced novelty. In other words, the effort after meaning is a quest for an ordered patterning of experience with a recognition of the correspondence between an experience as given and the instantiation of that given in memory, while the effort after truth is a systematic search for anomalies in our experience of a given. The former is common to people everywhere, while the latter is rare and is the fundamental impetus to real science—that is, when the "science" is not merely another form of ideology. Indeed, we are wired to seek meaning and to modify meaning in relation to experiences. Infants will naturally spend more time scrutinizing *discrepant* anomalies than *novel* anomalies (Kagan 2013: 41-42). Thus, we may suggest that when we speak of the anomalous aspects of ASC, we can distinguish between two kinds: (1) the anomaly may be in addition to familiar perceptual aspects of the experience, or (2) the anomaly may be totally novel, and thus create dissonance in the neophyte's mind—the anomaly may be "mind-blowing." Those truly seeking truth will tend to be comfortable with the latter kind of anomaly. The effort after meaning tends to support group ideologies, whereas the effort after truth is frequently ideology transforming. We will return to this distinction time and again, and especially when we discuss ideology in the Conclusion.

As we shall see, whether a contemplative practice is productive of meaning or of truth will depend upon the cultural background to the activity (Paper 2004). The results of contemplation may operate as either positive or negative feedback into the culture's worldview; again, dependent upon the contemplative's interpretive frame. Experiences had in ASC may operate as positive feedback into the culture and result in changes of the culture's worldview, while other such experiences may be treated as negative feedback reinforcing the worldview.

Monophasic and Polyphasic Societies

Societies vary in the extent to which they admit experiences into their consensus worldview. Every society on the planet enculturates ("passes down") its worldview—including its metaphysical assumptions—to subsequent generations. Anthropologists know that most non-Western, traditional worldviews acknowledge the value of ASC as windows into the spiritual—the normally invisible—domain(s) of reality (Bourguignon 1973; Bourguignon and Evascu 1977). We speak of such societies as having *polyphasic cultures* (Laughlin 2011: 62-66; Laughlin, McManus and d'Aquili 1990: 292-295); that is, they come to know about reality through experiences had in multiple states of consciousness—in dreams, visions, shamanic journeys, ritual dramas, drug trips, and so forth. Those societies that eschew alternative states as sources of serious knowledge about themselves and their world have what we may call *monophasic cultures* in that they tend to value knowledge gleaned only from what we Westerners call "normal waking" consciousness and institutional education systems. These societies tend to have materialistic and technocratic worldviews, and ignore, explain away, denigrate or reject knowledge attained in alternative states. The distinction between polyphasic and monophasic cultures is both important and fundamental to our project, for the contemplative path commonly leads to extraordinary experiences had in ASC. Hence, much of what I have to say in this book runs counter to a monophasic worldview.

Intent of the Book

This book is not intended as a manual, or "how to" handbook, for aspiring contemplatives. While I will often resort to descriptions of my own practices and experiences as a contemplative, I do so solely to render these as data in support of my conclusions (see also Bharati 1961; Paper 2004). I do not advocate that the reader follow suit. For instance, in the chapter on dream yoga, I mention that I built a sleeping box in which I slept sitting up for months. I do *not* encourage the reader to try this, especially if you must get up and go to work in the morning. The loss of sleep and weird experiences during meditation while sleeping sitting up can lead to confused and strange states of mind. Moreover, I was by then an experienced meditator and was not really perturbed by the results of the practices, although people around me—especially my university students—may have found my lectures a tad strange.

I do intend this book to be an exploration of the inherent capacity of the human brain to study itself under various psychological and cultural conditions. I am and have always been a scientist first and a contemplative second. My goal has been to render experiences and insights had during ASC into scientifically useful data—data of the phenomenological and ethnographic sort, rather than the limited, but very necessary, laboratory kind. I have for instance taken every *entheogen* and *empathogen* (psychotropic drugs used to produce spiritually salient experiences) that I can get my hands on that are used by traditional people to alter their state of consciousness in ritual circumstances. I have done so to have at least a modicum of experience upon which to base my understanding of why, as Erica Bourguignon (Bourguignon and Evascu 1977) showed, people all over the planet use drugs in ritual practices to attain ASC (Rush 2013) and have done so for millennia (Guerra-Doce 2015). Again, I do not advocate that my readers do the same, although I know many of you have done and will naturally bring your experiences to bear in our discussions.

That said, the book can be read passively, in which case it can feed the reader's intellect. But there is a deeper level of reading that is possible and that I fully intend. That is, I wish to invite the reader to participate as much as he/she can in seeking the contemplative insights upon which the whole project rests. You can read about Edmund Husserl's method of phenomenological reduction and file that information away for later use, or you can take the challenge that I am really making to try it out yourself. If you are already a contemplative, then many of the things I say will be transparent to you—you've been there, done that. If you have never attempted to meditate, to perform a phenomenological reduction, then the issue will remain conceptual and there will be a limit to how far you can understand what I intend to say. So, let me invite you to participate to whatever extent you wish, and enrich the experience with your own insights. As I said above, this is not a handbook of ASC, or a manual for how to get high. There are plenty of "how to" books out there already. So, have at it!

Contemplative Neuroscience: My Empirical and Theoretical Viewpoint

In *The Contemplative Brain*, I will take the broadest possible view of consciousness, incorporating wherever it is relevant research in transpersonal studies, phenomenology, experiential and phenomenological anthropology, mysticism, as well as more standard anthropology, neuroscience, psychology, biology and physics. Indeed, I will take any help I can get in making this project as complete and accurate as possible. I will often depend upon the insights available through different traditions of contemplation (Zen, Buddhism, Sufism, Gnosticism, shamanic meditation, Stoicism, etc.), for, although they usually come attached to ideological interpretive frameworks (Paper 2004), they are usually empirically rich and fed by tried-and-true phenomenological methods. There are, of course, "how to" books and teachers in all of these traditions to help you on your way.

Again, the task absolutely requires state-specific science—something like an anthropological version of *contemplative neuroscience* (Deikman 1982; Wallace 2006, 2007, 2011). At the same time, it requires a science that opens its arms to everyday contemplative practice (Chauhan 2015). If there is one great methodological failing of ethnographers, it is their reluctance to enter ASC when their hosts clearly value experiences of that kind (as we shall see repeatedly). Let me give you an example. There is a syncretic cult in Brazil that practices possession trance states (see Chapter 10). Many anthropologists have been hosted by these wonderful people, yet none of them to my knowledge has ever undergone a possession ritual to the point of letting go and enjoying the experience. One of these anthropologists, Mattijs Van de Port (2005: 151) makes mention of this as well:

> I'm certainly not the only anthropologist to have observed that no matter how possession trance is tackled theoretically, its *most immediate experience escapes our understanding*. Janice Boddy..., Paul Stoller..., and Michael Taussig..., to name but a few, all have remarked that whereas the Otherness of the phenomenon (its uncanny inexplicability, its screaming incompatibility with Western notions of personhood, its seeming disdain for self-control, its radical otherness) demands explanation, and this explanation highlights the inadequacy of our conceptual categories rather than the phenomenon itself....

Ethnography without a phenomenological method is a kind of *mindblindness* (Baron-Cohen 1997) in which we as observers can describe our hosts' behaviors but haven't a clue as to what motivates them in terms of their inner psychological life. What is missing in the above case is the direct phenomenology of the possession experience, and nothing less will do if we are to understand how the brain produces such experiences. No amount of socioeconomic analysis, or speculations about whether spirit possession is or is not a form of dissociation, is or is not a form of psychopathology will help us in the least. In my opinion, Van de Port nailed it, and anthropology fails us at this very juncture in our understanding. I will have more to say about this failure of ethnographic methods as we go on.

I will unpack data available in ethnographic research from their context in often grandiose theories that have dominated anthropology since its inception, especially those grounded in extreme constructivism. For instance, I find it fascinating that Western anthropologists in past generations considered animism with its claims of hidden spiritual powers as "primitive" while at the same time seriously considering the views of physics with its "ether," "curved space," and later "quantum fields" and "dark matter"—none of which are directly observable—as the very apogee of advanced thinking. Even today with astrophysical models depending on the existence of "dark energy" holding sway, there is a tendency to consider traditional cosmologies involving Holy Wind, spiritual forces like *mana* and the like as pre-scientific (read "primitive") belief systems. What is blatantly obvious, to me at least, is that neither ethnography, nor modern physics is populated with mature contemplatives (or advanced phenomenologists) who are capable of routinely realizing the extent to which their own conscious and culturally conditioned brain is an ingredient in their "objective" observations, considerations and equations. It does not take much in the way of contemplation to realize that most of the causation operating in the world of our experience is invisible, nor is it hard to realize that virtually all cultures recognize this fact and consider it crucial to their worldview. Every intact traditional culture I am aware of has a worldview (usually a cosmology) that recognizes: (1) the essential ineffability of experience, (2) that causation is usually invisible to the senses, and (3) that reality is one vast monad in which everything is embedded and causally entangled. In addition, most of those cultures consider experiences had in ASC (dreams, trance states, drug trips, etc.) as informative to their worldview. This is far from being "primitive," for such peoples have learned that causation that is invisible in the "waking" state may be visible and informative in alternative states. Most peoples on the planet are, in other words, more "radically" empirical in their worldviews than are many Western scientists. This is why traditional cosmologies are applicable to the quotidian world of peoples, while the cosmologies of astrophysicists are not.

Consciousness is a principle function of nervous systems. *Thus, no nervous system, no consciousness.* There is no such thing as a disembodied consciousness. I do not mean that people do not experience disembodied spirits, ghosts, gods and goddesses—they most certainly do. Not only that, but people experience themselves as floating and flying outside their bodies, taking trips to distant places while leaving their bodies behind, and hovering over their bodies while on the operating table. What I am saying is that those experiences happen between their ears. The only consciousness people have is mediated by their brains. That is why our first chapter will center on the conscious brain. The brain is the prime synergistic organ of the body. It evolved over millions of years to intervene between the *extramental world* (the real world apart from our knowledge of it) and our physical responses to that reality. The brains of all creatures serve this function. Thus, *mutatis mutandis* with respect to evolutionary changes, all creatures with brains are conscious. There is now so much psychobiological and ethological evidence in favor of this view that it is now up to nay-sayers to prove creatures with brains are *not* conscious. The brains of all animals produce an internal movie they take to be their environment—let us call this inner movie their *brain world*. Brain worlds are structured in such a way as to present a subjective point of view toward perceived events that can facilitate adaptive interaction with the extramental world—for simplicity's sake, let's just call the extramental world the *real world*. The relationship between the brain world and the real world is what psychological adaptation is all about, importantly including child (pup, chick, calf, cria, cub, larva, *ad nauseum*) development.

Over and above these various considerations, I will privilege information obtained via mature contemplation over all other approaches. I will define "mature contemplation" in a later chapter. Suffice to say here that the term labels a skill at manipulating ASC for increasing self-awareness and the introspection of the mental acts that operate within consciousness. The topic of mature contemplation is so central to my approach that it will be our next port of call after considering *neuroconsciousness* (Dell 1993). All other perspectives, be they neuropsychological or ethnographic will be filtered through acts of contemplation.

Let me give a simple example to illustrate why I consider contemplation so central to this project. It is common for people everywhere to mangle the distinction between the sensory data of experience and interpretation. Sensory events and their interpretation happen so rapidly in the brain that almost everybody conflates the two. However, it does not take long for a contemplative to realize the difference between these quite distinct mental acts. The brains of all creatures are designed not only to produce a world of sensory experiences, but a world of *meaningful* sensory experiences. As we shall see, this is the prime directive of consciousness, and the mature contemplative knows the difference between sensing patterns in the world and cognizing about those patterns. This realization will lead us as phenomenological anthropologists to apply what I call the *Rule of Multiple Interpretations*—that is, *there is no such thing as a sensory experience that is amenable to one and only one interpretation*. We will return to this issue throughout the book.

DESIGN OF THE BOOK

Preliminaries over, let me sketch-in the course of the book. We will begin by looking at consciousness as a function of the brain. Chapter 1 will examine many possible definitions of consciousness, insisting all the while that a modern take on consciousness must be congruent with the neurophysiological processes that mediate it. Consciousness is not some epiphenomenon that somehow floats above the body and that is conveniently separable after death, or during *near death experiences* (experiences had when the heart and breathing stops and later starts again) and out of body experiences. The world of our experience, regardless of the state of consciousness, is constructed moment-by-moment between our ears. We shall see that consciousness is best described as an energy field which is mediated by numerous structures in the brain. We will explain why the common separation of the mind and body occurs—why the mind-body problem persists in human thinking. More than this, we will account for how the brain's sensorium works to produce a sensory environment, this being the missing ingredient in most theories of consciousness.

Because this book is about contemplation, we focus upon the importance of the prefrontal cortex, the most dramatic physical feature in the evolution of the human brain, and the organ that makes contemplation possible. Consciousness is a function of all brains, not just human brains, so we will trace the emergence of consciousness during evolution and show how different the world of experience can be among different species of animals. Different, yes, but incorporating many of the same properties, not the least of which is the ability to focus attention upon important stimuli in the environment—this process being the principal anlagen of contemplation.

Our analysis will show how culture and neural development interact—how the "culture-ready" brain fulfills its destiny as the engine of experience and fulfilment of cultural expectations and worldviews. This evolutionary occupation is one of constructing meaning, thereby rendering stimuli into symbols, and activating them within ASC, often with the encouragement and facilitation of culture. One of the powers of culture is the construction of ritual methods of incubating states of consciousness by vectoring an individual's volition and concentration under circumstances that produce experiences that usually confirm the culture's worldview, especially in the domain of the supernatural and spiritual. In part, this engagement with the spiritual evokes communication between the conscious and unconscious processes in the psyche and may possibly even involve reciprocal interactions with the universe at a quantum level.

Chapter 2 will begin our discussion of contemplation per se with an introduction to neurophenomenology. We emphasize that explaining contemplation or any other mental act without reference to neuroscience is no longer tenable. We outline for you the history of the concept of neurophenomenology and show that there are really two schools of thought, one anthropological and the other psychological. There are many phenomenologies in philosophy, but what we are interested in is Husserlian transcendental phenomenology, for it is a discipline that produces mature contemplatives. The elements of the Husserlian method are discussed in part to show what a remarkable thing it is for the human brain to be able to study its own processes directly via introspection. The discussion underscores the importance of learning and realizing the "phenomenological attitude," the only stance that can facilitate the study of mental acts without distortion by cultural conditioning—the "natural attitude" about things we learn from our parents, peers and schools. In developing the phenomenological attitude, we learn the power of the "searchlight" function of awareness, and its power to penetrate to the truth of mental formations.

Mature contemplation is arguably the most important skill to learn for those wishing to study their own consciousness. We show why this is so and why that skill does not produce a solipsistic view of the world. To underscore this importance, the example of a neurophenomenology of time-consciousness is offered. We show how the brain produces the phenomenologically experienced sense of on-going time, as well as "chronesthesia," the ability to mentally whiz back and forth from the past lodged in memory to the now to the anticipated future and back again. Fully understanding how this sense of time and time travel operates is grounded in mature contemplation, for only by an exercise in phenomenological reduction are we able to perceive the real "now" moment as distinct from memory and anticipation. It is then possible to account for the ways that cultures encode time, both as a lineal "arrow" of time and as cycles within cycles. It is also possible to better understand the transformation in our time sense when entering ASC.

Chapter 3 takes us into an exploration of self-contemplation via meditation. As we have already mentioned, meditation involves ritual procedures for preparing the mind for optimal concentration. There are numerous meditation traditions found all over the planet, but most of those practiced in North America are derived from Asia, including Hindu yogas, different schools of Buddhism, and even certain shamanic traditions. Depending upon which practice we are discussing, a wide variety of neuropsychological systems are active in mediating the practice and resulting experiences. When novel—even extraordinary—

experiences do arise from time to time, there tends to be ready-made interpretations available for making sense of experiences. This negative feedback system is what we call the "cycle of meaning," which we discuss at length, and will encounter repeatedly over the course of the book. We also re-emphasize the important distinction between those cultures that value and encourage ASC and those, like ours, that do not.

Of course, we define "meditation" in terms of its phenomenology, and then get into an exploration of the neurophysiology of meditative acts. Again, we show the extreme importance of the prefrontal lobes in guiding the "searchlight" feature of awareness, as well as the areas and processes responsible for calming the body and mind preparatory to insight practices—especially those systems that mediate "empathy," "loving-kindness" and "mindfulness." The different areas of the prefrontal cortex and their functions are described.

Most meditative systems are embedded in a cultural matrix of intentions, sanctions, roles, practices, institutionalized meaning systems and language, as well as overarching worldviews that influence the how, when, where and who of meditative activity. The act of meditation upon some object will have inevitable consequences, independent of culture, but the meaning of which, post-experience, may be culturally framed. Again, there is a "cycle of meaning" involved which is fundamental to virtually all spiritual traditions that utilize meditative techniques. Still, anomalous experiences had in meditation may produce positive feedback into the system of meaning and cause change, especially a change in individual understanding. Much depends upon whether the orientation of the meditator is toward the effort after meaning or the effort after truth. Several "meditation cultures" are described to give a flavor of the interaction between contemplative acts and culture.

In Chapter 4, the issue of psychic energy and its relation to contemplation and meditation are discussed. The human nervous system is, to put it bluntly, a *trophic system* (Purves 1990). That means that brain cells and networks must "eat" to function. Shut off the energy to the neural cells, they stop functioning and will quickly die. Voila! No consciousness. Moreover, advanced meditators know that a major ingredient of ASC are energy events: blisses, rushes, streams of energy up and down the center of the body, energy whirling around "energy centers," etc. These experiences are often interpreted as healing and as a source of spiritual powers (see Sharp 2014). Several psychic energy traditions are sampled, again to give an empirical flavor of the kind of experiences had across cultures.

The chapter then goes into the details of what we know about the neuropsychology of psychic energy phenomena. Energy is moving all over the body all the time, even when we are sleeping. However, only some of this movement becomes conscious, especially those energies associated as meaningful within an interpretive frame. Because we experience such psychic energy events—feelings, emotions, frissons, blisses, pains, movements, rushes, raptures, ecstasies, etc.—we can empathize when others experience the same phenomena. By studying these phenomena, the contemplative can understand the extent to which his body and psyche are transcendental relative to his normal ego functioning. To understand the underlying bioenergetics mediating psychic energy experiences, we have recourse to Ernst Gellhorn's theory of *autonomic-somatic integration*. Using this perspective, it is easy to understand how ritual procedures can drive internal processes, and how extraordinary energy experiences may result in transforming the emotional salience of previously conditioned states of mind. In this chapter I describe some of the techniques used in Tibetan Tantric Buddhist *tummo* (psychic energy) practice, as well as some of the experiences I had doing this work. My focus becomes the elaboration of several universal attributes of psychic energy experiences, and how these are mediated by the body and brain. These features of energy movement and evocation help to account for different ASC that may be encountered during a contemplative's career.

Chapter 5 is perhaps best viewed as an interlude, an autobiographical description of my own path toward becoming a mature contemplative. Much of what I say about consciousness is as much motivated by my own phenomenological work as it is about the science of consciousness. Many of the things I claim to know about the mind are derived from direct experiences during a lifetime of exploring various traditions of spiritual awakening. Instead of confining these experiences and reflections to the background, I think it is useful to describe them as best I can so that they become a part of the narrative—part of the story about how one can become savvy about one's own consciousness and use that wisdom to evaluate various scientific approaches to and theories about consciousness. This, of course, was precisely what Husserl intended, and I think he was correct. We anthropologists are long past trying to disguise our personal involvement in our ethnographic projects by imposing a phony third person narrative, a change in style that goes back at least to Laura Bohannon's 1954 revelations in her book, *Return to Laughter,* about her personal experiences doing fieldwork with her husband Paul among the Tiv people of Nigeria. She felt the necessity to publish her delightful memoir under the pseudonym, Elenore Smith Bowen, to avoid criticism from the third person traditionalists in her discipline. Happily, this is no longer necessary, and modern anthropologists have found it useful to read about the experiences had by their colleagues in the field.

In this chapter I describe my early attempts at meditation that garnered me some understanding of psychic energy phenomena like bliss and ecstasy, as well as the ability to willfully calm the mind and body. The meditative life is one of an unfolding series of causally related events that cannot be predicted, but can, in retrospect, be comprehended as a maturation process. Integral to this process is learning to calm the mind, to focus the "searchlight" feature of awareness upon the object of meditation, and ignore distractions like pains and itches, discursive thought, mood swings and so forth. Learning to do this is in preparation for contemplation. Along the way experiences pop up that are considered "signs" that have meaning to an advanced meditator and signal the extent of the student's development along certain lines. Among the more important experiences are the so-called "absorption states," which are discussed at length. Also described is the realization of no-self—that is, the realization that the mind contains no permanent ego-entity that is sitting somewhere in the core of the brain watching the movie.

I describe as much as language will allow my experience of "stream-entry;" i.e., the first absorption into and realization of *nirvana.* Little can be said about this experience *per se*, but the consequences of the realization were as automatic as they were profound. Any state of consciousness is caused by prior states and factors (*karma*) interacting with states to transform them. So, it is with stream-entry. But there is no way I know to research stream-entry other than introspection. First person reports are rare but are all we have available to work with.

Chapter 6 returns us to an aspect of the contemplative's life that can be researched—namely dreaming. Indeed, there is a voluminous literature on the neuropsychology of dreaming, both as a source of meditation and involving traditional methods for producing so-called "lucid dreams." To understand the role of contemplation in the spiritual life of peoples around the globe, we must rid ourselves of the very Western bias that contemplation occurs only in what we call "normal waking consciousness." For many peoples, contemplation in ASC is important, for in ASC it is possible to imagine and assess otherwise invisible forces. Contemplation of dreaming allows the isolation of the structures of dreams. Some of the cross-culturally common attributes of dreaming are discussed and some of the characteristics typical of dreaming in polyphasic societies are emphasized. It is critical to understand that, unlike Westerners, in most societies on the planet people routinely pay attention to, and keep track of their dreams, for they find them informative and sometimes of great utility. Of interest to us are dream cultures that include some kind of dream yoga—a set of practices utilized to incubate and assess dream material.

I practiced Tibetan Tantric Buddhist dream yoga for years, and in this chapter, I describe what that adventure was like. I came to understand many things about dreaming and its role in self-discovery. I also learned that dreaming can become largely "lucid," and that dreaming for polyphasic peoples is likely more lucid than is normal Western dreaming. We shall see that the trick of maintaining lucidity in dreaming involves controlling consciousness across the point of transformation between waking and sleeping. Dream work has been fundamental to my spiritual life. Thus, I am aware of the importance of dream-calling found cross-culturally among shamans and healers. Dream-calling is a factor in the contemplative life that requires some discussion. This raises questions, of course, about why humans and other animals dream. This chapter considers this question, again from a neuroscience point of view.

Chapter 7 takes up one of the central foci of contemplation, that being self-discovery, or contemplation of the self. As any advanced meditator knows, the ego is an impermanent standpoint upon the world, including the self. Transcendental phenomenology, of course, is entirely about self-discovery. Traditional cultures exhibit myriad ways of conceiving, conceptualizing, imaging and talking about the self. From an ecological view, we can best understand that self-construal is an adaptational process no different than adaptation to external reality. Enduring social relations require that there be a consensus, habitual and customary understanding of the social person, and everyone must conform to some extent to social expectations to be perceived as a group member. Cultures recognize that such self-models are incomplete and changeable, at least implicitly reflecting the greater mystery of the true self which is largely unconscious to individuals and transcendental relative to any knowledge of the true self.

It is reasonable to posit that the more pressure there is in a society for people to conform to a fixed and shared concept of the social (economic, political) self, the less the culture will recognize and encourage transpersonal explorations. If a society does encourage transpersonal experiences, they will apply rituals to that end that incorporate "drivers" (drumming, dancing, psychoactive drugs, etc.) to incubate ASC. These ritual activities operate upon the organs of the body, especially the brain, nervous and endocrine systems, to produce changes in mind-state, which in turn facilitate contemplation of extraordinary revelations of self. Indeed, we will speak of "the self and its brain," for as I have emphasized, there is no self without a brain. Mind is far greater than ego, and the maturing adult must eventually come to realize that there is a vast untapped resource to be found in his or her unconscious.

Chapter 8 is an extension of self-contemplation focusing upon the cross-gender aspects of one's self. As I am a male, I can only address the topic phenomenologically from the male point of view. My cross-gender or cross-sex self is called my *anima*, while that of a female is called her *animus*. There is little I can say about the animus, because it is not really the mirror image of the anima. Contemplation of the animus requires a female contemplative. Contemplation of the anima is most often done by reflecting upon the significance of images that pop up in dreams, visions, fantasies and the like. I will show that most human societies consider anima visions as visitation by spirits, ancestors, goddesses or demons, depending upon whether they are affectively positive or negative. Anima possession may be viewed as soul-loss, or possession by some spirit for healing or killing.

In this chapter I will emphasize the cross-cultural aspect of anima experiences, not because ethnography is the stock-in-trade of the professional anthropologist, but because of the apparent ignorance of cross-cultural factors often found in the Jungian literature today. During the years that I have worked with meditators of all ideological stripes and cultural backgrounds, I have been impressed with the extent to which people can uncritically accept the interpretations most amenable to their own personal worldview. The failure to take into consideration the relativity of interpretation is not only antithetical to what Jung taught, but is also a blind-spot in the development of transpersonal studies. Yet, by the same token, it is very important to understand that a "Jungian" hermeneutic is just as culturally-loaded as any other. It is the purpose to which the interpretation is put that matters. From the standpoint of personal maturation, the Jungian approach will probably carry one to greater maturity than will traditional cycles of meaning. The latter are normally more concerned with social integration of meaning than with aiding the individual to optimize his or her own psychological growth. Be that as it may, the chapter will underscore the inevitability of cross-gender encounters during self-contemplation and shows that how that encounter is handled depends a lot on the tools of interpretation offered by the culture or the interpretive frame of the contemplative.

Chapter 9 begins our exploration of mystical experiences, often the consequence of intense meditation and contemplation. We discuss some of the issues around defining "mysticism" and "mystical experience" which is made more difficult because of constructivist accounts that deny that any such thing as a universal mystical experience exists. I take the side of the universalists, not out of mere preference, but because I have experienced mystical states and know better. The chapter will discuss several properties of these states, including absorption into the void, distortion of time and space, spontaneity vs. intentional quest, and bliss and numinosity. Culture has a lot to do with the ritual circumstances and interpretation of these experiences. These factors, as is discussed earlier in the book, involve a cycle of meaning that will link the worldview, the ritual practices and interpretive frame to ASC. Mystics usually lodge their intuitive knowledge of totality and causality in one of three alternative frames: (1) a self-generated ideology, (2) a revitalized ideology from their society's distant historical past, or (3) an ideology borrowed from another culture. Several examples of mystical experiences within their respective cultural contexts are described.

One of the interesting results of having a mystical experience and the inherent encounter with totality is that one's comprehension of reality comes very close to the nature of the universe that modern physics depicts for us, specifically the implicate nature of physical reality. Both astrophysics and quantum physics hold that reality is essentially a monad in which everything, including our body and mind, is embedded and causally entangled.

In this chapter we also glimpse the nature of the "ascetic impulse" that motivates contemplatives to seek solitude and simplicity, and to avoid the hindrances and irritants of the quotidian social world. We also see that virtually all institutional spiritual traditions, including the world religions, tend to co-opt the drive to asceticism by constituting subcultures more to the liking of the contemplative member.

Chapter 10 carries on with the discussion of mystical experiences by exploring these experiences among shamanic traditions. We anthropologists tend to lump spiritual traditions, especially those involving ASC, among societies with simpler socioeconomic systems under the umbrella term "shamanism." It is often the case that there exists a role of ritual specialist in those societies that practice some form of meditation. Thus, shamanic meditation cultures are important to us for at least two reasons: (1) The shaman is usually the most advanced meditator in the society and indeed may depend for his or her reputation on the ability to enter ASC and utilize their skill for the benefit of the people, and (2) contemporary shamanic traditions are as close as we can come to the original meditation cultures of the Upper Paleolithic, and hence the role of the ritual specialist, and of meditation, in the origins of religion. The knotty problem of defining what constitutes a "shaman" is addressed. I differ slightly from other anthropologists in that I suggest that there is a "shamanic principle" underlying most religions, regardless of the complexity of their political and economic systems (Laughlin and Rock 2014). This principle will be developed, and several examples of shamanic contemplative traditions will be given.

In Chapter 11 we will take up one of the most important ingredients of mystical experiences, loving-kindness. Mystical love may be considered as a "universal solvent" in the sense that it is love, and only love, that can naturally counter anxiety, greed and hatred, all which pose major hindrances to absorption states. Many of the mystical traditions we encounter in this book have developed techniques for eliminating ego-centered mind-states in preparation for the experiences and sequelae of mystical realization. This chapter will examine the affective processes involved in empathy and bonding, including among non-human monogamous social animals. The parts of the brain that mediate empathy and love are distinguished, and their cognitive-affective operations traced, including the pairing of love with sexual attraction and the drive toward reproduction, and the evolution of the social brain. We will focus particularly on loving-kindness meditation techniques used to counter negative aversion to absorption. We will see that those who practice loving-kindness become less anxious (particularly about death). Also covered are types of compassion meditation which operate to enhance the wisdom aspect of loving-kindness. I finish the chapter by discussing one of the most powerful meditation traditions, the Tibetan Tantric Buddhist meditation on Chenrezig, the deity of compassion.

Chapter 12 extends the discussion of loving-kindness into death contemplation. Sooner or later, a contemplative will inevitably confront the fact of one's own mortality. This awareness or "mortality salience," as psychologists like to call it, peels back layers of self-illusion and compensation, as well as cultural conditioning and ideology to reveal a stratum of death anxiety. We will discuss the importance of Ernest Becker's "immortality project" and the influence upon our quotidian lives of the existential dilemma posed by our "creatureliness." Becker's writings gave rise to three decades or more of what is called Terror Management Theory which we will explore for insights into the reasons why loving-kindness and other types of meditative techniques work so effectively to counter "denial of death" mind-states. All cultures on the planet recognize in one way or another the salience of death—the existential dilemma of being encountering non-being. We look at some death cultures and isolate some of the ways human societies have come to grips with the facts of death and dying. Of course, we are not the only social animals that die, and we find that non-human animals also recognize death as special, perhaps even salient, for they demonstrate distinct behaviors when perceiving the death of their own. We end the chapter by examining a few traditions of formal death contemplation, and how these practices are used to alter the salience of mortality, as well as exposing the culturally conditioned states of mind and behavior that buffer people from fully confronting their own inevitable demise.

Chapter 13 examines closely some of the sociocultural barriers that may arise to thwart the contemplative life. Foremost among these hindrances are being ensnared by ideologies and misguided by ideologues. We raise the question of whether one needs a guru or not to explore the mind using phenomenological and other contemplative methods. This is a ticklish question, because there is a subtle balance between helpful mentoring and demagoguery. We also suggest that the need for a mentor may cease when one realizes one's own inner Guru.

In the Conclusion, we take up some repercussions of our study of contemplation. One of those is to return to the question of language. However briefly, we look at the role played by language in communicating about contemplative experiences. We will be much clearer about the issue of ineffability, and at the same time about the power of language to help in evoking experiences and communicating those experiences to other contemplatives. We will also look at the rise of "contemplative studies" in education and science, as well as the promise of cyborg technologies for future augmentation of the contemplative path.

PART ONE

The Conscious Brain

CHAPTER ONE

Neuroconsciousness

By "consciousness," I simply mean those subjective states of sentience or awareness that begin when one wakes up in the morning from a dreamless sleep and continue throughout the day until one goes to sleep at night or falls into a coma, or dies, or otherwise becomes, as one would say, "unconscious."

– John Searle (1993)

As far as we can discern, the sole purpose of human existence is to kindle a light in the darkness of mere being.

– C. G. Jung, *Memories, Dreams, Reflections*

Anything that we are aware of at a given moment forms part of our consciousness, making conscious experience at once the most familiar and most mysterious aspect of our lives.

– Susan Schneider and Max Velmans (2008: 1)

We have reached the point in the history of social science where a discussion of methods that is not grounded upon both a neuroepistemology and a neurophenomenology will not be worth considering. Why? Because we know that consciousness is a function of the organization of the brain (Koch, 2004; Changeux 1985; LeDoux 2003b; Damasio 2010; Nunez 2010; Purves 2010; Penfield 2015; Dehaene 2014; Osaka 2003; Atkinson, Thomas and Cleeremans 2000; Berlin 2011). Every thought, image, feeling, intuition, awareness and sensation we experience is mediated by our organ of experience— our brain and its brain world. Thus questions having to do with how we know, what we can and cannot know, gender-related styles of knowing, the symbolic nature of knowing, how consciousness develops its brain world, and how it interacts with the unconscious psyche are really questions about how the brain is organized, how it develops and functions, as well as what limiting factors are imposed upon knowing by the organization of the brain and by the physical and sociocultural environments of the developing brain (Mesquita, Barrett and Smith 2010). All this is just as important to the study of contemplation and meditation as for any other aspect of consciousness (Lutz, Dunne and Davidson 2007). But we must first understand consciousness from both a phenomenological and a neuropsychological point of view.

What is Consciousness?

The challenge is to define, describe and interpret consciousness in terms that allow *both the phenomenological (knowing from the inside-out) and neurophysiological (knowing from the outside-in) perspectives to be in synch.* This is no small effort. The task is a challenge precisely because of the inherent mind-body dualism built into our English language, and the culturally conditioned thoughts of English speakers (see Atkinson, Thomas and Cleeremans 2000 for a review). We can easily write whole books about consciousness without ever referring to the physiology of the body, or the organs and metabolic processes that make consciousness possible. Likewise, we can write a library full of books about the body and its organs without ever mentioning subjective, somatic experiences. I summarily reject this schism in our language and thought, and more so the mind-body split in our beloved anthropology. There really is no alternative to a *neuroanthropology* (Laughlin and d'Aquili 1974; Laughlin, McManus and d'Aquili 1990; Lende and Downey 2012), which includes fully operationalized *neuroethnographic methods* (Domínguez Duque 2012; Domínguez Duque *et al.* 2009; Lewis, Turner and Egan 2009) and a special focus upon *neuroenculturation* (Laughlin 1991; Whitehead 2010a, 2012)—that is, how the development of the neural system is influenced by society.

Yet to depend upon the neurosciences alone for a definition of consciousness would be to limit ourselves to non-phenomenological and experimentalist agendas—quite useful in their place, but not in a study oriented toward mature contemplation and an anthropology of experience. Take for example Stanislas Dehaene's suggestion that modern neuropsychologists seem to agree that consciousness exhibits three major features (Dehaene 2014: 8-9):

Vigilance. When we are conscious we are awake to our experience. Objects and happenings are arising and passing before our mind. We may become awake in any state of consciousness, not just normal waking consciousness. Vigilance is characteristic for instance of "lucid" dreaming.

Attention. When we are conscious, we are conscious "of something," even if that something is a factor of consciousness instead of a thing or happening. We can focus our faculties upon one of innumerable potential objects that are before the mind.

Access. Objects of which we become aware become meaningful and, at least to some extent, reportable to others.

Dehaene is a cognitive neuroscientist with an interest in artificial intelligence (AI), and of course his definition of consciousness is conditioned by his desire to develop experimental data on the subject. In part he wants to define consciousness in such a way that measurable data may be obtained in laboratory conditions. He also wants to define the term in such a way that it is applicable to machine AI. Thus, he emphasizes conscious access to objects in his description of consciousness. For our purposes, however, this limited view of the topic is inadequate. In the first place we are interested in the naturalistic fact of consciousness; that is, we anthropologists take consciousness (1) as we experience it, (2) including all aspects of its nature, including its evolution, (3) as experienced during the process of phenomenological study, (4) as it changes moment by moment and across ASC, and (5) as described by peoples of other cultures. Indeed, we are not interested in measuring anything, save for examining states in which a measuring-type act may be occurring.

On the other hand, we do not want to leave the brain and body behind. Purely spiritual definitions of consciousness are frequently tainted by religious ideology. And they are most unlikely to refer to the brain or to the physiology of the body in any modern sense. For instance, any definition of consciousness that requires the inclusion of an immortal soul or homunculus runs counter to phenomenological scrutiny, as we will see in the next chapter. A definition that is based upon mental operations that culminate in reincarnation—Hindu and Buddhist notions of karma often imply this kind of operation—will not do, for there are no neuroscientific or phenomenological methods that can possibly falsify such a claim about consciousness. The immortality theory that at the end of life karma sort of adds-up and forms a single image or thought moment which then passes on to a future life is simply beyond the pale of scientific confirmation. Mind you, it may be true, but there is no scientifically tenable way to know.

A theory of karmic psychology in *this* life is another matter and can be quite useful in modeling the causal relations between mental acts and their developmental consequences to the actor. It is easy to see how people can realize karmic action in their own lives, and then project those relations into an imagined death process. For example, a close reading by an advanced meditator of the *Bardo Thodol,* or *The Tibetan Book of the Dead* (see Evans-Wentz 1960) will reveal that all the experiences described for the bardo period also arise during meditation and spontaneously in dream states. One type of meditation retreat is done in complete darkness for days (so-called "dark retreat;" see note on "bardo retreat" by Trungpa Rinpoche in Trungpa and Fremantle 2000: 18; see also Lowenstein 2003) and often leads to bardo-like experiences. That raises the possibility (to my mind, *the probability*) that meditation-related experiences are projected upon the period after death—remember, dear reader, the Rule of Multiple Interpretations introduced in the last chapter. For reasons that will become clearer when we speak of phenomenology in the next chapter, what we require is a definition of consciousness that makes no culturally tainted assumptions, whether religious or otherwise.

There are of course purely psychological accounts of consciousness based upon one typology or another. One that has been proposed by Ned Block (Block 1995; Young and Block 1996) suggests several different types of consciousness:

> **Access consciousness (A-consciousness).** A-consciousness allows us to act upon our experiences and to report inner states. There is

reportable content to the brain state which may lead to planning, judgements and willful actions.

Phenomenal consciousness (P-consciousness). P-consciousness covers the qualitative nature of our experiences, including somatic, visual, auditory and-so-on sensations. We can recognize similarities and differences among patterns of sensation.

Monitoring consciousness (M-consciousness). M-consciousness refers to the thoughts we have about what we are perceiving.

Self-consciousness (S-consciousness). S-consciousness covers the awareness of our self, including thoughts we have about our self.

While typological accounts of consciousness can provide useful heuristics by pointing out one or another function of consciousness, they cannot constitute a definition of consciousness itself, for obviously typologies always leave stuff out, like the coherence of phenomena, the illusion of "puffed-out" space, or the phenomenon of synchrony across the sensorium.

Consciousness as an Energy Field

For various reasons I will discuss in a moment, I am partial to a field theory of consciousness. However, attempts by neuroscientists to posit a field theory have often fallen short of phenomenological credibility, for they frequently drift into metaphysical claims that do not really take experience into account. Moreover, they are more than a little enamored with the electromagnetic field theories developed in physics and astrophysics. A partial exception to this charge is the work of Benjamin Libet in modeling consciousness and brain as a *conscious mental field* (CMF) in a way that is very close to my own when he suggests, "…we may view conscious subjective experience as if it were a field, produced by appropriate though multifarious neuronal activities of the brain" (1994: 120). But he goes on to suggest:

> The putative CMF would not be in any category of known physical fields, such as electromagnetic, gravitational, etc. *The conscious*

mental field would be in a phenomenologically independent category; it is not describable in terms of any externally observable physical events or of any known physical theory as presently constituted. In the same sense as for all subjective events, the CMF would be detectable only in terms of the subjective experience, accessible only to the individual who has the experience. An external observer could only gain valid direct evidence about the conscious mental field from an introspective report by the individual subject. In this respect the conscious mental field would differ from all known physical fields, whose existence and characteristics are derived from physical observations. (1994: 120)

Libet has said that his CMF theory is testable. He proposes an experiment in which a slab of cortex is totally isolated from the rest of the brain—as for instance in a patient that is undergoing surgery for removal of that bit of the brain—and then see if stimulating the tissues in the slab are reportable by the patient. In practice, it is very near impossible to carry out such an experiment and has not yet been accomplished.

Again, there is the tendency for Libet, like Karl Popper and John Eccles's (1977) *three worlds* hypothesis, to create a model that requires a mind-body, mental-physical split. I must insist that a viable model of consciousness *not* require an ontological and epistemological independence of consciousness from its neurophysiological substrate— independence from the brain and body. What I feel we need is a model that is fully embodied (see Varela, Thompson and Rosch 1991; Rockwell 2005) and that allows us to move back and forth between subjective and so-called "objective" accounts of consciousness, with the subjective being privileged with respect to empirical disconfirmation. Such a model will, for instance, allow an explanation of how conscious mental acts can cause and be caused by physiological acts.

New Zealand neuroscientist, Susan Pockett (2000, 2012), has proposed an interesting *electromagnetic field* theory (EMF) of consciousness which considers consciousness to be nothing less than an electromagnetic field generated by the cytoarchitecture of the cortex of the brain. As such, consciousness becomes an epiphenomenon which is in principle equally applicable to AI. Once again, the separation of mind and body seems to be ineluctable for neuroscientists: "This theory proposes that conscious experiences are identical with certain spatial EM patterns generated by neural activity in the brains of conscious subjects. While the EM field theory is an identity theory, it differs radically from the psychoneural identity theory in that (like functionalism) it predicts the possibility of producing consciousness without neurons" (Pockett 2012: 193). Like Libet, Pockett claims the EMF theory is testable, and suggests various ways it has been and can be confirmed. However, also like Libet and so many other neuroscience theories of consciousness, there is little or no appeal to phenomenology, and certainly not to mature contemplation. To make matters even more awkward, she suggests that the cortical neural systems must be 6-layer systems, and as many animals do not have 6-layer cortexes, *ipso facto* they can't be conscious—as we shall see, a patently absurd conclusion.

The Phenomenological Root of the Mind-Body Gap

At this point, I feel we must better understand why the mind-body problem is so pervasive in theories of consciousness. In a word, the problem is a natural outcome of naïve phenomenology, and the application of mature contemplation can ease the problem, if not eliminate it. The problem is the consequence of how our brains are designed to process information about the world, a design that creates the illusion that there is a gap or schism between our intentional and physical acts, a gap we normally take for granted, and which is operating in all human beings, regardless of their cultural background.

To illustrate what I am talking about, let me suggest a phenomenological experiment that my friend and colleague, Jason Throop, and I have found useful (Laughlin and Throop 2009). Lay your arm on the table before you in a relaxed position and let your mind be as calm and thought-free as possible. Then slowly flex your fingers, bunching them into a loose fist. Focus at first on both the external image of your hand grasping and the internal feeling of your movements. Look at your arm and feel the movement and see how much of your arm is involved in the process of grasping. Then close your eyes and just feel the process of grasping from the inside. Feel where movements begin and end. Then use your other hand to feel your grasping hand and arm to track the muscle movements involved in grasping. Using all the visual, tactile and internal (somesthetic) information available to you, decide how far up your arm you can detect the movements. You will probably notice both visually and somesthetically that the effort involves your fingers, hand and forearm—that the act of grasping disappears somewhere around your elbow.

What you want to do for present purposes is become familiar with the physical processes that are involved in grasping something—a ball, handle, whatever. Explore the movements in your hand and arm and define the boundaries to the activity that we call "grasping" and the limits of your awareness of what is happening in your body during that activity. For instance, flex each finger independently and in combination with other fingers. Notice the different muscle movements that produce each combination. Notice how hard it is to flex your third and little finger at the same time without one or more of your other fingers moving as well. As silly as it sounds, notice that you cannot make a fist in the opposite direction—that is, toward the back of your hand instead of the palm side. You cannot will the hand to do what it is structurally incapable of doing. If you were to tape your thumb to your palm, this would impose new limitations upon your ability to grasp objects. There are clear limits to the grasping movements you can make, and these limits are determined by the structure of your hand and arm.

Now, when you have explored the physical act of grasping, shift your attention to the mental act of willing your hand to grasp. Relax your fingers and then will them—cause them—to grasp. You gaze at your hand and will it to grasp and virtually simultaneously with the intention, your hand moves. But now reflect upon the linkage between the will to grasp that arises within your conscious mind and the actual act of grasping by your hand. You may have already ascertained that the physical act of grasping occurs out at the end of your arm. You have seen that the grasping action stops at your elbow (or wherever). There is no obvious physical connection linking the act of grasping to the sphere of your will, intention or awareness. Yet every time you will the act to occur, it does so, as if by magic. This lack of any directly experienced linkage between your mental intention and the physical act of grasping provides experiential data indicating a mind-body gap. If you will extend this exploration to your other physical activities, you will discover that this gap is apparent in every one of them, from walking to opening and closing your mouth to blinking your eyes and typing on a keyboard.

If you have carried out this exercise seriously and with sufficient concentration, you have probably been able to isolate and directly experience your own mind-body gap. This can be a subtly profound realization. We become aware that although we have the freedom to will our hand to move, we cannot be aware of and track the causal mechanism between our conscious act and our physical hand and arm. Yet, as Rodney Cotterill (2001) has argued, the evolution of consciousness makes no sense without viewing the link between neural systems and skeletal musculature as fundament to adaptation. Failure to fully lodge consciousness in the body leads inevitably to epiphenomenal accounts of consciousness.

Of course, we all know something about this linkage between brain systems and muscle systems. For that matter, the Desana, a hunter-gatherer group in Amazonia, know a great deal more than most Westerners about the relationship between brain and behavior, based upon their observations of the effects of head injuries on the behavior of game they hunt (Reichel-Dolmatoff 1981). We know our body comes equipped with a nervous system that connects the higher brain functions mediating our consciousness and intentionality, and the muscle groups that move our limbs. We take this physiological information so much for granted that it may well get in the way of fully realizing the mind-body gap as it arises in direct experience and thus inhibit our intuitive comprehension of the gap. We may naïvely project the information we have of anatomy and physiology into our experience of the mind-body relationship and fail to appreciate the lack of any directly experienced link between our conscious will and our physical activity. Yet if we do the exercise while dropping all preconceptions, we can come to appreciate how people in traditional societies experience the mind-body relationship without knowing anything about modern neurophysiology (for more on this issue, see Laughlin and Throop 2009; Leder 1990).

Phenomenological Theories of Consciousness

Privileging phenomenology means that how we define consciousness requires that consciousness be commensurate with descriptions of experience (Jack and Roepstorff 2002). It is easy enough to define consciousness by pointing out all the various features we, as meditators, may describe. For example, Venkatesh *et al.* (1997) isolate the following features of consciousness based upon self-reports of meditators: body image, perception, meaning, time sense, joy, sexual excitement, love, anger, sadness, fear, imagery amount, imagery vividness, direction, concentration, self-awareness, state of awareness, internal dialogue, rationality, volitional control, memory, and arousal. This is a fulsome catalogue of aspects of consciousness. But there are other dimensions that are left out, most importantly the *unitary nature of experience* (see d'Aquili and Newberg 1999). I take a very Diltheyian view of experience, as does my colleague Jason Throop: "…experience is granted a certain primordial structure, coherence or selfgivenness that exists prior to the active conceptual patterning of sensation…. [T]he coherence of experience is given directly in experience itself and is not solely a product that is actively constructed by acts of consciousness" (Throop 2002: 4).

The Missing Ingredient

There is a missing ingredient in virtually all theories of consciousness, and one that is the key to comprehending how the brain produces a brain world that is both coherent and seemingly "puffed-out" in an illusion of space. This key is the particulate nature of sensation. All sensory experience arises in the *sensorium*—the sensorium is the "seat of conscious sensations," the highest level of sensory processing in the human cortex.[2] When speaking of consciousness, it is the entire field of sensory information before the aware mind (see Ong 1991). When I use the term sensorium, it includes the neurophysiological structures mediating our sensory experience. Recent research in the patterns of synaptic connectivity among neurons forming neural nets suggests to me that neurons and networks may link sensations in stereotyped ways when stimulated by sensory input (Reimann *et al.* 2017). However the neural nets are integrated to produce patterned activation of pixels, we must address this missing ingredient before we can define consciousness in a meaningfully neurophenomenological way.

---

[2] The sensorium is a time-honored term in science and medicine (Newton used the term in the 17th and 18th centuries).

It is apparent to some mature contemplatives that sensory data are pixelated, particulate or granular to perception (Laughlin 1992; Laughlin, McManus and d'Aquili 1990: 108-112; see also Chapter 5). In other words, there is a specific state of consciousness within which the contemplative can perceive that their entire sensorium is made up of a field of pixels (dots, granules, particles, *bindus, yods,* etc.)— an aesthetic nod here to France's Georges-Pierre Seurat, Japan's Yayoi Kusama and sundry Australian Aboriginal artists. After realizing this state, the sensorium is thereafter experienced as a field of pixels that is perceptually and cognitively distinguishable into sensory modes, and within sensory modes into forms and events—in other words, patterns of pixels. The fundamental act of perception is the abstraction and reinforcement of invariant features within the order of an unfolding and dissolving field of pixels (Figure 1.1; see Gibson 1979).

In my experience, apprehending the pixelated nature of the senses is easiest to realize visually, but eventually sound, taste, touch and feeling are all seen to be made up of "clouds" of sensory particles. Once one realizes this self-nature, one may easily apprehend the texture of the sensorium at will. Furthermore, when concentration upon sensory molecular pixels reaches a sufficient intensity, awareness of gross sensory objects is lost, as is awareness of past or future (see next chapter). The easiest exercise for realizing pixelation is in visual perception. In very subdued light, as at dusk or in a dimly lighted room, pick a small bright patch of light and scan it, then shut your eyes and watch the afterimage of that patch dissipate. As the image deteriorates, you can discern the individual visual pixels blink out. The same can be done with bits of other sensory modes. Do the same thing with the auditory sense by dinging a bell and watch how the sound diminishes and deteriorates. This is a common practice in Buddhist *pujas,* or elaborate ritual meditations. Auditory pixels will become obvious. Vision is the easiest to work with, while sound, taste and touch require far greater concentration and ignoring of "thingness" in perception (see next chapter on "bracketing" and "suchness").

Whether a theorist has attained this "pixel" realization is evident by how they report and think about their own consciousness, and what understanding of consciousness they project upon others. For instance, Australian philosopher of mind, David Chalmers, has famously defined what he calls "the hard problem" of consciousness (Chalmers,

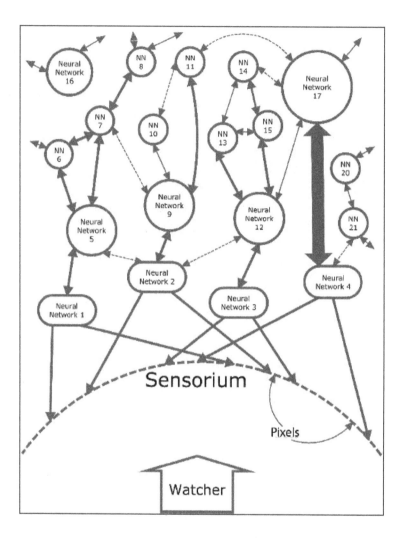

Figure 1.1. Fanciful Model of the Pixelated Sensorium. The pixelated structure of the sensorium is mediated by specialized sensory networks (the circle of dashes) which produce a seamless, "puffed-out" brain world for the consumption of the Watcher. Behind the patterns of pixels lie myriad neural networks (NN) that mediate recognition, identification and knowledge associated with the sensory patterns. NNs compete to control what is relevated into awareness. NN # 1-4 are those most directly mediating the brain world, but they all enjoy reciprocal (< >) interactions with many other NNs, while some NNs (#20 and 21) have minimal influence upon the brain world, and other NNs (# 16) have no influence whatsoever—in fact they may be actively dissociated via inhibitory links. Each NN in a network complex (e.g., # 5-8 and 12-15) has influence (heavy lines vs. dotted lines) upon the additive influence of the complex.

1996). By that he means, after we explain all the mental functions by reference to their underlying neurophysiology, the fact of experience remains a puzzle. "Why is it that when our cognitive systems engage in visual and auditory information-processing, we have visual or auditory experience: the quality of deep blue, the sensation of middle C? ...It is widely agreed that experience arises from a physical basis, but we have no good explanation of why and how it so arises. Why should physical processing give rise to a rich inner life at all" (Chalmers, 1995). Nowhere in his presentation of the "hard problem" does he evince the pixel realization noted above. He does not seem to realize that his patch of "deep blue" is (1) pixelated, and (2) a cognitive operation of his own brain. A patch of blue is the brain's symbolic representation of electromagnetic energies striking the retinae over a distributed area. In other words, blue pixels are the brain's way of representing a specific range of electromagnetic frequencies to itself. When one realizes that all sensory experience is a cognitive act on the part of the brain, then the so-called "hard problem" vanishes, or is at least made easier.

Answer the Bloody Question!

Alright then, enough futzing around with preliminaries. My working definition of consciousness is as follows: Experience arises in the sensorium, and as we have seen, our sensorium is distinctly human, conditioned by the structure of the body we inherit. The sensorium and assorted cognitive associations, most especially those structures mediating awareness, is not so much a physical location as a *neural phase space* (Nolte 2010).[3] A neural phase space is a kind of field that is made up of all the various functional areas of the nervous system that may potentially become entrained to the network mediating the brain's dynamic "stream of consciousness" (see Koch 2004). Consciousness is a neural phase space, not merely any particular function within that

---

[3] The idea of "phase space" was introduced by Willard Gibbs in the early 20th century *to model all possible states of a system.* The concept has been used in mathematics, mechanics and physics for decades, and is more recently being applied to the neurophysiology of functional organization and experience (e.g., Calitoiu, Oommen and Nussbaum 2012; Laughlin 1988; Werner 2011).

space (i.e., qualia, core consciousness, awareness, object of this moment's attention, so forth). Consciousness is *not* an epiphenomenon somehow floating above the brain like an ethereal EMF.

We know that consciousness is a field of some sort by realizing the unitary characteristic of experience. Moreover, we know that experience includes both the object of awareness and the ecology within which the object is selected and evaluated. Everything we focus our attention upon comes with a context, and the context impacts the interpretation and associated knowledge we bring to bear on the object. It does not require much advanced contemplation to comprehend that everything in experience is relative to and entangled with every other thing. Moreover, we can see that this quality of our brain world models the very nature of the real world itself—a realization which, when it comes-on strong in meditative experience, becomes the core realization of a full-blown mystical experience (Otto 1923; d'Aquili and Newberg 1999; Davidson 1976; Whiteman 1961; Forman 1997, 1998, 1999; Stace 1960; see Chapter 9). This, by the by, is why all traditional peoples build a worldview that is essentially a *cosmology*—a world conceived to be a monad within which all things are embedded, entangled and implicated (Robbins 2012). Our physical sciences, especially physics and astrophysics have found that they must model the real world as a cosmology—a universe of entanglement (DeGrasse Tyson and Goldsmith 2004)—in much the same way as virtually all traditional peoples have done (Flood 1993b: 2).

Even how we interpret color is context specific, and very human (Thompson, Palacios and Varela 1992). How animals perceive color (or not) is species specific. Color, of course, is not "out there," it is "in here," inside our brain world. We perceive only those colors that represent electromagnetic wave lengths in the real world that our visual system is designed to detect. Moreover, how we categorize color is wired-in—that is, we are born categorizing colors *prior to learning language* (Ozturk *et al.* 2013). Turns out that honey bees operate along similar lines. Their eyes contain trichromatic color receptor cells just as ours do. They use color in perception to learn about their environment, and exhibit inherent color categories as well, just as we do (see Avarguès-Weber, Mota and Giurfa 2012). But in the case of bees, the range of colors perceived includes electromagnetic frequencies to which we are blind. We see in the red range of the spectrum, but cannot see in the UV range, while honey bees see in the UV range and cannot see in the red range (Srinivasan 2010). Interestingly enough, there are rare humans whose retinae are blessed with four cone types—so-called *tetrachromats*—who are capable of ten times the color discriminations that most of us are able to manage (Jordan *et al.* 2010). Their color vision is far richer than the rest of us, and we have no way of appreciating the difference this makes in their visual brain world.

Each sensorial pixel is the conscious product of a tiny neural circuit that we cannot see. We only see what the neural circuit *does*. Using metaphors for the moment, each pixel is like the shining dot of light at the end of a black flashlight, the glow at the end of an invisible wand. Focusing on color patches, the bright colors are made up of colored pixels that are produced by their respective neural circuits. Millions of them produce a color patch. But also, blackness that we may interpret as the absence of color is in fact mediated in the same way. Black pixels are mediated by black dot circuits. Sensorial circuits are the Wizard of Oz behind the curtain that produce the world of appearances, white, black, gray or tri-colored. Everything that we perceive as "world" is made up of sensorial and other neural circuits and networks doing their "thing" in order to construct the brain world upon which our adaptation to the real world depends.

All the senses operate upon the principle of *topographical projection* by which spatial and other relations among sensory fields are reproduced at every level as the (afferent) neurons project their information into the cortex. Another way to see this is that spatial and other relations at the periphery of the body are represented and "mapped" onto the sensorium. The projections from the visual cells in the eyes are projected through neural tracts "retinotopically" into the visual cortex. This is called *retinotopy* or *retinal mapping*. The mechanoreceptor cells at the base of hairs are projected into the cortex via neurons that preserve the *somatic mapping* of their spatial distribution. Nociceptor cells in the skin relay their signals onto the cortex to retain their somatic position on the map of the body surface. The inner hair cells in the cochlea of the ear project *frequency-topically* into the cortex to conserve the relationship among "sounds" in the sensorium (*frequency mapping*). This is all very complicated, too much so to get into in detail. Suffice to say that the pixels of the sensorium represent in a very complex way the points of sensing by cells at the periphery, and the topographical relations of sensory cells are reproduced in an adaptive and veridical manner in the points arising in the sensorium.

One of the problems I have puzzled over for years is just where in the brain does the sensorium "come together," so to speak, to produce the typical unity of experience. We have known for some time that the various features of perceptual reality (the perceptual brain world) are processes in different areas of the brain in a "distributed parallel" manner (McClelland and Rumelhart 1986; Rogers and McClelland 2014). My hunch is that the synthesis occurs in the frontal area of the brain, at least among big brain mammals, including us "nearly hairless apes." More specifically, I have suggested that the sensorium arises somewhere in the region of the *anterior cingulate gyrus* and adjacent *prefrontal cortex* (PFC)—specifically the orbital and medial areas of the prefrontal cortex; see Figures 1.2 and 1.3). I have made this suggestion because: (1) this is the only single area of the brain where all sensory modes are represented, and where attention to cross-modal congruence of information is recognized, (2) this area exerts motor control thus linking the sensorium to action, and (3) this area is connected to the limbic system, thus linking the sensorium and affect (see e.g., Laughlin 1988; Laurienti *et al.* 2003; Groenewegen and Uylings 2000; Barbas 2000).

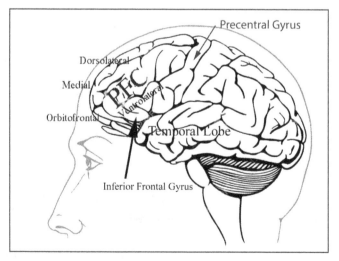

Figure 1.2. Left Cortical Hemisphere of the brain. Shown are the approximate locations of the different areas of the prefrontal cortex (PFC), the dorsolateral, ventrolateral, medial and orbital areas, as well as the temporal lobe and inferior frontal gyrus.

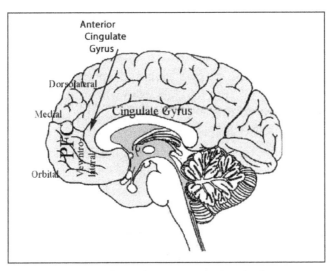

Figure 1.3. Areas of the Prefrontal Cortex (PFC). The brain is cut down the middle (sagittal view) showing the normally hidden aspects of the prefrontal cortex, including the dorsolateral, ventrolateral, medial and orbital PFC, as well as the anterior (forward) portion of the cingulate gyrus.

Critical to our understanding of this system is that the prefrontal cortex does *not* receive sensory information directly from the periphery, but rather from secondary association areas elsewhere in the cortex (Crick and Koch 1998). By the time sensory experiences arise in the sensorium, the information has been considerably processed. For instance, color processing and form processing occur in different areas of the brain but come together seamlessly in the sensorium. However, some sensory inputs are siphoned off at subcortical levels of the brain and used for various other functions that do not require awareness. For instance, visual data are used at the level of the midbrain to control eye, head and arm movements that can occur unconsciously because no direct link exists from that area of the midbrain directly to the prefrontal cortex/sensorium system.

THE EVOLUTION OF THE CONSCIOUS BRAIN

One of the great advantages of a neurophenomenological perspective on consciousness is that it allows for grounded speculations about the evolution of consciousness as a biologically adaptive, somatic activity. Inferences have long been made about when and how the "modern mind" arose among our ancestors. The archaeological and paleontological remains of past hominin[4] species have been picked over for generations looking for clues as to when this or that capability arose—the first use of fire, the first manufacture of stone, bone and wooden tools, the first domestication of plants and animals, the first evidence of burying the dead, and the first indications of mobiliary art have all been used to infer advancement of intelligence, consciousness and culture in our prehistoric past. But linking consciousness to neurophysiological structures and functions also allows us yet another avenue, and one that allows us to work our way back, not merely a few thousand or a few hundred thousand years, but for millions of years (Donald 2003; Cotterill 2001). It certainly allows us to reflect upon the apparent increase in the size of the hominin brain over the last few million years (Figures 1.4 and 1.5). And most of us would like to assert that this increase in the size, and of course complexity of the brain signals an increase in the complexity of consciousness.

But consciousness did *not* begin with the rise of the hominin line. It began long before there were any primates that could begin to evolve in our direction. We can say with some surety that consciousness arose when the first creature became capable of selecting one object and its cognitive associations from within its neural phase space. Put another way, consciousness originated with the ability to focus attention upon part of the sensorium to the exclusion of other potential objects and to act accordingly. We may also hypothesize that *animals evolved to experience before they became conscious.*

Evolving Experience and Consciousness

At some point in the evolution of animals, the first primitive forms of consciousness appeared, and this point was way before the evolution of humans, or even primates, mammals and large-brained invertebrates (see e.g., Edelman, Baars and Seth 2005; Boly *et al.* 2013). The

---

[4] The term "hominin" refers to all the creatures in the direct line of primate evolution leading to our own species, *Homo sapiens sapiens.*

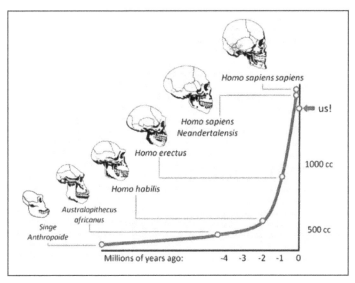

Figure 1.4. The Evolution of the Hominin Brain. Most of our evidence for the increasing size of our ancestors' brains comes from fossilized skulls from different periods in evolution. This means that the size of our distant ancestor Australopithecus living on the plains of Africa over 4 million years ago had the largest hominin brain in the world at the time, and it was barely, if at all, larger than that of the modern-day chimpanzee. Three million years or so later, our ancestor's brain had more than doubled in size. Modern human adult brain size averages around 1260cc for males and 1140 for females, the difference having to do with the ratio of brain size to body size.

evolution of the animal kingdom began with the origin of single cell creatures (first the *procaryotes*, then the *eucaryotes*) who very likely also experienced their environment in some very rudimentary way (Schwab 2012). Single cell animals alive today adapt to their environment by moving in space-time to avoid dangerous UV light and to optimally store energy. That means there must be some mechanism, however primitive, of internally depicting their environment as information, and acting accordingly. "Photoreceptive compounds, including the rhodopsin family, photolyases, and cryptochromes, and chlorophyll all would be helpful to early cells in several ways" (ibid: 9). We know that single cell *eucaryotes* like *euglena, amoeba* and *paramecium* can sense variations of light and chemistry and move with that information "in mind." *Euglena* features an "eyespot" that contains photoreceptive rhodopsins that allow the creature to orient and move toward or away from high light density stimuli (ibid: 13). I doubt much "learning"

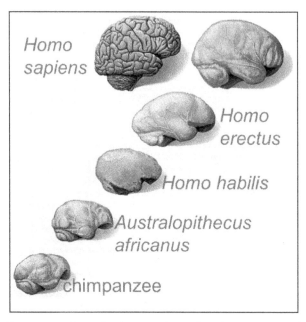

Figure 1.5. Comparing Brain Endocasts along the Hominin Line. The brains of human ancestors not only became larger, but larger in relation to the size of their bodies. Notice the exceptional development of the frontal lobes.

is going on, nor am I suggesting that these primitive life forms are conscious, in the sense I have defined the term. However, future research may surprise us. Experience first arose as an adaptation to a dynamic environment within which animals had to find food and avoid dangers. J.R.R. Tolkien's imaginary *Ents* aside, land plants do not adapt to their environments by moving their position in space, and thus may not have evolved the mechanisms necessary for mediating experience.[5] However, in my opinion, the jury is still out on plant consciousness (Gardiner 2012).

The emergence of multicellular animals further developed the reliance upon experiencing and moving in space-time. They had to develop mechanisms for coordinating somatic activities so that potentially autonomous cells did not render concerted action impossible.

---

[5] Some plants are phototropic, and thus have a rudimentary ability to orient their leaves to maximize sunlight. Also, there is some evidence that a plant's root systems may communicate within the system to maximize nutriment.

This necessity eventually led to the specialization of control cells that evolved into neurons and eventually simple neural nets (or circuits) typical of creatures like the jellyfish (Figure 1.6; see Sanes, Reh and Harris 2005: Chap. 1).

As animal species increased in size and cellular complexity, so too did the neural networks become more complex to maintain control of otherwise autonomous somatic systems (Sporns 2010: 142-148). Eventually, these primitive neural circuits formed a neural tube with multiple sensory organs, typical of (say) triploblastic worms like those that evolved a billion years ago (see Ghysen 2003). It is thus very likely that experience mediated by a primitive nervous system—a conscious system that included awareness operating selectively within a multi-modal sensorium—arose in the earliest stages of multicellular animal evolution (see Crist 2002 on Darwin's fascinating research demonstrating "intelligence" and experience among earthworms; Figure 1.7).

There is a clear process of cephalization in the evolution of species (Jerison 1973). That is, there is a trend in which larger and more complex nervous systems are selected for along most evolutionary lines. We are thus far the culmination of that process among primates. The octopus is the culmination of that process among invertebrate cephalopods. The octopus has the highest brain-to-body mass ratios of any other invertebrates (Wells 2013; Zullo and Hochner 2011). The evolution of

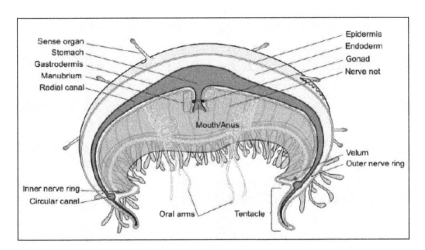

Figure 1.6. Inside a Jellyfish. The jellyfish has been cut in half to show the internal organs, including its neural ring and nerve net. Note also the sensory organs.

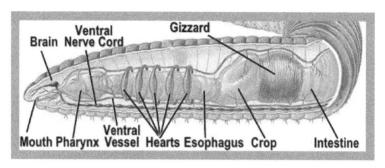

Figure 1.7. Front End of an Earthworm Showing Internal Organs. Notice the small brain attached to the ventral nerve cord. Small as it is, the brain is capable of remarkable intelligence.

the nervous systems of animals in different classes has led to many homologies and differences in the structure and function of the brain. This is in part because body structures are the result of adaptation over millions of years of selection, and the environment of the octopus is radically different than that of big-brained mammals like elephants, lions and humans. Consider: the octopus lives in a world with little gravity. It can move freely in all directions and can conform its body (no bones!) to any configuration and skin camouflage it desires. Thus, it has a more distributed nervous system: three fifths of its nervous system are in its arms allowing exquisite control over semi-autonomous movements of each arm (Young 1971). In the arms are suckers that both "touch" and "taste" their surroundings. At the base of each arm is a sub-brain (ganglion) which has control over that arm, and accumulates sensory information that is then sent to the brain. Their brain has an enormous visual system and collates visual data and data from the sensory systems in the arms. The octopus has the most advanced cognitive and learning system among the invertebrates.

It is very likely that the entire brain world, its sensorium and most of consciousness of higher mammals is mediated by cortical structures of the brain (Seth, Baars and Edelman 2005). It is very common for people to think of the cortex as a recent innovation in evolution, but this is not the case, as the primitive cortex and its precursors date way back to the brains of invertebrates living during the Precambrian era, some half a billion years ago or more (Tomer *et al.* 2010). Part of the confusion about this issue is semantic. The outermost surface of the invertebrate brain is called a *mushroom body* (rather than a cortex; Figure 1.8), a structure found in the brains of many worms and arthropods today that mediates learning and memory—the two most important precursor functions to the selection for the symbolic processing of reality during evolution.

All vertebrates have a similar layer of neural surface tissue that is called the *pallium*, which serves the same function, shares the same genetics as the invertebrate mushroom body, and dates to roughly 360 million years ago. It is also much more complex and advanced in birds and lower mammals than was once thought, due to the mistaken notion that the *pallium* consisted only of what we would call the basal ganglia in the human brain (Jarvis 2004). The pallium expanded and complexified over time and became the cerebrum of lizards, and then birds and mammals between 220 and 280 million years ago (Figure 1.9). This suggests that experience involving making sensory patterns meaningful was operating from nearly the inception of brains as the prime adaptive organ. Hence symbolic imagery has been fundamental

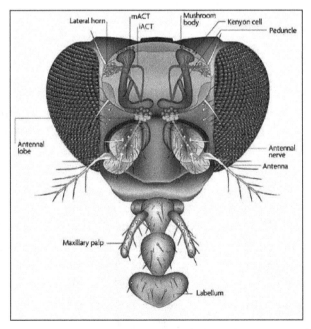

Figure 1.8. The Head of a Fruit Fly (*Drosophila melanogaster*). The inside of the head of the fly shows its mushroom bodies (*corpora pedunculata*) and associated nerves. The mushroom bodies are the higher centers of the fly nervous system associated with learning and memory.

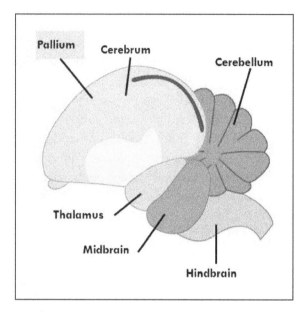

Figure 1.9. A Typical Bird Brain. The drawing shows the relationship between the pallium and other lower centers common to avian and mammalian brains.

to consciousness since at least the beginning of the Cambrian era some 540 million years ago.

Just to make things clearer, there are three types of neurons in the mammalian brain: (1) *afferent neurons* that carry sensory information from sense organs into the sensory association brain centers, (2) *efferent neurons* that carry commands from within the brain's control areas out to organs and muscles, and (3) *interneurons* (or *local circuit neurons*; Sporns 2010: 3) that connect to each other to form local circuits—kind of like wee biocomputers. These latter are cells that neither deliver sensory data from the surfaces of our body or organs, nor carry commands to muscles and organs, but inhabit an intermediate space between those information-in, information-out functions. Simple local circuits make our reflexes work (Figure 1.10). When the doctor taps you on the knee with her little rubber hammer, it is the reflexes in your spinal cord that transform sensory input into action. More complex systems of interneurons comprise the sensory association areas, memory circuits and higher cortical functions that intervene between sensory input and action.

There are many times the number of interneurons relative to afferent and efferent neurons in the brains of more advanced animals, and the higher on the evolutionary scale, the higher that proportion of interneurons becomes. Interneurons organize to mediate experiential models (or "schemas") of extramental reality (Hensch 2005).[6] In other words, without the emergence of interneurons intervening between sensory input and behavioral output, complex experience—our inner "movie," or our "controlled hallucinations" as Anil Seth (2017) would say—as we humans know it would not be possible.

Somewhere along the long course of the evolution of consciousness, the structure of the body began to make a marked difference in the sensoria of different species. The physical structure of the body and the layout of its sensory systems led to species-specific variations in the brain world of the world's creatures. I am sure that most anthropologists do not dwell upon the difference between our human sensorium and that of another species, say that of the hammerhead shark (*Sphyrna sps.*), but they ought to. Hammerheads have their eyes out on the side of their broad scalloped heads (or *cephalofoil*) and because the eye balls swivel and the shark yaws its head from side to side as it swims, its visual sensorium incorporates views of nearly 360 degrees around its body with sufficient overlap in front for binocular vision (McComb, Tricas and Kajiura 2009). On top of this, the *Sphyrna*:

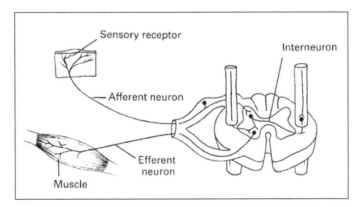

Figure 1.10. The Typical Reflex Arc. This diagram shows how afferent neurons bring information in from the peripheral sensory cells, and efferent neurons channel commands out to the muscles. The interneurons in the spinal column carry out rudimentary information-processing. The entire nervous system is made up of these three types of cells.

... have one of the largest olfactory bulb (collection of sensory cells for smelling) to brain ratio of any species and must rely heavily upon this sense. The scalloped hammerhead has an olfactory bulb that occupies 7% of its total brain mass as compared to approximately 3% for sharks in other families. Additionally, much of the forebrain in these sharks is devoted to the interpretation of odors. (Schwab 2012: 83)

As if this were not enough, the hammerhead in company with other sharks have a facility for detecting small electrical fields emitted by other animals (Campagno, Dando and Fowler 2005: 33). There are sensors under their nostrils called the ampules of Lorenzini which are linked to long jelly-filled tubes that connect via neurons to their brains. When there is insufficient light to see, they are still able to locate prey through their slight muscle movements, even when buried in the sand. Moreover, a "lateral line" of sensory hair cells runs down the side of the shark which allows it to sense vibrations created by movements in the water around it.

It is hard to phenomenologically comprehend the difference between a hammerhead's brain world and our own. However, one can imagine what it would be like to extend our visual acuity to nearly 360 degrees around us. We too move our heads back and forth to increase the angle of our visual field. If we do not move our head, our eyes can see a horizontal arch of roughly 115 degrees. Our vision is distinctly binocular, thus providing stereopsis because we evolved a visual system adapted to arboreal life in which estimation of distance to the next limb was essential. The hammerhead by contrast has less overlap producing stereopsis, but also, because the eyes are placed so distant apart, there is a triangular blind spot right in front of its nose. The shark cannot see what is right close in front of it. Of course we humans—like most vertebrates—have color vision, but sharks generally do not, so our imagined hammerhead brain world is visually one of shades of grey.

---

[6] I prefer the term "model" to the old gestalt "schema" used so effectively by Jean Piaget (1977). These earlier theorists had no way to ground the organization of representations of reality in neuroscience, but now we do. My use of model denotes a neurophysiological structure that mediates experience of the self or extramental reality.

Now, if we close our hypothetical hammerhead eyes to simulate complete darkness, we still can monitor our surrounding environment by our other senses. We can smell odors, sense movements of air touching our skin, and hear various sounds. People who are blind from birth show remarkable adaptations, especially auditory ones that allow them to safely move through their environment. However, there is no way we can appreciate the vast amount of information arising in the hammerhead's olfactory sensorium. The shark can detect the smell of tiny amounts of blood from miles away and follow the gradient to its source. We cannot imagine a 360-degree felt environment driven by the thousands of tiny shifts in vibrations in the water, nor can we imagine how the shark experiences the small electrical fields all around it, and discriminates which fields are food and which are to be ignored. All we must do is imagine ourselves as a blind person donning scuba gear and then sinking to the bottom of a lake. How easily could we find our way around? We could smell nothing; our touch would avail us little as we scurry about the bottom. Our hearing would be virtually useless as we could not detect direction with any acuity. We would have no electrical field sense, no sensorium full of wee vibrations, no sense of a magnetic compass. We would be relatively helpless.

With a bit of imagination and knowledge of the neurophysiology, we can to some extent put ourselves in the phenomenological shoes of other creatures and increase our appreciation of just how much the physiology of different bodies can influence quite different sensoria and hence consciousness, especially among big-brained critters like ourselves.

CONSCIOUSNESS AND CULTURE

The moment-by-moment shift in consciousness is the place where sensory materials arise to meet the cognitive functions mediating the meaning of things. The prime directive of the experiencing brain is to seek out patterns in sensed reality and to render those patterns meaningful. Of course, we all realize that most of the mental activities of the nervous system occur outside of the stream of consciousness (are sub-conscious or un-conscious) and many of these may never actually rise into consciousness—as we saw with the grasping exercise above.

We also saw that we do not have within our neural phase space the rich variety of odors, vibrations and electrical fields available to the hammerhead sensorial repertoire. We can only experience what we are neurophysiologically prepared to experience.

Neurognosis and the "Culture Ready Brain"

Many of the perceptual and cognitive associations constituting "meaning" are already available at or before birth. My colleagues and I have called this primitive, species-specific way of knowing *neurognosis*, a concept that will prove important in understanding various archetypal meditation experiences later in the book (Laughlin, McManus and d'Aquili 1990). My late friends and colleagues, John McManus and Gene d'Aquili, and I concocted the term "neurognosis" to label the genetic background of knowing. "Neuro-," of course, points to the brain, while "gnosis" refers to inherent knowing in the Greek (*gnôsis*) sense of insight, or intuition, rather than reason or intellectual knowing. Our concept is very similar, but not identical to Carl Jung's notion of *archetype*, but more on that later (see Stevens 1982). We are born with an experiential world "already there"—with a sensorium already vibrant with olfactory, visual, auditory, tactile, gustatory, and other sensory objects, movements, memories and relations, as well as space and time (Laughlin and Loubser 2010; Laughlin and Throop 2008; Throop and Laughlin 2002; Trevarthen 1995; Lagercrantz 2016). At no time in our development, pre- or perinatal, is our brain world chaotic (Laughlin 1991). Our brain is already equipped with a library of nascent categories and images that lay the foundation for development of intuitive knowing patterns selectively abstracted from the sensorium (Gazzaniga 2002; Count 1973; Holtkamp 2012; Laughlin and d'Aquili 1974; Stevens 1982; Wilkinson 2006; Williams 2012). Much of this library seems to be in the right hemisphere of the brain (Schore 2000, 2003, 2008). As neuroscientist Dale Purves (2010: 233) notes,

...the circuitry of nervous systems such as ours has evolved to contend with one fundamental challenge: How to generate useful perceptions and behaviors in response to a world that is unknowable directly by means of sensory stimuli. The strategy that has emerged to deal with this problem is governed by history, not logical principles or algorithms. Based on feedback from the empirical consequences of behavior, accumulated information about operational success is realized over evolutionary time in inherited neural circuitry whose organization is then modified to a limited extent by individual experience.

We humans are a species of social ape, and our neurognostic world is thus inherently social (Whitehead 2010b; Trevarthan 1995; Arbib, Liebal and Pika 2008; Lagercrantz 2016; Kagan 2013). We are born prepared to be enculturated—as Charles Whitehead put it, we have "culture ready brains" (Whitehead 2010b, 2012, 2016). Enculturation begins before birth. We all spent much waking time in our last trimester in the womb learning about the range of phonetics used by our parents and are born with an auditory bias toward that range of sounds. We are born knowing faces and breasts and the distinct smell and gaze of our mother (Laughlin 1991; Thoman 1979; Verny and Weintraub 2002; Lagercrantz 2016). We are also born with the innate, intuitive knowledge of totality, the monistic and entangled nature of reality. It is the latter type of neurognostic structuring that leads meditators in any full-on tradition anywhere on the planet to the realization of what has been called *absolute unitary being* (AUB; see d'Aquili and Newberg, 1993, 1998, 1999, 2000; Newberg and d'Aquili 2008; we will discuss AUB experiences later in the book). Our brain develops rapidly during our early life and this development involves cell growth and the establishment of interconnections between cells into neural circuits, and circuits into larger networks of cells and circuits. Development is both driven by internal biological dynamics (LeDoux 2003b) and influenced by environmental and sociocultural constraints. The degree of plasticity of any specific neural structure will vary from function to function, and with the period of development. Much of what anthropologists call enculturation is the influence our social upbringing exercises on the growth and plasticity of neural networks (Cacioppo, Visser and Pickett 2005; Decety and Ickles 2009; Huttenlocher 2002; Stiles *et al.* 2012). A good example is our heightened awareness of the range of sounds used in our natal language. Indeed, there is no more germane relationship between our physical nature and our cultural conditioning than the social and environmental influences on our sensorium.

Mirror Neurons and Social Consciousness

Another important element of our social natures is the existence of areas of our brain that contain what are called *mirror neurons* (Kilner and Lemon 2013; Gallese 2005; Gallese, Eagle and Migone 2007). These are cells within neural networks that become active, both when the animal does something, or when the animal perceives another animal do that same thing. It is hypothesized that mirror neurons are part of the social brain that subserves *empathy*—the capacity of normal humans to put themselves in another's shoes, to feel what they feel, to see things the way they do (Decety and Jackson 2004; Decety and Ickles 2009). As such, empathy can be both emotional and cognitive. Mirror neurons are found in the brains of primates and birds and seem to be a fundamental feature of social adaptation. In the human brain, they may be found in the premotor and supplementary motor cortex, the primary somatosensory cortex and the inferior parietal cortex (Molenberghs, Cunnington and Mattingley 2009; see Figure 1.11).

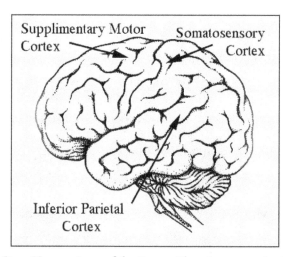

Figure 1.11. Mirror Neuron Areas of the Cortex. The primary areas in the human brain within which mirror neurons operate are the premotor and supplementary motor areas, the somatosensory area and the inferior parietal area of the cortex.

Emotional empathy is linked to the insular cortex that is buried inside the lateral sulcus (see Figure 2.4; see also Eres *et al.* 2015). Culture has little to do with whether people have any particular sense, for the various sensory modalities are inherent in the organization of the body and its nervous system (Barlow and Mollon 1982; Purves 2010). However, how the senses develop is very much conditioned by upbringing (Shore 1988). Because culture is humanity's principal way of socially adapting to reality, sensory development is quite sensitive to the society's collective brain world rendition of the physical and social environments (see, e.g., Seeger 1981 on the perception of nature among the Suyà Indians of Brazil). An excellent example is the fact that we Westerners have a hard time speaking about odors because our languages have few if any abstract olfactory terms. Certain hunter-gathering cultures however include languages that are rich in abstract terms for odors (Majid and Kruspe 2018). The ease with which these peoples can discuss odors is due to their upbringing, and languages exquisitely sensitive to the olfactory stimuli in their environment. Because of the importance of sensory enculturation, a lot of attention has been paid to the senses in anthropology over recent decades (Geurts 2002; Howes 1991; Moeran 2007; Stoller 1989; Throop 2010). This is to my mind a very hopeful development in the movement toward a full-blown neuroanthropology.

Neurognosis and the "Primordial Mind"

In one of the most insightful books I have read in a long time— psychiatrist Michael Robbins' *The Primordial Mind in Health and Illness* (2011)—Robbins posits the existence of a *primordial mind* that predates thought and which operates in parallel with rationality. The primordial mind is pregnant with meaning and supplies knowledge that is often difficult if not impossible to render into language. People in Western technocratic societies that operate primarily in the domain of the primordial mind are often marginalized as weird, kooky, or crazy. Traditional people of the sort I call polyphasic are more in tune with their primordial minds which are accessed more fluidly in ASC; i.e., in dreams, drug trips and trance states. As qualitatively different systems of mind, the two are related by analogy, not by linear causality that applies when one is working within a single system, based on the assumption that all mental activity is a subset of symbolic representational thought. This two-system model of mind based on analogical principles and transformations of meaning is nested within a larger multisystem model consisting of genetic endowment, brain, mind, interpersonal relationships, social structure, and culture. (Robbins 2011: 207)

The primordial mind is essentially neurognostic in its neurocognitive foundations and more fully develops in polyphasic cultural environments. Access to this level of pre-linguistic knowing—or "thought without language" (Weiskrantz 1988)—is experienced as intuition and imagery. Such access is common in ASC, particularly dreaming. For typical Westerners and other peoples with more materialistic, monophasic cultures, knowledge from the primordial mind requires rationalization, the rational account often being more an interpolation than a true account of the knowing (Laughlin 1997a). Yet the two systems of knowing remain with us all and run parallel to each other daily. In our fantasy lives, our intuitive grasps, our dreams, our primordial thoughts burble-up into consciousness, revealing to the introspective mind the comprehensions from the depths of our psyche. We in the West are taught to disattend these meanderings, but in many other cultures they are more readily attended and utilized in storytelling, myth-making and ritual procedures. As we shall see, engagement with the primordial mind becomes the essence of self-exploration in Jungian "active imagination" and other types of psychodynamic traditions that take one to the level of archetypes (see Chapter 7).

States of Consciousness

While phenomenological scrutiny can easily ascertain that no two experiences are exactly alike, humans identify recurring states that are characterized as selective abstraction, "...the process of focusing on a detail taken out of context, ignoring other more salient features of the situation, and conceptualizing the whole experience on the basis of this element" (Beck and Alford 2009: 204). States of consciousness are the product of the activity of innumerable neurophysiological systems that combine in a distinct organization making each state they mediate familiar and subjectively identifiable. For example, I am "tipsy" because

I feel elated, less coordinated and more sociable due to drinking alcohol. I am "dreaming" because I can get out of my body and fly around. I am "awake" because physical reality impedes my will. I am "hallucinating" because others cannot see what I am seeing. Just what recurring factors are selected for abstraction has a lot to do with our upbringing, how we talk about experiences, and hence our cultural background.

The neural processes that mediate each moment of experience are componential in their structure (Purves 2010). Most of the neural structures that combine to produce a familiar state of consciousness are common to other states as well (Pagel 2008). For instance, common to all experiences had in any state of consciousness is what Damasio (1999: 16) called *core consciousness* that "provides the organism with a sense of self about one moment—now—and about one place—here." Core consciousness is mediated in part by several evolutionarily older neural centers, including areas in the brain stem and in the somatosensory and cingulate cortex (Figure 3.5). These areas mediate arousal, the sense of the body in space, and emotion within consciousness. Damasio (1999) made the point that damage to other and newer cortical areas may lead to impairment of some functions, but not to core consciousness itself.

The Symbolic Brain

The myriad of different internal systems within the brain isolate and process patterns of selectively abstracted sensory input from reality or from imagery generated internally. Once again, the prime directive of this processing is to seamlessly meld pattern with meaning within the flow of experience. When this facility breaks down, as happens among patients with advanced Alzheimer's disease who may be perfectly able to recognize a face, but are no longer able to recognize faces (e.g., their son's face), then we are able to see that normal perception involves cognizing, including the association of images with emotions. The merger of pattern and meaning is so rapid and automatic that we are rarely aware of the activity, although seasoned meditators may apperceive a slight lag at times between stimulus and recognition. We do become a bit more aware of the process when it fails, as when we see a flash of blue through the trees and interpret it as water, only to find that the blue was sunlight reflected from a barn roof.

The act of knowing something is always an exercise of the *symbolic process* (Laughlin, McManus and d'Aquili 1990), the perceptual and cognitive act of matching patterns with their respective meanings stored in memory. Virtually all knowledge in primitive invertebrate animals is neurognostic with far less neural plasticity of networks and hence learning involved in experience. In higher animals, neurognosis is the initial, primitive, species-specific form of the symbolic process. Neurognosis mediates the universal aspects of pattern recognition and meaning. We rapidly develop our library of meanings after birth by repetitive interactions with the local physical and social environments, including our own body, and processing information through neural models having their initial structures as neurognosis.

As consciousness evolved, it by no means in any sense of the word left its essentially symbolic nature behind. Nothing could be further from the case. As George Lakoff (2014) and others have made clear in their research, our thought is riddled with metaphorical concepts—concepts that are mediated by distinct neural circuitry. Lakoff (2014: 1) offers an example used by his colleague Michael Reddy (1979):

> Reddy found over 100 classes of expressions for this metaphor. Examples include: *You finally **got through** to him. The meaning is right there **in the words**. **Put** your thoughts **into** clear language. Your words are **hollow**.* And many more. His point was that the generalization covering the linguistic metaphors was not in language, but in the metaphorical concept of communication as sending idea-objects in language-containers.

Metaphorical thought pervades our lives and is inherent not only in how we speak of things, but how we conceive of things. As Lakoff (2014) notes, morality is spoken of in terms of food—morality is linked to purity, immorality linked to rottenness. This is a metaphor that is virtually ubiquitous across cultures (Douglas 1966). Metaphors go on and on: we "devour" knowledge, "consume" goods and services, "digest" opinions, "grope" for truth. We won't "sit still" for that kind of treatment, we can't "fathom" why he did that, we "fabricate" lies, and we "run" the program. One of the most pernicious conceptual metaphors that haunts the American political psyche generation after generation is that of war (see Lakoff 1991). We see wars everywhere; the war on drugs, the war on poverty, the war on terrorism, the war on crime, the war on cancer, and on and on.

> This should not be thought of as a mere laundry list of cases. What links them together are the mechanisms that create the *neural metaphor system*—the neural learning mechanisms, the mapping circuits, the bindings, and the best-fit condition. "Best-fit" is more accurately called the conservation of energy law, namely, maximize the activation of existing circuitry with strong synapses that takes the least energy. Why, for example, should smelling fishy be behaviorally connected to suspicion…? (Lakoff 2014: 8; emphasis mine)

The key point here is that there exists a systematic neural structure that mediates metaphorical thought. It is pre-linguistic and neurognostic in its formation and is undoubtedly one that we evolved from within our phylogenetic line. It was operating long before hominins evolved language. Let Lakoff (2014: 5) spell it out for us:

- The human brain is structured by thousands of embodied metaphor mapping circuits that create an extraordinary richness within the human conceptual system. They largely function unconsciously.
- These mapping circuits asymmetrically link distinct brain regions, allowing reasoning patterns from one brain region to apply to another brain region….
- Each circuit characterizes a different form of metaphorical thought. Though metaphorical in content, the circuits reflect a reality, namely, real correspondences in real-world physical and social experiences starting in infancy.
- Where the experiences are essentially the same across cultures, the metaphor mappings tend to be the same. They appear to be learned by experience via neural learning. The asymmetry of the mappings appears to arise via STDP—spike-timing dependent plasticity— from which metaphor sources and targets can be predicted.
- Simple metaphorical thought is learned prior to, and independent of language, and plays an important role in the shaping of grammatical form….

- Complex metaphorical thought is formed via a neural binding mechanism....
- Complex metaphorical thought shows up not just in language, but in gesture, imagery (paintings, movies, dance, etc.), in mathematics..., science..., and in moral and political ideology.
- The compositional properties of language, not surprisingly, lead to an unbounded range of complex metaphorical thought expressed linguistically.
- In the theory of neural cascades..., bidirectional cascades of neural activation link complex form (most notably, linguistic form) to complex metaphorical meanings characterized via [neural] connections to and from many brain regions.
- Metaphorical inferences arise via the neural simulation of situations that are understood, at least in part, via the activation of metaphor mapping circuits characterizing how the situations to be simulated are understood.
- The compositional properties of language allow for an even greater unbounded range of complex metaphorical thought, but still understood via embodied primitive concepts and primary metaphors.

Neural circuitry allows these cascades of metaphorical links to be built in a virtual pyramid of comprehension. Recognition of novelty in the sensorium is quickly reduced to redundancy by the projection of metaphorical concepts upon the sensory event. It is this automatic cascading of inferences that, as we shall see in the next chapter, is suspended in the practice of advanced phenomenology. It is also this understanding of the essentially metaphorical nature of our thought that makes it easier to understand why the relationship between our conscious and unconscious minds is made possible by an enormous library of shared metaphors.

Culture and Alternative States of Consciousness (ASC)

Complex states of consciousness are relatively stable, recurrent over time, recognizable by the individual, and cognized and communicated within the individual's social group as distinct from other states. All cultures on the planet recognize, conceptualize and communicate about states of consciousness. Yet, the role played by states of consciousness in developing social identity and in local theories of reality can vary enormously across cultures. Experiences had in alternative states are systematically downplayed in technocracies, which are characterized by monophasic culture (Laughlin 2011). As we shall see, meditation systems that do not involve ingesting psychoactive drugs have become relatively popular among monophasic Western cultures, whereas those involving such drugs are usually proscribed. Among other things, this has caused a bias in the way Western psychology has approached meditation cultures.

Throughout the anthropological literature on traditional spiritual traditions, we constantly run across the term "trance." For the transpersonalist, this is a red flag signaling the author probably does not know what the experience had by his or her host is all about, nor has he or she had such an experience. I will be using the term "trance" all through this book, because it is the term that other authors have used. In most cases, whether evoked by use of drugs or some other ritual practice, the term *trance* should be read as ASC, unless otherwise stipulated (see Inglis 1990). In other words, the word is used to signal that some sort of ASC has been detected as happening and as relevant to a group's spiritual or healing activity. Of course, there are many kinds of "trance," not just one monolithic trance state; e.g., channeling trance, hypnotic trance, possession trance, psychedelic trance, magical trance, and so forth. For a discussion of the neurobiology and cross-cultural incidence of "trance" states, see Hove *et al.* (2015), Winkelman (1986, 2010) and Glicksohn and Ohana (2011).

Volition

What most English-speaking people mean by being conscious is that they are aware of something, as in, "I hear the phone ringing," "I see that tree," so forth. But what is really implied in most people's understanding is that consciousness is an experiential phase space within which any selectively abstracted object (e.g. image, motion, relationship, tone, texture) stands out as the focus of attention—the pivot point for organizing cognition (Posner 2004; Posner and Peterson

1990; Osaka 2003: 106-117). However, when Navajo people speak of consciousness or awareness, they use the same term (*áháshyq*, "to be aware or conscious"). Consciousness also equates with mind (*bíní*, "mind" or "volition"). If one loses consciousness it means to a Navajo speaker that their mind has literally vanished (Reichard 1950). Traditional Navajo have no way of speaking about an unconscious mind—for them it would be a contradiction as mind implies consciousness.

An act of perception involves creating a mandala of experience with the selectively abstracted object at its center. This is a fact easily proven and is the same for every normal person regardless of culture. An old mindfulness exercise of use here is to sit quietly, preferably out in nature, with one's eyes closed, focusing on the field of sounds around one. In this exercise, one first attempts to hear all sounds equally without focusing on any particular sound. When one can do this, ignoring any impulse to focus on any particular sound, one then chooses a sound to focus upon (like the bird singing, the wind in the trees, the gurgling of the stream). One watches how the selective abstraction of one sound over others affects the entire field of consciousness. In this exercise, one oscillates between focusing on one sound, then letting it go and focusing on the entire auditory surround. This is a deceptively simple but powerful meditation that may lead to realizations of a profoundly gestalt nature. This kind of flipping back and forth between global and specific is known as "sword and stream" meditation—contrasting the single-pointed and flowing possibilities of awareness.

This meditation also allows a phenomenological bracketing of volition, i.e., one can study the effect upon experience of exercising one's perceptual will-power. Every moment of the normal stream of consciousness is focused and organized around some object selectively abstracted from the total field of awareness, even if the field itself is the object. Most of the conscious faculties of the mind (i.e., sensing, cognition, recognition—literally *re*-cognizing—feeling, intention) become organized around the abstracted object of the moment. Normal waking consciousness is a stream of ever-changing foci as the mind scans its internal movie for objects of potential interest. When it finds something of interest, perhaps some novel object or event in the environment, the focus will become more intense and scrutiny more detailed until the novelty becomes redundancy and the mind moves on to another object (see Hobson 1994; Koch 2004). This is what Raichle *et al.* (2001) call the *default mode* of consciousness. Brewer *et al.* (2011) have shown that the default mode is subserved by networks in the medial prefrontal and posterior cingulate cortices, areas that in advanced meditators of all stripes are significantly deactivated in favor of strong links between the posterior cingulate, dorsal anterior cingulate and dorsolateral prefrontal cortices—areas known to subserve self-awareness (Figure 3.5; see also Short *et al.* 2010). Attention directed at an object speeds up internal processing of information about that object (Koch 2004). Yet, speaking phenomenologically, volition itself tends to withdraw from our awareness. Despite this fact, it is precisely volition we must place centermost in understanding what meditation means from a cross-cultural view.

Volition and Culture

Volition has received scant attention by psychological anthropologists (but see Murphy and Throop 2010). My contention is that this failure to address the issue reflects a phenomenological ignorance on the part of ethnographers, partially because of the tendency of the will to withdraw from our awareness, much like steering a car disappears from awareness once we have become proficient. All we are normally aware of is driving the car, as much of the volition involved in our mental acts is accomplished at an unconscious level. Another reason for avoiding the subject of volition is that when analyses of the term remain at a philosophical, semantic and linguistic level, the discussion becomes, as Murphy and Throop (2010) demonstrated, fuzzy in the extreme. This fuzziness is because (1) natural categories are fuzzy by their very nature (Kosko 1993; Laughlin 1993; Rosch 1978), (2) different languages have different ways of parsing volition, and (3) such analyses fail to address the structural, neurocognitive processes that mediate volition. The tendency of anthropologists has been to limit their study to the surface of things and make their contributions by describing variations in sociocultural forms. We have already seen that, if I am right, and consciousness arises in the frontal pole of the human brain, then we are neurognostically prepared to integrate sensory information, time-binding plans, modulation of feeling and appropriate adaptive behavior, all from within the area of our brain that is the evolutionarily newest and most advanced neural circuitry.

Introspection and Self-Awareness

Webster defines "self-awareness" as "knowledge and awareness of your own personality or character." The topic of self-awareness is fraught with all sorts of confusion and controversy. For a long time, we thought that only humans with their big brains and hefty anthropocentric egos could be self-aware. Then, in fits and starts all through the 20th and into the 21st century, evidence piled up that other animals are capable of *self-recognition* in mirrors. Put a spot on a chimpanzee's forehead where he can't see it, put him in front of a mirror and he will begin fiddling with his forehead, trying to figure out what's with the dot. Turns out, the same happens when you carry out this mirror experiment with elephants, pigeons, magpies, and dolphins (DeGrazia 2009; Parker, Mitchell and Boccia 2006). Self-awareness is of course a complex phenomenon, far more entangled than just being able to see a dot on the forehead and can be looked at from many vantage points (Ramachandran 2012). For example, *somatic self-awareness* is the awareness that I inhabit a body, and my body is different than the rest of the world. Experience of my body is via various senses— vision from the outside in, and proprioceptive channels from the inside out. *Social self-awareness* exists among social animals who live within a social structure in which statuses and roles occur. I am aware of myself as a "male," a "friend," a "group member," and as a person with social responsibilities. Research among monkey troops provides ample evidence of almost constant awareness in one's position relative to other group members. Both self-recognition and social awareness involve neural networks in the insular cortex, the part of the cortex folded away inside the lateral sulcus and one that is virtually identical in all primates (see Figure 2.4; also see Bauernfeind *et al.* 2013; Philippi *et al.* 2012; Seth, Suzuki and Critchley 2011).

Introspection is another matter. *Introspection* may be defined as the observation of one's own mental processes. There is a decades-long, very protracted debate in science over whether any good evidence can be gleaned from introspection, or "first person" reports (see Boring

1953; Lyons 1986). We now understand that introspection by other labels has been fundamental to social science all along (Clegg 2013), and with the advent of modern neuroimaging technologies, there has emerged a bolder acceptance of reports of introspective evidence, especially from adepts (Butler 2013; Jack and Roepstorff 2002; Jack and Shallice 2001; Hurlbert and Heavey 2001; Wilson 2003, 2004). I will not go into the philosophical arguments devaluing introspection as a method in science, for most of them are phenomenologically naïve and beside the point anyhow as we shall see when we take up neurophenomenology in the next chapter. As this book stands witness, there are many kinds of introspection and the utility of a particular method is of course tied to the greater scope and methods of inquiry (Gould 2013). What is characteristic of all disciplined methods of introspection is that one observes and learns about the processes of one's own mentation.

Introspection, as I am using the term, is a process that requires the dominance of prefrontal cortex activity (see Figure 1.2 and 1.3), an activity that can be suppressed when the mind is involved in non-introspective tasks—for instance, processing visual imagery categorization (Goldberg, Harel and Malach 2006). The capacity for introspection is the precursor evolutionary development (the anlagen) leading to the possibility of phenomenology. Put another way, introspection is a pre-adaptation for phenomenology, or phenomenology is an "exaptation" (Gould 1991) derived from introspection. When a meditator begins a disciplined path of self-discovery, it is his prefrontal lobes that he is exercising, and eventually his brain will be significantly different than that of non-meditators (Cardoso *et al.* 2007; Davidson 2003; Fox *et al.* 2014; Hasenkamp and Barsalou 2012; Kang *et al.* 2012; Lazar *et al.* 2005). I assume, and may well be proved wrong, that all big-brained vertebrates, and perhaps some big-brained invertebrates, are capable of introspection, but not phenomenology. The isolation of introspection as a set of distinct ASC is likely a human ability. Moreover, there are probably societies where no one meditates and hence no one is an advanced phenomenologist, while other societies contain many such. The role of culture in encouraging and supporting an institutionalized form of phenomenology is crucial.

THE UNCONSCIOUS

We have already referred to unconscious processes underlying the production of the sensorium, the brain world and consciousness. We have said that an explanation of consciousness or conscious states without considering the underlying neural processing is no longer tenable. The same goes for the unconscious mental acts that make up most operations of the psyche (Berlin 2011). Indeed, the activity of most neurognosis goes on at an unconscious level.

Although philosophers and poets had previously remarked upon the unconscious, we have Sigmund Freud (2005[1915]) to thank for really emphasizing how important unconscious processes are to understand our everyday experience, and for developing a mature psychology of consciousness:

> Thus, we have attributed three qualities to mental processes: they are either conscious, preconscious, or unconscious. The division between the three classes of material which have these qualities is neither absolute nor permanent. What is preconscious becomes conscious, as we have seen, without any activity on our part; what is unconscious can, as a result of our efforts, be made conscious, though in the process we may have an impression that we are overcoming what are often very strong resistances. When we make an attempt of this kind upon someone else, we ought not to forget that the conscious filling up of the breaks in his perceptions—the construction which we are offering him— does not so far mean that we have made conscious in him the unconscious material in question. All that is so far true is that the material is present in his mind in two versions, first in the conscious reconstruction that he has just received and secondly in its original unconscious condition. (Freud, quoted from Ellmann and Feidelson 1965: 360)

Indeed, it is safe to say that most of what goes on in our brain occurs at an unconscious level, including thought (Lakoff 1997; Wilson 2004) and affect (Schore 2003; Sato and Aoki 2006). Freud placed great emphasis upon the role of repression in forming processes in the unconsciousness—indeed therapists today hold that fear-generated repression is fundamental to understanding conscious-unconscious conflicts (Ginot 2015). But in modern times, there is a growing understanding that much of what the brain does for us occurs at biochemical, and possibly even quantum mechanical levels outside the bounds of consciousness and operating at speeds far faster than conscious processes can manage (Berlin 2011; Oschman and Pressman 2014; Laughlin 1996; Laughlin and Throop 2001; Globus 1998; Osaka 2003; Wilson 2004). This means, of course, that the unconscious is not merely the result of repressed and unwanted material, but rather is a very necessary and adaptive system—what Timothy Wilson (2004) likes to call the *adaptive unconscious*. He emphasizes the thousands of information-processing circuits that make conscious experience possible, but which cannot be accessed by consciousness. My only quibble with Wilson's thesis is his disdain for introspection. In fact, introspection in the sense of mature contemplation can indeed facilitate access to previously unconscious information-processing systems, as we shall see in the next chapter. Neuropsychiatrist Allan Schore has also argued very persuasively that much of what we call "unconscious" is mediated by the right hemisphere of the brain (Schore 2003). The right hemisphere clearly functions in a different and more complementary way than does the left hemisphere, and the indications are that we are normally less aware of right brain functions than we are of left brain functions. This is especially true with respect to emotion. For instance, people who suffer from chronic depression have overactive right hemispheres, and the roots of this malady in unconscious right hemisphere cognitions may be profound (Rotenberg 2004; Weinberg 2000). As we shall see, much that goes on in meditation and self-contemplation has to do with balancing the awareness of right and left hemispheric processes.

Germane to the interests of this book, it is fair to say that much of what arises in meditation is driven by previously unconscious personal materials involved in constructing our brain world, as well as the eruption of previously repressed or inaccessible feelings, thoughts, intuitions, images, attitudes and actions. Any meditator encumbered by a nasty little neurosis as I am will know all about such eruptions. This is a process that Arthur Deikman (1966) famously called *de-*

automatization—reconnecting with previously habituated unconscious material during meditation.

It was the great Swiss psychiatrist Carl Jung, who worked at a phenomenological level more sophisticated than Freud's, or any of Freud's protégés for that matter, who was to make the unconscious a far more interesting scope of inquiry (Chapter 7). He agreed with his mentor that the unconscious plays a significant role in forming personality, but unlike Freud he added a deeper level to the unconscious. The *personal unconscious* level of the *psyche*—the latter being the entirety of the brain's psychological processes—contains all the processes and contents that have been suppressed and repressed in the formation of the conscious personality. But underlying the entirety of the psyche, including the personal unconscious, is the *collective unconscious*—the fundamental, inherited structure of mental processes upon which development is grounded. The collective unconscious contains the "whole spiritual heritage of mankind's evolution, born anew in the brain structure of every individual" (Jung 1969a [1946]: ¶342). Jung's collective unconscious is the psychic domain of neurognosis (see above; also see Laughlin and Tiberia 2012). I will have a great deal more to say about Jung's archetypes in later chapters.

Nothing going on in the unconscious can become conscious unless and until it is represented in the sensorium—i.e., by awareness of sensations, thoughts, feelings, intuitions or images before the mind. Much of the communication between the conscious and unconscious mind is by way of images and metaphors (see above). Some states of consciousness are more permeable to communication from and to the unconscious than what we call "normal" waking consciousness. Much of our dream life is a movie produced by unconscious processing *relevated* ("lifted," "deautomatized" into consciousness) to the sensorium and associated knowing. In traditional societies with full-on "dream cultures" (Laughlin 2011: 197-231), this process of relevation looms large in how people interpret and act upon their world. Also, meditations that focus attention upon breathing (e.g., Buddhist *anapanasati*) inevitably result in eruption of previously repressed memories and feelings. Indeed, recent research has shown that the neural systems in the brain stem mediating the breath cycle directly network with and alter higher neural functions mediating cognition (cortical), feeling (limbic) and consciousness (prefrontal cortical; see Herrero *et al.* 2018). In addition, archetypes may express themselves in imagery that can inform the meditator about activities in the deep unconscious—a process that may well potentiate archetypal development and integration of these bits of ourselves into consciousness. All this said, the unconscious nature of most mental processes places a limitation on the utility of introspective methods (Wilson 2003, 2004).

The tendency of the psyche is toward the development of wholeness. However, fragmentation can and does occur in the organization of consciousness. Formations (Jung called them "complexes;" see Chapter 7) can be created during development, especially when the individual experiences traumatic events in their childhood. The formations can form quasi-egos that can "inhabit" consciousness under certain circumstances. During meditation or other trance-like states, these formations may present themselves, and even erupt in emotional outbursts, postural change and violent actions. I have personally experienced these eruptions, as I suspect any meditator will if they are, like me, a neurotic. This is probably one of the mechanisms underlying "possession" states across cultures (Bourguignon 1976). However, it is not my intent in this book to get sidetracked into a discussion of psychopathology, so enough said.

Quantum Consciousness

I mentioned that there is now some suspicion that the brain may be involved in rapid computations at a quantum mechanical level. Indeed, there has been a flurry of interest in the direct interaction between the brain and the quantum universe (e.g., Beck and Eccles 1992; Deutsch 1985; Lockwood 1989; Penrose 1989; Stapp 2009; Laughlin 1996; Loewenstein 2013; Bischof and Del Giudice 2013; Gardiner, Overall and Marc 2010). This raises the question of how the neurocognitive processes that mediate consciousness may also influence and be influenced by events happening between neural cells and quantum energy fields. For instance, are memories stored and retrieved at the quantum level (Jibu, Pribram and Yasue 1996)? We have wondered whether some neural networks may be organized to operate as transducers into consciousness of patterned quantum level activity within and between cells, and reciprocally from consciousness into quantum energy fields. Transformations of neural activity may produce transformations in the local structure of the sea of energy in which we are embedded and with which we interact. Moreover, perhaps local causation based upon biochemical interaction among neural cells may be transposed into non-local causation based upon biophysical activity between cells and the quantum sea. Brains that could interact subjectively with other brains and objects through quantum links would account for the very robust data we now have about distance causation events like remote viewing (Puthoff, Targ and May 1981), consciousness-machine interactions (Jahn and Dunne 1987), and other psi phenomena (see Radin 1997, 2006)—phenomena not unlike the sort (e.g., co-dreaming and telepathy) that are reported for traditional peoples by some ethnographers (George 1995).

The suggestion that the brain and quantum sea may interact directly remains a tantalizing hypothesis now. To my knowledge, no one has unequivocally demonstrated quantum effects of cellular activity, other than the significant findings in the field of biophysics pertaining to bioluminescence (see Popp 1998; Gu and Popp 1993; Ho, Popp and Warnke 1994; Popp and Beloussov 2013; Mothersill *et al.* 2014). However, there are several promising avenues of research into possible mechanisms, avenues that are sufficiently interesting that they have led several serious scholars to consider processes that mediate brain-quantum interaction (see Laughlin 1996 for a review). Although there has not yet been a definitive demonstration of direct neural-quantum sea interaction, the evidence is sufficiently suggestive to prompt some authorities to hypothesize that brain-quantum sea interpenetration may operate something like a "quantum computer" (Deutsch 1985, 1992, Wallace 1993a, 1993b). That is, information and "computations" may be organized within the pattern of coherent quantum activities. These "computations" may be detectable by neural networks and used as intuitively derived information in higher order neurocognitive processing. While I do agree with Penrose's (1989) arguments against narrow AI-type computational models of consciousness, it does seem possible on the strength of parapsychological and ethnographic evidence that information exchange of a broader kind may be occurring between the conscious brain and the quantum sea (see Puthoff, Targ and May 1981, Walker 1973, 1975 and Radin 1997 who also relate quantum physical and parapsychological phenomena). Perhaps most importantly, the vast, energetic real world may exert a kind of corrective pressure through the cells of neural networks against extremely unrealistic worldviews. Working with experienced meditators and the classic double-slit experiments, parapsychologist Dean Radin and his associates (2012, 2013) have shown that consciousness is a factor in determining the results of these experiments.

If you follow developments in quantum physics, you will be aware that the most promising account of the energetic universe is that of *zero-point energy* or *ZPE* (Kragh 2012; Milonni 1994; Puthoff 1987, 1989, 1990). This is a notion that at first glimpse is hard to wrap one's mind around—and it is quite controversial, for it in effect reintroduces the idea of the "ether" back into physics calculations. Take the most complete vacuum in outer space or take a hypothetical jar and suck all the matter out of it, modern physics tells us that most of the energy is still in that vacuum. It is ZPE that accounts for the existence of so-called *dark energy* without which our universe could not expand as it does—or so modern physics tells us. One way to look at ZPE is that it consists of all the non-coherent energies that permeate everything—"non-coherent" meaning that the frequencies of vibration of all this energy are random (hence the phrase "random fluctuations" of ZPE). To make matters even more interesting, if you freeze the vacuum down to absolute zero (that's −273.15°C or −459.67°F), ZPE is still jiggling around in there—hence "zero-point." I told you it is mind-boggling. Yet it is the ZPE nature of the quantum universe that may create the possibility that cells interact with and through the vacuum.

If we do find in time that brains operate in interaction with the vacuum much as "quantum computers," this surely would mean that much of what we call "the unconscious" must exist not only at the cellular level, but at the biophysical level as well. When advanced meditators delve deeply into themselves and their unconscious processes, it would seem likely that many of the advanced absorption states they experience (Chapter 3) may involve representations of what the brain knows about its biophysical and quantum interactions with the real world. This would amount to quantum-driven intuition.

However future research on biophysics goes with respect to quantum links between the brain and reality, it is crucial to keep in mind that for information to reach consciousness, the information must relevate into the sensorium and associated neural networks. We do not, and cannot apprehend the quantum universe directly, but only by transposition by systems of neural cells into the sensorium. I cannot emphasize too much that consciousness here on planet Earth—the only consciousness we are aware of thus far—is a product of the systemic interaction of millions of biological cells. The evolution of the cell in the guise of single cell animals and plants was the precursor event in the evolution of consciousness. So far as I can tell: no cells, no consciousness. Period.

SUMMARY AND SEGUE

Consciousness is the entire neural phase space of which we are aware. Our brain world arises and passes away in a stream of awareness and is mediated by the sensorium of the cortex of our brain. The sensorium is comprised of sensory material that comes in from the periphery and that is processed elsewhere in the brain at an unconscious level. Patterns of sensation are automatically linked to information stored in memory and both sensory patterns and cognitive associations are merged. Although there are many neural systems operating to process information in the brain and nervous system, only those that are directly involved in mediating the sensorium and associated meanings are conscious (Tononi and Edelman 1998). Nothing enters consciousness except by representation in the sensorium as sense perception or knowing.

We are social primates, and our brain is prewired to operate in a social way. As with other social animals, we come equipped with mirror neurons and other neural systems that mediate empathetic reactions to the behavior of others. These systems are but one example of the genetically prewired (but dynamic and amazingly flexible) systems— neurognostic structures—that mediate symbolic processing, categorical and metaphorical thought, imagery, feelings and reactions to events in the real world. As Jung would say, neurognosis is the sum of our species-typical processing of information. We are born with our very human brain world already there, operating between our ears, and portraying for us an ongoing stream of experiences that occur in a variety of states of consciousness, including wakefulness to the external world, dreaming, fantasy cycles, and so forth. Our brain is also susceptible to alteration by chemical and other means to produce ASC which may be used by society to probe the normally invisible aspects of reality (Flood 1993a). The evolution of these faculties in effect provided a preadaptation to introspective exploration by consciousness of its own internal properties. By this means, humans eventually learned that there is more to their being than most are normally aware of—that there are unconscious mental acts that under the right circumstances can speak to us through symbolic and metaphorical channels.

These developments prepared humans to become contemplatives. That is, we evolved to the point where the application of disciplined introspection could turn the faculties of awareness, perception and cognition, normally focused upon external events, inward toward the exploration of our own being. In so doing, we came to understand that we construct our world of experience—our brain world—and that the properties of our mind are impressed upon that world, whether it be involved with external reality or internal nature.

CHAPTER TWO

Neurophenomenology

I am therefore simply a contemplator of the world; the only act which is peculiarly mine is contemplation.

– Albert Schwegler, *A History of Philosophy in Epitome*
(1890: 209)

In 1986, Professor Kiyohiko Ikeda of Yamanashi University, Japan, invited me to an international meeting to discuss the role of structuralism in biology. Biologists from around the world had begun applying structuralist theory to the origin of the species and to other problems that they felt were not amply explained by Darwinian Theory. Professor Ikeda had read our earlier work, *Biogenetic Structuralism* (Laughlin and d'Aquili 1974) which had been translated into Japanese and thought I might have something to contribute. The workshop on structuralism in biology occurred at the Biological Laboratory, Kansai Medical University, Osaka, Japan, over 7-11 December 1986. Approximately 50 scholars attended the meeting, among whom were biologists Brian Goodwin, David M. Lambert, Atuhiro Sibatani and David Elder (Sibatani 1987).

Francisco Varela (Figure 2.1) also attended, and it was with him that I had the most interesting discussions about my paper, which was entitled "The Prefrontosensorial Polarity Principle: Toward a Neurophenomenology of Intentionality" (Laughlin 1988). He was very taken with the idea of neurophenomenology, and later in 1989 wrote to ask me to do a book exploring the idea to be included in the Shambhala Publications New Science Library series which he edited at the time. The book I did with my late colleagues John McManus and Eugene G. d'Aquili entitled *Brain, Symbol and Experience: Toward a Neurophenomenology of Human Consciousness* (1990) came out in that series (later republished by Columbia University Press). Among other things, the book explored the phenomenology of the great philosopher, Edmund Husserl (1859-1938), and argued that the essential elements and properties of mind discovered during phenomenological investigation must be mediated by universal structures of the nervous system. We will hear more about Husserl in a moment.

Varela appropriated the concept of neurophenomenology from our work and made it his own (Varela 1996, 1999)—e.g., "In brief, I approach temporality by following a general research direction I have called neurophenomenology, in which lived experience and its natural biological basis are linked by mutual constraints provided by their respective descriptions" (Varela 1999: 267). So far as I know, Varela never gave our group credit for having developed either the concept or the approach. But what is far more important here is that he effectively caused a schism in the neurophenomenology literature into two streams of thought, one that for simplicity's sake I will label the *cognitive neurophenomenologists* and the other the *cultural neurophenomenologists*. They are distinct strains and are usually characterized by not referencing the works done by the other—a silly state of affairs when you think about it.

Figure 2.1. Francisco Varela with the Dalai Lama. Varela (1946-2001) was both a neuroscientist and an avid Tibetan Buddhist and co-founded the Mind and Life Institute to facilitate a dialogue between science and Buddhism.

The Cognitive Neurophenomenologists

The cognitive neurophenomenologists are primarily philosophers and neuroscientists influenced by Francisco Varela (Varela 1996, 1999; see Rudrauf, Lutz, Cosmelli, LaChaux and Le Van Quyen 2003 for a summary of Varela's work), who defines the approach in a way that requires the naturalization of phenomenology (Varela 1997). Varela notes:

> On the one hand, we are concerned with a process of external emergence with well-defined neurobiological attributes, on the other, with a phenomenological description that stays close to our lived experience. The nature of the sought-after circulation one seeks is no less than that of mutual constraints of both accounts, including both the potential bridges and contradictions between them. What is the specific nature of the passages between these two accounts in the case at hand? (Varela 1996: 305)

Following Varela's lead, cognitive neurophenomenologists tend to define the approach within the philosophy of mind and cognitive neuroscience. Psychologists who do apply neurophenomenology tend to do so to experimental work, while philosophers use the approach as a kind of "naturalized epistemology" (Kornblith 1985). Cognitive neurophenomenologists have worked on a variety of interesting problems, including the embodiment of consciousness (Thompson and Varela 2001; Thompson, Lutz and Cosmelli 2005), self-consciousness (Lutz 2007), the "hard problem" of consciousness (see last chapter; Bayne 2004), hypnosis (Cardeña, Lehmann and Jönsson 2007), Whiteheadian metaphysics (Marstaller 2009) and the "spontaneity" of consciousness (Hanna and Thompson 2003). I will be drawing from their research and insights where appropriate throughout the book.

The Cultural Neurophenomenologists

The cultural neurophenomenologists are mainly anthropologists working in the areas of dreaming, the senses, medical anthropology, symbolism, and of course *transpersonal anthropology*, the study of culture and alternative states of consciousness (Krippner and Combs

2002; Staniford 1977; Campbell and Staniford 1978; Laughlin 1989, 1994b; Laughlin, McManus and Shearer 1983; Laughlin and Throop 2009; Lahood 2007; Gaffin 2012; Bharati 1961, 1975; Young and Goulet 1994; Goulet and Miller 2007). Research is almost always naturalistic and non-experimental. If there is one characteristic that distinguishes this branch, it is that, unlike most academic philosophers and psychologists, there is a primary focus on culture. Indeed, the lack of serious concern for culture and cross-cultural comparison has been an ethnocentric bias that has typified psychology for decades. "On the one hand, it is generally agreed that the need and ability to live in the human medium of culture is one of the central characteristics of human beings. On the other hand, it is difficult for many academic psychologists to assign culture more than a secondary, often superficial role in the constitution of our mental life" (Cole 1996: 1).

In keeping with the field of anthropology, the value of cultural neurophenomenology is naturalistic and introspective, and application is directed toward diverse subjects encountered in cross-cultural comparison, and ethnographic and applied fieldwork; e.g., consciousness (Laughlin 1988), emotion (Laughlin and Throop 1999; Throop 2000, 2010), religion and spiritual practices (Dornan 2004; Laughlin 1992, 2011; Winkelman 1996, 2010; Krippner and Combs 2002; Peters 2004; Vásquez 2011; Rodd 2002), theory (Peters 2000; Throop 2003a; Laughlin and Throop 2006; Laughlin, McManus and d'Aquili 1990), time consciousness and culture (Laughlin 1992; Laughlin and Throop 2008), dreaming and dream cultures (Kirmayer 2009; Laughlin 2011), the structure of the ancient mind (Dornan 2004; Laughlin and Loubser 2010) and healing (Groisman and Sell 1996).

HUSSERLIAN PHENOMENOLOGY AND MATURE CONTEMPLATION

The most direct method for ascertaining the relations between consciousness and the nervous system is by way of combining phenomenology and neuroscience into a kind of neurophenomenology. Neurophenomenology is a powerful method that relies upon a dialogue between descriptions of the essential properties of consciousness as ascertained through trained contemplation on the one hand, and the structures and processes of the brain mediating those essential properties on the other hand.

There are two phenomenologists who have most influenced anthropology, one of those being Maurice Merleau-Ponty (1962, 1968; see also Jackson 1996) with his phenomenology of the body and perception, and Edmund Husserl (Figure 2.2) who I have already mentioned. When I originally defined the method of neurophenomenology, I paired a neurophysiology of experience with Husserlian transcendental phenomenology, and ever since I have found Husserlian phenomenology the most useful for anthropological projects, as well as being very close to the Buddhist phenomenology that I have practiced for years (Chapter 5). There is a very good reason for my selection, for there are as many phenomenologies as there are phenomenologists (Kockelmans 1967). However, for many phenomenologists (like Heidegger and his notion of *Dasein*), the term simply means what we learn from reflecting upon our own experience. But for me, that definition refers to what might be called "naïve" phenomenology—philosophical reflections on the order of: "As I reflect upon the green of the leaves on the tree outside my study window...." In my opinion, the value of neurophenomenological research depends both on the advances in neuropsychology and in the disciplined and skilled application of what my colleagues and I call *mature contemplation* (Laughlin, McManus and d'Aquili 1990, Chap. 11; d'Aquili, Laughlin and McManus 1993). Varela did pick up on this element of our program, for he was, as d'Aquili, McManus and I were, a practicing meditator. He clearly had more than naïve phenomenology in mind, as noted by Rudrauf *et al.* (2003: 48), as evidenced by his discussion of Husserl, Merleau-Ponty and Heidegger (Varela, 1999):

However, *a simple undisciplined introspective approach is not the solution; the 'just-take-a-look' or 'seeing inside' attitude must be overcome.* Neurophenomenology implies "gathering a research community armed with new pragmatic tools for the development of a science of consciousness." This involves a "call for transforming the style and values of the research community itself," in other words, that researchers themselves, as they are specialists in neurosciences for instance, become specialists in the phenomenology of conscious experience: "My proposal implies that every good student of cognitive science who is also interested in issues at the level of mental experience, must inescapably attain a level of mastery in phenomenological examination in order to work seriously with first-person accounts" (Varela and Shear 1999).

Although I am a practicing Buddhist, my work in phenomenology focused upon the compatible method of Husserlian *transcendental phenomenology*—that is, introspection carried out by a trained meditator who has succeeded in "bracketing" or "reducing" all received assumptions (what Husserl called the *natural attitude*) about consciousness and who has realized the real (and illusory) nature of the ego. Only then can a phenomenologist accurately discover the essential properties of consciousness and then seek to explain such elements by way of neuroscience. Indeed, Husserl's intention was that scientists learn to be phenomenologists before they carry out science so that they understand how much the structure of the mind influences how reality is observed (see Chauhan 2015 on this issue). This bracketing or "setting aside" of one's natural attitude leads to a state of consciousness Husserl (1977[1931]) called the phenomenological or transcendental *epoché*.

Figure 2.2. Edmund Husserl (1859-1938). Husserl was a profound contemplative and philosopher who led the way toward transcendental phenomenology.

The Phenomenological Attitude

Part of the problem with operationalizing Husserl's methods is that he wrote in very formal, philosophical German and we English speakers get his words through translation. Also, he relies upon concepts that are hard for us to understand. Yet his method is very straightforward. Let me give a simple example. I am sitting here typing away on my keyboard, sunlight is sparkling upon the table being filtered through half-closed venetian blinds, the air conditioner is buzzing loudly in the background of my awareness, I feel the pressure of my bottom on a hard bench, and dozens of other sensations and potential distractions. Yet when I am really into the writing, all the distractions fall away from my awareness and I am principally aware of my thoughts and words as they appear on my laptop screen. This is the "searchlight" function of awareness, to select out of the enormous range and variation of perceptual objects (light streaks, humming sound, feelings of fingertips on the keyboard, hardness of the bench, and on and on) the object I wish to attend to the exclusion of all else. In a very natural way, my brain "brackets," or "reduces" all other objects and ignores them so that I can settle in on the one activity I wish to focus my mind upon. We all do that all the time. Our minds flit from one object to another, minute after minute, hour after hour, if we are aware. The same in our sleep, for if we become aware in our dreaming, our mind continues to flit from one image to the next until we lose consciousness again.

This scanning, bracketing and focusing of the searchlight of awareness is how the brain builds and displays our brain world. It is wired-in, and it is adaptive. All people's brains work the same way, but what objects people attend will vary depending upon all sorts of factors. This activity is mediated by what neuropsychologists call the *default mode network* (Sood and Jones 2013; Brewer *et al.* 2011; Taylor *et al.* 2012). What is very unusual, however, is for a person to begin to study their own brain processes (seeing, feeling, thinking, dreaming, moving, breathing), taking control over that self-same system and using it as their research tool. To learn to take control of awareness is the root method of Husserlian phenomenology (see also Irrmischer *et al.* 2019). To master the turning of the searchlight inward to the structures of consciousness is to go a long way toward acquiring the *phenomenological attitude* toward any object of consciousness whatsoever.

The pursuit and maturation of the phenomenological attitude (Husserl 1931, 1977; Koestenbaum in Husserl 1967: *xx*; Miller 1984, p. 175; Schmitt 1967) produces a state of mind marked at times by astonishment and wonder, and by a cognition relatively free of the constraints of received, culturally conditioned frames of reference (see Fink 1981: 24; for an Eastern view of this state of mind, see Suzuki 1970). This freedom allows the inner-directed study of the factors of consciousness as objects of awareness, rather than conditioned attention to phenomena naïvely presumed from the natural attitude to be "out there" somewhere in the "real world" and requiring response (see Funke 1981: 72). The contemplative comes to realize that each state of mind is componential and unitary. In addition, the mature contemplative can slow the process of entrainment down to the very simple to discern the atomic levels of experience: pixels, temporal epochs, impermanence of objects, purity, parallel processes, componential nature of the empirical ego, or "me" (and cognized ego, or "I"), visible and invisible causation. Only through contemplation can one come to realize a level of awareness that is essentially contentless—conscious only of consciousness-in-itself, or what some call "mystical consciousness" (Josipovic 2019).

Attaining the phenomenological attitude is not easy. Philosophers will speak of "adopting" the attitude, as though we can decide to acknowledge the value of the attitude and, "voila!" we are a mature contemplative. In fact, it is very hard to learn, and requires among other things discipline, unlearning life-long habits of reaction to stimuli, thought about things and perception of things, calming the formations of mind, etc. There are images in the East that depict the normal person's consciousness as a monkey being pulled along by a rampaging elephant (conditioned mental activity). Gradually the monkey climbs up on the elephant's back and learns to slow the elephant down and eventually control its actions and directions. The monkey learns to determine the path instead of the elephant. This is, of course, a metaphor for gaining control of the searchlight of awareness and learning to direct it toward whatever object one wills. During the maturation of our phenomenological attitude, the habitual and "taken for granted" knowledge is bracketed. This is the *phenomenological reduction* of which Husserl speaks about over and over. The *reduction* or the *epoché* is *nothing less than an alternative state of consciousness typical of mature contemplatives who are able, like the monkey on the elephant's back, to take control of the searchlight of their own consciousness and use it to focus upon and study the nature of their own minds.*

Husserl's method of contemplation is, like all such systems across the planet, a staged process; first do this, then do that, then do that, and eventually you will come to know. There are three grand reductions about which Husserl had lots to say.

The Phenomenological Reduction. Husserlian method depends upon a gradual backing away from the natural attitude about reality; that is, the naïve assumption that the brain world is the real world. The first great reduction is thus a suspension of the question of whether the real world exists outside of our knowing about it. The Buddha also refused to get involved in this kind of metaphysical speculation, this refusal coming down to us as some of the Buddha's unanswered questions (Skt: *avyākṛta*). What remains for scrutiny are the "essences," the universal properties of mental acts revealed to consciousness, regardless of whether there is a real world. This stance is an alternative state, not a metaphysical claim, but among some followers of Husserl, especially Heidegger, the significance of this was missed and led to confusion about solipsism (see below).

The Eidetic Reduction. Once the question of real or unreal worlds is set aside (bracketed), the contemplative focuses on the essences, or essential elements in the structure of consciousness. This is done by systematically uncovering how the mind builds its brain world as it naturally occurs, and sometimes by carrying out thought experiments, like varying elements and seeing what happens. Principal among his teachings is learning to "return to the things themselves," or "things as they are in themselves." That is, we become aware of the way perceptual objects present themselves immediately before the mind *prior to any apperceptive attributions, cognitive, intuitive, language or other associations, feelings or thoughts intrude upon the experience* (Husserl 1982 [1913]).

A rudimentary example of the method of reduction brought Husserl as close as he came to the realization of sensorial pixels (Chapter 1). This is to be found in his discussion of *hyle*[7] or *hyletic data* (Larrabee 1973; Føllesdal 1978, 1990). Hyletic data are the contents of sensation as reduced to a snapshot in time (the "now moment;" see below).

---

[7] "Hyle" derives from the Ancient Greek ὕλη, and means "matter," or "stuff."

...we recall that all living experiences, hyle included, are immediately experienced or lived through; they are not objects in any sense of the word.... In order to analyze a living experience, we must use reflection upon it; consequently, the living experience becomes an "object" of reflection and is thereby mediated by reflection. Becoming an object of reflection somehow modifies the living experience, since before reflection it was not an object. (Larrabee 1973: 197-198)

When we apprehend the sensory field, we discover that it is already distinguished into sense modes, and within sense modes into qualities. These are "primordial" in the sense that they are not objects, unless we reflect upon them, in which case they become objects of reflection, a process that changes the *lived through* experience (Husserl 1982[1913]). Moreover, the hyle is non-intentional, for the hyle is "already there" before any abstraction occurs. Moreover, it is the hyle—pardon me if I put words in Professor Husserl's mouth, the *field of sensorial pixels*—that "fills" our percepts yet is already there before we apprehend the percepts (Husserl's term is *noema*; Husserl 1970 [1900-01]). The apperception of hyle is equivalent to the Buddhist experience of *suchness* (Skt: *tathātā*) which has been elaborated among Chan and Zen practitioners (Suzuki 1970; Austin 1998: 549-553, 2006: Chap. 82). I will return to the experience of "suchness" in Chapter 3. Meanwhile, "return to the things," hyletic data, suchness—these are three ways of referring to the reduction Husserl considered *the* fundamental skill that must be nurtured for a mature contemplative to attain the phenomenological attitude. As we shall see in a moment, contemplation at this level implies a specific orientation within and toward the arrow-of-time.

The Transcendental Reduction. At some point along the path of self-discovery, one focuses awareness on the elements that one identifies with as "me." Gone is the assumption that there is a little "me" somewhere in my brain that is sitting around watching the movie. In fact, all that we discover about me that is not an intentional and interpretive act is the fact of watching. "I" am thus reduced to a Watcher. There is watching and there are the intentional objects being watched, and when the Watcher focuses upon features and characteristics previously identified as "me," they turn out to be intentional acts by the Watcher and are moreover impermanent. Lo and behold there is no tiny homunculus anywhere in the brain—there is only the Watcher and the movie being watched. "I" am thus merely a standpoint of awareness in the construction of the brain world.

While in the state of consciousness denoted by the phenomenological and then the eidetic reductions, all culturally received knowledge is bracketed, set aside, disattended—including all cultural interpretations, pre-evaluations, biases, feelings, identifications, verbal descriptions and reactions. Eventually, and as an automatic consequence of the maturation of his attitude, the contemplative comes to realize the impermanence and illusory nature of the empirical ego or natural attitude self-identification, and the ego itself is reduced. The contemplative learns that the only enduring aspect of the ego is awareness itself (Hood 2002). In Husserlian terminology, the empirical, conditioned ego is reduced and what is left is the *transcendental* ego (Husserl 1977[1931]). This reduction—the *transcendental reduction*—was as fundamental to Husserlian methods as it is with Buddhist *vipassana* meditation (Mahasi Sayadaw 1978; see Chapters 3 and 5). As Husserl himself realized, "I stand above the world, which has now become for me, in a quite peculiar sense, a phenomenon" (1970[1937]: 152). It was Husserl's dream that all scientists, including all psychologists, would master the phenomenological attitude before carrying out more standard scientific research so that they might understand how their own minds worked prior to using them to build theories and evaluate research findings.

This is a very crucial point, for even if we have access to the very finest neuroscience available, if the phenomenological data are naïve (pre-epoché, pre-reduction), then very likely the neurophenomenology will be naïve as well, and quite likely erroneous (see Jack and Roepstorff 2002). Let me offer an example. It is apparent to many mature contemplatives that sensory data are pixelated, particulate or granular to perception (Laughlin 1992; Laughlin, McManus and d'Aquili 1990: 108-112; see Chapters 1 and 5). In other words, there comes a time when many contemplatives reach a specific reduction of "thingness" within which they can perceive that their entire sensorium (sensory field) is made up of pixels. After the reduction, the sensorium is experienced as a field of pixels that is perceptually and cognitively distinguishable into sensory modes, and within sensory modes into things and happenings. The fundamental act of perception is the abstraction and reinforcement of relatively invariant features within the order of an unfolding and dissolving field of pixels (see Gibson 1979). In my experience, apprehending the pixelated nature of the senses is easiest to realize visually, but eventually sound, taste and touch are all seen to be made up of sensory particles. Once one realizes this epoché, one may easily apprehend the texture of the sensorium at will. Furthermore, when concentration upon sensory molecular pixels reaches a sufficient intensity, awareness of gross sensory objects falls away.

Necessity of Mature Contemplation

Some scholars accept the importance of disciplined phenomenology and some do not. Following Varela's lead closely, neuroscientist Antoine Lutz (2002) notes that neurophenomenological investigation, "...requires a specific, rigorous technique. What is needed here is to overcome the 'just-take-a-look' attitude with regard to experience that is pervasive in cognitive protocols or the dominant philosophy of mind. Western and Eastern phenomenological traditions have been favored, as we will see later, as appropriate pragmatical tools, but other first-person approaches are being explored. The phenomenological methodology relies on the cultivation of a gesture of reflexive awareness, called phenomenological reduction.... The goal of this methodological reduction is to attain intuitions of the descriptive structural invariants of an experience." In a subsequent study, Lutz (Lutz, Dunne and Davidson 2007) applies the method to correlate self-awareness of seizure onset with the underlying neurobiology of awareness—an ingenious project that involved training epileptics to recognize the "prodromes," or onset signals that arise before seizure.

By contrast, philosopher Lars Marstaller (2009) has applied the perspective to the process philosophy of Alfred North Whitehead. He argues that Whitehead's "phenomenology" can be used to "extend" the range of neurophenomenological exploration. While I have long considered Whitehead to be a remarkably astute contemplative (Laughlin and d'Aquili 1974: 76-77), by no stretch of the imagination can his approach be considered a phenomenology in the disciplined Husserlian sense, or even of the Buddhist *vipassana* variety. Whatever value Marstaller's essay has for metaphysics, it demonstrates to me just how rapidly the application of neurophenomenology can be watered down in the phenomenology department. This slippage into naïve phenomenology is further apparent in Laurence Kirmayer's (2009) study in which he uses the term neurophenomenology merely as a shorthand for emphasizing the relationship between the experience and neurobiology of nightmares. Indeed, some writers have gone so far as to question the need at all for phenomenological training in carrying off a neurophenomenology. Philosopher Tim Bayne (2004: 351) writes:

> At the heart of neurophenomenology is the claim that Husserlian phenomenology has a unique and privileged method of describing the first-person nature of consciousness. Phenomenology is unique in that it is importantly different from the standard first-person methodologies employed in consciousness studies; and it is privileged in that it is more rigorous than such methodologies. I have my doubts about both claims. *I say this with some tentativeness, for my knowledge of the phenomenological tradition is limited.* But let me explain why I am inclined to think that the phenomenological method is neither unique nor privileged. (emphasis added)

Bayne is honest about his lack of familiarity with phenomenology and goes on to exhibit a very typical ignorance of phenomenological methods. This kind of criticism has been leveled at Husserlian phenomenology for decades, both in philosophy and in psychology, almost always by scholars who have not trained themselves in any contemplative method, and who have not experienced the distinct states of consciousness these methods evoke, and in fact depend upon.[8] I will repeat, only a contemplative is able to realize (not know about, but *realize in direct experience*) non-dual awareness or "contemplation-as-such," and thereafter be able to accurately incorporate that realization into contemplative neuroscience (Josipovic 2019).

---

[8] Those readers wishing to read more about how to actually accomplish a Husserlian transcendental phenomenology project might wish to consult: Cairns 1976; Funke 1987; Ihde 1977; Moran 2000; Giorgi 2007.

A Quick Word about Solipsism

It is perhaps evident by now that I far prefer doing phenomenological explorations than ruminating over endless philosophical considerations and arguments pertaining to Husserlian vs. Heideggerian or other phenomenologies. I want to know how my mind works, not get bogged down wondering whether the fact that solid wax melts and shape-shifts is critical to Cartesian metaphysics. But there is one issue we do need to acknowledge in passing, and that is the charge that the phenomenological reduction leads to a metaphysics of solipsism. "Solipsism" labels the belief that only mind exists, and that the real world is a figment of our imagination (Watson 2014). Husserl of course never made such a claim, in either its extreme or partial form. But critics, including Heidegger, claimed that the phenomenological reduction (misinterpreted as a metaphysical claim or assertion) creates problems of intersubjectivity. If I presume that the only consciousness that exists is mine, then how do I know that you exist? How can I relate to you from inside a phenomenological reduction? This question is just silly because empathy is inherent in normal human consciousness. Husserl never considered this criticism as serious.

Moreover, we now know that human and non-human brains include systems of mirror neurons that automatically relate the behaviors of others to ourselves (Decety and Ickles 2009; Keysers and Fadiga 2017; Whitehead 2010b; Chapter 1). In other words, we humans and other social animals are wired to cognize and mimic the behavior of others. We are wired to know the Other. Basically, mirror neurons become active when we institute goal-directed behavior—like lifting a cup to our lips. The very same cells become active when we observe others do the same thing. These cell systems in effect "mirror" the behavior of others as though the actions were our own. Added to this is that any mature contemplative also knows that the deeper one gets into the meditative life, by way of whatever path, the more we calm the body and attain greater self-awareness, there is an automatic (and transcendental) increase in empathy and loving-kindness (Skt: *metta*) directed at others within the field of consciousness (see Chapter 11). Eventually one comes to realize Totality which incorporates empathy for all beings within a single vast monad in which we are all embedded and entangled. Indeed, we recognize that there is the rare person who grows up without the capacity for empathy, and who do have an essentially solipsistic brain world—we now call these people *psychopaths* (Fallon 2013; Fecteau, Pascual-Leone and Théoret 2008; Brook and Kosson 2013).

THE NEUROPHENOMENOLOGY OF CONSCIOUSNESS

A factor that is often missed by philosophers debating phenomenology is that mature contemplation often leads through a series of transpersonal experiences, resulting in irreversible changes in self-awareness and ego-identification. I will trace the path of my own development as a contemplative in a later chapter but suffice to say here that these changes allow "seeing" in new ways, ways that pre-epoché commentators cannot know from direct experience—the kind of difference in seeing alluded to in such Zen aphorisms as "before awakening chop wood, after awakening chop wood."

There are numerous realizations pertaining to the essential structures of consciousness that are available to mature, disciplined phenomenology I could mention that are also amenable to a neurophenomenological treatment. One of the problems that attracted both Varela (1999) and me (Laughlin 1992)—I assume independently—was the structure of time-consciousness. This was a very natural problem for phenomenologists, and Husserl wrote one of his finest studies on the subject, *The Phenomenology of Internal Time-Consciousness* (Husserl 1964 [1905]; see also Kortooms 2002).

Both Varela and I grounded our analyses upon the Husserlian reduction, which I discuss at length, but which Varela for some reason declined to discuss at all. In any event, Husserl (1964: 48; see also Landgrebe 1981: 59; Miller 1984: 85) saw the "primal impressional datum" of perception as being a synthesis of recently past acts of perception ("retention"), of the streaming present ("now points") and of the anticipated future ("protention;" Figure 2.3). As Husserl (1964: 49-50, 76) notes:

...the continuity of running-off [unfolding] of an enduring Object is a continuum whose phases are the continua of the modes of running-off of the different temporal points of the duration of the Object. ...Since a new now is always presenting itself, each now is changed into a past, and thus the entire continuity of the running-off of the pasts of the preceding points moves uniformly "downward" into the depths of the past. ...Every primordially constitutive process is animated by protentions which voidly constitute and intercept what is coming, as such, in order to bring it to fulfillment.

These three phases of temporal unfolding constitute a "perceptual epoch" (not to be confused with the epoché): retention, the "now point" and protention combining to form the naïve "present." The relations among memories of patterns abstracted from recently past epochs are, as Husserl (1964: 81) noted, "primordial;" that is, fundamental to how consciousness works, fundamental to the neural organization mediating perceptual acts. These are cognitions that entrain with what is happening in the sensorium "right now" to produce the perception of enduring objects and the sense of causal continuity of events.

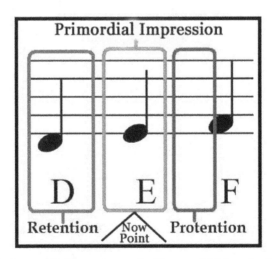

Figure 2.3. The Primordial Perception of a Temporal Object. In this simple model we use the sound of unfolding musical notes to depict both the naïve perception of time which blends the recent memory (retention) and anticipation (protention) with the present in hearing a change of notes. In consciousness of the unfolding "now moment" there is only the "e" note.

The phases of the perceptual epoch are not merely theoretical distinctions, they are phenomenologically apparent. Not only that, but reduction of awareness to the moment is fundamental to the experience of "things themselves," the hyle, and suchness, as discussed above. The suchness experience is the perception confined to the moment, not to the naïve "now." As a contemplative's concentration upon the flow of sensory experience increases and the mind slows down its processes, the sensory flow is revealed to present in a continuous, but pulsing, iterative flow (Damasio, 1999: 126; Dainton 2006: Chap 5). It is by studying the discernable fine structure of perceptual epochs, the relations between epochs, and the temporal binding of epochs that we can discover the essential and universal nature of time-consciousness—what Maurice Block (1977: 284-285) called "universal time;" the experience of time that underlies the very structure of our subjective life regardless of our cultural heritage. The mature contemplative after completing the requisite reductions is prepared to watch this process unfold in his own experience. Not only is the sensorium comprised of pixels, it flickers, and this flickering is quite distinctive. But it is harder to realize than seeing sensorial points.

For one thing, the so-called "now-point" is not a "durationless interface between past and future" (Dainton 2006: 120; Wittman 2011). Perceptual epochs are not instantaneous. We know this as contemplatives because the reduction to the pure "now" involves the falling away of retention and protention until all one is aware of is the intermittent streaming of sensory data (hyletic data), as well as patterns and topological relations among patterns (color, tonal, textural relations, spatial and geometric relations, etc.) as they arise and pass away in the sensorium. In this reduction to the actual now, all gross cognitive and behavioral acts like recognition, anticipation, reaction, rememoration, so forth, have dropped away. The stream of data (e.g., in the case of speech, the sounds transmitted through the air by the speaker's vocalizations) arise simultaneously within epochs and then pass away. There is clearly some very short duration involved in this process, but it would be impossible to measure it using phenomenological methods alone. Were this not the case, then it would be impossible to discern the passing away of the pixels during the now moment. Perceptual epochs are not snapshot-like. They are neither static, nor instantaneous. They are themselves what Husserl called "temporal objects;" they are objects of experience that have a durational expanse, however minute. The data that arise and pass away in epochs "take time" to present. But all data or patterns arising within any one epoch are experienced as simultaneous (see Gho and Varela 1987; Pastor *et al.* 2004; Bogen 1998).

The temporal organization of experience is thus a very complex matter and involves areas of the brain in addition to those mediating perceptual epochs. For instance, subjective time varies depending upon which ASC one is in, the state of one's emotions (bored, excited, in pain or in pleasure) and how much interoceptive body awareness is involved (Wittmann 2015). When we become absorbed in some activity (as in meditation of one kind or another) we may enter a state of "flow" in which we totally lose track of time (Csikszentmihalyi and Csikszentmihalyi 1988).

It would not be unfair to say that the whole brain is involved in temporal processing, depending upon which aspect of temporal processing we are discussing (Wittmann 2015). The role of the brain's prefrontal cortex (PFC) in selecting, exciting and ordering sensorial activity into a temporally meaningful plan has been discussed elsewhere (Laughlin 1988; Laughlin, McManus and d'Aquili 1990: 105-119; see also Pribram 1971; see Figures 1.2 and 1.3). I have suggested elsewhere that phenomenal experience is constituted within the dialogue between PFC imposed order ("intentional meaning") and sensorial order ("perceptual meaning"). Part of the dialogue between prefrontal and sensorial structures seems to involve septal-hippocampal centers in the midbrain (see Figure 12.1 later in the book). Orbitofrontal projections from the prefrontal cortex richly innervate the hippocampus and dorsolateral prefrontal projections enter the lateral septal area (see Gray 1982: 65ff). These areas are also connected to secondary sensory areas and seem to receive sensory information that is already abstracted from the initial processing in primary sensory cortex. All this processing is designed to extract, make meaningful and act upon the world as portrayed by perceptual epochs. Temporal-causal associations, durational motion in space, the general sense of the "streaming" of consciousness are all grounded upon the primordial structure of the perceptual epoch.

We now know that normal perception in mammals involves a continual comparison between sensory experience and cognitive predictions (Leinweber 2017; Huang and Rao 2011). Keeping track of durations of time, as well as making temporal predictions seem to involve the insular cortex (Figure 2.4). The insula is cortex that is buried inside the lateral sulcus that separates the parietal and temporal lobes. These areas are heavily connected to the PFC which seems to also be involved in these functions. The insula is also implicated in mediating emotional empathy (Eres *et al.* 2015).

Chronesthesia: Our Janus Nature

Cognitive neuroscientist Endel Tulving (2002; Nyberg *et al.* 2010) has pointed to the importance of mental "time travel," or *chronesthesia* to the neurophenomenology of subjective time:

> Chronesthesia is defined as a form of consciousness that allows individuals to think about the subjective time in which they live and that makes it possible for them to mentally travel in such time.... Our findings show that under conditions in which variables other than the imagined moments of personal past, present, and future are held constant, some brain regions exhibit differential activity that is systematically related to the subjects' conscious, "chronesthetic" states. (Nyberg *et al.* 2010: 22356)

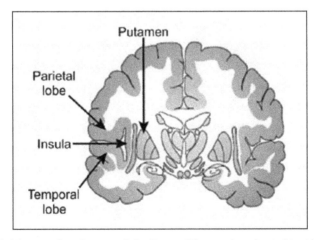

Figure 2.4. The Insular Cortex of the Brain. The insula is buried inside the lateral sulcus that separates the parietal lobe from the temporal on each side of the brain.

Chronesthetic consciousness is a discrete state of consciousness presumably shared by all peoples everywhere—the ability to internally imagine episodes held in memory or imagined along an arrow of time from past through present and into the future. Naturally it was first thought that only humans are capable of this mind-state, but subsequent research has indicated that we share that ability with other animals, including great apes (Osvath and Osvath 2008; Martin-Ordas *et al.* 2010) and birds (Clayton, Bussey and Dickinson 2003).

As contemplatives, we may bracket immediate external intentions, perhaps sitting quietly and disattending the outer world—ignoring our present sensations entirely. We may then imagine doing some simple act in the present, say, digging a hole to plant a rose bush in the garden. We may then shift to the memory of having dug a hole for a rose bush in the past. Then again, we can imagine digging a hole to plant a rose bush in the garden tomorrow. These different imaginings are easily differentiated vis-à-vis our subjective time travel—what might be called our inherent Janus nature (Figure 2.5). We have no trouble distinguishing that which has happened, is happening and will happen. Moreover, the cognitive and imaginary associations that accrue to each are different. Another exercise is to run a movie in your head from the now moment backwards from image to image, each further back in

Figure 2.5. The Roman God Janus. Janus was the Ancient Roman god of time, depicted here on a bronze coin struck in 102 BC during the republican period before the emperors. One face considers the past, the other the future. Today we might call Janus the god of chronesthesia.

time to perhaps yesterday, then forward again, through what is before the senses now and then into the future imagining how the day before you is imagined. When you do this back and forth, always including the sensory now, it becomes easier and smoother to do. You can feel the brain shifting its gears to access memory, moving into the now with its lucid sensations and then into imagination of anticipated happenings later in the day. This is the "time travel" of which Tulving speaks.

In any event, we know that how the brain mediates these three mental acts is a complex affair involving several structures in our brain. Compared with imagining digging the hole right now, remembering having dug the hole and forecasting the digging of the hole involve shifts in activity in the left lateral parietal cortex of your brain, in addition to areas in the left frontal cortex, the right cerebellum and the thalamus (see Szpunar, Watson and McDermott 2007). Presumably the same alterations occur in the time-travel sequencing of back and forth imagery.

Cultural Neurophenomenology and Time Consciousness

Although Husserl's method is rarely viewed in this way, it is thoroughly cognizant of the role played by culture in conditioning consciousness. It is, after all, culture that plays a major role in establishing a person's "natural attitude" toward phenomena, and that must be bracketed before mature contemplation may be accomplished. Furthermore, there are really two directions of study implied in Husserl's approach, one inward to the discovery of the structures of one's own subjectivity, and one outward to explore the historical and cultural influences on that subjectivity. One is incomplete without the other, and what we are terming a cultural neurophenomenology is predicated on the integration of both movements. Indeed, this is precisely the point that Husserl was making in his classic work, *The Crisis in the European Sciences and Transcendental Phenomenology* (1970[1937]: 72), when he argued:

...[for] an autonomous philosopher with the will to liberate himself from all prejudices, he must have the insight that all the things he takes for granted are prejudices, that all prejudices are obscurities arising out of a sedimentation of tradition—not merely judgments whose truth is as yet undecided—and that this is true even of the great task and idea, which is called 'philosophy.' All judgments which count as philosophical are related back to this task, this idea. A historical, backward reflection of the sort under discussion is thus actually the deepest kind of self-reflection aimed at self-understanding in terms of what we are truly seeking as the historical beings we are.

Let us return to the neurophenomenology of time consciousness and show how the addition of the cultural ingredient allows for a cross-cultural application of the method. We have seen that all brains process the temporal dimension of perception in the same way. The brain retains and binds a working memory of recently past now moments (retention) to the real now point and anticipated future now points (protention). The now point is the sensorium refreshing its presentation every fraction of a second, and to the mature contemplative may appear as a flickering of the sensory field. If data present in the same now point, then they are perceived as simultaneous. If they are presented in different now points, they will be perceived as occurring in time. This is a rudimentary cognitive act, and is the primordial structure of lineal time, the building blocks of chronesthetic experience.

In the past, much was made in anthropology about how the time maps of traditional peoples differ from those of Western society. Traditional (earlier called "primitive" or "savage") peoples, according to this view, have a fundamentally different mentality than so-called civilized folk, and thus live more in the present and cognize time as a system of recurrent cycles, while Westerners live with their minds riveted on the future and cognize time in a lineal series of episodes (see e.g., Levi-Bruhl 1966[1923]; Evans-Pritchard 1939). The "modern" time-map was assumed to be the product of the industrial revolution and facilitated by the invention of clocks. Such dualistic accounts of cultures and their time-maps have more recently come into disrepute as being both over-simplistic and empirically inaccurate, not to mention patronizing (Adams, 1990: 16-19; TenHouten 2005: 2-3; Gell 1992: 34). A moment's reflection about our own Western time-map shows that we live out our lives in a welter of recognized, recurring cycles—day and night, a weekly round of days ("TGIF!"), seasons, recurring holidays like Christmas, Easter, Veterans Day, Ramadan, birthdays, annual vacations, a daily cycle of ritualized meals (breakfast, lunch, high tea, dinner, night time snack), annual round of sports seasons, and on-and-on. By the same token, as Gell (1992: 34) points out, if traditional peoples are only aware of cycles of recurring events, how is it possible that they can distinguish last year's events from other different events of the same kind in previous years—an ability they obviously have, otherwise they could have no sense of history, not to mention chronesthetic awareness.

Culture does influence the way we orient ourselves to duration—usually durations over minutes, hours and years, even generations, centuries and eras. As with other aspects of experience, we become conditioned to integrate our quotidian lives within a worldview that emphasizes a standpoint with respect to time, causation and history. We all experience sensory time-consciousness in the same way, regardless of cultural conditioning, but just which objects and events receive our awareness will vary from person to person, from group to group and from period to period through history. How we integrate our sense of temporal continuity and cyclicity will be informed from our personal history and our society's worldview. The most dramatic and forceful of influences will be our group's cosmology, including its stock of lore and mythic stories, its cycle of ritual enactments, its subsistence patterns and relation with its environment and the teachings of its primary enculturators (thinkers, shamans, healers, parents, instructors, teachers, leaders, and so-forth).

ASC and Time Consciousness

As any mature contemplative can attest, meditative states, and indeed ASC in general may alter one's time sense, even to the extreme of stopping time or making time irrelevant. As Ulrich Ott (2013: 105) has noted:

In ordinary waking consciousness, subjective time is usually in good agreement with physical time as measured by clocks. However, subjective time experience can be severely altered under certain conditions. Slowing and acceleration of time and the complete loss of the sense of time are common during altered states of consciousness. Obviously, the brain mechanisms that provide a time framework in the service of instrumental behavior can be transiently suspended. Conditions known to facilitate this process are, for instance, dream sleep, hallucinogenic drugs, and states of absorption, where all representational resources are engaged by an intensive experience.….

Of importance is the disappearance of any time sense during absorption states, especially those we might class as "mystical experiences" (Chapter 9). This does not mean that consciousness becomes static, like a snapshot. Rather, it is a dynamic experience during which one is not aware of the passage of time. The experience may in retrospect have lasted a minute or an hour. One cannot tell from memory alone. Moreover, it would seem that the anticipatory, or prediction mode (Leinweber 2017), of perception drops away and there is left the ongoing flow of atemporal sensory experience.

SUMMARY AND SEGUE

Neurophenomenology is a powerful explanatory and research tool that goes a long way toward controlling for the consciousness "gap" between our brain world and extramental reality (Laughlin and Throop 2009). It is especially powerful when the phenomenology utilized is that of mature contemplation, and not merely first-person descriptions of experience (Gallagher and Sørensen 2006). Unfortunately, there is and will continue to be a temptation on the part of researchers to water-down the need for skilled phenomenology. In some cases, there will be no alternative, as when the researcher is depending upon first person reports of subjects and patients who may or may not have been trained as phenomenologists. But learning to become a mature contemplative—a pre-requisite for anything like a Husserlian transcendental phenomenology—is a transpersonal project. And it is arduous. One cannot become a mature contemplative without transforming one's self, one's ego. Hence, there will be a resistance on the part of many to undertake the rigors of training.

We have only begun to explore the range of problems that might profitably come within the purview of a neurophenomenological analysis. For cognitive neurophenomenology, the implications are radical, in that the approach requires considerable alteration in the design of laboratory or clinical research protocols, as well as the training we give nascent scientists. For cultural neurophenomenologists, the challenge is to acquire the requisite training in neuroscience (or add a neuroscientist to the team) as well as learn to use transpersonal field methods to access the experiences had by one's non-Western hosts while in ASC.

I have sketched in my view of consciousness and then have outlined a major approach to neurophenomenology that has proven itself nicely in the exploration and analysis of experience and consciousness. Next, I will take up the subject of meditation more broadly and show how the natural functioning of the conscious brain is able to be turned, like the monkey on the elephant, to the study of itself. While one advantage of a Husserlian approach is that it has been formulated outside of any specific religious or spiritual tradition, all other full-on phenomenologies of which I am aware are found in the spiritual traditions of other peoples. Once we spread our net wider for insights about mature contemplation, I will then share with you my own personal adventures as a contemplative, if for no other reason than it will give a flavor for what the contemplative life can be about.

PART TWO

The Meditating Brain

CHAPTER THREE

Meditation I:
The Structure of Self-Awareness

By taking just a few extra seconds to stay with a positive experience—even the comfort in a single breath—you'll help turn a passing mental state into lasting neural structure.

– Rick Hanson, *Hardwiring Happiness*

What's encouraging about meditation is that even if we shut down, we can no longer shut down in ignorance. We see very clearly that we're closing off. That in itself begins to illuminate the darkness of ignorance.

– Pema Chodron

Science has taken a tremendous interest in meditation over the last several decades (Goleman 1996; Goleman and Davidson 2017; Murphy and Donovan 1999; Shapiro and Walsh 1984; Tart 2001; Wallace 2007, 2009; West 1990; Varela and Shear 1999; Haruki, Ishii and Suzuki 1996; Walsh and Shapiro 2006; McMahan and Braun 2017; Brandmeyer, Delorme and Wahbeh 2019), reflecting perhaps the increased popularity of Asian spiritual traditions among Western societies (Taylor 1999; Bush 2011). In a survey by the American Center for Disease Control of the complementary and alternative medical use of meditation, 9.4% of the 23,393 U.S. adults sampled had used meditation in the past 12 months (Barnes, Bloom, and Nahin 2008).

Not surprisingly, most of the research in the psychological literature has focused on the nature and effects of the more popular types of Asian meditation traditions, including hatha yoga (*hatha vidya*), Transcendental Meditation (derived from the Hindu tradition), Zen (a Japanese form of Buddhist meditation training), Theravada

Buddhist *vipassana* (a form of mindfulness training from southern India, Burma and Thailand), and Tibetan Buddhist Tantric ("arising yoga") training (Murphy and Donovan 1999; Child 2016). There are many other traditions of meditation, whether derived from Asian traditions or elsewhere, including those associated with the teachings of George Gurdjieff, Jiddu Krishnamurti, Jainism, Sufism, Stoicism and Christianity (Goleman 1996; Heinze 1993). Yet these various types of meditation tend to be those associated with the major world religions. Anthropologists, however, tend to cast a wider net with respect to cultures and spiritual traditions. I say "spiritual tradition" because most of the world's languages have no word that easily glosses "religion" (from the Latin *religio*, "worship, sanctity, awe") in the Western institutional sense of the term. For instance, religion for the Navajo people of the American southwest is ritual; the closest to religion one can come in Navajo is the term *nahaghá*, meaning "go about ceremonially."

It is no longer possible to ignore the research done on meditation by neuropsychologists who have shown that phenomenologically reportable states of consciousness achieved during meditation are mediated by discrete neural systems (see Lutz, Dunne and Davidson 2007 for a review). Depending upon what kind of meditation is being done, a wide variety of neurophysiological networks are involved (Bærentsen *et al.* 2010). In this chapter, I wish to place meditation and the cultural systems in which meditation traditions are embedded in a broader, more cross-cultural frame. This requires that we first define what we mean by meditation in a neuropsychological context that follows on from our previous discussion of phenomenology, and then show that in intact traditional cultures, the practices of meditation are always lodged within a system of feedback between a people's worldview and their individual spiritual experiences. This will allow us to examine not only meditation practices cross-culturally, but also both the experiences evoked by meditation practices and how the people share, evaluate, cognize, interpret, and utilize such experiences.

In the late 1970s, I developed an interest in the sociocultural aspects of transpersonal experiences and ASC, and how these play a role in the formation and maintenance of spiritual and religious systems. Readers familiar with anthropology will know that ethnographers follow a methodology called *participant observation* that inclines us to learn about peoples by living with them for extended periods of time and studying their cultural practices by personally doing them. During my ethnographic fieldwork among Tibetan Buddhists in Nepal and India, I became a monk (Figure 3.2) in the Sakya monastic order for many years and studied Tantric meditation techniques under several lamas, including my preceptor, Venerable Chogye Trichen Rinpoche (Figure 3.1) and my root guru, Venerable Karma Tenzin Dorje Namgyal Rinpoche (1981), the latter being a Canadian monk who studied meditation during the 1950s in Burma. I have practiced both the Vajrayana and Theravada versions of Buddhist meditation, and have also practiced other meditation traditions, including those of the Hermetic Order of the Golden Dawn, the transcendental phenomenology developed by Edmund Husserl (Chapter 2), and active imagination developed by Carl G. Jung (Chapter 7). After ending my exploration of Tibetan Buddhist monastic culture, I spent some years studying the Navajo ritual healing system, which among other things involves meditation upon complex symbols (so-called sand paintings) very similar in fact to those used by Tibetan Tantric practitioners

Figure 3.1. Chogye Trichen Rinpoche Eating at His Monastery in Lumbini, Nepal.
Rinpoche was my preceptor and gave me most of the higher empowerments leading to the meditations I carried out in the Tibetan tradition.

Figure 3.2. The Author as a Tibetan Monk with His Fellow Monk, Ven. Chee Han Seng, at Chogye Rinpoche's Lumbini, Nepal, Monastery. Chee and I befriended the little white dog who later became the monastery's mascot.

(Krippner 1997b). What all this means for present purposes is that the discussion that follows carries with it the benefit of direct experience with a variety of meditation systems and cultures.

The Cycle of Meaning

It is relatively easy to account for meditation and culture within a strictly ethnocentric Western frame. It is quite another to gain an understanding of what happens when the same practices are carried out in a variety of Western and non-Western societies. To make things clearer, I would suggest that any person having an ASC will most likely comprehend their experience within a culturally patterned, interpretive frame (see Paper 2004). We can model this frame in what may be called a culture's *cycle of meaning* (see Figure 3.3; Laughlin 1997c, 2011: 200-208; Laughlin, McManus and d'Aquili 1990: 214).

Intact traditional spiritual worldviews nearly always manifest as a mythopoeic symbol system which includes myths and other stories, pre- and proscribed behaviors, rituals, and perhaps even specialized social roles. People participating in mythopoeic activities, including ritualized meditation disciplines, eventually have direct experiences that are in turn interpreted in terms of the society's worldview. There may be shamans, priests and other experienced guides to help the neophyte interpret their experience (Steadman and Palmer 1994). The experience is usually interpreted in such a way as to instantiate the society's world theory—in other words, provides negative feedback into the worldview. Occasionally, experiences may arise that are not straightforwardly representative of the worldview, and thus may cause a change in the society's theory of the world—in other words, aberrant experiences may operate as positive feedback into the worldview. In such a way, a society maintains a living worldview, susceptible as it is to change relative to what is always a dynamic reality.

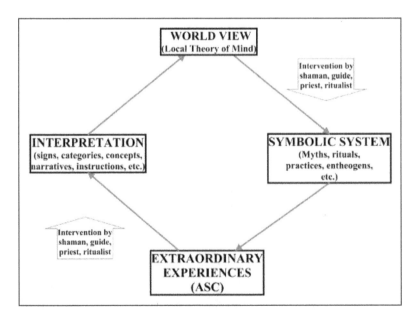

Figure 3.3. The Mystical Cycle of Meaning. A society's worldview, often a cosmology which includes its local theory of mind and consciousness, gives rise to symbolic representations of knowledge in the form of a myth-ritual complex, stories, art, drama, texts and drivers. Participation in the "mysteries" described in myth, drama, text, etc., may lead to direct ASC that are then interpreted, perhaps with the aid of a shaman, priest, elder, etc., in such a way that the experience instantiates, enlivens and verifies the society's worldview.

Polyphasic societies quite frequently require some or all its members to participate in mystical rituals (with or without the use of entheogens, or spiritually evocative psychotropic drugs; Ruck *et al.* 1979; Rush 2013; Richards 2015; McKenna and McKenna 1975). For instance, members of the Sun Dance religion among certain Plains Indian societies may dance for hour upon hour to the beat of drums after dieting and purification rituals. Some dancers eventually enter a trance state in which they become one with the spirit entity (see Voget 1984). When a dancer is seen to be in this state, he is immediately attended by shamans who help him to understand what he has experienced. The interpretation is, of course, always in terms of the society's worldview and local theory of mind. Similarly, members of the cult of Asklepios (the god of medicine) in ancient Greece would seek help at ritual sites where they prepared for direct encounters with the god while dreaming. After dreaming the patient told what he or she experienced to the priest who then gave the patient an interpretation. The interpretation was, again, in terms of the Asklepiosian worldview (Kerényi 1959).

Phenomenology of Meditation

When discussing meditation in a cross-cultural context, we must keep in mind that the word "meditation" is English; a term that derives from the Latin term (*meditari*) for certain forms of contemplation. The root meaning of meditation, like its cousins median, medicine and moderation, implies the centering of the four humors or energies. Also, our English term contemplation literally means "in the temple," implying that one is entering a holy place, or a mind-state that apprehends the whole, the divine, the totality of things. These are good enough translations for such eastern terms as the Buddhist and Hindu *dhyāna*, or the Hebrew *hāgâ*, which implies both chanting and contemplation. However, for most societies, just as there is no word for religion, it is also fair to say that few have a word that clearly glosses meditation as a distinct practice.

To define meditation so that, in principle, it can apply across the world's estimated 4,000 cultures, we must look more closely at what the mental act of meditation entails, i.e., the neuropsychological properties that mediate the universal aspects of meditation (Laughlin, McManus and d'Aquili 1990; Winkelman 2010). When I speak of "a culture" I mean a system of information and knowledge that is available to members of a group (Goodenough 1971). What most authorities mean by meditation involves extraordinary application of mental functions that otherwise operate in the everyday experience of everyone on the planet, regardless of cultural background. At the practical center of meditation is a practice that (1) applies concentration or mindfulness upon some object (flickering light, image, breath, sound, rhythm, movement and so on), and (2) is single-mindedly maintained against all distractions over a sustained period (Raffone and Srinivasan 2010). Meditations can be relatively quiescent, as with zazen, or active as in San trance-dancing or Sufi *semazen* (whirling dance). All forms of meditation fundamentally depend upon the brain's wired-in capacity to direct its searchlight faculties to an intended object.

THE MEDITATING BRAIN

Neuropsychological research has now evolved to the point that interesting things may be said about the neurophysiological processes mediating meditation practices and experiences (Fábián 2012; Nicholson 2010; Tang, Hölzel and Posner 2015), and this body of information allows us to better define meditation in a way that is applicable across cultures. Unfortunately, many of the definitions of meditation in the psychological literature do not have this cross-cultural application. For example, meditation has been defined as a relaxation technique, a set of body postures, and the presence or absence of body movements (see Deshmukh 2006; Shapiro 1984).[9] Although many different ritual techniques are used in meditation systems, they do not define meditation itself. To focus more exclusively on the universal attributes of meditation, we should limit our definition to mental acts and to those acts that produce the range of states of consciousness considered to be meditative in quality (Winkelman 2010). As I am one

---

[9] Meditation has also been defined as the "sustained awareness aimed at nonreactive and nonattached mental observation, without cognitive or emotional interpretation of the unfolding moment-to-moment experience" (Braboszcz, Hahusseau and Delorme 2010: 1910).

of those who hold that for every state of consciousness there is a discrete neurophysiological system mediating it, any valid and useful definition of meditation must therefore be couched in neurophenomenological terms. For instance, Tibetan loving kindness (*metta*) meditation appears to involve the left medial prefrontal cortex, insular cortex and the anterior cingulate gyrus, areas known to mediate empathy and feelings of happiness and wellbeing (Engström and Söderfeldt 2010; see also Hofmann, Grossman and Hinton 2011).

Meditation may be defined as a state of consciousness, driven by an extraordinary exercise of will or volition, in which bottom-up or top-down driven focal attention to, or concentration upon (Koch 2004; Posner 2004; Bærentsen *et al.* 2010) a single object is maintained over a period to the exclusion of all competing, bottom-up demands for attention (see also Davidson, Goleman and Schwartz 1976; Goleman 1996; Heinze 1993; Odajnyk 2011; Winkelman 2010). Behaviorally speaking, meditation may also refer to the ritualized procedures for attaining specific meditative and contemplative mind-states (d'Aquili, Laughlin and McManus 1979; Laughlin, McManus and d'Aquili 1990; Davis-Floyd and Laughlin 2016). It is the case that when traditional peoples wish to control knowledge and skill, they "educate" their young (Rossano 2012), and when they wish to control ASC, they ritualize the procedures intended to incubate and evoke those experiences. Many of these ritual procedures require discipline and skill to enact (e.g., the Sun Dance, Hatha Yoga).

Phenomenologically, a meditative state of consciousness is characterized by a single-minded attention to, and perhaps even an absorption into, one object while all other potential objects of consciousness are suppressed or ignored (Ott 2007; Laughlin, McManus and d'Aquili 1990). An *absorption state* (Skt: *samādhi*, *jhāna*; see Gunaratana 1988; Snyder and Rasmussen 2009; Bryant 2009: 78; Austin 2006: Chap. 74) is any state of consciousness in which the experienced distinction between self and object dissolves (Ott 2007). When we are "absorbed" in a good book, there is just the unfolding story—the awareness of self and book being separate entities disappears. The same happens very rapidly when we attend a cinema. When the movie starts, we are almost immediately "lost" in the story. Experienced meditators are very familiar with absorption states which tend to occur under conditions of intense concentration upon a single object to the exclusion of all other objects (breath, heartbeat, image, sound; see Chapter 3).

Mindfulness and the Prefrontal Cortex (PFC)

Attention is primarily mediated by the prefrontal cortex, especially the right hemisphere, in humans (Posner and Peterson 1990; Newberg and Iversen 2003; Manna *et al.* 2010; Lou, Nowak and Kjaer 2005). By object, I do not necessarily mean a material thing because the entire field of experience may be taken as the object in a meditation (see Lutz *et al.* 2008 on focused and open monitoring in meditation). In the Buddhist tradition of meditation, the term "mindfulness" is often used to label concentration, but in a much more specific way. *Mindfulness*:

> Is characterized by dispassionate, non-evaluative, and sustained moment-to-moment awareness of perceptible mental states and processes. This denotes continuous, immediate awareness of physical sensations, perceptions, affective states, thoughts, and imagery. Mindfulness is nondeliberative: It implies sustained paying attention to ongoing mental content in the present moment without thinking about, comparing, or in other ways evaluating the ongoing mental phenomena that arise during periods of practice. Because of this emphasis on direct awareness, minimally filtered by active evaluation or analysis, mindfulness is often described as "bare attention" to mental events and processes... Thus, mindfulness may be seen as a form of naturalistic observation, or more precisely participant-observation, in which the objects of observation are the perceptible mental phenomena that arise during all states of waking consciousness. (Grossman 2010: 88)

"Bare attention" is the key to understanding such Buddhist meditation techniques as *vipassanā*, a practice designed to explore and understand the real nature of mind and the realization of impermanence, suffering and no-self. By *bare attention* (Pali: *sati*) is meant that one studies elements of consciousness like a naturalist would study a colony of ants, with dispassion and keen observation leading to understanding (Wallace 2006).

We should keep in mind that the normal operation of consciousness is in service to adaptation. The brain's scanning mission is to track one object after another, moving on from an object when it is rendered redundant and uninteresting to another, potentially novel and interesting object (Irrmischer et al. 2019). The object of meditation may be an image in the sensorium of something external (e.g., a flickering flame, a skull on a pole, an audio tape of people chanting, one's breath), or an internally produced image or other internal feature of consciousness (e.g., a sublingual mantra, an image of a deity, spirit or other mythological symbol, an attribute of consciousness like an itch, phosphine, feeling, or even the entire dynamic stream of experience). Theoretically, any object may be the focal point of meditation; hence, one may have as many meditations as there are objects. However, traditional meditation cultures define the objects of meditation (external or internal) for their own purposes, almost always to instantiate the cultural worldview in direct individual experience. By the way, when I speak of a *meditation culture* I am speaking of all the elements of a culture that inform, condition and socially organize meditation practices, and all those elements that experiences had during meditation impact.

Meditation may characterize any state of consciousness in which willfully sustained attention is possible. For example, during trance states, drug trips (ritual procedures involving ingestion of datura, ayahuasca, magic mushrooms, peyote, ecstasy, etc. are all very common across cultures), dreaming (particularly during lucid dreaming), sleep onset (hypnagogic imagery) or sleep offset (hypnopompic imagery) and, of course, waking states. Also, meditation may be carried out while lying down, sitting or standing still, or while moving (running, walking, exercising, eating, swimming, prostrating, undergoing an ordeal, so forth). What makes a state of consciousness a meditation is the extraordinary exercise of volition, regardless of the other attributes of the state. By this definition, there are many societies in which no meditation culture exists, for there may be no rationalization for meditating, or traditional rituals and other procedures for evoking the requisite sustained attention.

Prefrontal Cortex, Volition, Attention and Meditation

The neurophysiological system mediating a meditative state will vary depending upon the object, qualities and behavioral involvement of the state (Newberg *et al.* 2003; Wang *et al.* 2011). Meditating upon auditory objects is mediated by a different entrainment of networks than, say, the meditation upon one's breath or heartbeat, upon the phosphines produced by putting pressure on one's eyes (Nicholson 2009), or upon the repetition of a mantra or prayer. Obviously, a major variant will be the sensorial components of the state. However, what will be common to all meditative states will be a notable entrainment of areas of the PFC (see Koch 2004; Lou, Nowak and Kjaer 2005).

The PFC is the anterior part of the frontal lobes, the latter being the part of the brain from about the middle of the cortex forward that is given over to the mediation of actions of all sorts (e.g., expression of emotion, movement of the eyes, speech, movement of the limbs, so forth; Fuster 2015). The PFC is perhaps the most important part of our frontal cortex from the perspective of the anthropology of volition because (1) the PFC is the one area of the cortex that is interconnected with every

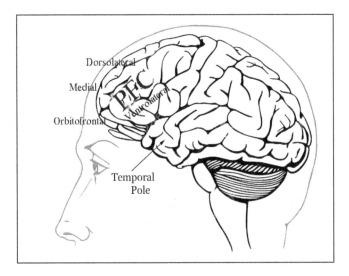

Figure 3.4. The Areas of the Prefrontal Cortex. Pictured is the left lobe of the human brain showing the approximate location of the various areas of the prefrontal cortex (PFC), including the orbitofrontal, ventrolateral, medial and dorsolateral PFC, as well as the inferior frontal gyrus.

other functional area in the brain, (2) the extent of PFC involvement as a component in the structure mediating our experience makes an enormous difference in intentionality, quality, lucidity, continuity and planning, and (3) the evolution of the PFC among hominins is the single most important reason why we humans developed the higher cortical functions and rich cultural diversity we enjoy today. The PFC is the evolutionarily youngest part of our brain (Jerison 1973, 2007; Rilling and Insel 1999) and has expanded in proportion to the overall neocortex relative to the brain of apes, while the motor areas of the frontal lobes have proportionally shrunk (Corballis 2011; Deacon 1997; Geary 2005; Schoenemann, Sheehan and Glotzer 2005). The human PFC constitutes as much as one third of the neocortex, much larger proportionally than other primates (LeDoux 2003b). In addition, the human PFC exhibits more interconnections when compared with ape brains, both within the lobe and between the lobe and other areas of the brain. This is the area of neocortex that makes our foreheads bulge out above our eyes more than, say, a chimpanzee's or the family dog's, and that makes our species of "nearly hairless apes" so very clever.

The PFC is the seat of our brain's executive functions and intelligence (Changeux 1985; Fuster 2003, 2015; Hobson 2002; Geary 2005; Goldberg 2009; Miller, Galanter and Pribram 1960; Pribram 1971; Roberts, Robbins and Weiskrantz 1998). This is the part of the cortex that integrates and temporally orders lower action centers, contributes along with other cortical areas to general intelligence and problem-solving, that moderates and suppresses emotion, that binds time in spatiotemporal bundles and makes plans (Amodio and Frith 2006; Miller, Galanter and Pribram 1960), that generates ideal simulations of the world, and that mediates working memory (Fuster 2015). Dietrich (2003) has even suggested that the PFC is the principal area involved in changing from one alternative state of consciousness to another. If we wish to carry out a complex, purposeful activity over time, simulate an ideal solution to a problem, delay motor responses until the situation is assessed, the involvement of the PFC as a component of our neural activity is essential, as it is for all other primates. Germane to our discussion of volition, one of the prime functions of the PFC is the inhibition of emotions and behavior. It is the PFC that allows us to disconnect from competing stimuli and reactions (Fuster 2015).

Research has shown that volition (or "will") is mediated by areas in the dorsolateral PFC and the anterior cingulate cortex (Frith *et al.* 2016; see Figures 1.2 and 1.3), and that meditation is accompanied by increased activity of prefrontal lobe executive functions and a moderation of emotional reactions (Teper and Inzlicht 2012; Hölzel *et al.* 2007a, 2007b; Brefczynski-Lewis *et al.* 2007).

Meditation Transforms the Brain

We now have many morphometric studies that show that long-term practice of mindfulness and other types of meditation results in permanent alteration and growth in those parts of the brain that mediate meditation. Bretta Hölzel and her colleagues (2007b) studied 20 experienced *vipassanā* meditators whose mean practice was 8.6 years meditating for at least 2 hours a day. Using MRI, they compared the thickness of gray matter of these meditators with a matched group of non-meditators. They found:

> ...a distinct pattern of gray matter concentration in meditators, who spent a significant part of their lifetime training non-judgmental acceptance towards internal experiences that arise at each moment. Regular meditation practice is associated with structural differences in regions that are typically activated during meditation, such as the inferior temporal gyrus and hippocampus as well as in regions that are relevant for the task of meditation, such as the insula and [orbital PFC]. Using the whole-brain unbiased objective technique of VBM... the present study extends the findings by Lazar *et al.* (2005) and suggests a wider network of brain regions involved in meditation show long-term structural differences.

In a meta-analysis of numerous imaging studies, Fox *et al.* (2014: 68) found that several cortical and subcortical areas are involved in, and are perhaps altered by, meditation:

> These include regions key to meta-awareness and introspection ([right lateral PFC]), exteroceptive and interoceptive body

awareness (sensory cortices and insular cortex, respectively), memory consolidation and reconsolidation (hippocampus), self and emotion regulation (anterior and mid-cingulate, and orbitofrontal cortex), and finally intra- and interhemispheric communication (superior longitudinal fasciculus and corpus callosum, respectively). Notably, except for primary and secondary somatomotor regions, consistent differences were found almost exclusively in higher-order ('downstream') executive and association cortices. *This suggests that meditation preferentially recruits such general, higher-order brain regions.* (emphasis added)

Not only that, but there is clear evidence that long-term meditation, or what I have called mature contemplation, may lead to permanent rewiring of certain executive areas, particularly those related to attention and control of distractions such as discursive thoughts (Cahn and Polich 2009; Hasenkamp and Barsalou 2012; Mograbi 2011):

Participants with more meditation experience exhibited increased connectivity within attentional networks, as well as between attentional regions and medial frontal regions. These neural relationships may be involved in the development of cognitive skills, such as maintaining attention and disengaging from distraction, that are often reported with meditation practice. *Furthermore, because altered connectivity of brain regions in experienced meditators was observed in a non-meditative (resting) state, this may represent a transference of cognitive abilities "off the cushion" into daily life.* (Hasenkamp and Barsalou 2012: 1; emphasis added)

These and other morphometric researches are showing that long-term meditators—mature contemplatives—develop neural systems significantly altered from non-meditators (see Desbordes *et al.* 2012; Kang *et al.* 2012; Sood and Jones 2013; Kurth *et al.* 2014; Fell, Axmacher, and Haupt 2010; Vestergaard-Poulsen *et al.* 2009; Lazar *et al.* 2000, 2005; Baron Short *et al.* 2010; Chiesa, Calati and Serretti 2011; Garland *et al.* 2010; Jha, Krompinger and Baime 2007; MacLean *et al.* 2010; Murphy and Donovan 1999; Shapiro *et al.* 2006; Davidson and Lutz 2008;

Luders, Toga, Lepore and Gaser 2009; Luders *et al.* 2011; Vestergaard-Poulsen *et al.* 2009; Grant *et al.* 2010; Lutz, Slagter, Dunne and Davidson 2008). There is also evidence of growth of gyrification among meditators (Luders *et al.* 2012). Of specific interest to an understanding of contemplation are studies showing that long-term meditation increases general intelligence, or Spearman's *g* (Singh and Talwar 2012; Bera, Barik and Bera 2017). General intelligence is a cognitive facility mediated by the lateral prefrontal cortex (Duncan *et al.* 2000; Figure 3.4). It is possible that this effect may be due in part to meditation enhancing working memory (*hypermnesia*; Manjunath and Telles 2004).

With respect to the organization of dream states, lack of PFC involvement in what Westerners typically consider normal dreaming is the reason why there is a relative poverty of recall, continuity, temporal plot-line and reflexive awareness, as well as enhanced affect, in dream recall (Pace-Schott 2007, 2011). It was long thought that dreaming was basically deficient in cognitive functioning and intentionality (e.g., Purcell, Moffitt and Hoffman 1993). The implication here is that only by recalling dream content and the application of waking interpretive functions could order and meaning be brought into dream material, an implication common in psychoanalytic treatments of dreams (see Laughlin 2011). However, with the discovery (by science, but long known to many traditional peoples) of "lucid dreaming" this view has come into question. In lucid dreaming, a transience of PFC activation during the dream state will operate to alter the components of the neural network mediating the dream (Dietrich 2007), entraining not only some or all the executive functions of the brain, but also the level of arousal, of involvement of midbrain vestibular system mediation of spatial orientation (Snyder and Gackenbach 1991), emotion, and autonomic system tuning (LaBerge, Levitan and Dement, 1986). Dream yoga meditations thus also involve intense activity of the PFC (Laughlin 2011; see also next chapter).

The PFC is the seat of volition and thus the principle organizer of any meditation (Austin 1998, 2006; Cahn and Polich 2006; Dietrich 2003; Newberg and Iversen 2003; Fell, Axmacher and Haupt 2010; Vestergaard-Poulsen *et al.* 2009; Frith *et al.* 2016). The PFC is customarily divided into three anatomical areas in each hemisphere of the brain (see Figures 3.4 and 3.5):

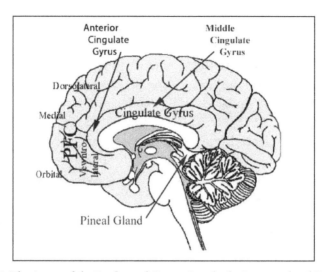

Figure 3.5. The Areas of the Prefrontal Cortex Inside the Longitudinal Fissure. The two hemispheres of the brain are cut apart (sagittal view) showing the location of the inner areas of the prefrontal cortex (PC), including the dorsolateral, medial, orbital and ventrolateral PFC, plus the anterior cingulate gyrus.

Orbital Prefrontal Cortex. This is the area of the PFC that lies just above our eye sockets. It is laid out on the undersurface of the cortex of both hemispheres (Rolls 1998). This area is intimately interconnected with the limbic system and is known to inhibit and control emotional reactions and behavioral responses to stimuli (Damasio 1994, 1999). This area seems to be involved in connecting behavioral responses to incentives (i.e., rewards and punishments; Rolls 1998), as well as working memory related to emotion (LeDoux 2003a). Apropos to meditation, it is this area of the PFC that inhibits instinctual reactions to fearful stimuli (LeDoux 2003b). Serious damage to this part of the cortex often produces hyperactivity and over-reaction to perceptual stimuli. The condition also produces a deficit in the ability to pay sustained attention and to avoid distraction stimuli (Fuster 2015).

Medial Prefrontal Cortex. This is the area of the PFC that lies inside the fold between hemispheres. It is found on the medial surface of the cortex of both hemispheres just above the orbital PFC. The medial PFC is involved in attention, as well as in motivation, self-reflection and planning, or goal orientation (Fuster 2015; Jenkins and Mitchell 2011). It is, like the orbital PFC, intimately connected with the limbic system and mediates the kind of time-binding we sometimes call intention or will. The area is also implicated in self-reflection and inferences about the states of others (Mitchell, Banaji and Macrae 2005), a function directly associated with meditation (Cardoso *et al.* 2007). It appears to be directly involved in mediating mood in Zen practitioners, adjustment of mood, increased serum serotonin, and increased slow wave alpha band activity and decreased theta band activity in the region (Yu *et al.* 2011), and associated with retuning of the autonomic system (Takahashi *et al.* 2005).

Lateral Prefrontal Cortex. This is the largest area of the PFC and is located on the convex surface of the anterior brain just in front of the pre-motor area of the frontal lobes of both hemispheres. This very large and complex area is unique to primates. While other animals have a PFC, only primates, including humans, have this large expanse of cortex given over to the brain's executive functions (LeDoux 2003b). The lateral PFC is involved in placing ideas, images, and sensory perceptions in a wider, more global perspective (Damasio 1985). Damage to any part of this area of the PFC will result in various manifestations of what is called the *Lateral Syndrome,* all of which are rooted in attention deficit disorder. Attention in this sense has two aspects: inclusive, which means that the mind can focus upon one aspect of experience, and exclusive, which means the ability to suppress anything that would interfere with inclusive focus (Fuster 2015)—in other words, the two prime characteristics of meditation. It is primarily the inclusive aspect that is lost with Lateral Syndrome. This area is also involved in time-binding, planning, maintaining working memory, temporal organization of behaviors, and maintaining single-focus on internally generated images.

All areas of the PFC are involved in one way or another in maintaining top-down, willfully selective attention to objects and exclusion of alternative objects. An example of a top-down meditation might be the selection to focus on a Zen *koan*[10] or a Sufi story to the

---

[10] A *koan* (Chinese: *gongan*) is a statement, question, story or some other verbal challenge that a Zen meditator will meditate upon. *Koans* are neither puzzles nor meaningless—they do have answers and appropriate responses that help the teacher diagnose where the student is on the path to *satori* (see Heine and Wright 2000).

exclusion of all other bidders for attention. Of course, the PFC works in concert with other functional areas to mediate the working memory, emotion, sense of self and skeletal muscular tone that is a requisite for meditation (Bunge *et al.* 2001). PFC activity in the theta and alpha ranges appear to be involved in producing a blissful experience with certain types of meditation (Aftanas and Golocheikine 2001; Sharp 2014). One cannot over-emphasize the remarkable development of the prefrontal brain in our species. It seems very doubtful that any other primate is capable of meditation in the sense I am using the term. Meditation depends upon developing the skillful application of attention and countering the natural and highly adaptive scanning searchlight function of consciousness—i.e., the default mode network.

I do not wish to imply that other primates are incapable of developing skills involving willful attention along other dimensions. Indeed, as primatologist Donald Sade (2012) has suggested, the development of abilities influences the development of the biological self. For example, one of the more remarkable rhesus monkeys that Sade and others observed at the Cayo Santiago rhesus macaque colony was an individual designated as WK (Sade 2012; Sade *et al.* 1988). WK was an unusual individual in many respects. He became the alpha male in one group, and then moved to another group where he also became alpha male. More to the point, WK was the first monkey to be observed cracking open husked coconuts. While all the other individuals would eat coconut meat if available, they could not intentionally crack open a husked coconut. WK was the only monkey to actively crack them open. In time, other members of the group would hear WK cracking open a coconut and gather around him, wanting to share the goodies. WK rarely ate more than a few bites of meat and then left the rest for others to eat. He clearly experimented with different techniques for opening the nut before settling on one technique he apparently found to be most effective. WK worked on opening a coconut for as much as an hour at a time, and usually succeeded in accessing meat. After a period, during which he lost rank and gradually became peripheral to the group, WK would open his coconuts out of view of higher-ranking monkeys. Eventually, he left his group and became a solitary male, spending much of his time hanging out in the mangroves on the island shore.

I recount WK's story because he was an exceptional individual who apparently discovered the technique of sustained attention to a problem (cracking open coconuts) and the utility of solving the problem. It is significant that this skill (1) was developed by WK over a period and required sustained attention, and (2) was not passed on in a cultural way to others, even though other monkeys routinely observed his methods. We do know that among primate species generally, the more advanced the brain, the longer the animal will focus upon and explore novelty, as well as the potential utility of new objects (Menzel 1963, 1966, 1972). However, there is no reason to suppose that any non-human primate is capable of meditation in the present sense. Indeed, it seems likely that the exercise of some kinds of meditation did not occur prior to the Upper Paleolithic period; that is, after about 30-40 thousand years ago when we have our first evidence of intense symbolic and shamanic activity (Lewis-Williams and Dowson 1988; Pearson 2002; Ucho 1977; Ucho and Rosenfeld 1967; Winkelman 2010). Indeed, Matt Rossano (2007) has argued, I think persuasively, that early meditation may have resulted in selection for enhanced working memory (*hypermnesia*) in the brains of Paleolithic peoples.

Although my colleagues and I suggested the importance of the PFC in mediating meditation, lucid dreaming and other ASC over three decades ago (Laughlin, McManus and d'Aquili 1990), recent studies have brought more focus to this aspect of neuropsychological functioning (e.g., Allen 2012; Engström and Söderfeldt 2010; Newberg *et al.* 2003; Wang *et al.* 2011). There is now clear evidence of neuroplastic changes in brain structure due to the development of meditational skill (Jiang *et al.* 2020; Shen *et al.* 2020). Moreover, there is considerable evidence that certain types of meditation involve lateral asymmetry of PFC functioning (e.g., Earle 1981, 1984; Glueck and Stroebel 1975; Newberg and Iversen 2003). It is also heartening to see an increase in work done by experienced meditators on the neuropsychology of their own experiences (Austin 1998, 2006; Nicholson 2009; Varela and Shear 1999), a shift in neuroscientific epistemology in keeping with the anthropology of experience (Turner and Bruner 1986) and transpersonal anthropology (Gaffin 2013; Laughlin 1988, 2011, 2012; Winkelman 2010).

Of course, there is far more going on in the body during meditations of various kinds. Sustained meditation can impact the entire body, especially the systems that control metabolic activity. I will have a lot more to say about how these systems work in the next chapter when we address psychic energy.

CULTURE AND MEDITATION

Meditation systems vary enormously depending upon their intent, object, ritual procedures, expectations, social conditions, and personal development (Brown 1986; Heinze 1993). Yet, all meditations involve the mediation of PFC functions that make willful, top-down, sustained attention possible. Much of the variation in type of meditation is due to the culture within which practitioners are reared and enculturated. Meditation cultures are formed because of one of the invariant properties of meditation—the accumulation of memories of experiences and meanings clustered around the object of meditation. Furthermore, the evidence noted above is that systematic meditation produces measurable effects on both the brain and the immune system of practitioners, especially of those who have become mature contemplatives (Davidson 2003; Manna *et al.* 2010; Short *et al.* 2007; Vestergaard-Poulsen *et al.* 2009).

We should consider this: it is possible to meditate on anything, on any object perceived to be outside or inside our body. We can meditate on any sound, any somatic process we can perceive or imagine. We can meditate on any rock, tree, body of water, image, light reflection, animal, painting, nothingness, dream image, sensorial pixels and so forth. No matter what the object we choose to meditate upon, eventually that act will evoke and potentiate other experiences, memories, and intuitive insights, and these associations become the meaning of the object (Laughlin *et al.* 1984, 1986). If we meditate upon the Zen *koan* "*mu*," all the experiences and evoked associations resulting from that meditation become associated in memory with *mu*, i.e., become the meaning of *mu* for the meditator (Odajnyk 2011). It is precisely these experiences and associations that are intended by the meditation culture in the enculturation of practitioners, and always relate to the culture's worldview in some way.

Arising Yogas

Many types of meditation involve the visualization or auditorization of the object of focus, and each type of meditation is mediated by its own distinct neural organization, an organization that may change over a lifetime of meditation (Lehmann *et al.* 2001; Wang *et al.* 2011). Visualizations require the meditator to focus attention upon an image while auditorizations focus upon imagined sounds. Visualization practice may begin with focusing upon the image of something in the environment, but eventually the image is internalized and becomes the focus of concentration (Laughlin, McManus and d'Aquili 1990; Laughlin, McManus and Webber 1984). One may begin chanting a mantra out loud, but eventually the chant is internalized and wholly sublingual. There is a common structure to the meditative complex developed in these kinds of meditations. Borrowing from the Tibetan Tantric tradition (see Child 2016), I will call these kinds of meditations *arising yogas*. Virtually all meditative traditions, including modern latter-day alchemical practices (Chapter 9) and "guided visualizations" of all sorts, include arising yoga techniques.

The first phase of a typical visual arising yoga practice involves producing a stable image, an internalized image that may be constituted before the mind's eye at will—the ideal goal being an *internal image* of great vividness and stability. This may involve various ritual procedures for purification and producing an internal image from an objective image (the *parikamma nimitta* in Buddhist psychology; e.g., a picture, painting, mandala, geometric drawing). Sometimes, the practice involves creating an object which one scans to internalize its image—an object that in Buddhist practice is known as a *kasina* (see Buddhaghosa 1976).[11] One shifts from scanning the object to concentrating upon the afterimage with the head turned away or eyes closed. Once the afterimage is formed and stabilized as the focus of attention, it becomes the inner image, and the practice is to maintain the concentration upon

---

[11] *Kasinas* are usually smaller, more portable objects like paintings, bowls, crystals, and so forth. But they may also be very large man-made objects like a labyrinth, a geometrical form that has been used for thousands of years to evoke a contemplative mind-state (West 2011).

the inner image, perhaps accompanied by a chant, song, or some other combination of ritual driving stimuli.

Ritual drivers are any behavior, drug, element, substance, activity, sensation, etc. that directly causes the body to alter its activities in a desired way (see Lex 1979; Gellhorn and Kiely 1972; d'Aquili, Laughlin and McManus 1979; Laughlin and Loubser 2010; Laughlin, McManus and d'Aquili 1990; Davis-Floyd and Laughlin 2016: Chap. 5). Rhythmic stimuli such as chanting, clapping, drumming, dancing, flickering lights, etc. drive the autonomic nervous system into alternative energy configurations, sometimes leading to profound ASC and psychic energy experiences. Drivers may be packaged into a complex ritual (Laughlin, McManus, Rubinstein and Shearer 1986; Davis-Floyd and Laughlin 2016: Chap. 5) or may even be interlaced within the tapestry of a complete way of life, as in the various *ascetic life-styles* of hermits, monks, *sadhus*, and other folk who have forsaken the worldly way of life (D'Aquili and Newberg 2000; Valantasis 2008; Wimbush and Valantasis 1998a).

No matter the form of the internalized image (known in Buddhist psychology as the "acquired sign," the *uggaha nimitta*), eventually concentration upon the image will result in experiences arising that have to do with the esoteric or mystical meaning of the image. There may arise a stable image called the "secret sign," or the "counter-point sign" (*patibhaganimitta*) in Buddhist psychology. This is where neurognosis comes in (Chapter 1). For instance, meditating upon one's breath may result in seeing bubbles, spheres, fish eggs and the like before the mind's eye.[12] These universal experiences do not depend upon the culture of the practitioner, only the interpretation of their meaning does. They derive from the nascent, inherited mechanisms of the human brain. These evoked images are predictably common but are not logically entailed by the internal image. In other words, there is no rational way of predicting that meditation upon the breath will cause some meditators to see bubbles. However, because these archetypal images commonly arise during specific meditations, the teacher or guru will know about them and can gauge from their

---

[12] Many other images pop up during breath meditation, including blue sphere, moon, mist, red light, etc.

arising the maturity of the meditator's practice (e.g., among Tibetan Buddhist "arising yoga" practitioners, among Zen *koan* practitioners, Jungian active imagination practitioners). Depending upon the practice, the meditator may shift focus to the evoked image (see Griffin 1989; Laughlin and Tiberia 2012), in which case, concentration upon the evoked image will itself unfold and evoke further imagery and experiences. Again, these experiences become associated with the culture's or religion's worldview by way of their interpretive frame.

Meditation, Culture and the Cycle of Meaning

Traditional worldviews are expressed through the society's symbolic system, which includes their mythology, ritual, mobiliary and parietal art, architectural constructions, drama, performance, sacred landscape and games. All the different symbolic media are interconnected within the context of cosmological understanding. The symbols are variant expressions of a single reality as understood by the people. In those societies that do have a meditation culture, the object(s) of meditation will usually be drawn from the symbolic material available within their mythological system. This is the culture's cycle of meaning in action (see above).

The worldview as expressed symbolically is part of a living system of meaning for people born under the influence of an intact and relatively stable traditional culture. As the Ridingtons, ethnographers living among the Dane-zaa or Beaver Indians of Alberta, Canada, noted:

> Mythical cosmologies [like that of the Beaver Indians] are not the attempts of savages to explain in fantasy where empirical knowledge of reality is absent, but are rather the opposite— statements in allegorical form about knowledge of the interrelations between what we would call natural (objective), psychic (psychological), and cultural (learned adaptational) aspects of reality. Myth and science are opposites, not because one is wrong and the other right, but because myth metaphorically portrays reality as it is experienced while science postulates a reality that is thought to exist but can never be experienced. Myth unveils what is known to be true, while science experiments to

build realities that are thought not to be untrue. Myths through their symbols allow men to enter directly and experientially into the realm of meaningful reality.... (1970: 49-50)

The cosmology at the core of the worldview and its symbolic representations are lived and, in the living, the cosmology is animated and self-validated within the crucible of each person's consciousness. The cosmology is mainly carried around in people's brains, aided by symbolically rich, mnemonic materials like myths and other stories. Myths and stories are a living reality among people who have an intact cosmology (Laughlin and Throop 2001). The associations, principles and assumptions upon which a traditional cosmology is founded are rarely, if ever, worked out by people (Ortiz 1972). Rather, most people accept and participate in accordance with the worldview they inherit from their culture's pool of knowledge. This participation results in real life experiences that are in turn interpreted in terms of the cosmology, thus completing a semi-negative feedback loop which instantiates the cosmology in individual experiences and which also self-validates the truth of the people's system of knowledge (Ricoeur 1962, 1968; Walsh 1990).

Specialists are sometimes involved in the ritual and the interpretive phases of the cycle. Shamans and priests are often ritual specialists and keepers of the esoteric teachings pertaining to the spiritual domain of life. In some meditation cultures, these specialists take the form of a teacher or guru. The teacher may set the meditation for the practitioner and more than likely will be involved in the interpretation of experiences and insights. Meanings of meditation-related experiences are almost always interpreted in terms of the culture's worldview. Insights arising during Buddhist meditations will be interpreted in Buddhist terms; likewise, for Sufi, Western mysteries, Jain, Shogendō, Apache, Medicine Wheel, Sun Dance, and any other culturally-linked meditation system.

A society's cycle of meaning is never static. It is never totally closed to input and change. Some positive feedback is essential, for direct experiences can lead to alterations in interpretations, which in turn can change the worldview and its meditation culture. Obeyesekere (1981) has suggested that a great deal of creative impetus in culture change stems from ritually induced experiences had in meditations, dreams and other ASC. He explained that these states are characterized by their great creative capacity and their ability to "generate subjective imagery and cultural meanings" (1981: 169). Moreover, he argued that myth is itself directly produced from and influenced by ASC, thus requiring an integration of the creative and conventional sides of culture. The experiential byproducts of ASC can be "reworked by the conscious mind, and [as such] brought in line with the needs of the individual and the demands of culture" (1981: 181). In keeping with the cycle of meaning, Obeyesekere reasoned that culture and myth therefore "feed back into the [alternative state of consciousness], influencing the thought structure of these states" (1981: 181).

This process of rendering creative subjectivity into socially shared mythopoeic symbolism and ritual action is quite common. As Brock (2000: 15) noted, "Studying idiosyncratic doubts and ambivalence can yield important information on cultural processes. Social and cultural creativity are often most dynamic where idiosyncratic ideas influence well-established constructions, or what is, by consensus, regarded as real." These two attributes of the cycle of meaning—creativity and conservation—are probably ubiquitous to all meditation cultures on the planet.

We live in a world today in which globalization and rapid culture change are accelerating. The connection between a society's worldview and the direct experiences of individuals can be broken. This has happened historically when some political authority has outlawed ritual practices designed to evoke ASC, as happened to practitioners of the Sun Dance in the 19th century (Voget 1984). Christian missionary interference with local spiritual traditions was notorious for this kind of destruction. Meditation cultures are quite vulnerable to external interference because not everyone reaches full realization of an esoteric path. Often it is the individual who goes further (rises "higher") who becomes the shaman, prophet, guru, road chief, healer, oneirocritic, or visionary and who acts as a guide to others on the meditative path. Individual achievement is consistent with the stated goals of the system and its interpretive frames. But sustained interference may break the realization-teaching cycle. The various practices and techniques of meditation in time no longer operate and experiences are not evoked that are consistent with the various mythopoeic elements of the system. This is a dead system in which achievement cannot lead to the intended goal. Shamans, if they still exist in such a society, resemble priests in a dogma-dominated institution bereft of its esoteric or occult inspiration. Direct experience no longer instantiates the worldview and natural revitalization feedback into the worldview no longer operates. Such systems, under certain historical circumstances, may be revived or reestablished. This happened, for instance, late in the 20th century when various ritual practices used previously in the Sun Dance were resurrected (Voget 1984). Moreover, meditation techniques removed from their traditional cultural roots and cycle of meaning will tend to become diluted and lose their significance (Bruce 2002). Profound meditations within the traditional cultural context may be rendered little more than a relaxation exercise.

A society's cosmology and symbolic system are ultimately the product of the creative imagination of its people. This is not imagination in the mundane fantasy sense (i.e., imagined unreality), but rather the *Imaginatio* in Corbin's (1969) sense: the exercise of the creative, intuitive faculties associated with imagery by which the essentially invisible aspects of reality become envisioned (Flood 1993a). Modern Western culture is marked by a vast chasm between its conception of reality as described by science and reality as imagined by people: "In short, there has ceased to be an intermediate level between empirically verifiable reality and unreality pure and simple" (Corbin 1969: 181). In traditional societies this intermediate level by which reality is imagined is the spiritual domain and seamlessly bridges the gap between knowledge about the world and direct experience, the latter being derived in some cases by meditative methods.

Although dynamic and open to some change, traditional worldviews do tend to be conservative of meaning. They resist change in knowledge, for the principal function of a society's worldview is to assure both a complementarity of experience for society's members, as well as to reflect the authenticity of experience. The traditional cycle of meaning is the product of an inherent *effort after meaning* (Bartlett 1932) as opposed to an *effort after truth* (Count 1973; Garro 2007; Laughlin and Throop 1999, 2001). As we have seen earlier, the cognitive processes of the human brain operate to associate what is arising moment by moment within the sensorium with information stored in memory. The effort after meaning is the effort expended by the brain to interpret experience as redundant, as an instantiation of a pattern already stored in memory. The effort after truth, however, shifts the orientation from attributing meaning to the given toward discovering what is novel in the given and then evaluating the veracity of meaning by comparison with the experienced novelty. In other words, the effort after meaning is a quest for the correspondence between an experienced given and information in memory, while the effort after truth privileges anomaly over redundancy of a given. Most meditation systems orient the practitioners toward the effort after meaning, while a few systems, such as Husserlian transcendental phenomenology (Chapter Two) appear oriented toward the effort after truth.

As the cycle of meaning model implies, the information encoded in sacred stories and other symbolic media informs lived experience, and that is why myth is found to be so intimately associated with ritual activity. Durkheim (1995[1912]) long ago held that ritual is a mechanism through which individuals can harmonize their subjectivities with one another and with the cosmological system as expressed in a society's corpus of myths. His view of the close connection between ritual and mythology is evidenced in his assertion that "If myth is withdrawn from religion, ritual must also be withdrawn.... Indeed, the rite is often nothing other than the myth in action" (1995[1912]: 79). More recently, Victor Turner (1985, 1992; Turner and Bruner 1986) have argued that embodied ritual, not disembodied myth, is the cornerstone of religion. As is implied in the cycle of meaning model, the spiritual life of a people is an active process with ritual enactment at its very core (d'Aquili, Laughlin and McManus 1979; Laughlin 1989; Laughlin et al. 1986; Davis-Floyd and Laughlin 2016; Rappaport 1999). Meditation cultures operate in the same way, to harmonize the cultural theory of reality with individual subjectivities to instantiate and confirm the society's worldview or, if necessary, alter it such that harmony is reestablished, and the cycle of meaning is rejuvenated.

Meditation as Cultural Incubation

While all intact traditional societies have a worldview, as well as ritual procedures designed to *incubate* (aid the development of) experiences that instantiate and vivify their worldview, some societies have procedures that incorporate meditation; i.e., train initiates in techniques of sustained attention to a set of spiritually salient symbols (chant, song, image, thought, text, somatic process, emptiness) to evoke culturally prescribed experiences. For example, many cultures incorporate methods to incubate important dream experiences and some of these utilize ritual techniques to enhance attention within the dream (Laughlin 2011; Meier 2009; Tiberia and Laughlin 2016). Very often the sustained attention is accompanied by ritual drivers that operate to produce changes in somatic processes and states of consciousness (Laughlin, McManus and d'Aquili 1990; Laughlin and Throop 2003; Davis-Floyd and Laughlin 2016). Drivers include activities such as walking, running, dancing, whirling, drumming, chanting, singing, manipulating beads, flickering firelight, painful ordeals (e.g., flagellation), fatigue, dieting, sweat baths, exotic postures, sleep deprivation, and ingesting herbs and psychoactive plants.

Once again, I must remind the reader of the important distinction between monophasic and polyphasic cultures (Chapter 1). The great majority of human societies living today are polyphasic. That is, groups of people who value ASC because they allow people to access the normally invisible spiritual world, converse with gods, ancestors and spirits, and gain crucial information about the causes of blight, catastrophe, and disease (Flood 1993a). Most human societies utilize psychoactive drugs in their religious rituals (Bourguignon 1973; Bourguignon and Evascu 1977; Richards 2015), and as archaeological evidence suggests, have done so for millennia (Guerra-Doce 2015). Yet, most of the meditation systems practiced by people in Western monophasic cultures tend to be those that do not utilize entheogens during meditation (psychoactive drugs tend to be proscribed in materialist societies generally), save for modern rave culture, the Native American Church and other social movements that imbibe psychotropics (Chapter 11). These tend to be meditation systems associated with the World Religions (Buddhism, Christianity, Islam, Hinduism and Judaism), despite historical evidence of many mystics in these traditions having once used such herbal aids. And, of course, most of the neuropsychological and transpersonal research carried out with meditators tends to draw from these demographics. Thus, psychological research on meditation is severely biased toward meditation systems derived from largely modern, monophasic technocratic societies. Yet, this is not the whole story, for the body itself produces endogenous hallucinogens, pain killers and other mood-altering substances (Barker, McIlhenny and Strassman 2012). For instance, the pineal gland (Bradley 2010; see Figure 3.5; but cf. Nichols 2018) can produce its own psychedelic hormone called DMT:

Under circumstances of heightened activation, pineal enzymes can also endogenously synthesize the powerful hallucinogen 5-methoxy-dimethyltryptamine (DMT). Several studies have linked DMT to a variety of mystical states, including out-of-body experiences, distortion of time and space, and interaction with supernatural entities. Hyperstimulation of the pineal at this step, then, could also lead to DMT production that could be associated with the wide variety of mystical-type experiences associated with that hallucinogen. (Newberg and Iversen 2003)

Despite this anti-drug bias, some Westerners (including myself) have in fact sought to augment their meditative practice with the help of psychoactive substances, sometimes under the guidance of traditional shamans (Dobkin de Rios 1984; Dobkin de Rios and Winkelman 1989; Winkelman 2005; Hagens and Lansky 2012), but these practitioners are in a minority. Taking as an example the use of ayahuasca teas in spiritual practices, Hoffmann, Keppel-Hesselink and da Silveira Barbosa (2001: 28-29) noted that "Ayahuasca seems to induce and expand the hypnagogic or twilight state (correlated with an increase of theta) and at the same time keeps the individual awake and conscious (correlated with an increase of alpha)." They also suggested that "in some respects the ayahuasca altered state is comparable to meditation and it is quite conceivable that ayahuasca facilitates meditation" in that "ayahuasca opens up people to their unconscious feelings and memories and gives them an opportunity to explore new psychological insights" (see also Hagens and Lansky 2012).

Riba *et al.* (2006: 93) carried out regional cerebral blood flow research on ayahuasca users and found that:

Ayahuasca administration led to significant activation of frontal and paralimbic brain regions. Increased blood perfusion was observed bilaterally in the anterior insula, with greater intensity in the right hemisphere, and in the anterior cingulate/frontomedial cortex of the right hemisphere [Figure 3.5], areas previously implicated in somatic awareness, subjective feeling states, and emotional arousal— including emotional empathy (Eres *et al.* 2015). Additional increases were observed in the left amygdala/parahippocampal gyrus, a structure also involved in emotional arousal.

Again, the ritual use of ayahuasca had many of the effects upon the PFC and associated structures that we have come to expect with meditation. As a matter of fact, sustained attention is combined with the ritual use of the drug when shamans initiate apprentices (Rock and Krippner 2011; Rodd 2006; Rodd and Sumabila 2011).

Regardless of the exact design of meditative systems cross-culturally, and regardless of the blend of ritual drivers slotted into a ritual practice (Laughlin, McManus, Rubinstein and Shearer 1986), the intention of any meditation system is to incubate specific experiences and states of consciousness, thus influencing individual development in a way that is required and sanctioned by the society and congruent with the society's worldview. Thus, whether a meditation is done privately by the individual, or by groups of people practicing together, traditional meditation systems are always social processes. The goals, design of practices, inclusion or exclusion of ritual drivers, place and timing of practice and interpretation of experiences and insights are all determined by the society for its own collective ends.

MEDITATION CULTURES

The phenomenology of meditation utilizing all the available psychotropic substances and other ritual drivers is far too complex a matter to go into here (see Devereux 2008; Dobkin de Rios 1984; McKenna 1992; Rudgley 1993; Schultes, Hofmann and Rätsch 1998; Davis-Floyd and Laughlin 2016: Chap. 5). However, to illustrate the kinds of meditation cultures that are less likely to appear in psychophysical studies of meditation, let me offer several examples to broaden the ethnographic scope of the field.

Contemplative Subcultures: Monasticism, Asceticism, Eremitism and Retreating

One way that cultures have of training, incubating and controlling ASC and spiritual development is by offering those members so inclined an alternative subculture—a lifestyle more conducive to meditation, contemplation and self-discovery. In our modern times, people in many traditions across the planet have recourse to *retreats* and *retreat centers*— that is, they take a period during which they shut out the normal world and concentrate upon their respective spiritual practices. I have done many retreats lasting from a few days, to a few weeks, to months. I have "retreated" in my own home by stocking up on food, "pulling the plug" on outside contacts, and eliminating all predictable distractions for the duration. I have entered monasteries, both Christian and Buddhist, here in the United States, and in Europe and Asia. I have also gone to retreat centers that specialize in accommodating the needs of full-time meditation. I have never had recourse to the mendicant ascetic lifestyle, for that does not go over well in North America. Our society is not mendicant friendly, to put it mildly. In contrast, in Indian Hindu tradition, there is an age-old model of four states of life (*ashrama*): The childhood/student stage (*brahmacharya*), the householder stage during which one raises a family, carries out a career and supports dependents (*grihastha*), the retired "forest dweller" stage (*vanaprastha*) and the *sadhu* (*sannyasi*) or renunciation stage (*sannyasa*; Olivelle 1993). In the third "forest dweller" stage, one passes on the responsibilities of the householder to the younger generation and "retreats" into relative seclusion to focus upon one's spiritual liberation (*moksha*). Most people do not enter the fourth stage of becoming a *sadhu*. In both the third and fourth stages, it is permissible to beg for food.

Ascetic Impulse

I have concluded after nearly four decades of meditation-related adventures that asceticism is a natural manifestation of the spiritually questing mind which will be easily understood by any mature contemplative (Wimbush and Valantasis 1998a), and which may be termed the *ascetic impulse*: the ineluctable desire for simplicity, solitude, tranquility ("silence," "stillness"), anti-ego-centered mentation and a stress-free environment (Scudder 1912: 100; Mazrui 1967: 237; Chaudhuri 1972: 6; Clark 1998: 505-510).[13] In the meditative life, one learns very early that the pressures of one's daily life—one's occupation, family responsibilities, demands of household maintenance, noise and chaos of urban existence, and so forth—become a hindrance to meditation and undistracted contemplation. I have known many contemplatives who, within the first months of taking up serious meditation, find there is a long list of things (relationships, jobs, habit patterns, personal desires, diet, etc.) they are no longer willing to do, because they recognize that their previously "normal" lifestyle drags them back from the direction in which their spiritual practice is propelling them. For instance, I have known several serious meditators who took high-paying seasonal jobs in Alaska to accumulate enough money during the summer to spend the rest of the year taking meditation courses and attending retreats.

Societies are quick to co-opt the process of spiritual awakening, especially those that are polyphasic in their worldview. In virtually every instance, asceticism is brought under the purview of institutions that make sure the results of contemplative work are situated in the institution's cycle of meaning (see Kaelber 1998; see also Vallely 2002 for Jain, Behr 2000 for Christian and Eskildsen 1998 for Taoist ascetic traditions). Because of cultural embedding of individual asceticism, most of the world religions early-on developed monastic institutions that house, feed, clothe and take care of the health of male and female "monks."[14] The oldest monastic tradition that we know anything about developed around 600 BCE by earlier groups of predominantly *eremitic* (Gk: *eremos*, "desert;" hence "desert dweller;" aka "hermit") practitioners of renunciation and contemplation. Generalized ascetic

---

[13] The term "ascetic impulse" (aka, "ascetic instinct") has been used throughout the 20th century to label the drive to seek the non-material, yogic, spiritual or monastic life. The earliest reference I have found for the term was in V. D. Scudder's book, *Socialism and Character* (1912: 100).

[14] In Asia both male and female monastery dwellers are called "monks," while in the Christian West we distinguish between male "monks" and female "nuns." I will not use this western sexist distinction and will refer to all monastic ascetics as monks.

daily lives seem to be endemic to organized spiritual paths wherever they arise. Early Christian leaders extolled the virtues of maintaining strict virginity and sexual abstinence, undergoing self-effacing ordeals like fasting and mortifying the flesh, sleeping directly on the ground, and ridding themselves of any wealth or possessions (Vidmar 2014).

The roots of the various forms of institutional renunciation are undoubtedly found in the practices of shamanic recruitment. Neophyte shamans often seek solitude during their transformative phase—during their initiation, training and asceticism (Walsh 1994). While some shamans are recruited out of a severe illness, others undergo a subtler change:

> [S]ometimes there is not exactly an illness but rather a progressive change in behavior. The candidate becomes meditative, *seeks solitude*, sleeps a great deal, seems absent-minded, has prophetic dreams and sometimes seizures. All these symptoms are only the prelude to the new life that awaits the unwitting candidate. His behavior, we may add, suggests the first signs of a mystical vocation, which are the same in all religions and too well known to dwell upon. (Eliade 1964: 35; emphasis added)

We shall see in Chapters 9 and 10 that these and other practices form part of the tool kit of contemplative traditions whose goal is the evocation of mystical experiences. They are essentially processes of *metanoia*—lifestyle changes that have the effect of loosening the strictures of cultural conditioning and allowing for anomalous experiences and self-transformation (see Laughlin 1990a; Avanessian and Hennig 2017). These folks establish a daily life divorced from the concerns of the worldly householders, and from activities that feed the "me, mine, more" ego-centered attitudes. These subcultures are often the direct antithesis of the mainstream culture, and yet usually depend upon the material and legal support of the wider culture.

Cynic and Stoic Meditation

Aside from Judeo-Christian traditions, there were several "pagan" philosophical schools that practiced various forms of asceticism and meditation, especially the Cynic and Stoic schools of ancient Greco-

Roman philosophy (Finn 2009: 25-27; Long 1996). Much of what these schools taught has been lost, but there are sufficient writings surviving to suggest that these ascetic practices were intended to evoke mind-altering and even mystical experiences. It is important to understand that ancient Hellenistic philosophies were intended, not to create and transmit academic theories of metaphysics, ethics and virtue, but to show normal people how to live the good life. So it was with the teachers of Cynicism who espoused an extreme form of asceticism in which one was to live a simple life, much like a beggar, a life based upon the pursuit of virtue and in accord with nature (Branham and Goulet-Cazé 2000). Contrary to other competing schools of the day, the Cynics taught that by the application of reason and discipline, one may come to understand that to experience happiness one should embrace poverty and avoid those ego-inflating pursuits common in society like wealth, pleasure, and power. One should be satisfied with having only those things that nature provides.

Stoicism was very similar to Cynicism in that devotees focused upon adhering to the natural and virtuous life, but unlike the Cynics, they emphasized moderation in their asceticism, pointing to the causal interrelations between virtue and tranquility (Irvine 2008; Mac Suibhne 2009). It has been erroneously claimed that the Stoics were anti-emotion. Rather, they eschewed *negative* emotions like anger, greed, hatred and fear, and demonstrated how, by living in a virtuous way, the *positive* emotions like happiness, love and, above all, tranquility can flourish. One should train oneself to take each moment as it arises and not expend energies seeking pleasure, wealth, sexual satisfaction and the like, or avoiding fear or pain. Each of us has a part to play in the natural unfolding of things and focusing upon discovering that part will lead us to virtue and thus tranquility. The Stoics were essentially contemplatives who focused upon what in the East would be called *karma*, that being the causal relationship between mental acts and consequences. Living life by practicing natural virtue produces a tranquil state of consciousness, and one living in a tranquil state of mind automatically lives virtuously. One of the cornerstones of Stoic practice was cultivation of self-awareness, and awareness of what psychological conditions produce tranquility, or thwart it (Irvine 2008: Chap. 21). The contemplation upon the self necessitated developing a kind of "watcher" who observed what we are doing while we are doing it and evaluating how close to the Stoic ideal we have approached in our daily activities (ibid: 121).

Alas, we have no descriptions of the ASC experienced by any of the Stoics or Cynics. What is quite clear, however, from surviving accounts is that Cynic and Stoic ascetic disciplines and their characteristic meditations upon nature led to cosmological worldviews typical of mystical traditions:

> The universe itself is God and the universal outpouring of its soul; it is this same world's guiding principle, operating in mind and reason, together with the common nature of things and the totality that embraces all existence; then the foreordained might and necessity of the future; then fire and the principle of aether; then those elements whose natural state is one of flux and transition, such as water, earth, and air; then the sun, the moon, the stars; *and the universal existence in which all things are contained.* (Chrysippus, quoted in Cicero 1997[45 BCE]; emphasis added)

Shamanic Meditation Cultures

The role of the shaman may be significant in a meditation culture (see Chapter 10). Indeed, it seems evident that all traditional meditation cultures originated in shamanism (Johnson 1982; Winkelman 2010). Shamanic meditation cultures are important to us for at least two reasons: (1) The shaman is very likely to be the most advanced meditator in society and indeed may depend for his or her reputation on the ability to enter ASC and utilize their skill for the benefit of the people (Price-Williams and Hughes 1994; Rock and Krippner 2011; Krippner and Combs 2002), and (2) contemporary shamanic traditions are as close as we can come to the original meditation cultures of prehistoric times, and perhaps of the entire Upper Paleolithic, and hence the importance of the role of the ritual specialist, and of meditation, to uncovering the origins of religion (Lewis-Williams 2002; Ridington and Ridington 1970; Whitley 2004; Winkelman 2010). It is important to keep in mind that all shamanic meditation cultures are found in polyphasic societies. In virtually all such systems, reality consists of the visible (mundane) and the invisible (spiritual). The spiritual world becomes visible during dreams, trances and other ASC during which spiritual forces may be perceived, approached, communicated with and appealed to for help and information. Meditation states are one avenue for making the normally invisible forces visible. A shaman is a specialist, skilled in the procedures for accessing the invisible (Townsend 2004). But studying the role of meditation in the shaman's life is not an easy matter. Shamans by their very role operate in public forums (ceremonies, healing rituals, initiations, etc.). But shamans often meditate in seclusion, especially in their formative years, or in informal social situations. Few anthropologists have apprenticed to shaman adepts, and so there is a lot we do not know (see Rodd 2006).

One of the meditation techniques utilized by shamans is the meditation upon mirrors (MacDonald *et al.* 1989). Shamanic mirrors were normally not made of glass and did not reflect in the way that modern mirrors do. They were normally opaque and made of metal, slate or wood. They were and are still used to create a visible portal between the mundane physical world and the spiritual world. Traditional peoples all over the planet recognize the significance of doorways as a liminal stage between spaces (e.g., see MacDonald 1984 for the Tsimshian people of the northwest coast of North America). One type of shaman's mirror used in North America was made of slate in the form of a palate (something like a narrow table tennis paddle). One surface was ground into a slightly concave surface such that when water was placed in the concavity, it would form a reflective mirror that slowly shrank to a pinpoint and then vanished, much like a closing iris. Experiments with this kind of "scrying device" were carried out by some of my colleagues and me which tended to confirm the efficacy of this type of meditation device (MacDonald *et al.* 1989). Polished metal mirrors are used in one of the most important initiation meditations among Tibetan Tantric Buddhist practitioners, the so-called mandala offering (*dkyil-'khor*) during which one builds a mandala of rice grains on a mirror (another kind of *kasina* practice) and then sweeps them off. This is done over and over for perhaps a hundred thousand repetitions while chanting an appropriate mantra (Beyer 1973).

Marabout Meditation

The role of the shaman-like marabout in North and West African Islam is crucial, for they are usually Qur'anic scholars, oneirocritics (dream interpreters), spiritual guides and ritual practitioners. Most marabouts in West Africa are also Sufis and are valued for their *baraka* or divine nature and knowledge. The great marabouts are also masters of meditation (*khalwa*; Butler 2004; Dilley 1992). *Khalwa* occurs in solitude, often taking the form of dream meditation, to attain a closer relationship with their spiritual natures and with God. They also will meditate on behalf of others who wish a talisman blessed or some other spiritual boon. The marabout can summon spirits and access their power. They may also lead group chants which, accompanied by drumming, may lead to trance.

The Kogi *Mámas*

The Kogi Indians live high in the Sierra Nevada de Santa Marta Mountains of Colombia. They are the only surviving remnant of pre-Columbian culture in the Americas and have one of the most remarkable social structures and spiritual cultures in the ethnographic literature (Reichel-Dolmatoff 1949-1950, 1976). The Kogi are a subsistence agricultural people who are ruled by male priests called *mámas* who are ritual specialists and master meditators, and who undergo what is perhaps one of the most strenuous, years-long contemplative apprenticeships on the planet. A novice is chosen as a small child by a *máma* in trance communion with the Mother-Goddess or by dream-divination. Then begins a long period of training that lasts until the novice is initiated as a new *máma* during early adulthood. During the many years of training, the novice lives among the family of a *máma* and never sees the light of day, quite literally. He sleeps in a ceremonial house during the daylight hours, and only emerges during brief intervals at night for meals and for training, always accompanied by a *máma*. If the moon is out at night, he must wear a special hat that blocks out the direct light of the moon. All during the night he is being trained and indoctrinated. He undergoes many ritual drivers, including repetitive chanting, dietary strictures, fasting, rhythmic singing and dancing, total sexual abstinence, meditation and breathing exercises, and ingestion of various psychoactive drugs. "The youth is taught many divinatory techniques, beginning with the simple yes-or-no alternatives, and going on to deep meditation accompanied by exercises of muscular relaxation, controlled breathing, and the 'listening' to sudden signs and voices from within" (Reichel-Dolmatoff 1976: 280).

The whole point of a novice *máma's* arduous education is the gradual introduction of direct experience and mastery of ASC, including lucid dreaming and meditative trance, accompanied by proper indoctrination as to the meaning of experiences as they arise. For the apprentice *máma*, this is a long process by which sensory deprivation is accompanied by ritual drivers that evoke inner spiritual encounters that result in the experiential instantiation of the Kogi cosmology and culminate in union with the divine—the experience typical of mystical realization, termed by C. G. Jung *the coniunctio* (or "conjunction," the union of all opposites; see Edinger 1995; von Franz 1980). This lengthy period of light deprivation is a type of "dark retreat," also used by Tibetan Tantric practitioners and other wisdom traditions (Lowenstein 2003).

As Reichel-Dolmatoff (1976: 284-285) stated:

...the aim of priestly education is to discover and awaken those hidden faculties of the mind that, at a given moment, enable the novice to establish contact with the divine sphere. The *mámas* know that a controlled set or sequence of sensory privations eventually produces altered states of consciousness enabling the novice to perceive a wide range of visual, auditory, or haptic hallucinations. The novice sees images and hears voices that explain and extol the essence of being, the true sources of Nature, together with the manner of solving a great variety of common human conflict situations. In this way, he is able to receive instructions about offerings to be made, about collective ceremonies to be organized, or sickness to be cured. He acquires the faculty of seeing behind the exterior appearances of things and perceiving their true nature. ...The entire teaching process is aimed at this slow, gradual building up to the sublime moment of self-disclosure of god to man, of the moment when Sintána or Búnkuasé or one of their avatars reveals himself in a flash of light and says: "Do this! Go there!" Education, at this stage, is a technique of progressive illumination. The divine personification appears bathed in a heavenly light and, from then on teaches the novice at night.

Totemic-Animistic Meditations

The worldview of many traditional societies is rooted in what anthropologists call *totemic thought* (Levi-Strauss 1971; Friedrich 1991; Winkelman 2004). Winkelman (2004: 207) defines totemic thought in this way:

Totemic thought uses analogical processes, establishing a homology between animal species differences and the differences among human groups; differences among human groups are represented through the differences among animal species. Totemism distinguishes human groups by attributing the characteristics derived from the animal world, representing group identity and intergroup differences through models provided by animal species. The use of animals for social and cognitive modeling is a fundamental aspect of metaphoric and analogical thought…, a universal human system for expression of meaning and creation of social and personal identity.

Totemic worldviews hold that human society is in intimate connection with nature and derives much of its meaning from perceived relations among animals and plants. As Ridington and Ridington (1970: 49) state, "Totemic symbols are not merely syllogistic but refer to a systematic conceptualization of natural, psychic, and cultural reality that in mythically oriented traditions can best be called a cosmic structure…." Cosmological worldviews are typically grounded in a monistic conception of the world of nature and the world of consciousness and culture as being two sides of the same coin. This conception of the unity of being (the mystical realization of which is the *coniunctio*) is emphasized in the formal, symbolic association of persons and groups, and the interrelations among these, with the interactions among animals and plants in the environment. Totemic meditations are usually carried out in association with various ritual drivers (sometimes including psychoactive drugs) and are often a procedure for establishing either an intimate experience of unity or a personal relationship with one's totemic animal or plant.

The Shugendō religion of Japan offers an example of this kind of meditative work. Shugendō is one of the syncretic sects that emerged during the great influx of religious influences from China during the Heian Period (794-1185 AD; see Earhart 2004). Combining the mountain worship, animism-totemism and spiritualism of earlier Shinto with the asceticism and meditation of Buddhism, the practitioner (*shugenja*, "one who has power, a mountain ascetic," or *yamabushi*, "one who lies down in the mountains") seeks enlightenment and supernatural power through unity with the mountain spirits or gods (*kami*). The practitioner undergoes rigorous training (*shugyō*) that involves mastering rituals, ascetic practices and meditation (*meisō*).

Contemporary Shugendō is focused upon several sacred mountain sites around Japan (Rill 2011). Without going into detail about the intricate ritual practices carried out by the practitioner who has climbed onto a sacred mountain, the intent of meditation, both sitting, and walking forms often accompanied by mantra recitation and preceded by fasting and purification, is a state of absorption into the object of focus during which all duality disappears from awareness and the consciousness is as one with the subject. Practicing absorption meditation—fundamental to all meditation[15]—leads eventually to the skill necessary to enter and prolong absorption into the All (again, the *coniunctio*). The objects that are used as meditation foci may be certain Japanese characters. "Shugendō also uses the five meditations for calming the Mind, meditations on purity, compassion, the chain of causation, the four elements, and breathing..." (Rill 2011: 244). As Rill (2011, p. 28) notes:

> The idea of peeling back the layers of the lotus flower is an inversion of the typical metaphor in Buddhism. The unfolding of the lotus flower is meant to represent the opening of human consciousness to something greater, something more intimately connected with the cosmos. Ultimately the Goal is a complete

---

[15] As Pagano and Warrenburg (1983: 188) have noted, "...absorbed attention may be an important prerequisite for successful long-term practice of meditation."

unity between human consciousness and the source of the universe, Dainichi Nyorai.

Dancing Meditations

One of the most interesting examples of meditation culture is the Sun Dance among the Plains Indian cultures of the United States and Canada. Traditional Crow Indians practiced individual fasting to evoke dreams that would give them power and knowledge about their future with respect to the Dance (Voget 1984). In the old days, people received their Sun Dance bundle through dreaming and were thereafter able to sponsor a Dance. These ceremonies were normally concerned with revenge and killing enemies. They practiced self-torture by hanging from the lodge poles by hooks piercing the chest, a painful ordeal that would drive visions (Lowie 1915). Today, any high-status male can sponsor a Sun Dance, often after having a dream directing him to do so. Dancers participate in a Sun Dance either because they feel the need, or they have been told to participate by a spirit person in a dream. The dancer fasts, prays and offers the spirit person tobacco to "bind" him. After fasting and dancing for hours or days, while concentrating upon the Buffalo symbol on the central pole, a dancer may have a vision or dream of one or more of the spirit persons that becomes a source of ecstatic power for the dancer and his group (Jorgensen 1972; Walker 2012).

Practitioners among the Oglala people may meditate upon a special bed of sage under the guidance of their guide, seeking visions pertaining to their participation in the Dance (Walker 2012). Lewis (1972: 44) had this to say about a potential Sun Dance participant:

He was expected to rid himself of possessions, to give feasts, to see that his family and *tiospahe* [extended family] members provided equipment, presents, food, and offerings to the Powers. He received an oral education in history and tradition. He was expected to fast, to seek a vision, to consecrate his thinking and behavior. He was expected to observe (and might also be closely supervised therein) a strict code of conduct which included meditation, control of emotion and action, sexual abstention, social withdrawal, silence and concentrated thought.

A half a world away, we find the now famous healing trance dance of the !Kung San of the Kalahari Desert, South Africa (see Katz 1982; Katz, Biesele and St. Denis 1997; Biesele and Howell 1981; Keeney and Keeney 2013). The San hold that there exists a supernatural power called *n/um* (*n/om*) that healers access through a dance practice and use to heal people. "In !Kung culture, *n/um kxao-si*, '*n/um* owners,' are curers of the kind referred to in English as 'medicine men.' I have accepted this paraphrase. From it follow two other paraphrases: *n/um tshxai,* the dance at which the medicine men go into trance and perform their curing rite, I term the 'medicine dance;' and *n/um* itself, the supernatural potency from which the medicine men derive their power to cure, I term 'medicine'" (Marshall 1969: 347). Keeney and Keeney (2013: 73) note that: "*N/om* refers to both the changing and one's experience of feeling it, as well as to the creator god's inspiration for creating. It evokes an enhanced state of awareness accompanied by ecstatic emotion." *N/um* is thus a divine energy that permeates the world and that can be accessed directly by adepts who enter "trance" (read ASC) in which they experience being filled with energy and which allows them to heal others.

Richard Katz focused on the experience of trance dancers, and describes for the Kalahari San a "transcendental experience" called *!kia* (*!aia*), an extraordinary state of consciousness during which:

> ...a !Kung experiences himself as existing beyond his ordinary level of existence. !Kia itself is a very intense physical and emotional state. The body is straining against fatigue and struggling with convulsion-like tremors and heavy breathing. The emotions are aroused to an extraordinary level, whether they be fear or exhilaration or fervor. Also, a !Kung practices extraordinary activities during !kia. He performs cures, handles and walks on fire, claims x-ray vision, and at times says he sees over great distances. He does not even attempt such activities in his ordinary state. (Katz 1976: 287)

One of Katz's adepts stated:

> You dance, dance, dance, dance. The *n/um* lifts you in your belly and lifts you in your back, and then you start to shiver. *N/um*

makes you tremble; it's hot. Your eyes are open but you don't look around; you hold your eyes still and look straight ahead. But when you get into !kia, you're looking around because you see everything, because you see what's troubling everybody... Rapid shallow breathing, that's what draws n/um up... then n/um enters every part of your body, right to the tip of your feet and even your hair. ...In your backbone you feel a pointed something, and it works its way up. Then the base of your spine is tingling, tingling, tingling, tingling, tingling, tingling, tingling...and then it makes your thoughts nothing in your head. (Katz 1976: 286-287)

Notice also that the San utilize quite common ritual drivers in their healing dance, including flickering firelight (associated directly with n/um), hours of repetitive dancing to chanting and rhythmic drumming and clapping, as well as "yogic" breathing. Note also that experienced meditators commonly experience shaking and twitching as the body alters its energy distribution and centers (see Desjarlais 1992 for this phenomenon among Nepali healers; see also Hume 2007: Chap. 4).

The reader familiar with Hindu Kundalini practices will recognize the techniques and phenomenology of the Bushmen practices (Vivekananda 1956). This is an example of how movement, rhythm and other ritual drivers are combined with intense concentration to produce an alternative state of consciousness of value to the society.

Navajo Healing Diagnostic Meditations

The contemporary Navajo seer or diagnostician (Levy, Neutra and Parker 1987; Wyman 1936) uses one of two extant techniques for divining the causes of disease, as well as discovering the location of lost persons and articles, stolen property, sources of water, and witches: hand-trembling (ndilniihii) and stargazing (deest'ii'; including moon-gazing, sun-gazing and crystal-gazing). Each of these is a technique intended to evoke an ASC in which internal visual images spontaneously arise in the practitioner's mind and a diagnosis is rendered by interpreting those images. The diagnostician may also be a healer, although this co-mingling of roles is quite rare. He or she may or may not formally discuss the disease with the patient before entering the alternative state, but as he/she likely knows all about the patient's condition beforehand, in most instances the diagnostician enters the procedure with some relevant knowledge. Also, the information about the disease is coming directly from the Holy People, especially Gila Monster and Dark Wind with whom hand-tremblers are closely allied, through the intervention of the diagnostician. If a healing ceremony is indicated, the patient will often undergo a short segment of the indicated ceremonial (e.g., the "blackening") to test whether the diagnosis is correct before undergoing the great expense and effort of the full ceremony. Failure of a prescribed course of treatment is evidence of a false diagnosis.

Hand-trembling is the most common technique used among the Navajo today. Unlike the medicine man and the other types of diagnostician, individuals become hand-tremblers by way of a calling. For instance, a person may spontaneously enter an alternative state and exhibit characteristic trembling and convulsions during participation in a healing ceremony (especially auspicious during a Hand-Trembling Way ceremony) and are then recognized as having the gift of divinatory sight. Usually a woman, hand-tremblers will first bless their arm with corn pollen and then hold it over a patient, and once the trembling begins they enter an alternative state in which their normal personality is submerged and during which they may see images that indicate both the cause of the disease and the remedy, be that treatment by herbals or by a healing ceremony, or both. The hand-trembler may also draw images on the floor of the *hogan* (traditional Navajo round, six-sided or eight-sided house) while in her alternative state, thus utilizing a kind of automatic writing, to produce a diagnostic image such as a lightning bolt, a circle or a hole which will indicate a diagnosis.

Stargazing is a skill that must be learned. The stargazing ritual may involve making an appropriate sand painting, or not, depending upon circumstances. An apprentice stargazer is assigned an appropriate star by his teacher. The small sand painting will represent his star. With or without the sand painting, the stargazer will bless his eyes and the eyes of the patient with powder made from the lenses of the eyes of certain birds. He then goes outside and sings appropriate chants and prays for his star to show him the cause of the patient's distress. He will stare either at his star directly, or at the light from that star filtered through a crystal held up in front of him. He will enter an alternative state in which images appear that are indicative of the correct diagnosis. The stargazer will often describe to the patient what he has seen and ask what the patient or other participants have seen during the ritual and will render a diagnosis based upon his interpretation of these images. Sometimes the diagnostician may use the moon or sun as the source of light.

Buddhism and Suchness

One of the most productive and narrowly focused traditions of contemplation on the planet involves the various practices used in certain Buddhist schools toward the realization of suchness (aka *thusness*; Skt.: *tathātā*, or *dharmatā*). As I mentioned in Chapter 2 when we were discussing phenomenology as contemplation, what Husserl meant by "return to the things themselves" is equivalent to Chan and Zen Buddhism's experience of suchness. I came to realize suchness from a distinctly different route—at least I think I did. I have shared with you the realization of the pixelation of the sensorium in Chapter 1 and will give a more personal description of the experience in Chapter 5. What I want to focus on here is one of the ramifications of the realization of the pixelated sensorium, the ability of the mind to become absorbed into the suchness of the sensorium.

First, descriptions of the suchness experience do not usually mention pixelation but do implicate a discrete ASC defined by an absorption state with the structure of the sensorium as focus. These descriptions also note the layering of perceptual, cognitive and linguistic significance that almost immediately follow pattern detection in the suchness. In evoking the suchness realization, contemplation reverses the normal layering until nothing is left but the suchness. Neurologist and Zen practitioner James H. Austin has this to say about suchness in his remarkable book *Zen and the Brain*:

> Real suchness is not a concept. It is an experience beyond reach of the intellect. Is there no way a finger can point, even in the same general direction as this experience? Let us try, first by looking at what seems to be an ordinary pebble. In the early milliseconds, we will have already taken it away from itself. We will have processed the wavelengths and transformed them into a percept framed in

our own *personal* terms of reference. Thoughts wandering, as usual, we might even go on to discriminate whether it was a light or heavy pebble, igneous or metamorphic, etc., etc. If its black surface and white quartz veins seemed aesthetically pleasing, we might succumb to the rock hound's powerful impulse (almost primal, it seems) which drives the "collector's need" to take it home. Or if it were flat enough, and we had energies to burn, we might hurl it skipping along the water's surface.

What happened to the stone *itself* in all this? The pebble got lost. For its true suchness is none of these extra, human, layers. It is the stone, seen thoroughly but spared from being processed further. And seen not as *our* object. But *just as it is*, the thing-in-itself, uncomplicated by any of our autobiographical references. In suchness, viewing perceives that very stone, and it relates directly to it. Immediate perception. Uncluttered by any personal reverberations. (Austin 1998: 549-550)

Culture has a lot to do with obscuring the natural suchness of perception. As the great Zen authority, D. T. Suzuki wrote in his book, *Zen and Japanese Culture* (1959):

The Primary Nature functions in its purest form in our infancy, when we are held in our mother's arms and fed from her breasts. As the baby is sufficient unto itself with the Nature, so even as adults we must be sufficient unto ourselves when the Nature is permitted to work in its own way with no interference from the side of relative consciousness. Unfortunately, as soon as we begin to grow up we are indoctrinated by every means accessible to us. Because of conceptualization, our sense-experiences inform us with an incorrect picture of the world. When we see a mountain, we do not see it in its suchness, but we attach to it all kinds of ideas, sometimes purely intellectual, but frequently charged with emotionality. When these envelop the mountain, it is transformed into something monstrous. This is due to our own indoctrination out of our "scholarly" learning and our vested interests, whether individual, political, social, economic, or religious. The picture thus formed is a hideous one, crooked and twisted in every possible way. Instead of living in a world presented to the Primary Nature in its nakedness, we live in an artificial, "cultured" one. The pity is that we are not conscious of the fact. (ibid: 174-175)

From the Zen point of view, "culture" refers to how society utilizes the raw data of suchness for its own purposes by fragmenting nature and attaching significance to the bits and pieces abstracted from nature. This process is, of course, quite adaptive, as we saw back in Chapter 1, but lost along the way is the ability to *de*-layer perception back to the suchness and dwell in that state until enlightenment dawns. As neuroscientist Naoyuki Osaka (2003: 107-107) has shown, when we visually pick out objects from the environment to scan and process, we lose track of, and are unconscious of, what is happening in peripheral vision. In other words, we miss out on most of what vision is portraying. Realizing suchness is enlightening but may well be maladaptive in the strictly biological sense. Research on action-readiness among meditators has shown an increased striatal dopamine release which is associated with a decrease in action-readiness—in other words, meditators tend to let stuff arise and pass away without responding (Kjaer *et al.* 2002).

Second, suchness is said to be empty or void (Skt.: *śūnyatā*). This takes us back to the mirror as a symbol for the "canvas" of the pixelated sensorium. The emptiness does not in any sense imply a vacuum or "nothingness." Rather, it is the emptiness of significance in the initial suchness of perception. There are many different methods used to realize the emptiness of suchness. I have mentioned how I did it because of an initial realization of sensorial pixels in visual perception (Chapter 1) and will elaborate on this experience in Chapter 5. There are other methods, some of which are thousands of years old.

Let me give you an example of another method from my own experience. During my "foundation work" (Tib.: *ngondro*; see Nydahl 1990) in Tibetan Tantric Buddhism, I completed over one hundred thousand repetitions of what is called the *mandala offering* (Tib.: *kyil khor*; Figure 3.6). The "mirror" as used by Tibetans is really an upside-down, flat-bottomed bowl or pan with a translucent sheen. Tibetan materials and practices can get very elaborate with multiple bowls or rings made of silver and gold stacked on top of each other. Most of the pictures of the mandala offerings you will find on the internet are very elaborate because they are used as symbols in rituals and placed upon altars.

The "real" esoteric mandala offering is very simple and straightforward and uses only one bowl and a lap-full of rice. I was taught to make a "mirror" out of a small round shaving mirror removed from its mounting and glued to the bottom of a dish. I sat in half-lotus posture with a sheet covering my lap into which I poured a heap of rice that had been dyed yellow with food coloring. I would hold the mirror with my left hand and take up a fist-full of rice in my right, and as I repeated the appropriate mantra, I constructed a mandala-form mound of rice on the mirror, offered it up to the Buddha, then wiped all the rice back into my lap. This procedure was repeated over and over, the number of repetitions being counted by a mala (rosary) also in my left hand. I did most of these repetitions during retreats and found that most of the experiences that arose because of this practice occurred during lucid dreams (see my description in MacDonald, Cove, Laughlin and McManus (1989) and Laughlin, McManus and d'Aquili (1990: 328-331) for much more detail).

If you imagine that this process reproduces, however grossly, the moment-by-moment perceptual epoch—the real now moment

Figure 3.6. Tulku Khejok Rinpoche Performs a Mandala Offering. The practitioner constructs a wee mandala of rice grains (or beans, tiny semiprecious gems, or any other tiny objects) upon an upside-down bowl (the mirror) while repeating a mantra. Then he wipes the mirror clean and starts building the mandala again.

(Chapter 2)—during which sensorial pixels (rice grains) arise and pass away, you will see the utter simplicity and beauty of the technique for evoking an instantaneous realization of suchness. Moreover, this technique is far older than Buddhism, and was in one form or another borrowed by Buddhist teachers from earlier shamanic practices. Shamans have used many kinds of objects as meditation (or scrying) devices, including any object that could contain liquid and crystals. Perhaps the most widely used were mirrored surfaces and scrying bowls (or baskets; see MacDonald, Cove, Laughlin and McManus 1989). One North American example is the Plains Indian practice of burning wooden boards in fire and burnishing the blackened area to a high gloss. With European contact, Plains shamans increased the reflectivity of the boards by inserting pieces of mirror. There is some evidence throughout northeastern North America of different types of scrying bowls being used. For example, the Micmac Waltes game uses a wooden bowl also used extensively in divination and social gambling games. This combination of gambling and divination with water containers also occurs among the Pomo people. Another interesting example of bowls used as meditation objects is to be found in the archaeological record of the Mimbres peoples of the American southwest. Mortuary remains indicate that pottery bowls were punctured at their bottoms, or "killed," to let the soul out of this world into the next (see MacDonald, Cove, Laughlin and McManus 1989 for many more examples of mirrors as meditation devices).

Another technique used by Chan and Zen Buddhists for suchness-oriented meditation is the so-called "rock garden" or "dry landscape garden" (Jap.: *karesansui*). Figure 3.7 is the Ryoan Ji Temple rock garden in Kyoto, Japan. The temple belongs to the Myōshin-ji sect of the Rinzai school of Zen Buddhism. It was created during the Muromachi era (1333–1573 CE) and is one of the type of "dry landscape" gardens specifically designed as a meditation object, or *kasina*. The meditation upon such gardens is intended to evoke experience of suchness. One can meditate upon the garden from benches that run along the monastery to the right of the garden. As with any *kasina* practice, the image of the garden may be internalized, and the internal image meditated upon until counter signs arise. The patterns raked into the garden have been scientifically analyzed and shown to be integrated with the temple itself

Figure 3.7. Ryoan Ji, a Zen rock garden in Kyoto, Japan. The famous Ryoan Ji Temple rock garden is in Kyoto, Japan, and belongs to the Myōshin-ji sect of the Rinzai school of Zen Buddhism. It was created during the Muromachi era (1333–1573 CE). It is one of the type of "dry" gardens specifically designed as a meditation object, or *kasina*. The meditation upon such gardens is intended to evoke the ASC known as "suchness." One can meditate upon the garden from benches that run along the monastery to the right of the garden.

(see Van Tonder, Lyons and Ejima 2002). My hunch is that the entire temple was designed precisely to facilitate monks gazing at the garden, then move inside the temple building to continue the "arising yoga" process, but I have no proof of this.

Third, in my opinion, these types of suchness-oriented contemplation are the most direct traditional routes to both the realization of "no-self" (Austin 2009) and "stream-entry," the experience of Nirvana (*nirvāṇa, moksha, satori*; see Chapter 5). Indeed, for those capable of going at the "awakening" project directly, the practice of *zazen* (Figure 3.8) utilized especially in the Sōtō school of Zen Buddhism is the simplest and most efficacious traditional method I am aware of (Suzuki 1970). The method is so simple that any attempt to describe it ends up sounding more complicated than it really is. Unless the additional method of *koan* meditation is used, as it is in the Rinzai school, zazen is just sitting, chilling out and maintaining an empty mind—cultivating bare attention and empty of thoughts, fantasies, feelings (known in Japanese as *shikantaza*; see Austin 2006).

Plotinus and Attainment of *Henosis*

Suchness is not a cultural production, but rather a universal property of perception. Neither Zen, nor Buddhism generally, are the only methods that bring a contemplative to the realization of suchness. I have already discussed Husserl's "return to the things themselves" in Chapter 2 as essentially a "reduction" of the "natural attitude" to the perception of suchness. The same process can be seen operating in the ancient Greco-Roman mystic and philosopher Plotinus' *Enneads* (Plotinus 1992; see also Ho 2016). Plotinus (Figure 3.9) was a Greek living in Rome during the 3ʳᵈ century CE whose philosophy was Neoplatonism, but whose inspiration was mystical. We have no idea when or under what conditions he had his mystical experiences, but we do know that he had them at least four times in his life (Jugrin 2015: 104). The object of contemplation for Plotinus was union (*henosis*) with the One (Gr.: εἶδεν), and all one need do to experience union with the One is "negate" (Gr.: ἀποθήζη; read "reduce" in the Husserlian sense) all the layers of cognition that are a barrier to absorption into the One:

Figure 3.8. Sitting Zazen. The practice of zazen utilized in the Sōtō school of Zen Buddhism is the simplest and most efficacious traditional method for realizing suchness.

[T]he ultimate reality called the One is naturally present in man's natural condition. Since man is already in Its presence, there is no need to strive to attain *henosis*. However, he does need to dispel the illusion that the One is separate from him and that labor is required in order to attain *henosis*. To this end, the practice of Plotinus' negative theology plays two roles. First, it highlights the illusive preconception that *henosis* can be attained by man's own striving. Second, it exposes the failure of man's striving, and thereby lets man dispel his illusive adherence to it. (Ho 2014: 151)

The One is not God—in fact it isn't a thing at all. It is our natural state, according to Plotinus. Thus, the experience of *henosis* can only occur when all distinctions have been negated such that one's mind is in synch with the One which is already in us.

Our thought cannot grasp the One as long as any other image remains active in the soul. To this end, you must set free your soul from all outward things and turn wholly within yourself, with no more leaning to what lies outside, and lay your mind bare of ideal forms, as before of the objects of sense, and forget even yourself, and so come within sight of that One. (Plotinus 1992: 6.9.7)

Figure 3.9. Plotinus (204/5 – 270 CE), Greco-Roman Mystic and Philosopher. Plotinus taught a method for negating the mental acts that distract from contemplation of, and absorption into the One.

In short, one practices an asceticism that allows the stripping away of distinctions, desires, preconceptions, aversions—Husserl's "natural attitude"—until the primordial state of suchness is revealed. Contemplation of suchness sets the condition for absorption into the One (Ho 2016).

The above is but a sampling of the variety of meditation cultures that are different in some ways from the meditation systems usually researched by psychologists. We can see that what remains the same across cultures is the development of skillful concentration of attention upon some object, be it a chant, an image, a light, a body movement and so forth, and resulting states of consciousness that the application of this skill may produce.

Ancient Judaic Meditation

Judaism has used meditation techniques for experiencing and gaining intuitive knowledge of the Divine for several thousand years (see Kaplan 1995; Verman 1996; Verman and Shapiro 1996). Rabbi Mark Verman and meditation researcher Deane Shapiro (1996) have discussed the history of five different techniques used in Jewish meditation: meditation upon oneness, the breath, chanting, light imagery and the heart.

> One way to concentrate upon the oneness of God is by repeating a specific phrase with great concentration upon the Hebrew word for "one," *ehad* (or *echad*) and especially the last letter or stop phoneme of the word called the *dalet* (or *daleth, daled*). *Ehad* has a varied set of meanings, but the essential connotation is of undifferentiated oneness, pointing to the mystical state of being one with God (i.e., absorption into the godhead). The *dalet* (phonologically: /d/ as in "cod," or /ð/ as in "mother"), as with all Hebrew letters, has spiritual significance, in this case referring both to its numerical association (the 4th letter of the Hebrew alphabet, emphasizing the four cardinal directions) and to the name of God. Rabbinical teachers would emphasize the great attention to be given to each sound in the chant as it is slowly repeated (ibid: 101).

In the meditation on breathing, the emphasis is upon the significance of the cycle of inbreath, outbreath and the gaps in-between:

> On our inbreath, we should concentrate on receiving life from God. That inbreath is life-sustaining. On our outbreath we should give everything we have back to the universe. Our outbreath may be the last we ever take, and, at the end of our life, we want to make sure we have given everything we have back to the world. ...Imagine on each outbreath letting go and giving forth all you have to the world. Then, if a new inbreath occurs, there can again be a feeling of gratitude and thanksgiving. The "pause" between the inbreath and outbreath in the Zohar [central texts of the Kabbalah] is known as *"metzarim,"* narrow passes or straits. These narrow passes can be understood as parts of us that want to keep taking in and are not ready to shift the cycle into letting go. Focusing on our breath, therefore, can be an opportunity to breathe in with thankfulness, notice the parts of us that cling and hold on inappropriately, our narrow places; and then allow ourselves to experience letting go and giving back all that we have received. (ibid: 107)

There is an important distinction between concentrating upon the breath solely as a physical act, as in Buddhist *anapanasati* meditation, and concentrating upon the cycle of breathing as cognitively significant. The inner signs will differ and the interpretation of experiences that arise are already partially pre-defined. The practice invites absorption and the experience will be interpreted as absorption into the godhead, with all the cognitive associations that will link the experience to a Judaic cycle of meaning.

Jews often move their bodies when they pray, a practice known as *shuckeling*, and which is said to increase concentration and bliss (Eisenberg 2004). An allied practice may be used conjointly with breathing during which one nods up and down with the speaking of the letters of God's name. With the inbreath, the head lifts toward heaven, nodding once for each pair of letters. Vocalizations are thus locked to the breath and to the nods. Again, concentration is upon both the body and the significance of the vocalizations.

Jewish mystics have long used visualization practices that center upon the scriptural association between the divine presence and being bathed in light—e.g., Moses meets God through the intervention of a burning bush. The instructions suggest that the practitioner seek solitude for lengthy periods of time to let go of all worldly thoughts and endeavors. Then focusing upon God above them, imagine the presence of the Lord as a brilliant light that envelops their body and mind (Verman and Shapiro 1996; see my description of "star group" meditation in Chapter 10). There are instructions as well to put slight pressure on the eyeballs by lolling the eyeballs upward, or around and around, or massaging the front of the eyeballs with the thumbs, all of which will produce light with the eyes closed. This is a technique also used by the New Age guru, Maharaji—he of the Divine Light Mission—by (DANGEROUSLY!) pressing the eyeballs inwards from the sides until patterns of light (aka, "phosphenes") occur. An adept may be able via intense concentration to keep the light growing, without pressure, until everything is light, and the light takes on the form of a vortex or tunnel leading to hypnagogic-type imagery. In other words, the phosphenes in the retinae and optic nerves trigger light experiences in the cortex which, for the adept, no longer require the phosphenes to propagate.

Finally, Verman and Shapiro (1996: 111-112) piece together what is known about the meditation upon the heart in Judaic tradition. This practice involves two simultaneous foci, the visualization of the name of God ("YHVH"), and the opening of the heart center:

With your mind's eye. Visualize the four letters of the Unique Name as if they are infinitely large. At the same time, open your heart to the Ayn Sof, the infinite, hidden most aspect of the Divinity. Two different modes: a conceptual exercise designed for the mind, and an encounter with the infinity for the heart—simultaneously, two complementary meditations, *like the arms reaching out to embrace the Divine that is within.* (ibid: 112; emphasis added)

Each one of these Jewish meditations has a single intent, a dissolution of the normal perceptual, cognitive and emotional barriers between the ego and the All. We will return to this discussion with respect to mystical experiences in Chapter 9.

SUMMARY AND SEGUE

Research into the mechanisms and phenomenologies of meditation systems requires a definition of meditation that may, in principle, be applied cross-culturally. Meditation defined in terms of PFC-mediated, willful selective attention may be easily studied in all cultural contexts. However, linking the term to any of the subordinate, culturally determined aspects of meditation (e.g., relaxation, seclusion, breathing exercises, exotic postures) confounds the scope of inquiry and renders the concept inapplicable to many meditation cultures available in the ethnographic literature, as well as those better known major religious traditions. In point of fact, defining meditation in other than volitional terms is ethnocentric (Keith 2011), for it is conditioned by the great World Religion-associated meditations that eschew psychotropic drugs and other "alien" or "pagan" ritual drivers. Most of the research in the psychological literature has been upon such practices as Transcendental Meditation, Buddhist mindfulness meditation, Hindu yoga and the like, most of which tend to link concentration with quiescence and relaxation (e.g., Deshmukh 2006; Shear 2006; Takahashi *et al.* 2005; Deepak 2019).

Part of the problem may be laid at the feet of ethnographers who usually have not practiced the meditation techniques they are reporting. Therefore, their narrative may contain little phenomenology about techniques used or experiences evoked. This will no doubt be frustrating to specialists researching the psychology of meditation. Yet, this is no excuse for ignoring the broader scope of meditation cultures that can flesh out our understanding of the sociocultural conditions in which meditation systems are embedded. Whether the researcher is a psychologist or an anthropologist, our discussion underscores the importance of both the exact design and conditions of a meditation system (i.e., what cocktail of ritual drivers are combined with willful, selective attention in the practice, and the interpretive frame). Interpretive frame is as important as the experiences had during meditation. An intense, ecstatic bright white light experience may be interpreted by a Christian as a visitation from the Holy Spirit, by a Buddhist as one of the *arūpajhānas* ("formless absorption" states) on the path to awakening, and by a Hindu yogi as perhaps an experience related to the *sahasrara* chakra, the same or similar experience given three different interpretations derived from three different meditation cultures.

Perhaps, neither the psychology nor the anthropology of meditation systems fully appreciate the importance of neurognostic, or archetypal, elements of meditation-related experiences. Nothing less than an archetypal account will explain the common imagery that informs religious iconography across cultures—motifs such as the Tree of Life, the tunnels with light at the end, mythical creatures such as were-beasts, mandalas, goddesses associated with fire, marriage as the unity of opposites, glowing spheres (or *bindus*), and so on (Griffin 1989; Jung 1997b; Laughlin and Tiberia 2012; Stevens 1982). The imagery that is often evoked from concentration upon a culturally defined object tends to be universal forms. It may well turn out that all meditation systems have as their unconscious goal the direct experience of the ultimate reality of both psyche and the cosmos. Such experiences, when they eventually occur, are frequently accompanied by intense energies in the body, sometimes reaching ecstatic proportions. We will now turn our attention to the energy aspect of contemplation and encounters with ASC.

CHAPTER FOUR

Meditation II:
Psychic Energy

While I stood there, I saw more than I can tell and I understood
more than I saw; for I was seeing in a sacred manner...

– Black Elk (Neihardt 1961: 43)

Transpersonal experiences range widely in their qualities. They include so-called parapsychological (or psi) phenomena (remote viewing, telepathy, co-dreaming, precognition, psychokinesis, magical causation or causation "at a distance," synesthesia, out-of-body experiences, and the post-death survival of bits of one's personality (see Kierulff and Krippner 2004; Cardeña, Lynn and Krippner 2000; Radin 1997, 2006). These are experiences of greatest interest to parapsychologists and transpersonal psychologists. In addition, anomalous experiences also include numerous phenomena of greater interest to anthropologists such as the use of psychotropic substances (iboga, ayahuasca, peyote, "magic" mushrooms (e.g., fly agaric, *Psilocybe sp.*), datura, and other entheogens; see Wasson *et al.* 1986; Rush 2013; Richards 2015; McKenna and McKenna 1975; St John 2018; Schurr 1995), lucid dreaming (co-dreaming, encounters with spirit beings in dreams), soul flying, spiritual healing, trance states, vision quests, apperception of ghosts and other spirit beings, and shamanism (see Hume 2002; McClenon 2002; Winkelman and Baker 2015). Anthropologists are especially interested in the relationship between ASC and anomalous experiences on the one hand, and ritual practices on the other (Laughlin, McManus and d'Aquili 1990; Winkelman 2000; Davis-Floyd and Laughlin 2013; E. Turner 2011; V. Turner 1985; V. Turner and Bruner 1986; Hume 2002). A virtually universal aspect of many of these experiences is the apperception of the movement of energies inside the body and mind. Emile Durkheim (1995 [1912]) pointed out the importance of these energy movements in his notion of "collective effervescence" (see Throop and Laughlin 2002; Child 2016). I will refer to these energetic movements as "psychic energy."

By *psychic energy* I refer to any subjectively experienced energy flow within the body and mind of an individual. I am specifically NOT referring to psychic energy as theoretically defined by psychoanalysts (Freud, Jung, etc.). I am using the term strictly *to label a set of somatic/ spiritual energy experiences.* The word "energy" derives from the Greek *energeia* which means "activity," the concatenation of the two roots *en,* "in," plus *ergon,* "work" or "action." And, of course, the word "psychic" comes from the Greek *psyche* which means soul or mind, and which is also associated with the principle of life, or "breath." Thus, the term psychic energy as I am using the term denotes the energetic activity occurring within embodied consciousness.

Operationalizing the term within the present transpersonal framework, we may say that psychic energy refers to the experience of the activity of an individual's body as apperceived within the sensorium. The direct perception of psychic energy, as usually described in "higher" (i.e., non-trivial) psychic energy experiences, may be interpreted as the perception of the movement, unfoldment, transformation, or flow of somatic activities as experienced in consciousness. Psychic energy experiences range from very subtle frissons through various bliss states to profound ecstatic states, and numerous phenomena in between. They may occur in any part of the body, or more globally encompassing all of consciousness. Such experiences may be perceived by any or all the senses: somesthetically as energy rushes up the *central channel* or swirls in energy centers, visually as images, lights or streams moving in parts of the body, auditorily as a buzzing or wind sounds, and so forth.

One of the most profound and yet commonplace experiences of psychic energy eruption is during orgasm which, depending on various factors, may be experienced locally as pleasure in the genital area or globally throughout the body (so-called "full-body orgasm," also "oceanic feeling").[16] Profound psychic energy experiences occur, often

---

[16] It is interesting that the French sometimes refer to an orgasm as *petite morte* ("little death"), for it is not uncommon for mystics to interpret intense ecstatic absorption experiences with death.

unbidden, during ritual practices and that may lead in retrospect to spiritual interpretations. Before continuing, let me offer one of many such experiences that I have had during years of exploring Tibetan Tantric Buddhism. It occurred during a weekend "loving kindness" (Skt: *metta*) retreat in 1979. Part of the work was to imagine a rose in the heart region while repeating the famous mantra, *Om Mani Padme Hum*, associated with the deity, *Chenrezig*. Numerous visual images spontaneously arose during this retreat, including a rose-colored sun emitting radiant rays of rose-colored light, two rose-colored geometric planes, one above me and one below me formed by conjoined bubbles, a bush sprouting innumerable red roses, blue tubes spewing rose energy, and a long lake between mountain peaks with a golden mountain at the end of the lake.

At one point while in a steady state of absorption and blissful peace, the image of a beautiful blond female figure dressed in a red shift appeared from behind me and walking away from me in my left visual field. At first, I intended to ignore her as I routinely did with all other distractions from the object of my meditation, but then I intuited that "she" was an archetypal expression of my anima. So, I sent her a blast of loving feeling visualized as a laser beam of rose-colored light emanating from my heart. Both the female figure and my bodily self-awareness instantly exploded into a rapidly expanding sphere of rose colored energy. Within a split second, my consciousness was in a state of intense absorption upon boundless space filled with pulsing, shimmering rose colored particles and my body was awash in ecstatic, oceanic bliss—a bliss state far greater than any orgasm. There then followed the eruption of a soundless scream and another energy explosion from the depths of my being that culminated in the awareness of the visual image of a tunnel or birth canal.

After corporeal awareness gradually returned, I spent a couple of hours in complete tranquility, either contemplating the essential attributes of mind, or in absorption upon this or that symbol as it arose before the mind's eye. Because of my understanding of Carl Jung's model of the psyche, I tended to interpret what I had experienced as *mana* in Jung's sense (Tibetan's call this energy *tummo* (*tumo, gtum-mo*; see Laughlin 1994b, 2011: 187-190; David-Neel 1971; Child 2016)—as the eruption of the vast energy available to the self, available in the unconscious. I could just as well have interpreted the experience as having been that of the Holy Spirit, for I had been raised a Christian. Considering I was working within a Tibetan Tantric frame of reference, I could also have interpreted the energies I felt as grace waves from the goddess *Dorje Pakmo* (or *Vajravarahi*).[17] In my case, my experience was "pre-interpreted," thus offering several ready-made interpretive frames due to my immersion in Jungian depth psychology, Christian upbringing, and familiarity with Tibetan Buddhist iconography. Once again, I can point to the applicability of the Rule of Multiple Interpretations (Introduction).

I will return to this very revealing experience in Chapter 8 when I discuss the significance of Jung's *anima* and *animus* for contemplatives. Meanwhile, there are many clear examples world-wide of psychic energy experiences, usually associated with ritual practices, often paired with imbibing psychoactive drugs. Let me summarize a few of these.

Sherpa Dancing

Spiritual traditions from many cultures around the world describe extraordinary experiences pertaining to the movement of psychic energy within the body. These experiences may be profound, may be the consequence of entering an alternative phase of consciousness, are often the consequence of various ritual practices, and may be culturally interpreted as both numinous (from the Latin *numen*, "divine") and sacred (from the Latin *sacris*, "holy"). Robert Desjarlais (1992: 5) has described his experiences in trance states while assisting a Sherpa shaman named Meme in Nepal:

> ...I would sit in a semi-lotus position to the right of my 'guru' and attempt to follow the curing chants. In time, Meme would begin to feel the presence of the divine, his body oscillating in fits and tremors, and my body, following the rhythm of his actions, would similarly 'shake.' Tracked by the driving, insistent beat of the shaman's drum, my body would fill with energy. Music

---

[17] For images of Dorje Pakmo (Vajravarahi), see: http://kallumkanchavumpinnecinemayum.blogspot.com/2014/05/thangka-paintings.html.

resonated within me, building to a crescendo, charging my body and the room with impacted meaning. Waves of tremors coursed through my limbs. Sparks flew, colors expanded, the room came alive with voices, fire, laughter, darkness.

Ritual drivers lead to an alteration of consciousness in which energy movements express themselves in body tremors and visual images. It is often the case that psychic energy reveals itself in multiple sensory modes.

San Healing Dance

The healing trance dance of the San (aka, Bushmen) of the Kalahari Desert, South Africa, is now well known (Chapter 3; see Katz 1982; Katz, Biesele and St. Denis 1997; Biesele and Howell 1981; Keeney and Keeney 2013) in the field of medical anthropology. The San hold that there exists a supernatural power called n/um (n/om) that healers access through a dance practice and use to heal people (see Marshall 1969 quote on San "medicine" above). Most ethnographers reporting on the notion of n/um, like most reporting upon mana in the Pacific, are engrossed in the cosmological, cosmogonic, mythological, social status, mystical beliefs, and other institutional and pragmatic associations with psychic energy, while giving scant time to the actual experience of n/um. N/um is thus an impersonal divine energy that permeates the world and that can be accessed directly by adepts who enter "trance" (read "alternative state of consciousness") in which he experiences being filled with energy and which allows him to heal others.

As we saw in the last chapter, anthropologist Richard Katz is the exception, for he focused on the experience of trance dancers, and describes for the Kalahari San a "transcendental experience" called !kia (!aia), an extraordinary state of consciousness during which practitioners evoked psychic energy experiences considered to bring about extraordinary healing and psychic powers. Notice also, for further reference, that San utilize quite common ritual drivers in their healing dance, including flickering firelight (culturally associated directly with n/um), hours of repetitive dancing to chanting and rhythmic drumming and clapping, as well as "yogic" breathing. Note also that experienced meditators commonly experience shaking and twitching as the body alters its energy distribution and centers—"center" being the root meaning of *med*-itation, *med*-icine, *med*-iate, *med*-ion and so on (see Desjarlais 1992 for this phenomenon among Nepali healers; see also Hume 2007: Chap. 4).

Hindu Yoga

A similar phenomenon has been described among Hindu yogis who recognize the existence of a primal, infinite source of psychic energy called *Kundalini* which is the font of all religious states of consciousness:

> Thus, the rousing of the Kundalini is the one and only way to the attaining of divine wisdom, superconscious perception, realization of the Spirit. The rousing may come in various ways: through love for God, through the mercy of perfected sages, or through the power of the analytical will of the philosopher. Wherever there has been any manifestation of what is ordinarily called supernatural power or wisdom, *there a little current of the Kundalini must have found its way into the Sushumna* [central channel]. (Vivekananda 1956: 58, emphasis mine)

The goal of yogic practice is to open the central channel (which runs up the center of the body just in front of the spine) to the flow of Kundalini energy. "When the current begins to rise through the Sushumna, we go beyond the senses, and our minds become supersensuous, superconscious; we go beyond even the intellect, where reason cannot reach" (ibid: 63). There exist several major energy centers lying along the central channel, but the most important are the Kundalini center at the base of the spine and the highest center in the head. "All the energy has to be taken up from its seat in the Muladhara [basal center] and brought to the Sahasrar [head center]" (ibid: 63). To this end yogis practice several techniques involving breathing and physical exercise to loosen and direct the Kundalini energies.

Probably the most famous and competent description of a Kundalini experience is provided by Pandit Gopi Krishna (1970). Pandit Krishna experienced a sudden awakening of Kundalini after years of patient meditation. While sitting in meditation one day, "suddenly, with a roar like that of a waterfall, I felt a stream of liquid light enter my brain through the spinal cord. ...The illumination grew brighter and brighter, the roaring louder, I experienced a rocking sensation and then felt myself slipping out of my body, entirely enveloped in a halo of light" (Krishna 1970: 12-13). The experience deepened for him until he experienced his consciousness as infinite and full of light. This single experience resulted in profound alterations in his cognition and in his life.

Please note again for future reference that Kundalini yoga practices involve numerous drivers including chanting, body postures and movements, special breathing techniques and visualizations. We will return to Kundalini in Chapters 9 and 11.

Malay Wind

Ethnographer Carol Lederman (1988, 1991), while doing fieldwork among the Malay people and particularly among Malay healing shamans continually ran across the concept of *angin* ("Inner Wind"), a native concept which labels an experience that sometimes occurs during healing rituals. She mentions that her informants declined to define the concept for her, insisting instead that she would have to experience *angin* herself to know what it means. For the longest time she was resistant to undergoing healing rituals herself. Eventually she gave in and undertook the healing ritual herself. "At the height of my trance, I felt the Wind blowing inside my chest with the strength of a hurricane." When she described her feelings to her informants, they responded, "Why did you think we call them Winds?" (1988: 806). [Incidentally, Janet Carsten notes that, "Women in Langkawi also spoke of 'wind' entering and 'rising,' *naik angin*, up the body" (1995: 231)]. Thereafter, Carol could evaluate the meaning of the "wind" metaphor from her own direct experience. *Angin* ceased to be merely a belief and was appreciated as a metaphorical description of a real and profound experience.

Navajo Wind

Many cultures equate spiritual energy with air, breath and wind. Not surprising then that in Navajo Indian cosmology the hidden vital, motivating dimension of things is called *nilch'i*, or Wind (McNeley 1981). Physical reality—indeed, all things in the perceptual world, including people—are motivated by this one, vast, cosmic Holy Wind that flows in and out of all things (*bii'asti*, the "animating energy within"), and that underlies and vitalizes the normally hidden totality of the universe. Wind underlies the vitality, dynamics and movement of nature, from the contemplation of which people may attain their intuitions about the purpose of existence. And it is an imbalance or disruption of that portion of the "wind that stands within" (*nilch'i hwii'siziinii*) each person that leads to disease and misfortune. The Navajo view is very similar to the Malay notion of *angin* discussed above.

Is *Mana* Another Word for Psychic Energy?

Although it is hard to prove, my hunch is that the root meaning of the famous concept of *mana* among many Pacific cultures refers to psychic energy experiences. Unfortunately, Pacific ethnographers have rarely asked the right questions, nor were they open to participating in ritual practices that might open them to transpersonal experiences. Yet sometimes the literature is so tantalizingly close to referencing psychic energy phenomena. Take for example Aletta Biersack's (2011a, 2011b) award-winning two-part study of the Highland New Guinea "Cult of Ain," as originally described by the late, great ethnographer Mervyn Meggitt (1973). Buried within Meggitt's and Biersack's accounts are descriptions of rituals carried out that suggest practitioners entered an ASC and experienced profound somatic energy events that they associated with the energy and wisdom of the sun. Meggitt notes that in the case that more commonplace rituals fail to heal a patient:

> They then turn to certain old men among them to ascertain what ritual to use in order to alleviate the situation. The old men go into seclusion for two or three days in a house hidden in the bush. Each *morning they look at the rising sun and experience a fit of shaking …that passes into a trance-like state, during which they look for signs* to indicate the appropriate ritual to be performed by the local group. (1973: 12; emphasis mine)

Reflecting on the key question of sun-gazing, Biersack writes:

> Why the sun? In the Ipili context, the answer is clear to me. The sun was viewed as the source of all knowledge or *mana*. Looking along the shaft of the spear at the sun was not only a way of communicating with the sun but of learning from him. Those who looked at the sun along spear shafts learned new *mana* or knowledge in preparations for conducting their lives in new and better ways. Within the ritual context, Ain's messages were supplemented or altered with new intelligence, communicated directly from the source of all knowledge. *Shakers sometimes spoke gibberish*, believed to be the words of the sun. (2011b: 236; emphasis mine)

Take note of the shaking theme again paired with speaking "gibberish." The latter is called *glossolalia* and along with shaking is typical of ASC among Pentecostal Christian practitioners (see Lewis 2000). Biersack also notes how the transpersonal element of the sun-shaking ritual is relatively unexplored territory:

> Meggitt's article was called "The Sun and the Shakers," and in many, perhaps most or all places where the Cult of Ain attracted followers, looking at the sun and shaking occurred. *This is one of the most unexplored aspects of the cult, with respect both to the shaking and the sun.* Sharp provides some insight [1990: 114], "….when offering cooked meat of sacrificed pigs while standing on a high platform L. [the cult leader] stared at the sun and his body shook violently…. Observers felt at this time that he was communicating directly with the sun deity, because cultural expectation is that shaking means communication with spirits" (2011: 235-236).

Allen Abramson (2005) has raised the issue of the use of psychoactive drugs in accruing *mana*. Some Fijians it seems look to imbibing of the psychoactive drink *yoqona* (made from kava (kava-kava) root, *Piper methysticum*) during rituals to access and attain *mana*. Kava-drinking is ubiquitous throughout Pacific cultures (Cawte 1985; Lebot, Merlin and Lindstrom 1997), and in some places like Tonga, the kava ceremony became quite elaborate and pregnant with symbolism (Newell 1947).

It seems evident to me that many anthropologists missed the subtle, but significant narcotic effects of kava drinking,[18] and these experiences are in many Pacific cultures considered *mana* (e.g., see Petersen 1995 for the people of Pohnpei, one of the Senyavin Islands which are part of the larger Caroline Islands group). An interesting question might be to what extent psychotropic drugs and *mana* accrual occurs, or once occurred, during rituals associated with accessing *mana*? Embedding a psychotropic substance in spiritually oriented rituals alters the range of experiences that may be influenced by the drug, however subtle its effects when imbibed outside the ritual context. Aside from Australia and New Guinea, it appears that more powerful psychotropic drugs were not used by traditional Pacific peoples in spiritual rituals (Rudgley 1993; Marshall 1987).

I suspect that the derivation of the idea of *mana* (and cognate terms) was and is experiential, in fact transpersonal—that *mana* is the Pacific equivalent of San *n/u*m, Hindu Kundalini, Chinese *chi*, Native American *orenda* (and cognate terms like *wakonda, oki, manitu*), and so forth. Keep in mind that I am not saying that modern day Pacific languages do not define *mana* in terms of supernatural force, efficacy, potency, political authority, sacredness and the like. Clearly, they do, and it is also clear that definitions vary across cultures. Rather, I am raising the epistemological question, how do (or did) people come to know that *mana* exists? I am suggesting that they know (or knew) *mana* from direct psychosomatic, psychic energy experiences, especially those encountered in ASC (ritual "trance," lucid dreams, psychoactive drug states, meditative states, etc.).

PSYCHIC ENERGY AND THE BRAIN

I reject any notion of psychic energy that does not ground its causation in somatic processes. This failure to ground psychic energy in physiology is a very distractive mind-body dualism perpetuated by psychoanalysis

---

[18] I have myself experimented with kava drinking, although using only commercially available powdered root. I can confirm the slight narcotic effects of kava drinking, and I suspect that the chew and spit method used by Pacific folks would enhance the effects somewhat.

for decades (see Applegarth 1971 for a review). If we experience psychic energy, then that experience must be mediated by neurophysiological and other trophic systems in the body. After all, the brain is the most complex trophic system in the known universe. The brain is roughly 1/50th of the body's weight and consumes on average 1/5th of the energy our body produces. And every activity of the neural circuitry of the brain is via electrochemical discharges. The brain is extremely energetic, and that is why EEG machines work by detecting outbursts of neural energy (see Purves 1990).

During our lives, we experience psychic energy events—feelings, emotions, frissons, blisses, pains, movements, rushes, raptures, ecstasies, etc.—and when we encounter other humans we presume they experience the same phenomena we do. This presumption is automatic, and we may further extend this projection to other non-human beings, to animals and plants, and perhaps even to non-animate things like rocks and pools of water, etc. The faculty of empathy (a type of psychological projection) is "wired-in" to most of our nervous systems. Babies exhibit empathy by paying attention to the distress of others, and respond with distress cries of their own, a concern about distress in others that becomes refined into appropriate helping responses as they age (Preston and de Waal 2002).

It is entirely possible of course for our empathy to lead us astray. We may have an experience and presume another person has had that experience when in fact they have not. Because of the goddess in the red shift experience I described to you above, and other such pairings of energy and images, the association of goddesses and other archetypal figures with powerful energies found in myths all over the world is quite transparent to me. If I had not had those experiences, I might conclude, wrongly I think, that the pairing of goddesses with cosmic energies is but a primitive cognition on the part of traditional cultures trying to explain the invisible forces that effect everyday life events. Psychic energy experiences are decidedly *not* invisible; they are palpably real.

Bioenergetics of Psychic Energy

Our body and its nervous system are, of course, part of the real world that our brain world experiences and makes sense of. In other words, our real body and brain are *transcendental* relative to any experience or knowledge we have of it. Most of the energies produced within the self are outside the awareness of the ego—they are transpersonal-by-definition. When we experience energy rushes in our body, those experiences are mediated by body processes that we cannot see and usually do not understand. Interoception (hunger, chemoreception, autonomic reactivity, etc.), proprioception, imagination and the like are the sensory "portals" into the reality of our self (Chapter 7).

To sketch in a model of neuro-bioenergetics that can go a long way in helping us understand how the body produces psychic energy and associated experiences, I will rely upon Ernst Gellhorn's theory of autonomic-somatic integration (Gellhorn 1967, 1970; Gellhorn and Loofbourrow 1963) developed out of the earlier theoretical formulations of the great Nobel laureate biologist, Walter Rudolf Hess (1925). I agree with Davidson (1976: 359) that Gellhorn's is the only currently existing theoretical formulation in the neurosciences that may account for phenomena that arise in "higher" experiences of psychic energy. The reason for this is simple. Typical textbook accounts of bioenergetics focus upon the body's *autonomic nervous system* which, "...regulates certain body processes, such as blood pressure and the rate of breathing. This system works automatically (autonomously), without a person's conscious effort."[19] The trouble with this definition is that it leads to the erroneous conclusion that the conscious brain cannot perceive, nor alter the activity of the ANS, when in fact it can and does (Green and Green 1977). In effect this view cuts metabolic regulation off at the neck, a mistake corrected by Gellhorn's model which incorporates central nervous system networks in association with the ANS. According to Gellhorn's model, the system in our body that controls emotion, as well as development of reaction to stimuli in the environment, is comprised of two complementary (sometimes antagonistic) systems, each of which organizes functions located at every level of the nervous system from the cortex down (i.e., segmental and suprasegmental organizations), and underlies the cross-culturally universal aspects of emotion (Scherer and Wallbott 1994). One system is called the *ergotropic system* and the other the *trophotropic system*.

---

[19] The Merck Manual (http://www.merckmanuals.com/home/brain,-spinal-cord,-and-nerve-disorders/autonomic-nervous-system-disorders/overview-of-the-autonomic-nervous-system).

The Ergotropic System: The *ergotropic system* mediates our so-called fight or flight responses; that is, the physiological components of our adaptation strategies to desirable or noxious stimuli in the environment. Anatomically, the ergotropic system incorporates the functions of the sympathetic nervous system (one half of the ANS), certain of the endocrine glands, portions of the reticular activating system in the brain stem, the posterior hypothalamus, and portions of the limbic system and frontal cortex of the brain. The principle function of the ergotropic system is the control of short-range, moment-by-moment distribution of metabolic energies to events in the environment. It is designed to come into play when the possibility of responding to external stimuli arises. It also shunts the body's resources away from long-range developmental activities and into carrying out action in the world directed either at acquisition or avoidance of things of interest to the organism.

Under generalized ergotropic arousal, a number of organic responses may be experienced, including shivering, constriction of the surface veins and capillaries (paleness of the skin), dilation of the pupils of the eyes, increased heart rate and blood pressure, increased muscle tone, decreased salivation ("dry mouth"), constriction of the throat, increased rate of respiration, erection of body hair ("hair standing on end"), and desynchronization of cortical EEG patterns (indicating disordered or disharmonic cortical functioning). These responses, all which make adaptation possible in one way or another, are commonly associated in experience with positive or negative emotion. Objects or events associated with responses will typically be perceived as desirable or undesirable, attractive or repulsive, friendly or hostile, beautiful or ugly, safe or dangerous. The ergotropic system prepares the organism to obtain objects (like food, water or a mate) required for the continued survival of the organism or species, and to avoid objects (like poisons, enemies and predators) dangerous to survival. A fundamental problem in nature is how to eat without being eaten. The ergotropic system in humans is the product of millions of years of selection for responses that solve that problem.

The Trophotropic System: The *trophotropic system* is far less dramatic in its activities but is nonetheless the system responsible for regulating energies going to the vegetative functions, such as repair and growth of cells, digestion, relaxation, sleep, and so on. Anatomically, the trophotropic system incorporates the functions of the parasympathetic nervous system (the other half of the ANS), various endocrine glands, other portions of the reticular activating system, the anterior hypothalamus, and other portions of the limbic system and frontal cortex of the brain. It is the trophotropic system that controls the somatic functions responsible for the long-term wellbeing, growth, development and longevity of the organism. This system operates to maintain the optimal internal balance of bodily functions for continued health and development of the body, and consequently of the mind.

Under the influence of the trophotropic system, a variety of physical and mental responses may be experienced, like warmth and "blushing" at the surface of the body due to release of sympathetic constriction of veins and capillaries, constriction of the pupil of the eye, decreased heart rate and blood pressure, relaxation of tension in the muscles, increased salivation, relaxation of the throat, slowing and deepening of respiration, erection of the penis and clitoris, and synchronization of cortical EEG patterns (indicating harmonized higher cortical functions). Relaxation (reduced arousal) and its concomitant processes are commonly associated either with disinterest in events in the environment, or with dispassionate concentration upon some object—as in calming meditation. Judgements as to desirability or undesirability of the object are suspended. The relaxed person is typically experiencing a comfortable, warm, womb-like indifference to the environment. The fundamental function of relaxation is perhaps less obvious than that of ergotropic arousal but is nonetheless crucial to the survival of the organism. It is mainly during relaxation, and particularly during undisturbed sleep, that the body processes nutrients and uses these to repair and grow. In other words, when the body is not finding food and avoiding becoming food ("ergotropic reactivity"), it is reconstructing and developing itself ("trophotropic reactivity").

Complementarity of the Two Systems: The ergotropic and trophotropic systems have been described as "antagonistic" to each other. This means that the increased activity of the one tends to inhibit the activity in the other. This is the case because each system is physically wired to inhibit the functioning of the other under most circumstances. If a person gets excited about something (angry, anxious, afraid, lustful, etc.) the ergotropic system not only produces the requisite physiological, emotional and behavioral responses, it also puts a damper (via reciprocal inhibition) on the trophotropic system which was previously subserving digestion and other metabolic activities. Likewise, when a person relaxes (say, after a heavy meal), the trophotropic system actively dampens the activity of the ergotropic system.

The relationship between the two systems would be better described as complementary, rather than antagonistic, for each serves the short and long-range wellbeing of the organism. It is really a matter of a balance of functions and distribution of energies in the body, the trophotropic system maintaining the homeostatic balance so necessary for health and growth while the ergotropic system facilitates the moment-to-moment adaptation of the organism to its environment. As such, they are not anatomical mirror images of each other. The wiring of the ergotropic system is designed to arouse the entire body for potential response to threat. Under normal conditions, when the ergotropic system is activated, the entire body/mind become aroused. Properly functioning, it is a turned on/turned off kind of system. By comparison, the trophotropic system is wired for the fine tuning of organs in relation to each other as the demands of internal maintenance shift and change. Its resources can be activated for one organ or body part, or it can turn on globally as during sleep when the entire skeletal musculature is "turned off." The point to emphasize is that whereas the trophotropic system is designed for continuous activity, the ergotropic system is designed for sporadic activity. We are wired for short, infrequent bursts of adaptive activity interspersed with relatively longer durations of rest, recuperation and growth. Prolonged ergotropic reactivity may cause depletion of vital resources stored up by the trophotropic system in various organs, and may cause fatigue, shock, body damage, and in extreme cases, death.

Tuning the Two Systems: The distinct balance of ergotropic and trophotropic activities under particular environmental circumstances is susceptible to learning and there is evidence that their characteristic balance under stress is established in early life. The learned (conditional) ergotropic- trophotropic balance relative to any environmental stimulus is called *tuning* (Gellhorn 1967: 110, 1970). When we say that someone "gets uptight around authority figures," we are referring to a discrete ergotropic-trophotropic tuning relative to people perceived to be in authority. Or when we say that someone "chilled-out when he got a back-rub," we are referring to a different discrete tuning relative to being stroked.

A learned change in the characteristic ergotropic-trophotropic balance relative to a stimulus is called *retuning* (Gellhorn 1967, 1970). Events like football games, childbirth, rock concerts and combat patrols that previously elicited excitement (ergotropic reactivity) may after retuning be met with a relatively relaxed response (trophotropic reactivity). Some researchers have argued that ritual control of ergotropic-trophotropic balance forms a basis for traditional healing techniques and for evoking ASC (Gellhorn and Kiely 1972; Lex 1979; Laughlin, McManus and d'Aquili 1990; Grimes 2003; V. Turner 1985; Fischer 1971). It should be obvious now that we can integrate what we have earlier learned about ritual drivers with the model of ergotropic-trophotropic retuning. Discrete states of consciousness may be brought about by retuning the balance of ergotropic and trophotropic functions in the body. And retuning may be driven by ritual practices, including the use of psychotropic drugs.

Extraordinary Retuning: Anomalous psychic energy experiences arise due to extraordinary interactions between the ergotropic and trophotropic systems, particularly involving the two halves of the ANS (see d'Aquili 1985; Newberg and d'Aquili 2000; Saniotis 2009; Fischer 1971). The most common but often profound psychic energy experience is the orgasm which is mediated by the simultaneous discharge of both the sympathetic and parasympathetic nervous systems. However, other more exotic energetic experiences such as accompany emotional catharsis, intense ecstasy and so-called spirit possession trances also are mediated by simultaneous ergotropic-trophotropic discharge and subsequent retuning (see Lex 1979; Winkelman 2013). Indeed, it is suggested that such extraordinary retuning is responsible for the therapeutic benefits of cathartic experiences and the resulting relief of distress during ritual healing (Winkelman 2010).

Anomalous psychic energy experiences may result from practices that drive either the ergotropic or trophotropic system until suddenly both react. What we may call *ergotropically driven reactivity* occurs when practices depend upon excitation of the body (Hageman, Krippner and Wickramasekera 2008), as in long distance running (Callen 1983; see also David-Neel 1971 for Tibetan *lung-gom* or "trance runners"), "trance" dancing (like the San dancing described above), or painful ordeals (like those once used by Sun Dance practitioners among Plains Indian cultures; e.g., see Dorsey 1905). In these practices, the ergotropic system typically dampens its complementary trophotropic activity, but after a certain point, sometimes after hours of repetitive driving and excitation, the inhibitory dampening flips and both systems react simultaneously, leading to ecstatic bliss accompanied by visions, insights, intuitions, realizations, and perhaps catharsis. These ASC are often accompanied by an intuitive realization of *Totality*—that is the entanglement of one's self with everything, an experience sometimes called "cosmic consciousness" (Bucke 2009[1961]).

Driven trophotropic reactivity initiates the process from the other side of the complementarity. This is the route taken by meditators who sit quietly and concentrate upon the breath, heartbeat, an eidetic image, and so on, perhaps augmented by chanting, fingering beads or other relaxing somatic activities. As calm deepens the enhanced trophotropic activity dampens ergotropic reactivity which can be experienced as warming skin, loss of muscular rigidity, feelings of bliss and central channel rushes. At some point, the reciprocal dampening may reverse and both systems may simultaneously react. One may then experience the kind of global energy eruption I described above as the "goddess in the red shift" episode. Methods for producing this kind of experience may underlie the efficacy of healing rituals, such as the Coyote Way ceremony among the Navajo of the American southwest (Merkur 1981), or healing rituals among Peruvian *curanderos* (Joralemon 1984), the latter being augmented by imbibing the mescaline-bearing cactus.

Simultaneous discharge of both ergotropic and trophotropic systems may set the stage for retuning the autonomic relationships conditioned to traumatic memories and images (Gellhorn 1970; Gellhorn and Loofbourrow 1963; Lex 1979; Levine 2010; Lehrer 2003). I have long suspected that enhanced trophotropic reactivity in people suffering from anxiety neuroses may in effect pull the ergotropic energy-rug out from under repressions, thus releasing pent-up tension and sometimes resulting in cathartic release and autonomic system retuning. Perhaps more importantly for transpersonal anthropologists, simultaneous discharge would seem to mediate the classical mystical experience, which again would seem to exhibit cross-cultural structural invariants (see Scharfstein 1973: Chap. 10; Stace 1960; d'Aquili 1982; d'Aquili and Newberg 1993). The hallmarks of mystical experience (Chapter 9) are its notorious ineffability (Braud 2002), realization of Totality (i.e., "cosmic consciousness;" Bucke 2009[1961]; see also Winkelman 2013), and transcendence of ego boundaries (Deikman 1966; Whitehead 2004). Ritual practices driving the ergotropic-trophotropic systems and resulting perhaps in the realization of mystical experience may or may not include ingestion of entheogens (Takahashi 2003).

Fischer's Cartography of ASC

My late friend and colleague, Roland L. Fischer, used the Gellhorn ergotropic-trophotropic system to develop a model of ASC, including those that arise during meditation as well as mystical states (Figure 4.1). The loop between the ecstatic extreme of ASC on the left and the yogic *samadhi* on the right in Figure 4.1 signifies the rebound effect that ecstatic states can have during meditation "trances," leaving the practitioner in a hypoaroused energy state typical of calm contemplation (see Laughlin, McManus and d'Aquili 1990: 319-320).[20] Fischer's model indicates the range of possible ASC depending upon ergotropic-trophotropic reactivity and tuning.

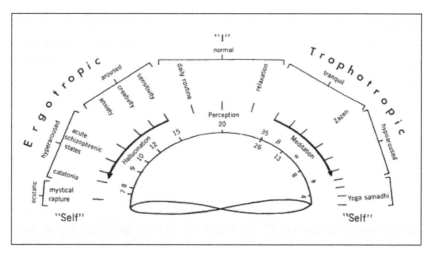

Figure 4.1. The Fischer Cartography of Ecstatic and Meditative States. Varieties of conscious states mapped on a perception-hallucination continuum of increasing ergotropic arousal (left) and a perception-meditation continuum of increasing trophotropic arousal (right). (Figure modified from Fischer 1971, with permission)

Auras and Psychic Energy

I have thus far not touched upon the issue of seeing auras, or the psychic ability to see (feel, smell) other people's "energy body." I have not done so for the very simple reason that I myself have never seen an aura, although I have occasionally seen colored light phenomena under the influence of various psychotropics (ayahuasca, MDMA, peyote and LSD) that I might have interpreted as seeing "auras" (see also Luke and Kittenis 2005). And I have known fellow meditators who have claimed to see auras as well (see Alvarado 1987 for a relevant review). Apropos to Edith Turner's dictum, "Why don't we believe our informants when they tell us they see things that we don't?"—I tend to believe these folks. I do not know what to do with the aura question, although if there are such things they must in some way be related to psychic energy (Figure 4.2).

The trouble with auras is that there is virtually no neuroscience to back up the claims made by psychics, and all sorts of researches have failed to confirm them. Some people who suffer from migraine headaches clearly see auras, probably due to synesthesia or "cross-modal" perception (Milán *et al.* 2012). Those suffering from certain types of epilepsy see auras as well (Bien *et al.* 2000). Yet despite this inability of laboratory neuroscience to get a grip on the neurophysiological underpinnings of psychic aura vision and related experiences, they nonetheless seem to be a common experience described by healers, psychics, mystics and other practitioners of various meditative traditions (see Moga 2017 for a survey of healers). Furthermore, the ability to see auras is correlated with measures of both cognitive and emotional empathy (Parra 2013) and with having had other psychic experiences (especially synesthetic experiences), engagement with fantasies, vividness of imagery and unusual interest in things psychic (Alvarado 1987, 1994). Summarizing their evaluation of several studies of aura vision, Zingrone, Alvarado and Agee (2009: 163) concluded:

---

[20] "The numbers 35 to 7 on the perception-hallucination continuum are Goldstein's coefficient of variation (46), specifying the decrease in variability of the EEG amplitude with increasing ergotropic arousal. The numbers 26 to 4 on the perception-meditation continuum, on the other hand, refer to those beta, alpha, and theta EEG waves (measured in hertz) that predominate during, but are not specific to, these states" (Fischer 1971: 898).

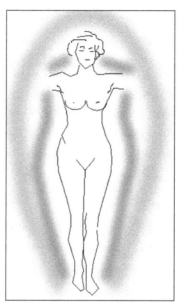

Figure 4.2. Psychic Energy in the Form of Auras. This is a black and white rendition of the colored drawing made by Dr. Walter John Kilner (1847-1920), a "medical electrician" at St. Thomas Hospital in London. Dr. Kilner (1911) wrote one of the first papers in English on auras (he called them "atmosphere") and their potential use for diagnosing and treating disease.

We feel strongly that the consistency of the results of all five studies reported here, both between studies and with previous findings, argue that aura viewers are a unique group of individuals with whom future work should be carried out. It is possible that some of these individuals are experiencing perceptual anomalies that may be linked to neurological disorders, but instead of treating them as symptoms and seeking medical help, the experiences have been conceptualized as positive or even healthy. If this is so, further studies of aura viewers, with this in mind, may provide insight into the impact of context on the interpretation of seeming perceptual experiences. Similarly, because aura viewers appear to report so many other relevant experiences, they constitute a group of individuals with whom a wide variety of experiences can be studied as one. Phenomenological, developmental, cognitive and experiential variables might be more readily explored in this population.

I most heartily agree and suggest that far more research be directed at the neuropsychological correlates of aura vision, not merely as untreated neuropathology, but as a capacity that may be a refined ability to perceive psychic energy fields (in Eastern terms, a *siddhi*) among some advanced contemplatives.

THE TIBETAN BUDDHIST *TUMMO* PRACTICE

> *Wind is mind moving.*
> *Breath is the inner wind.*
> *I am fearful of movement,*
> *Of change.*
> *I scream at the wind!*
> *Wind passes me by,*
> *Too pure for comment.*

> — The Author

While I was learning the various Buddhist meditation practices (Chapter 5) under the tutelage of my Tibetan Buddhist teachers, one of the practices I encountered was that of *tummo* (or *dumo*) yoga, one of the Six Teachings of Naropa (Chang 1991[1963]). The Tibetan tantric Buddhist conception of the psychophysical body is like that of the Hindu view. The body is made up of a system of channels (Skt.: *nadi*, Tib.: *rtsa*) through which psychic energy passes. This psychic energy (Skt.: *prana*, Tib.: *sugs*) may be experienced as breath and as psychic heat, or *tummo* (Tib.: *gtum-mo*; see Govinda 1960: 137-186; Evans-Wentz 1958: 172-208). *Tummo* may be experienced as concentrating upon distinct centers in the body, the so-called *chakras* (a Hindu term that literally means "wheel;" Kakar 1982: 201). Recognizing that the work of contemplation requires energy, there are ritual techniques for generating and distributing psychic energy in the form of *tummo* for energizing contemplation. In other words, the mind-state requisite to mature contemplation (Skt.: *mahamudra*, Tib.: *phyag-rgya-chen-po*; a term used both for the work of contemplation and the realization of the Void (Skt.: *sunyata*, Tib.: *ston-pa-nid*; see Wang-ch'uk Dorje 1978) is only possible when the psychic energy is active and appropriately distributed throughout the psychophysical body. When the energies are thus active and appropriately distributed, the mind-state of the mature contemplative spontaneously arises.

In the discussion that follows I will be mainly concerned with the experience of *tummo*, and only indirectly with the appropriate use of those energies to attain insights into the nature of mind (Chapter 3), or the state of contemplation itself. However, I should emphasize that in Tibetan Buddhism, as with all sects of Buddhism, the transpersonal experiences that may accompany the generation of *tummo* are not the goal of the practice and, if made the goal and thereafter clung to, are considered hindrances of the worst kind relative to the real goal, the realization of mature contemplation and the attainment of liberation.

Tummo Techniques

There are specific ritual practices in Tibetan tantric Buddhism designed to evoke experiences of psychic heat. What follows is a considerably simplified version of the yoga of psychic heat. The practitioner is directed to sit quietly and calm the mind, and then to imagine the body as an empty vessel. He then visualizes an energy center located in the navel area (Skt.: *manipura*, Tib.: *lte-bahi hkhor-lo*). He visualizes a small but intense flame in the navel center and then imagines a drop or radiant bubble in the energy center located at the crown of the head (Skt.: *sahasrara-padma*, Tib.: *hdab-ston*). While doing breathing exercises designed to bring the breath down through the two main side channels (Skt.: *ida* and *pingala*) to feed the flame in the navel center, the practitioner imagines the flame entering the central channel (Skt.: *susumna*, Tib.: *dbu-ma rtsa*). The flame starts out as a thin thread of iridescence and then becomes more intense as the breathing continues to fan it. It becomes more intense and longer until it reaches the crown center. The flame melts the drop in the crown center which becomes a bliss-nectar that flows down to permeate the entire body. The flame also is imagined filling the entire body. Awareness of the body is eventually lost, and all consciousness is a sea of *tummo*. The kinds of experiences that arise doing this meditative work may also arise spontaneously, or during other meditation practices, especially those involving the visualization of central channel or energy center images.

Numerous visual images have spontaneously appeared during my practice of *tummo* or related meditations. My impression from discussions with other meditators is that some meditators are more susceptible to experiencing these images than are others, but that among those that do experience them, their motifs are frequently universal. Those suggesting energy centers include a sphere floating in space, suns radiating energy, spinning planets with Saturnian rings. Those suggesting movement of energy through channels include a radiant sun over a torrential waterfall, tubes spewing smoke, bubbles or streams of energy. Any of these may be experienced as inside or outside of the body. For example, the body may be perceived as an image of myriad tubes through which passes energies moving away from or toward radiant spheres, spinning spoked-wheels or planets located up and down the central channel.

I discovered early in the *tummo* work that the practice was associated with increased sexual arousal. Feelings of lust would increase in both waking and dream states. I began to understand why psychic energy is often called "psychosexual" energies, or "libido." There came a point in the work, however, when I discovered that the energy activated in the central channel could be willfully switched from an outward direction which was experienced as sexual arousal to an ascending direction which was experienced as intense, but non-sexual bliss. I eventually learned during *tummo* practice to flip the direction back and forth so that one moment I was sexually aroused and the next in a tranquil, centered and blissful state. The energy in the central channel felt much like a hot fluid that was being shunted one way or the other at a "valve" or juncture in the system of channels. I realized that this experience accounted for why Tibetan yogis equate semen with the ascending fiery energy of *tummo*. It also became apparent why Freud initially conceived of the libido in sexual terms and later as referring to the entire field of life energy.

Practice of *tummo* typically led to an expanding and focusing of consciousness. The energies in the navel region would initially ascend into the head and the entire sensorium would seem to catch fire and discorporate into its constituent pixels. This was always associated with intense rapture. Then, as this intense experience subsided, the entire field of consciousness would have expanded and at the same time cleared of discursive chatter, fantasy, desire and other distractions. Subsequently, and for some period, the mind was free of distractions and could focus upon any object it desired to contemplate (an idea, a question, an image, an aspect of the sensorium, etc.). Concentration was exceptional and there was a free flow of insight related to whatever was the object of meditation. As a consequence of many such experiences, I recognize the essential similarity of these with the San *!kia* experience described above.

THE FLOW OF PSYCHIC ENERGY

Although psychic energy as defined here is apparent in a quite ordinary way and at any time to contemplation, I am primarily interested in certain regularities in the reported experiences of psychic energy had while practitioners in various cultures are in what they report to be extraordinary ASC. As I have described for my own experiences with *tummo* practice, these experiences are frequently dramatic and exhibit several invariant features which one may recognize in cross-cultural comparison. The reader should, however, remain aware that we label these "higher" states only because they are coded as such in their respective traditions. I make no claim that such dramatic experiences are in fact the highest form of mystical experience—indeed, there are mystical traditions such as Zen and Tibetan *mahamudra* that interpret such dramatic experiences as major hindrances on the path to mature spiritual awakening and associate them with low level awareness and immaturity, the healing or untangling of "energy blocks," and even neurosis. These traditions would hold that the very dramatic quality of these experiences signals the fact that the practitioner is spiritually off-balance relative to the goal of perfect awakening—incidentally, a view with which C.G. Jung would have agreed.

Flow

The experience of a greater flow of energy in the soma/sensorium seems to be an inevitable consequence of the exercise of sustained concentration, be that upon a physical task such as racing, dancing, swimming, and the like, or upon some object of contemplation.

Flow is the holistic sensation present when we act with total involvement, a state in which action follows action according to an internal logic, with no apparent need for conscious intervention on our part. Flow is experienced in play and sport, in artistic performance and religious ritual. There is no dualism in flow. *...Flow is made possible by a centering of attention on a limited stimulus field, by means of bracketing, framing, and often a set of rules.* There is a loss of ego, the self becomes irrelevant. Flow is an inner state so enjoyable that people sometimes forsake a comfortable life for its sake. (Turner 1979: 154; see also Csikskentmihalyi 1975; emphasis added)

Flow is an experience that may be associated with the unfettered release of all somatic and mental tension. Total flow experience is the experiential opposite of total, "up-tight" stress. Depending upon how blocked the energy resources are under stress conditions, flow may or may not involve the experience of a marked release or upsurge of energy which may be interpreted at the time as "floating," "bliss," "ecstasy," "exhilaration," etc. Full flow will be characterized by the cessation of verbal chatter and fantasy. Consciousness is notably clear of worry, defensiveness and ego-centeredness. Entering flow is commonly reported to be like "breaking through" to another plane of consciousness, as "attaining one's second wind," and as if the "bottom had fallen out from under" the normal range of consciousness. During the experience of full-on flow, there may be a sense of access to an endless source of energy, and the awareness of bodily movement as smooth, effortless and blissful (Csikskentmihalyi 1975; Sharp 2014).

Researchers have tracked the activity in the brain that mediates the experience of flow. Ulrich, Keller and Grön (2018) carried out fMRI measures of brain activity among a sample of people who were either bored, overstressed or in flow. Those in flow showed increased activities in several brain systems and a decrease in others: "Neural activation was relatively increased during flow, particularly in the anterior insula, inferior frontal gyri, basal ganglia and midbrain. Relative activation decreases during flow were observed in medial prefrontal and posterior cingulate cortex, and in the medial temporal lobe including the amygdala" (ibid: 496; see Figures 1.2 and 2.4).

Centeredness

A more refined, and presumably more advanced, form of flow involves the movement of energy toward (or into) or away from (or out of) the central axis[21] of the body. The centering of somatic energy in a vertical axis may be experienced directly as bodily (i.e., proprioceptive) sensations and symbolically in visual imagery.[22] One may see in a vision the movement of energy in a central tube or shaft, the trunk of a tree, a vertical stream of water, etc. The sensations of energy movement ("bliss") may radiate outwards to encompass the entire body, even the entire perceptual world. The variations are endless, and undoubtedly are related to the *axis mundi* motif in cosmological myth (Eliade 1964).

Circulation

Centered psychic energy is often experienced as circulating around the body axis, and often concentrated at one or more points along the axis. The classic example of circulating, concentrated energy is the chakra. Again, a discrete center of psychic energy may be experienced somesthetically as sensations of heat, bliss or movement at a particular place in the body, and symbolically as a scintillating bubble or sphere, a rotating wheel, ball of fire, "space station," lotus or other flower, rings around a planet-like sphere, etc. References to "circulation of light" within the body and cosmos to be found in the ancient Chinese meditation text, *The Secret of the Golden Flower* (Wilhelm 1962) would seem to provide one example of such perceptions.

Circulation of energy may be experienced as moving centrifugally away from the center, or centripetally toward the center (Woodroffe

---

[21] It is interesting that the word "axis" comes from the Latin for axle, thus denoting a center around which something turns.

[22] I had a relevant experience while participating in *Maulavi* (Sufi dancing) in which the task was to spin around to music while visualizing a central crystal-form axis running up the center of the body and colorful energy streams flowing out of the palms of the hands. There came a point in the dance when concentration became extremely intense and a shift of consciousness occurred during which energy seemed to center into that axis and the entire world of phenomena seemed to be spinning around the center of consciousness which was that axis. This was associated with intense and blissful energy movement in the central channel. A moment later concentration was broken by thoughts, and I fell down.

1974: 7). The center may feel like a spot of intensely hot and blissful energy that is radiating outwards from the body and into the world. One may perceive a radiant "sun," "moon," or other astrological body emitting rays of light onwards into the world. On the other hand, one may feel energy moving inwards and concentrating upon a spot in the body. One may see the image of an inwardly spiralling vortex of light, perhaps condensing at a spot.

Ascending and Descending

It is not uncommon for the report of centeredness to emphasize the ascending and descending direction of energy flow. Energy may be experienced as originating from below and moving up the body axis, originating above and moving down the axis, or both. Once again, the experience may be somesthetically one of a flow of energy from above or below producing bliss or ecstasy in the body. The experience may also have a visual component such as radiant light from a source above or below (see Eliade 1965, Bucke 2009[1961] for various descriptions), a waterfall down the central visual field, a shaft of light, tube of flowing particles, movement of a mist or cloud of energy, movement of consciousness up or down a shaft, stairwell or hole, etc. Movement of energy up and down the central axis is frequently associated with emotional outbursts and the spontaneous release of tension, the latter termed *dearmoring* by Reichian psychologist, Alexander Lowen (1976).

Of notable significance would seem to be the interaction of polarized energy sources, especially those associated with above and below, left and right. The higher states of consciousness and the more profound states of illumination or insight are frequently associated with the integration of these polarities by axes of energy flow, and perhaps eventually the realization of an even, unblocked and undifferentiated totality of energy flow in every moment of consciousness. In some cases, the establishment of a free flow of energy between an energy center above (e.g., in or above the head) and one below (e.g., the belly, genital-anal, or somewhere further below) is requisite for a state of consciousness during which profound and numinous experiences are attained. This ASC is commonly described in terms of a "clarification," or an "expansion," of consciousness, and is one during which superior power, illumination, transcendent insight and vision are attainable. It is in such a state (often described in the ethnographic literature as "trance," "ecstasy," or "altered state") that a shaman may experience a journey into the ethereal or chthonian realms—a common motif in both mythopoeic texts and dramas, and in dream reports.

Dreambody

The flow of psychic energy in the body, revealed in various ASC as somesthetic sensations and symbolically as visual forms, may be interpreted in some cultures as a *dreambody* (after Mindell 1982). The *dreambody* (i.e., "soul," "subtle body," "energy body," etc.) is the "real" body of perceived energy flow within the sensorium. The perception of energy flow within the body is, of course, dependent upon the state of consciousness being attended. Viewing the body as a concrete, physical "thing" or entity is typical of the states most concerned with adaptation to the external environment. Views of the body in other states (e.g., dream, lucid dream, meditation, hallucinatory drug trip, etc.) tend to be more evanescent in substance and plastic in form (see Kakar 1982: 187 on the Tantric "subtle body"). The dreambody is perhaps capable of extraordinary deeds, able to metamorphose at will, and free to travel to other worlds (see Poirier 1990 on Australian Aboriginal Dream Time experiences).

A Theory of Psychic Energy and ASC

I have presented the phenomenology of psychic energy phenomena, sampled how they are manifest in different cultural traditions and have described personal experiences had "in the field" that illustrate this phenomenology. I have also distinguished several structural invariants in the experience of psychic energy in "higher" ASC as evidenced by my own experiences and those of peoples cross-culturally. And I have examined theoretical concepts by means of which I may speak of the relations between neural and other somatic systems and sensorial events arising and passing in consciousness. I have suggested that the only currently available perspective from which to formulate a tentative theory of psychic energy is via Gellhorn's ergotropic-trophotropic model of metabolic energy distribution. I now wish to put these elements together to build an account of psychic energy experiences had in certain ASC.

All that we are, or ever can be, aware of is comprised therefore of psychic energy—the energies displayed in the field of pixels that make up the sensorium. And this includes our awareness of metabolic events occurring in our body. We know that we need nutriment when we feel hungry, that we are injured when we feel pain, that we are relaxed when we feel calm and aroused when we feel excited. Some people have unfortunate neurophysiological disorders (e.g., congenital insensitivity to pain syndrome; Thrush 1973) which cause them to be unable to feel when they have been injured. And many of us walk around unconscious of the fact that we are hypertense because we are "disconnected" from our bodies. But when the systems of the body are operating in a state of uninhibited or unobstructed *interpenetration*, we may say that a process of interpenetration exists between the sensorium and its activities and the greater organism and its activities (Chapter 7). It is tantamount to a microcosm-macrocosm relation—we might say one of partial isomorphism—in which events in the body are represented by, or produced by, patterns in the flurries of pixels within the sensorium. The cognitive system is designed to detect invariance in the patterns formed within the sensorial field and to construe a reality from the totality of such patterns.

Thus, patterns of sensorial psychic energy may in some instances be the consequence of metabolic events in the body, and in other instances produce metabolic events in the body. One feels pain when a finger is cut, but one can also produce somatic responses characteristic of injury by merely imagining a cut finger. The causality between sensorial and non-sensorial somatic events is reciprocal and thus interactional. Furthermore, the sensorium, like the rest of the nervous system, participates in the balance of ergotropic-trophotropic tuning. That is, the sensorium registers somatic events energized by the bicameral ergotropic-trophotropic system and is thus a part of their organization. Simply put, an excited somatic system produces an excited consciousness, and vice versa. A calm consciousness is mediated by a calm body. *There is no such thing as a calm mind in an excited body, or vice versa.* When tuning is in favor of trophotropic activity, this activity includes a predominance of trophotropic activity within the sensorium. The same may be said for predominantly ergotropic tuning. An ergotropically tuned sensorium may be a welter of rapid, even confused, thoughts, sensations and images, whereas a trophotropically tuned sensorium may be clear, uncluttered and even blank.

"Higher" Psychic Energy Experiences

Reciprocal relations between sensorial and non-sensorial ergotropic-trophotropic events hold as well for ASC and experiences of psychic energy encountered during them. From the model presented above, we may hypothesize four categories of ergotropic-trophotropic events and their sensorial concomitants that may occur during extraordinary ASC:

Hyper-trophotropic tuning. Trophotropic activity is tuned exceptionally high resulting in an extraordinary state of relaxation. This happens of course in normal sleep but may paradoxically occur during meditative states accompanied by keen alertness and vigilance. In extreme form, hyper-trophotropic tuning may be experienced as a sense of oceanic tranquillity and peace in which no thoughts or fantasies intrude upon consciousness and no bodily sensations are felt. The meditator feels like he is floating on a calm and wave-less sea. In Buddhist psychology such a state might be termed "access concentration" (*upacara samadhi*).

Hyper-ergotropic tuning. Ergotropic activity is tuned exceptionally high resulting in an extraordinary state of arousal and excitation. This may occur under a variety of circumstances where output of motor activity is continuous and rhythmical, as in dancing, long-distance running, swimming, rock climbing, etc., or where processing of information is continuous and so voluminous that interjection of thought and ego-centered decision making would prove disadvantageous, as in motor car racing, piloting a jet fighter, etc. This state will also be associated with keen alertness and concentration in the absence of superfluous thought and fantasy. The practitioner feels like he is a conduit for vast quantities of energy which are flowing effortlessly through his consciousness. This is the full-on flow experience noted earlier.

Hyper-trophotropic tuning with ergotropic eruption. As noted by Gellhorn and Kiely (1972), under certain circumstances both systems may discharge simultaneously. In this case, the meditator is in a state of oceanic bliss and perhaps by intensifying his concentration upon the object of meditation a bit more, experiences inevitably accompanied by the sense of a tremendous release of energy may occur. The meditator may experience one or another of the "active" blisses, energy rushes and other movements and sensations in the body.

Hyper-ergotropic tuning with trophotropic eruption. Simultaneous discharge of both systems may be attained via the opposite route. The practitioner may experience a trophotropic discharge during hyper-ergotropic tuning. Again, this may be the consequence of enhanced concentration, as well as trophotropic drivers such as rhythmic stimuli. The practitioner may experience an orgasmic, rapturous or ecstatic state arising out of a generalized sense of flow. This may occur because of practices like Sufi dancing and marathon running.

Driving Peak Experiences

Both the ergotropic and the trophotropic systems may be driven directly, either from the top down or from the bottom up. The dancing of the San adept which brings about the arising and ascension of enhanced psychic energy (n/um) may be interpreted as an example of hyper-ergotropic activity driven by rhythmic motor activity, resulting under proper conditions in a trophotropic eruption during which the !kia mind-state arises. The dancing is a bottom-up driver, as it is operating initially upon the lowest level of ergotropic-trophotropic hierarchy. Another common bottom-up driver is fasting, a practice often preceding or accompanying other more active ritual procedures (e.g., North American Indian vision quests). Fasting is known, not only to reduce caloric and other nutriments available to cells, but also to decrease the quantity of important hormones such as T3 in the blood, as well as their receptor cell sensitivity, thus providing a probable mechanism of energy conservation (Schussler and Orlando 1978). Fasting may thus be interpreted as a bottom-up driver of trophotropic activity, for it tends to have a tranquillizing effect upon the body. So-called "laughing meditation" is another bottom-up technique that can produce positive affect and relaxation (Kwee 1996: 139-142).

The two systems may be driven as well from the top down. This is frequently accomplished by concentration upon imagery, which I have already noted may produce an increase or a decrease in somatic arousal, depending upon the content. Prolonged and intense meditation ("devotion") upon a lotus above the head, or upon a Sacred Heart in the chest, may first result in an ever more enhanced concentration leading to hyper-trophotropic activity, and under the proper conditions, to an ergotropic discharge, perhaps a minor discharge to one or another of the sympathetic plexuses, or a full-on discharge throughout the system experienced as described in Pandit Gopi Krishna's (1971) "Kundalini awakening" in the Hindu tradition (see also Woodroffe 1974, Mookerjee 1982, Prabhavananda 1963, Sarandananda 1978, Vivekananda 1982), or St. Margaret Mary Alacoque's (Tickell 1869) sustained "rapture" in the Christian tradition (see also Stierli 1957 on St Catherine of Siena, Herambourg 1960 on St. John Eudes, Anonymous 1871 on St. Gertrude and Jeremy 1962 on St. Mechthild and St. Gertrude).

Cross-culturally, a very common driver is the repetition of a phrase, as in a prayer or mantra. The phrase being repeated may be meaningless to the practitioner, or may be significant, as in a prayer. Fundamentally, repeating a phrase either vocally or more often sublingually, causes a rhythmic vibration in the body—and vibrations, as we know, cause changes in the body's state (Bentov 1977). Take for example the repetition of the three Hindu and Buddhist *seed syllables* (Skt: *bīja*) OM AH HUNG—if you vocalize them slowly, you will find that the OM mainly resonates in the head, the AH in the throat and the HUNG in the chest. If you repeat them slowly the vibrations move down from the head to the throat to the heart, activating (driving) those three centers. All I need do to trigger warm bliss in my heart center is sublingually repeat HUNG and concentrate on the sound being in that region. The effect is greater if I repeat HUNG and imagine a flower in my heart. The meaning of the three sounds is irrelevant to this effect. Seed syllables are in fact meaningful within Buddhist symbolism, but I would venture to say that most meditators using those, and other seed syllables are unaware of their significance. We do know that mantra meditations do drive specific areas of the brain, particularly the bilateral hippocampus/parahippocampal areas, as well as both sides of the middle cingulate cortex and precentral gyrus (Figures 3.4, 3.5, 11.2, 12.1; see Engström,

Pihlsgård, Lundberg and Söderfeldt 2010). Repeating mantras, even among non-meditators, has a profound effect upon shutting down higher cortical activities (Berkovich-Ohana *et al.* 2015), and generally relaxing the brain and body (Shobitha and Agarwal 2013). *It is considered extremely important that advanced meditators can direct the vibrations of mantras to specific centers in the body.*

Concentration and Neurophysiological Recruitment

Psychic energy is usually felt as bodily sensations, or "seen" as visions of energy flows as I have described above. Occasionally there may be auditory or other sensory modal components to the experience. The point to emphasize is that the sensorial components of the experience bear a causal relationship to the ergotropic-trophotropic transformations associated with them. If they are expressions of those transformations, sensorial events are brought into linkage with the ergotropic-trophotropic events. If they are initiators of those transformations, then sensorial events bring the greater ergotropic-trophotropic events into action.

Whether top-down, or bottom-up drivers are operating, the key element is usually concentration upon a single process or object leading to eventual harmonious linkage of operating systems at all levels of the neural hierarchy. We can say that associated neural circuits become *recruited*: sustained concentration upon an object of contemplation, if carried out with sufficient intensity, will tend to cause the eventual recruitment and linkage of most, if not all somatic systems at every level of hierarchy within the body. Itzhak Bentov (1977) hypothesized that certain meditative procedures lead ultimately to the synchronization of all the standing waves of the body to the rhythm of the dominant aortic standing wave. If true, this could be considered a special case of recruitment.

Whether the experience of psychic energy flow is the result of explicitly applied drivers, or due to the spontaneous retuning of the systems as an unintended consequence of inadvertent drivers, the "higher up" the ergotropic-trophotropic systems the effect reaches, the more divergence may be expected in the experience. This is because the range of possible entrainments is most limited at the lower end of the hierarchy (i.e., in autonomic, endocrine and other somatic systems) while it is less limited in the midrange structures (i.e., midbrain and limbic systems) and least limited at the higher end (i.e., in cortical structures). In other words, we would expect the imagery and intuitive insights associated with psychic energy experiences to vary a good deal more from individual to individual, and from culture to culture, than we would expect variance in the somatic and affective components. Much of the apparent diversity in psychic energy experiences cross-culturally derives primarily from different interpretive frames used *after the fact* to describe the more symbolic aspects of the experience—precisely those aspects that are retained most easily in memory and most easily described in natural language and art.

Structural Invariants and Ergotropic-Trophotropic Tuning

As we have seen, there is a recognizable structural invariance in the reports of higher psychic energy experiences. I suggest that the sensation of flow so common to these experiences derives from the elimination of the simple body image in favor of direct linkage to proprioceptive fields (i.e., sense receptors that deliver information from muscles, tendons, arteries, etc., internal to the body). This amounts to interpenetration of proprioceptive neural networks and the neurocognitive systems mediating consciousness. The distinct sense of centering, as well as ascending and descending of psychic energy likely derives from proprioceptive sensing of autonomic and endocrinal activity, which for the most part is most active at the center of the body.

The most obvious origins of such activity are the two sympathetic trunks (part of the ANS and the ergotropic system), which lie on either side of the spine, and the great vagus nerve of the parasympathetic system (part of the ANS and the trophotropic system) that sweeps down from the base of the brain to emerge at the base of the spinal column, there to innervate the sexual and other organs. Sensations of circulation and heat at discrete centers of the body, such as the heart region, may be accounted for as proprioception from one or another of the sympathetic plexuses (see Motoyama and Brown 1978; Greenwood 2006). The root center may well be mediated by the pelvic and coccygeal plexuses, as well as innervation of the prostate and sexual organs. The navel center may be innervated by the solar plexus, the heart center by the cardiac and pulmonary plexuses, the throat center by the pharyngeal plexus and thyroid-parathyroid complex, the brow center by the carotid plexus, and the crown center by the pineal gland. Something like this model of the relationship between the plexuses and the chakras is fundamental to modern Ayurveda medicine (Mishra, Singh and Dagenais 2001).

The symptoms of dearmoring or destressing characteristic of many reports of psychic energy experiences may be interpreted as the development over time of: (1) local ergotropic-trophotropic tuning within individual organs or muscle groups, (2) asymmetry of functioning due to differential left-right tuning, or (3) differential tuning between various levels in the hierarchical organization of ergotropic-trophotropic functioning. In other words, retuning may not occur all at once, or in a harmonious way throughout the body. For example, retuning may occur asymmetrically due to asymmetrical functioning at the various levels of the system from the autonomic system up to and including the cortex. This may be expected especially in the case where a distinct ergotropic-trophotropic balance is linked to a phobic or other highly charged image. Many meditators may experience more dearmoring symptoms on the left side of their body because the right hemisphere specializes in linking images, and especially faces, to emotion. In such cases we might suppose that the right side of the body would become more relaxed than the left side of the body until sufficient retuning has occurred to balance the two sides.

Visual and other sensory components of "visions" may be accounted for in part as representations of some or all these proprioceptive inputs. As the usual body image is replaced by flow experience, the visual system may become linked to the process, thus providing the image of a radiant energy body, perhaps with glowing energy centers perceived as a radiant heart or lotus or sphere with Saturnian rings. The expectation set of the practitioner will have a determinate effect upon the details of the vision and the interpretation of symbolic material encountered.

In any event, the full-on, simultaneous discharge of the ergotropic and trophotropic systems would seem to set the stage for ultimate mystical experience, which again would seem to exhibit cross-cultural structural invariants (see Scharfstein 1973: Chap. 10; Stace 1960; d'Aquili 1982). Ergotropic-trophotropic retuning would seem to be a prerequisite for certain transcendent, transpersonal experiences that are often enough at the very core of religious belief and institutions. *!Kia*, visitations from Christ or the Holy Spirit, encounters with deities, as well as perhaps profound insight and attainment of "power" or "genius," would all seem to be accompanied by profound alterations in the flow and form of psychic energy.

SUMMARY AND SEGUE

The importance of considering the arousal and distribution of psychic energy is central to any study of contemplation and meditation, particularly since meditation traditions are often concerned with evoking psychic energy for contemplative purposes. It is useful to conceive of the nervous system as a trophic system (Purves 1990). If we should cut off the energy to the neural cells, they will stop functioning and will eventually die. Advanced meditators know that a major element of ASC are energy events: blisses, rushes, streams of energy up and down the center of the body, radiant figures, etc. These experiences are often interpreted as healing and as a source of spiritual powers. Several psychic energy traditions are sampled, again to give an empirical flavor of the kind of experiences had across cultures.

Energy is moving through the body all the time, even when we are sleeping. However, only some of this movement becomes conscious. Because we experience such psychic energy events—feelings, emotions, frissons, blisses, pains, movements, rushes, raptures, ecstasies, etc.— we can empathize when others experience the same phenomena. By studying these phenomena, the contemplative can understand the extent to which their body and psyche are transcendental relative to their normal ego functioning. Ernst Gellhorn's theory of autonomic-somatic integration is one of the most important tools for modelling how psychic energy experiences arise, are evoked, are utilized in meditative traditions and how they may be transformed. Using this perspective, it is easy to understand how ritual procedures can drive internal processes, and how extraordinary energy experiences may result in transforming the emotional salience of previously conditioned states of mind. I have described some of the techniques used in Tibetan Tantric Buddhist *tummo* (psychic energy) practice, as well as some of the experiences I had doing this work. I elaborated several universal attributes of psychic energy experiences, and how these are mediated by the body and brain. These features of energy movement and evocation help to account for different ASC that may be encountered during a contemplative's career.

I will continue to offer personal experiences as data in the next chapter. I will trace my own progress during the decades it took for my own practice as a contemplative to unfold. Some of this personal history was, as we shall see, rather hit and miss, while other periods were graced with remarkable teachers and competent guidance. It should become much clearer why I take the scientific positions that I do, not the least being a strong resistance to constructivism as any kind of explanation for the relationship between culture and transpersonal experience.

CHAPTER FIVE

Meditation III:
A Personal Journey

Far better than sovereignty over the earth, or far better than
going to the abodes of the devas, or far better than ruling supreme
over the entire universe, is the attainment of Sotāpatti Fruition.

– Buddha, *Dhammapada*, verse 178

A monk once went to Gensha and wanted to learn where the
entrance to the path of truth was. Gensha asked him, "Do you
hear the murmuring of that brook?" "Yes, I hear it," answered
the monk. "There is the entrance," the Master instructed him.

– C. G. Jung, *Psychology and Religion*, ¶878

The anthropological study of consciousness shows an increasing interest in questions about universal and culturally conditioned aspects of the development (growth, maturation) of consciousness. Naturally, this shift toward experience in turn lays the groundwork for a more sophisticated understanding of the psychology of consciousness across cultures, and models may now be generated that come closer to the way modern neuroscience understands how the brain develops consciousness.

As I have emphasized, ethnographers often work among polyphasic cultures—that is, among peoples who consider experiences had in ASC to be both real and significant. Hence, an experientially grounded ethnography will inevitably have to incorporate the more transpersonal domains of experience, and the realizations and psychological transformations that stem from such experiences. Such realizations often find their way into cultural expressions as narratives, mythopoeic symbolism, ritual enactments and art, the significance of which is often missed due to the lack of requisite transpersonal experience on the part of the fieldworker. As my colleagues and I have argued many times elsewhere, the study of transpersonal experiences requires transpersonal methods (Laughlin, 1989, 1994a, 2011; Laughlin, McManus and d'Aquili, 1990)—or as Belgian anthropologist Arnaud Halloy (2016) says, "full participation" in polyphasic cultural life. Simply put, if I want to know, I must do what is necessary to know. As Ken Wilber suggests in his book, *A Sociable God* (2005[1983]: 156), one begins the process of inquiry with the injunction "If you want to know this, do this." When one does "this" (i.e., meditate, dance, take the magic herb, carry out the ritual) then certain experiences consequently arise, and then perhaps a conversation ensues with one's hosts or guide and one learns what those experiences mean both for oneself and for one's host culture.

We have previously defined consciousness, seen how the human brain is pre-adapted to contemplate its own nature, and seen how the brain manages this remarkable process. In this chapter I want to share how transpersonal experiences arising for me along a path of spiritual inquiry may, in retrospect, be understood as part of a single maturational process. I will describe several experiences I have had over the course of a half century as a meditator, and roughly 35 years as a Buddhist mindfulness practitioner, six years of which were spent as a Tibetan Tantric Buddhist monk (see also Child 2016). I want to highlight these experiences to show how one follows the other in a *retrospectively* obvious and causally efficacious way. I will take the reader from my realization of the pixelated nature of sensory experience, through the realization of the impermanence of the self to the experience of what Theravada Buddhists call "stream-entry," the first conscious experience of Nirvana. I offer this story, not to replace the necessity of directly experiencing these way-points yourself—after all, "if you want to know this, do this"—but rather: (1) to sensitize ethnologists and transpersonal researchers to the developmental dimension of all paths of transpersonal experience, regardless of culture, (2) to underscore the empirical importance as evidence for states of consciousness that transcend sensory experience, (3) to demonstrate that the unfolding realizations upon which many full-on spiritual traditions are grounded may take years, even decades to unfold, and (4) to illustrate how the design of a contemplative path can determine the experiences that arise, and the kind of maturation that may eventually occur.

The terminology I will use will be from both Theravada Buddhism and Husserlian phenomenology. Although the goals of Buddhist and Husserlian phenomenology are different, I am mixing their terminology here because: (1) both held sway in my own journey, and I have used both frameworks in making sense of my experiences, (2) both Theravada Buddhist methods and Husserlian methods constitute transcendental phenomenologies (Hanna 1993a, 1995; Larrabee 1981), (3) both methods are conducive to good science (Chavan 2007), and (4) in some cases the Husserlian interpretations and terminology are less loaded with religious ideological baggage than are Buddhist accounts.

LEARNING TO MEDITATE

I was originally taught to meditate by one of my professors, the late Dr. LeRoy Johnson, while I was doing graduate work in anthropology at the University of Oregon in 1967. LeRoy showed me how to sit in half-lotus position and focus attention on the rising and falling of my belly. I quickly learned that with increasing concentration to the exclusion of distractions (other objects, verbal chatter, etc.) came a deeper and deeper calm leading to single-minded bliss-states I would later learn were typical of absorption states, and that the practice was in fact *samatha* work—cultivation of single-mindedness leading eventually to a special state of complete calm and one-pointed concentration that is called *upacara samādhi*, or "access concentration," so named because the mind is free to choose to concentrate upon an object or remain indifferent to the object, and thus may choose to enter absorption states or not.

In Buddhist meditation practice, a calming meditation (*samatha*) is used to chill-out the mind/body (again, no such thing as a calm mind in an excited body, and vice versa) and shut down the energies supporting discursive thought and slideshow imagery (together called the *saṅkhāra*, "formations") so that focus upon the object (breath, heart, belly, etc.) becomes progressively easier to retain. As we discussed last chapter, this calming process is mediated by a retuning of the ergotropic-trophotropic reactivity, particularly the tuning of sympathetic and parasympathetic control of metabolic energy. Only when the mind/body activity stabilizes at a maximum of relaxation does access concentration arise—a state in which the body is at dead calm, and the mind is sharp and able to direct its searchlight awareness at any object it wishes to contemplate: death, impermanence, anima, compassion, types of causation, and so forth. The meditation one does when shifting from the *samatha* object (usually the breath) to the object of contemplation is called "insight meditation" (*vipassana*). It is the latter that eventually leads to liberation in the Buddhist sense of the term.

But I am getting ahead of my story. At the time I learned to easily enter *samādhi* using belly concentration (remaining aware of the physical sensation of my abdomen rising and falling, to the exclusion of all else), I knew nothing about Buddhism or insight meditation, and simply meditated to relax and enter bliss-states from the rigors of graduate school. I became adept at what I later understood was, from the Buddhist point of view, "frozen ice" *samādhi*—frozen, because the state of mind is utterly devoid of any burning questions that would lead to any insight into the nature of mind, not to mention suffering. Inevitably, and after two years of practice, I grew bored with bliss-highs and dropped meditation work for the following decade or so.

When I took up meditation again, it was because I was having experiences that triggered questions about consciousness. A years-long process of unfolding dream-work that I will describe in detail later (Chapter 6; see also Laughlin 2011: 409-421), accompanied by taking up *hatha yoga* practice, under the guidance of my friend Patricia Kolarik, led eventually to spontaneous transpersonal experiences and serious questions about mind that had been absent from my earlier "frozen ice" work. I sought and found guidance from Buddhist teachers in Canada under whose tutelage I learned the causally entangled relationship between tranquil single-mindedness (*samatha*) and mindfulness (or *vipassana*; see Goleman 1984; Solé-Leris 1986; Thanissaro 1997; Johansson 1969: 88-102). It was during lengthy meditation retreats, ostensibly under the influence of Buddhist methods and guidance, that I learned to establish the phenomenological attitude, and to cultivate several reductions through direct introspection. As I have noted before, this shift in consciousness is not a momentary choice or foray but involves a fundamental reorganization of perception with life-long consequences. Arthur Deikman has argued that mature contemplation involves a process of *deautomatization*, "an undoing of the automatic processes that control perception and cognition" (1982: 139)—a freeing-up, as it were, of natural attitude conditioning requisite to the development of the phenomenological attitude.

I discovered over time that any discernable attribute of consciousness may be bracketed, "deautomatized" and studied using mindfulness methods. For instance, one may choose to isolate red and study the gradation of hues cognized as "red," or the feelings evoked by "reddish" hues. Or, one may choose to bracket the relationship between visual patterns on a page and the meaning they evoke as "words." Wine tasting under the guidance of a sommelier is essentially a phenomenological exercise leading to a more sophisticated understanding of the flavorful nuances of wine. The potentially bracketable qualities and processes of experience are virtually endless. However, some foci are more auspicious than others, depending upon the goal or ideology associated with the meditation being practiced. In Buddhist psychology, focusing upon the impermanence of phenomena is more important and developmentally productive than focusing upon discrete qualia. As we saw in Chapter 2, this whole process of self-inquiry is termed the phenomenological reduction (Held 2003: 21), the intent of which is to learn to parse raw sensory presentation (the "things themselves") from the naive blending of sense and interpretation.

If, instead of remaining focused on the original object (breath, internal image, sensations at the bottom of the feet in walking meditation, etc.), the meditator shifts focus to the countersign (Chapter 3), applying sufficient intensity of concentration may lead to absorption (*jhāna*) into the sign—that is, the collapsing of the watching-watched (subject-object) duality. Absorption is a natural function of an interested brain paying close attention to something. One normally experiences absorption when watching a movie in a cinema, or while engrossed in a good book. But the kind of absorption I am describing here is into an internal image produced wholly before the mind's eye. Moreover, the concentration may well be beyond the intensity one normally brings to reading or watching a film. In addition, the sign is usually simple and not very dynamic. Again, the sign is associated with the original object—it is a sign *of* the object—but it is in no way logically predictable. That is why one can never reason one's way to the answer of a *koan*.

Absorption states are frequently numinous, especially for beginning meditators. Among other things, the *jhānas* are often accompanied by bliss (*pīti*) of varying intensities, dynamics and locations in the body (Chapter 4). Meditators may describe themselves as feeling "a rush," joyous, centered, "high," exhilarated, pleasurable, ecstatic, and so forth. The loci of bliss may be in the chakras, perhaps also flowing up or down the central channel. For the duration of the absorption and for a period afterwards, the meditator feels good, comfortable, tranquil, alert and energized (Laughlin 1994b). Buddhist meditators are taught to utilize these experiences to energize their insight practice—like plugging-in to a psychic battery—but not to make the mistake of considering the absorption state as the goal of insight practice, no matter how numinous the experience may seem at the time. When I was early-on practicing "frozen ice" *samadhi*, I had become essentially a *pīti*-junkie.

During the process of bracketing a sensory object for scrutiny, and becoming aware of its various elements and features, the attention becomes so intense that the object *as a thing* disappears. Say an apple arises before the mind as an internal image, and one chooses to focus on it as a meditation object. One can become so focused on the color and texture of the apple skin that the apple-ness vanishes. All that remains is the patch of color. The same will happen if you meditate upon the black letters on this page. Your attention can be so focused on the form of the letters that the meaning of the symbols as words drops away. Try it yourself and you will see. Well, during this kind of meditation, I noticed that there is a pattern to the color patch or surface that is independent of the patterns or textures inherent in the object itself—like the spots and lines of color on the surface of the apple. That independent pattern was in every visual thing I took as a meditation image. The process was something like this. I would scan a thing I am perceiving (say, the apple) and then close my eyes and try to hold the image by concentrating upon the inner image as long as I could. As the image slowly faded, I noticed that it was a field of visual pixels that were fading. The visual object seemed to be made up of millions of these pixels.

I then experimented with very simple objects and watched the inner image fade, and every time, the fading was particles of light blinking out. The more intense and tranquil the state of mind, the easier it was to discern individual pixels. For example, walking in the snow I would focus upon a single bright spot of light emitted by a snowflake crystal, immediately shut my eyes and watch the wee light fade into a field of particles. Or, lying in bed at night in semi-darkness, or walking in a forest at twilight, I would "take in" a brighter patch of light and watch it deteriorate. I naturally concluded that my brain was somehow constructing visual objects out of pixels and began to puzzle about what structures of the visual cortex would produce these tiny building blocks. I got so excited, I involved my students in a game. I made cards of black cardboard with a small white dot in the middle. I asked students to scan the dot and internalize the image, and then watch it fade out with their eyes closed. I asked them to write down what they experienced and what the fading out looked like. Several students also twigged to the fading pixels.

Some later time, I had a sabbatical and was headed back to Nepal to be with my Tibetan guru. I had a stopover in Paris and was staying in a small hotel in the Rue des Escoles. During one memorable evening while meditating I suddenly realized that not only were visual objects made up of pixels, but also auditory objects as well. Then within a single hour I had realized that *all sensory objects are made up of pixels, regardless of the sensory mode.* Ever after, this became for me the "Rue des Escoles epoché." And it changed forever how I perceive sensory objects, and how I theorize about how the brain makes this happen. In my opinion, this state of consciousness and attendant realization is the essence of suchness (Chapters 2 and 3). Gone altogether are any gross "things," as well as thoughts, feelings, chatter, memories, expectations and so forth linked to thingness.

NO-SELF

Realizing that sensory experience is pixelated, and that pixels and fields of pixels arise and pass away each moment of consciousness leads quite naturally to understanding that all things constructed from these sensorial pixels are likewise impermanent, including thoughts, images, feelings, somatic sensations, perceptual qualia, and so forth. This is one route to realizing that everything we are conditioned to associate with the ego—the culture-laden self, the "me"—are also impermanent. Thus, it is not surprising that disciplined contemplation will eventually lead to the fall of the illusory, permanent ego (see e.g., Roberts 1993). This indeed happened in my case as a direct result of the "Rue des Escoles" epoché.

There is no better example of the transformational capacity of self-discovery than the realization of *no-self* (or *not-self*; see Thanissaro 1999; Mathers, Miller and Ando 2009); that is, the realization that there is no such thing as an ego, no permanent soul-entity, no little homunculus sitting inside the brain watching the sensorial movie. One realizes that the belief in a permanent ego is an artifact of cultural conditioning which is eventually dispelled by phenomenological self-reflection—by disciplined introspection leading to direct experiences that bring one's received self-concept into question. Because the realization of no-self is derived empirically—that is, introspectively—it is safe to say that any cultural tradition that encourages self-reflection as a path to self-knowledge and wisdom will lead inevitably to apprehending that nothing that arises in consciousness is permanent. This realization is not a matter of taste, not a matter of opinion or ideological commitment, not a matter of cultural custom, but rather is one of empirically "seeing" the self as it really is, a transcendental and dynamic self-system.

Anatta

The best-known tradition of self-reflection leading to the realization of no-self, and the elevation of that realization to a cornerstone of an ethno-phenomenology, is the Buddhist doctrine of *anatta* (aka, no-self or selflessness; see Austin 1998; Carlisle 2006; Collins 1982; Federman 2011; Flanagan 2011: 93-98; Harvey 1995; Metzinger 2009; Morris 1994; Smith 2010; Thanissaro 1999). In Theravada Buddhism, the realization of *anatta* occurs automatically as a fruit of insight meditation (*vipassana*). In a famous treatise on insight meditation, the great Burmese meditation master, Mahāsi Sayādaw (1994), noted that the belief in a permanent ego falls away during stage four of a 19 stage maturation process leading to the realization of Nibbāna and its fruits. What the Mahāsi's discourse obviously implies is that personal identification with an enculturated self-concept—George Herbert

Mead's "me"—is common to all people everywhere, even in Buddhist societies. This is a point that ethnographer Melford Spiro (1993) made about his Burmese Buddhist informants. Aware of the central teaching of *anatta*, he wished to see how that teaching influenced peoples' self-understanding. Spiro notes that:

> After a few months into my field work, however, it became apparent that I would have to change my research plans because I discovered that the Burmese villagers with whom I lived and worked do not internalize the doctrine of *anatta*. Instead, they strongly believe in the very ego or soul that this doctrine denies. They do so on two accounts, experiential and pragmatic. First, because they themselves experience a subjective sense of a self, the culturally normative concept of an ego-less person does not correspond to their personal experience. Second, and perhaps more important, they find the doctrine of selfless person not congenial to their soteriological [expectation of salvation] aspirations. (Spiro, 1993, p. 119)

Spiro's findings among the Burmese mirror my own among Tibetan Buddhist monks (see also Falcone 2010). Individuals rising to the realization of no-self are exceptional in any society; even those whose local epistemology or ethnopsychology describe the emptiness of the transcendental self. Tibetan Buddhist monks may learn texts by heart that extol the virtues of realizing no-self (the *anatman*), but few practice the advanced insight meditations leading to this realization. Indeed, if the realization of no-self were all that easy, disciplined methods leading to that realization would not be necessary. There is a profound difference between understanding at the level of concepts and complete realization.

Practitioners of certain Western phenomenological and spiritual traditions have reached the same realization based upon meditations focusing upon the impermanent contents of the "empirical" ego. Edmund Husserl concluded from his own introspection that the ego is essentially empty of content and is no more than an enduring point of view upon ever-changing content—a *transcendental ego* as Husserl liked to say, perhaps tongue in cheek (Husserl 1989: 103-104). The ego is an ineluctable focus of intentionality, a perpetual orientation of attention, perception, feeling and cognition directed toward the world of experience (Husserl 1969: 23). A meditator inevitably comes to this conclusion because she finds that every content she focuses upon as "me"—as "my" self—is impermanent; that is, all contents arise and pass away within the sphere of consciousness; hence, the old saw: "you can't step in the same river twice." All that remains of "my" self is an enduring point of view always present within the stream of consciousness, a point of view that is devoid of permanent content, and yet is identical to the unity of each moment of consciousness (Husserl 1970: 545).

Meditation and the Neural-Self

What we are able learn from the maturation of awareness reported by advanced meditators fits well with what the neurosciences tell us about how the brain develops consciousness. Insight meditation of any kind is essentially the disciplined turning of the spotlight of consciousness upon the internal processes of the transcendental self. It is clear now from research on the neuropsychology of meditation that the process of introspection is one that involves a reorganization of the *neural-self* (Davidson 1976; Damasio 2003, 2010; Deshmukh 2006; Luders, Clark and Toga 2011; Luders *et al.* 2012; Shapiro and Walsh 1984; Walach, Schmidt and Jonas 2011; Varela, Thompson and Rosch 1991; Varela and Shear 1999). Moreover, this picture is consistent with Carl Jung's insistence that when one takes an active, conscious role in one's own maturation, one ends up a qualitatively different person than if one's maturation unfolds unconsciously (see e.g., Jung 1967: ¶241).

A self-aware neural-self is different both experientially and structurally than a non-aware self or an empirical ego. Indeed, a concrete delusion of ego can distort both experienced reality and self-knowledge, as for example among people burdened with the so-called Dunning-Kruger Effect (Kruger and Dunning 1999) in which individuals of low ability perceive themselves as superior. Neurophysiologically speaking, awareness of self is mediated differently than awareness of the Other (Decety and Sommerville 2003). The introspective mind-state is mediated by a discrete organization in the brain (Heatherton *et al.* 2006), and as that system of networks develops through repetitive application of self-awareness, the introspective faculty grows, strengthens and reorganizes (Goldberg, Harel and Malach 2006; Gusnard, Akbudak, Shulman and Raichle 2001; Murphy and Donovan 1999). As we learn more about how the brain mediates its own self-reflection, there is a concomitant and growing realization among researchers of the value of introspective, phenomenological and meditative research in science (Tart 2001; Wallace 2007, 2009).

As reorganization of the neural-self progresses, direct experience may produce dissonance relative to culturally received categories and models of self and consciousness. Indeed, as Keith Murphy and Jason Throop (2010) have shown, received categories may become fuzzy in the extreme to remain adaptive to changing experience and neuropsychological maturation (Kosko 1993; Laughlin 1993; Rosch 1978). For example, in many cultures it is difficult and perhaps even irrelevant to make crisp distinctions among states of consciousness. For instance, Barbara Herr (1981: 334) has described the fuzzy boundaries Fijians make between what we call dream, hallucination and vision. Bill Merrill (1992) has described similar fuzziness of such categories among the Ramámiru of Mexico. A crisp distinction between dreaming and meditation becomes moot as well in the experience of advanced meditators in our own society. For instance, my late friend and fellow contemplative, Rodney Malham, shared this dream sequence with me:

I am looking down a long ramp. It is bright daylight, a blue white light. Attractive females appear before me beckoning me down the slope. I know these women, but not by name. They call me on, then as I get close they fade and another appears. The pace is slow and deliberate, no hurry. The sequence eventually fades to light.

A few nights later, I had another dream in which I enter a large space, like a gym, no ornaments or distractions. Ahead, I see an older man playing basketball with a few young boys, and I walk up to them. The older master notices me approaching and asks, "are you interested?" I don't need to answer verbally, it is understood, I am interested. He leads me to a side room. I sit, and he holds up a platter of small objects. I am to choose one. The master moves the platter to my forehead, and I am led to choose a small black bowl.

The third eye is now fully open with light streaming. The master's voice says, "you have chosen death." Everything dissolves into light and I am aware now of moving from a lucid dream state into fully conscious meditation with full concentration and at one with the universe, *samadhi*. The meditation now had its focus, or *koan*, the question had been answered. Calm, peaceful, abiding. To be reborn or to redefine ourselves, we need to experience the death of the self. We need to leave behind the constructs that impede our ability to see the true nature of mind.

The "true nature of mind" to which Rodney alludes is in part the inherent impermanence of all content in the stream of consciousness, including anything that might correspond to a fixed, enduring soul, ego, self or identity. This does not mean that all the feelings, perceptions, self-concepts, habits, etc. that used to define the "me" somehow magically vanish. The sequelae of realizing no-self really involve a years-long process of disengagement from and identification with those mental factors. What falls away is the belief that there exists a single seamless person, a permanent "me," that is at the center of all this mental and physical conditioning. What does remain is Husserl's transcendental ego (see above), the inevitable pure subjectivity in each moment of consciousness.

THE SAMYE LING RETREAT

My own experience of *stream-entry*[23] (first realization of Nirvana) occurred in 1982 toward the end of a two-month's long retreat at Kagyu Samye Ling Tibetan Buddhist meditation center in southern Scotland. At the beginning of the retreat I was alternating two types of meditation, one being a Tibetan Tantric meditation upon a deity known as Khorlo Demchog, a standing, blue, fierce male figure embracing the

---

[23] The penultimate experience in Theravada Buddhist *vipassana* meditation is *sotāpatti* ("stream-entry") or *nirodha-samapatti* ("cessation"). A meditator who has attained stream-entry is called a *sotāpanna*, or "stream-winner." In Japanese Zen, this experience is called *satori* or *kenshō*. Whatever term used, this experience is the first conscious absorption into and realization of Nirvana (see Amaro and Pasanno 2009; Bodhi 1999; Khema 1994; Thanissaro 2012a, 2012b; Suzuki 1959).

female deity Dorje Pakmo in sexual union while they dance together in flames. I was not using the complex instructions (*sadhana*) for the construction of the image of the deities. I was simply working from a photograph of the scene and internalizing it until I could evoke the internal image at will and in detail without the picture (another kind of *kasina* practice).

With this retreat my consciousness seemed to have "learned set" (as the great learning psychologist Harry Harlow used to say) and the visualization meditation developed far more rapidly than during previous practices and retreats. After a period of days, the Demchog/ Dorje Pakmo imagery "took on a life of its own" and the meditation no longer required evoking the image. The dancing couple would pop up and move around my sensorium performing different positions and movement that became meaningful to me at an intuitive level. The imagery was never so strong that I could hallucinate the imagery with my eyes open. The imagery was more like a dream or vision.

Because I was heavily influenced by C. G. Jung, I had always assumed that male and female deities in sexual union (*yab-yum*) were a symbolic representation of the male and female aspects of my own unconscious—the *syzygy*. Their movements, interactions, postures and so forth communicated to me what the relationship between my male and female (*anima*, as Jung called the contragender aspect of the male psyche; see Chapter 8) processes were up to in the moment. The dancing imagery became more and more autonomous, and I became more and more comfortable with the meditation taking its own course. Eventually, the imagery began to simplify, and the humanoid imagery transformed into two spheres of light (*bindus*, in Buddhist terms; Tibetan: *thig le*), one blue and the other rose, that "danced" (moved, jiggled, circled) around each other, sometimes separating, sometimes merging, sometimes one bigger than the other. Sometime later a much smaller third sphere would appear between the blue and rose spheres, usually a golden color. I interpreted the appearance of the third sphere as representative of the Watcher, identifying neither with the male nor the female aspect.

After a period of days, if I tried to construct the internal image of Demphog/Dorje Pakmo, the spheres would immediately pop up to take their place in the sensorium. I was no longer able to hold a complex *yab-yum* image of any kind without an immediate transformation of the imagery to spontaneous *bindu* imagery—a process I have learned to interpret as simplification and purification of countersigns (*patibhaganimitta*). Interestingly, the *bindus* became permanent. To this day, some thirty-six years later, all I must do is close my eyes and concentrate on the "screen" of the visual sensorium and the *bindus* appear, and their activity reflects the state of my consciousness at the moment. At some point in this retreat I realized how the classic "yin-yang" symbol originated in the direct experience of ancient contemplatives.

The second type of meditation was mindfulness of the breath (*ānāpānasmṛti*), as taught in Theravada Buddhism. I would either focus my attention upon the breath entering and leaving a nostril or follow the breath down to the pit of my stomach and then lodge my focus on one of the chakras along the central channel as I imagined it to be, just forward of my spine. I would often visualize a tiny pea-sized blue bubble (*bindu*) with a Buddha figure in it moving up or down the central channel or placed it in a chakra.[24] I used the breath concentration to deepen the calm and increase the concentration that I was using in the *yab-yum* work. Meanwhile, there were other interesting experiences going on as well, especially while dreaming (Chapter 6; see also Laughlin 2011: Chap. 13). These were directly related to the core work of the two alternating meditations I planned to do throughout the retreat.

However, as the two previously distinct meditations developed—or, perhaps more accurately, as my consciousness developed during the meditations—they merged into a single exercise of awareness that led eventually to stream-entry. Whether beginning with the *yab-yum*, or the breathing meditation, I quickly would reach access concentration. In that state I had the choice of meditating upon any aspect of consciousness to the exclusion of all else. The instructions one receives in Buddhist meditation training (so-called "pith instructions") is that regardless of what the original meditation, once access concentration is reached and stabilized, the focus of concentration should shift to the arising and

---

[24] This is a variation of breathing concentration combined with visualization that I learned from a monk in Thailand, a member of the sangha at Wat Pak Nam temple in Bangkok. At the time, each monk carried a small clear marble enclosing a golden Buddha figure which is used as a *kasiṇa*. I went to the Wat and bought one and used it for years. I have also used blue and red marbles as visualization devices.

passing of phenomena. I followed this instruction assiduously, and as the retreat proceeded, more and more time was spent in this state and upon this focus. I had realized some time before the retreat that if sufficient concentration were focused upon an object or other aspect of phenomena, an absorption experience would likely arise. As I have said above, in access concentration, the contemplative can choose to enter or avoid absorption (the *jhānas*; see above), using absorption and its numinous qualities to energize the focus of meditation, whatever that focus may be.

Yin Is Yin, and Yang Is Yang

During the Samye Ling retreat, I dined well. I was presented with meals brought right to my door by silent volunteers at the retreat, and I learned as soon as I began my retreat that the food preparation was supervised by a genuine chef who balanced the many small offerings on a plate based upon the theory of yin and yang energies. Save for one day a week, all foods were vegetarian. Once the internal imagery had begun to take on a life of its own, I became aware that as I took a bite of a specific dish, imagery would arise in my closed-eyed sensorium. Soon it became obvious to me that two patterns of images predominated, one being scenes of warfare (tanks, troops, battlefield) and the other being white floating clouds in a pink sky. A bit of research occurred to me. I asked the chef by note if she would collaborate with me and label each individual dish on my plate with a number, keep a list of whether the number was in her scheme of things either yin or yang. She agreed, and I wrote down on a list whether a martial or peaceful image arose when I sampled each dish. It did not take many meals for us to realize that every dish she considered as yin prompted a peaceful scene in my mind's eye, and every yang dish a martial one. It was thus that I realized an empirical basis for yin-yang food attributions. My body was sampling foods and sending images "upward" to the cortex of my brain to feed the interest I had developed in sub-conscious and unconscious processes.

Stream-Entry at Samye Ling

The constant, unremitting and concentrated focus of awareness upon the arising and passing of phenomena while in access concentration was usually upon the field of sensorial particles, and the residue of the two types of meditation had simplified into a choice between concentrating on the blue and red spheres and what they were telling me about the mind-state at the moment, or subtly shifting focus to the arising and passing of the particles that made up the sensorium in all sensory modes (visual, auditory, tactile, somesthetic, feelings, so forth), including those constituting the visual spheres. I spent most of the time for days opting to focus on the arising and passing of the pixels. Eventually a sudden realization arose (instantaneous intuition) that there was no arising, and that the entire sensorium was passing. From that moment my meditation focused upon the passing of the field of sensorial particles. This shift in awareness, so very subtle, led within hours to stream-entry. One moment I was concentrating on the passing of sensorial pixels, the next the entire sensorium fell away like a vast cosmic "dump" and all that remained was diamond-clear awareness with no field of pixels. The experience I came to realize as *pure consciousness* must have been momentary, but during its duration there was no sense of time, no sense of space (whether bounded or unbounded, whether full or empty), no arising or passing of phenomena [whether of form (*rupa*) or formless (*arupa*)], no thoughts, no feelings, no movement, no desires or aversions, no choice, no coming or going— total liberation from the tyranny of phenomena over consciousness. The experience is ineffable simply because the only way to describe Nirvana (Skt: *nirvāṇa*; Pali: *nibbana, nibbāna*) to others is by way of metaphors, which of course are drawn from the experience of phenomena. There is no way to speak of Nirvana, save using metaphor. Indeed, even the word Nirvana itself is a metaphor, meaning to "blow out" the flames of desire and aversion. For that duration there was not a scintilla of phenomenal reality. There was just what I would describe as *pure awareness*.

The moments following stream-entry were filled with inexpressible joy, for with the memory of the experience was simultaneous comprehension of its significance—that I had "won through" to the essence of mind, that I had realized *sotāpatti* (Mahāsi Sayādaw 1994: 32-34). Very soon after this realization, within minutes as I recall, I understood completely why the masters taught that "three fetters" automatically fall away as a consequence of one's first experience of stream-entry (see e.g., Thanissaro 2012b): (1) belief that I exist as a permanent phenomenon (for me this had largely fallen away earlier), (2) that there is any doubt about the goal of Buddhist meditation, and (3) that no rituals or other practices are the goal of the path to liberation. As the *Alagaddupama Sutta* notes, "In the Dhamma [the Buddha's teachings] thus well-proclaimed by me—clear, open, evident, stripped of rags—those monks who have abandoned the three fetters, are all stream-winners, steadfast, never again destined for states of woe, headed for self-awakening" (Thanissaro 2004). From my experience of the moments just post-stream-entry I had acquired apodictic knowledge of what constitutes the goal of Buddha Dharma, and that any practice that does not aid in attaining stream-entry is false and a hindrance to the path. I also understood the truth of the words one of my teachers, Namgyal Rinpoche, had said to me, "Complex meditations are for dull minds."

Consequences of Stream-Entry

There have been for me numerous consequences of the experience of stream-entry—usually summarized as the "fruits" (Skt: *sotāpatti phala*). For one thing, I came to understand that realization of sensorial pixels is neither a necessary nor sufficient condition for stream-entry. All that is absolutely required is the ability to enter access concentration and a tenacious concentration upon the arising and passing, and then the passing of phenomena. Others would seem to have experienced stream-entry in something like the way I did. For instance, Ekaku Hakuin (2010: 23) writes that: "At around midnight on the seventh and final night of my practice, the boom of a bell from a distant temple reached my ears: suddenly, my body and mind dropped completely away. I rose clear of even the finest dust. Overwhelmed with joy... ." In addition, Robert Bellah (2008: 201-202) relates the experience of an eighteenth-century Zen monk and teacher, Ishida Baigan who, after meditating for years, had this experience:

> Late one night, he lay down exhausted, and was unaware of the break of day. He heard the cry of a sparrow in the woods behind where he was lying. Then within his body it was like the serenity of a great sea or a cloudless sky. He felt the cry of that sparrow like a cormorant diving and entering the water, in the serenity of a great sea. After that he abandoned the conscious observation of his own nature.

For another thing, meditation for me boiled down to whatever work I have had to do to become centered and tranquil enough to enter access concentration, and then to focus upon the passing of phenomena. This work has continued to mature in very subtle ways. Very recently I came close to "entering the stream" for a second time, an event that is called *phalasamapatti*, or "attainment of fruition" (Mahāsi Sayādaw 1994: 34). This occurs when the knowledge of Nirvana, or "the stream" (the cognitive "fruits"), has matured sufficiently that one may re-enter the stream with greater awareness than the first time, and without aversive reactions that will hinder the "letting go" into the stream (Mahāsi Sayādaw 1994: 34-35). This happened for me in this way:

> I became lucid in a dream in which I was meditating (I believe I was in a temple of some kind) and turned my attention to the passing away of dream phenomena. So intense did the concentration become that I was no longer dreaming but was in access concentration watching the field of pixels that constituted hypnopompic imagery, and then the field of pixels alone without form—the imagery (thingness) had fallen away. At a moment, I realized I was headed back into stream—I recognized the symptoms as the field of pixels began to "dump" so that all that remained before the mind's eye was rapidly passing sensorial pixels. My foreknowledge of the experience of entering stream, which had been absent when I experienced *sotāpatti*, got in the way of letting go. At the last moment there was a small but sufficient aversive reaction to stop the process leading to *phalasamapatti*.

Despite having hindered the process of "letting go" into the stream, I experienced intense joy and after some moments realized that, while my clinging to phenomenal reality was still too strong to allow the experience a second time, the bonds were weakening, and I was getting closer. I also realized that it is only that aversion, that clinging to phenomena ("form;" Mahāsi Sayādaw 1994: 34), that stands in the way of my being able to enter the stream at will and remain there if I choose.

Post-Samye Ling

I stopped all formal meditation practice a few days prior to leaving Samye Ling and spent my days wandering around the moors and basking in the gorgeous southern Scottish landscapes. Within a week or so of leaving Samye Ling for the United States, some of the other consequences of stream-entry began to present themselves, some of them in the dream state. One particularly memorable dream occurred while I was staying in Philadelphia: I dreamed that I was standing hand in hand with my child-self under a fiery arch that had morphed from two enormous serpents that had arisen on each side of us and touched their heads above us. I was lucid and watching the scene from a position behind the fiery portal and my dream selves, so I could see they were located on a vast plain upon which stood the ruins of a city. I knew in the dream that I was looking at the transformation of myself after the realizations of the past [Samye Ling] retreat. I was beginning to awaken from the dream and was in a hypnopompic state when a fiery golden chariot being drawn by huge golden horses appeared out of an intense, almost blinding golden light, and a deep, booming voice called out, "Read Ezekiel!" This image could not have lasted more than a few seconds, but I awoke knowing that I had not (and indeed have never since) experienced a dream like that (Laughlin 2011: 191-192). Audible hallucinations like this are known as "mystical locutions" (Freze 1993).

I did not own a Bible and did not recall ever reading the book of Ezekiel, although I might have encountered the fiery chariot motif in my childhood Methodist Bible classes. I obtained a copy of the Old Testament later that same day and was astonished when I read of God appearing before the prophet Ezekiel in the form of a fiery chariot pulled by *Chayot* (mystical angels), and that much of the book was about the destruction of the old Jerusalem and the construction of the City of God upon its ashes. I also noted that the creatures pulling the chariot in my dream were definitely horses, and not the mythical angels of the Biblical imagery. This dream happened over thirty years ago, and it is still as clear, numinous and meaningful to me today as it was then. It was clearly an indication that the stream-entry experience was resulting in transformations at a very deep level of my psyche.

DISCUSSION

Turning the subjectivity of transpersonal experiences into scientifically useful data is sometimes not an easy thing to accomplish. I once addressed this as the "problem of the phenomenological typewriter;" namely, presuming that ethnographers, by means of participant observation, successfully attain the experiences intended by mythic drama, ordeal, drug trip, ritual and other aspects of an alien culture's spiritual tradition, how then do they describe those experiences so that they become publicly available data (Laughlin 1989)? As an anthropologist, my commitment is and always has been to science—to grounding experiential anthropology in a Jamesian "radical empiricism," if you will (James 1976 [1912]; Laughlin and McManus 1995; Taylor 1996). For the ethnographer, no experience had by human beings is too outré to be included as data under ethnographic scrutiny.

Ineffability and Poetics

The more extraordinary the experience (a commonplace in the study of mystical and transpersonal phenomenology), the harder it is to render the information gleaned from the experience into a scientifically comparative form. All too often the description of a rare experience is set aside as somehow too anecdotal to be considered scientific. It is often very difficult for others to "unpack" the metaphors used to describe experiences. This is especially true in the present case, for any attempt to describe "path moment" (*sotāpatti*) in natural language will perforce require that one resort to similes and metaphors—even the terms "path" and "moment," "stream" and "enter" for that matter, are similes. Indeed, with respect to the direct experience of *sotāpatti*, there is no path, no stream, no entering, no time-consciousness, no space (thus the term "empty" is also just a simile)—in fact phenomenally speaking, there is no anything.

Always remembering the Rule of Multiple Interpretations, one nonetheless develops a basis in transpersonal experiences for understanding how particular metaphors come to stand for what are largely ineffable states. This issue has been directly and tellingly addressed by *anthropological poetics* (aka, *ethnopoetics*; see Brady 1991;

Diamond 1986; Hymes 2003; Tedlock 1999), a field that studies the many ways that language is molded to express experiences across cultures—"focusing in particular on the oral communication of proverbs, laments, prayers, praises, prophecies, curses, and riddles shaped by the spoken, chanted, or singing voice" (Brady 2008: 296). All experiences are ineffable in that more is left out than can be expressed. Another way to say this is that while experiences are information rich, cognition and language are relatively speaking information poor. The problem in communication is for the speaker to send sufficient information—the right information—to trigger (or "penetrate to") a much larger field of information in the mind of the listener (Laughlin 1989). The challenge is even greater when communicating transpersonal experiences such as those I have described here. As most societies are to some extent polyphasic, people who have extraordinary experiences face the challenge of finding a language to share the purely subjective and express the ultimately inexpressible. They often have recourse to poetics, which likely was the first and oldest art form, for it allowed the sharing of not only sensory aspects of ASC, but also knowledge gleaned at the intuitive level. The Buddha himself reputedly used poetry to communicate such knowledge. The *Udana* (included in the *Sutta Pitaka*) is partly in verse, one of which expresses a consequence of Awakening (Buddha 1997, Ud 2):

When things become manifest
To the ardent meditating Brahman,
All his doubts then vanish since he has known
The utter destruction of conditions.

The Buddha's verse does *not* express a rational conclusion. Rather, it is an expression of the fact that with the first stream-entry experience, doubt about the path automatically drops away. It is an intuitive knowing that may give rise to poetic expression via imagination, metaphor and insight. Poetics is born of the challenge of expressing and sharing the ineffable. Many societies have their poetic forms for just this purpose. Yet in modern technocratic societies, a schism has been erected between poetic expression and science. This humanist-scientist dichotomy stands as a hindrance to doing transpersonal science, for it fails to rise to the challenge of sharing the most effective uses of esoteric language as scientifically useful data. Yet there is no reason (other than stubborn ideological loyalty) that transpersonal researchers cannot embrace what my friend and colleague, Ivan Brady calls *artful science*—a methodology that is grounded in the media of poetics. Specifically addressing anthropologists, Brady notes that artful science:

> ...pursues knowledge mostly ignored or formally discounted by the extremes of logical positivism. It advocates as a complement (not as a replacement) a kind of knowing and reporting that (a) promotes phenomenology as a philosophy that puts the observer (the seeker, the knower) upfront in the equation of interpreting and representing experience; (b) pushes interpretive anthropology back into the loop of sensual experience, a body-centered position that includes a consideration of but transcends the sweeping metaphor that everything (e.g., people, landscapes) can and should be rendered as texts to be interpreted; (c) finds some continuity in the structures and orientations of body-roundedness and myth despite important limitations posed by language itself and by epistemic interference between the present and our preliterate past; and (d) gives poets special cachet through their offering forms of knowing and saying (robust metaphors and more) that can engage the senses and visions of being-in-place in ways that both exceed and complement more conventional strategies in anthropology and history. (Brady 2005: 981-982)

This approach is especially useful for transpersonal researchers interested in understanding the religious art and architecture of prehistoric peoples, as well as the textual expressions of transpersonal experiences by long dead literate peoples.

More on Methods

Thus far there are no technological methods that may independently measure the activity of the brain while, say, an *arhat* (Pali: *arahant*; a person who is never apart from the stream; indeed, may be said *to be one with the stream*) is absorbed in Nirvana. They cannot take a camera with them and record the experience. They cannot tape record their description of the experience as it occurs. They cannot draw or paint the experience in other than metaphorical images. Most importantly, we do not know how the brain mediates stream-entry. Is *sotāpatti* mediated by isolating prefrontal cortical attention structures from the structures mediating the sensorium? Or does the sensorium simply cease to function for the duration of the experience, leaving in its wake something like "pure" consciousness, consciousness with only itself as object? We do not yet know. We do have a literature pertaining to the psychology of post-stream-entry *sotāpanna*. For example, Full, Walach and Trautwein (2013: 61) interviewed advanced Burmese Theravadā Buddhist meditators who presumably had experienced stream-entry to establish whether meditation at this level of maturity leads to significant and permanent changes in perception. They found evidence of such developments of perception: "Changes could be identified concerning the quality of perception, especially in aspects of clarity; comprehension of interdependences in perception processing, i.e., mental condition and perception; successive cessation of a subject/object-based perception; and finally, a non-conceptual perception including the deconstruction of the notion of I, self, or me." But the authors caution that their study could not parse-out cultural conditioning that may have influenced their data. I would add that being labeled a *sotāpanna* may in some cases be due to status factors in Burmese monastic culture—a way of acknowledging advanced status as a meditator or teacher—and is not a guarantee that the individual has experienced stream-entry. Again, there is yet no independent method of measuring stream-winners.

Obviously, there is also no way to draw a random sample from a known universe of stream-winners among all peoples everywhere. Thus, the use of parametric statistics in analyzing the data from a non-random sample of stream winners, even when available (as in the study above) would be invalid. Does that mean that the study of rare states of consciousness cannot in principle be "scientific?" Hardly. To require quantitative experimental evidence in such cases would amount to the most absurd kind of scientism, one that denies the foundations of all scientific disciplines in naturalistic research. As I noted before, by such an account, most of Darwin's work aboard the Beagle would not make the grade. In fact, as William James argued, much can be empirically learned from individual experiential case studies, and trait comparisons between such studies, even when the experiences are rare, and the universe of such cases remains unknown. The great neurologist V. S. Ramachandran addressed this issue in the following way: "By way of analogy, imagine that I cart a pig into your living room and tell you that it can talk. You might say, 'Oh really? Show me.' I then wave my wand and the pig starts talking. You might respond, 'My God! That's amazing!' You are not likely to say, 'Ah, but that's just one pig. Show me a few more and then I might believe you'" (Ramachandran and Blakeslee 1999: xiii). Neuroscience, as with transpersonal studies, is grounded in single case studies; often in-depth qualitative explorations upon which later multiple case meta-analyses are founded.[25]

Developmental Perspective

If there is a single lesson I have drawn from reflecting on the signal experiences I have had over the course of a lifetime of meditation, *it is that the processes of neuropsychological development are pivotal to both spiritual awakening and transpersonal studies.* Even when ethnographers appreciate the cultural significance of transpersonal experiences and even leave themselves open to having such experiences themselves (imbibing the host's entheogens, participating in the local healing and other rituals that evoke extraordinary experiences, or in the present case, following the path of meditation), they have all too often failed to realize that transpersonal experiences may occur for their hosts in a developmental continuum from, say, those associated with initiation early in life to those typical of elder masters (see Assagioli 2007; Chinen 1985; Wilber 1996). In other words, spiritual paths are developmental processes with various experiences marking way-points along the path toward full maturation. An American learning to become a lucid dreamer, for instance, is a far-cry from being a dream shaman. In spiritual awakening, transpersonal experiences may be both symptomatic of one's level of maturity, and the cause for a change in self-understanding.

With respect to the Buddhist path, my old friend and meditation teacher, Tarchin Hearn has noted (personal communication, 8 May 2014):

---

[25] Consider the impact of the strange case of Phineas Gage upon 19th century neuropsychology (Macmillan 2000).

Many people can apprentice in a spiritual system and become adepts and teachers of that tradition. Not so many people can as a result of their practice, transcend or go beyond the very tradition that nourished them. Buddhism teaches us how to live well in the present moment. It doesn't know what will unfold in the moment to come. This universe has not yet arisen. Namgyal Rinpoche once suggested to me that I should study Buddhism, realize it and walk on and then I should study western traditions, realize them and walk on. I've come to realize that the "walking on" is the forefront of this evolving universe in the collaborative act (with everything and everyone else) of creative being. Put in another way, when I was young I thought that I needed to understand and perhaps even master Buddhist teaching. I had no idea that Buddhist teaching was an attempt to skillfully nudge me towards a way of being and a field of questioning that, at the time, I was not able to even imagine and that today I discover hour by hour.

Numerous ethnographers have worked among peoples with polyphasic cultures. Relatively few of them have gone so far as to participate in a culture to the extent of attaining the alternative states fundamental to the hosts' worldview. This is the common pattern among ethnographers who have studied shamanistic religions, many of which require initiation into the proper use of entheogens and secret ritual practices, a process of apprenticeship that may last for years (see the articles by Robin Rodd, an ethnographer who has apprenticed to a South American shaman; Rodd 2002, 2006; Rodd and Sumabila 2011). There are cases in which the society's mythological system may reflect a developmental progression of understanding and realization from the simple levels of childhood through to the comprehension of the master. For instance, Dan Jorgensen (1980) discovered that the mythology of the Telefolmin people of Papua New Guinea has something on the order of ten distinct levels of complexity ranging from many short "just-so" stories for children's ears to a master's level in which all the many myths are integrated into a single story that takes days to narrate.

The course of meditational maturation—of *contemplative individuation*, to wax Jungian for a moment—is perhaps one of the most empirically available, because more and more dedicated meditators have become mature contemplatives. As mentioned in Chapter 3, we now have sufficient evidence from psychological and neuroscience research supporting the notion that meditation results in changes in perception, attention, affect and cognition (e.g., Brandmeyer, Delorme and Wahbeh 2019). It also seems very likely, as suggested by Ledi (2007), that most significant changes in neurophysiological, psychological and cognitive functions caused by meditation will be found among mature contemplatives. For instance, it is far easier for me to enter access concentration now than when I first experienced it so many years ago. Still, I am unable to access that state at will, a skill that is prerequisite for an *arhat*, which I am decidedly not. Notice that when I got close to a second absorption into the stream (*phalasamapatti*), there was sufficient aversion to letting go of phenomena to thwart the process. What I learned from this "near miss" is that my "clinging" to phenomena—to sensorial productions—and my emotional reaction to transformations in consciousness have not matured sufficiently to allow the experience to occur. The recognition of what was about to happen emotionally hindered the happening. I can project to a time when, should I live long enough, the emotional reaction will be either gone or too attenuated to thwart another entry into the stream.

Origins and Pervasiveness of Meditation

Meditation is neither a recent phenomenon, nor was it first invented by Eastern spiritual traditions (Goleman 1996). Indeed, most of the classic meditations used by the Buddha in his teaching were inherited from traditions that were ancient even in his time (Gunaratana 2002; Wynne 2009). As C. G. Jung (Hannah 1981: 3) noted years ago, human beings have very likely been meditating for millennia—possibly since humans have been both self-aware, and able to share and discuss subjective experiences such as fantasies, visions, dreams, hallucinations, drug-induced imagery—as well as meditative countersigns—and so forth. Of course, we will never know the precise evolutionary Rubicon leading to a "contemplative brain," for it is a matter of speculation and theory (Filmer-Lorch 2012: 6-7).

However, I would argue that prior to a certain point in prehistory, virtually all human cultures would have been polyphasic in their worldview, grounded in their belief that experiences had in ASC are different perspectives on reality (Laughlin 2013b). Many cultures would have discovered the practice of intense concentration upon images and other somatic phenomena available to their mind's eye, and this perhaps widespread practice could well have influenced the evolution of certain cognitive functions (see Mithen 2003; Rossano 2007). Doubtless also, meditation of various types would have played a central role in ancient shamanic mysticism and healing (Lewis-Williams 1992, 1997; MacDonald *et al.* 1987; Pearson 2002: 95; Peters 1989; Winkelman 2010: 72-73). The fact that countersigns often arise because of intense concentration upon any object is suggestive that many shamanic healing traditions involve the healer or diagnostician meditating upon ("reading") some pattern; e.g., bones, entrails, sandals, stones, etc. thrown on the ground, starlight passing through a crystal, images in a scrying bowl, so forth. Of course, short of an ethnographer with a time-machine, there is no way to know for sure when shamanism first became linked with meditation practices (Lewis-Williams 1997).

A pivotal distinction must be made here: Whereas most shamanic meditation practices very likely involved following and interacting with dynamic imagery in much the same way that C. G. Jung advocated in his method of active imagination (Chapter 7), Buddhist mindfulness discourages interacting with spontaneous imagery, except in Tantric traditions where more shamanic methods are used solely to energize the real work of mindfulness training, the realization of stream-entry and cessation of phenomena. Keep in mind that the Buddha considered that clinging to (dialoguing with) phenomena was a major cause of suffering (*dukkha*), and he wished to discover the "builder"[26] of phenomena by snuffing out this clinging and thereby embracing cessation (Rahula 1974). As far as I know, no known shamanic tradition is founded upon the realization, or even the knowledge of stream-entry. But again, for the methodological reasons mentioned above, we simply cannot know for sure.

---

[26] Verse 154 of the *Dhammapada* reads: "Oh house-builder! You are seen, you shall build no house again. All your rafters are broken, your roof-tree is destroyed. My mind has reached the unconditioned (Nibbana); the end of craving has been attained."

Husserlian and Buddhist Methods

As noted before, I recognized many parallels between Buddhist mindfulness practices and Husserlian transcendental phenomenology. Indeed, I early-on suspected that Edmund Husserl was to some extent what Buddhist psychology calls a *pratyekabuddha*, or "self-awakener"— someone who is sufficiently advanced in mindfulness that they rediscover the development of the path of awakening all by themselves and without instructions or teachers. It was clear to me that using either Buddhist mindfulness or Husserlian "reduction" would inevitably lead one into the same transpersonal domains of self-awareness (Hanna 1993b), and lead to the most accurate phenomenological understanding of consciousness. Moreover, considering Husserl as a *pratyekabuddha* seemed to me to explain why so many of his students and followers failed to "get it" with respect to attaining the phenomenological attitude and transpersonal comprehension. This failure for instance is at the very core of Husserl's disappointment with his protégé, Martin Heidegger, who ran off to teach university philosophy before becoming a mature contemplative (see Husserl 1997). Other of Husserl's students (e.g., Eugen Fink, Gerhard Funke, Ludwig Landgrebe) continued to hang around their teacher and did do the requisite mindfulness work, and their comprehension of, and reflections upon the phenomenological attitude are very useful to meditators wishing to understand Husserlian methods (see e.g., Fink 1995: Funke 1987; Landgrebe 1973).

It was part of the English-speaking Husserlian zeitgeist at the time I was reading his books that Husserl had not encountered Buddhism, or the Pali Canon, for he never mentions Buddhism in any of his major writings. Some scholars had acknowledged the similarities and differences between Husserlian phenomenology and various forms of Indian philosophy (e.g., Mohanty 1972). It turns out, however, that Husserl did engage with the Buddhist literature— the Pali Canon had just been translated into German—and even wrote a short note expressing his feelings about what he had read. Thanks to Fred Hanna (1995), we have an English translation of that 1925 note entitled "On the Teachings of Gotama [Gautama] Buddha." In that note Husserl seems to thoroughly identify with the aims and methods of Buddhist phenomenology:

That Buddhism—insofar as it speaks to us from pure original sources—is a religio-ethical discipline for spiritual purification and fulfillment of the highest stature—conceived of and *dedicated to an inner result of a vigorous and unparalleled, elevated frame of mind, will soon become clear to every reader who devotes themselves to the work.* Buddhism is comparable only with the highest form of the philosophical and religious spirit of our European culture. It is now our task to utilize this (to us) completely new Indian spiritual discipline which has been revitalized and strengthened by this contrast. (Hanna 1995: 367; emphasis added)

One important factor influencing my use of Husserlian methods was the simple fact that, coming from a wealth of experience while practicing Buddhist mindfulness (*vipassana*), Husserl's methods of bracketing, "reduction," the epoché, returning "to the things themselves," etc. were perfectly transparent. Despite his turgid prose, it was blatantly obvious to me what Husserl's project was on about. As Hanna (1995: 366) wrote: "Eugen Fink once told Dorion Cairns 'that the various phases of Buddhistic self-discipline were essentially phases of phenomenological reduction'" (Cairns 1976: 50). This statement is especially significant since Fink was Husserl's chief assistant and was considered by Husserl to be his most trusted interpreter. It is thus also significant that Husserl considered the effort of and dedication to attaining the phenomenological attitude inevitably impacts psychological development. Again, as Hanna (1995: 369) notes: "Husserl claimed side benefits of phenomenological seeing in terms of self-exploration and self-development. He said that the insights gained from performing the transcendental phenomenological method of seeing brings about 'a complete personal transformation'" (Husserl 1970[1936]: 137).

There is one other important factor that I do need to emphasize; I can find no evidence that Husserl himself experienced stream-entry. His use of the concepts of "transcendental phenomenology" and "pure consciousness" refer more to something like access concentration, a state few of his students and followers developed, if their respective writings are any indication. His descriptions of that state involve the falling away of all preconceptions, all discursive knowledge, and a complete openness to intuitive insight. His project was fundamentally different than the Buddha's in that Husserl wished to explore the essential structures of phenomenal consciousness and was not guided into a course of meditation that would lead him, or any of his students so far as I know, to *sotāpatti*; i.e., transcending phenomenal experience. Moreover, my hunch has always been that, given Husserl was perhaps a *pratyekabuddha*, he found it easier to enter access concentration without the disciplined calming and centering exercises (*samatha*) required by most of us to reach that state (see also Hanna 1995: 371).

SUMMARY AND SEGUE

I have had numerous extraordinary experiences over the course of the last half century of phenomenological exploration, especially while dreaming. What I have described above are three of the most seminal experiences arising during mindfulness work—the realization of sensorial pixels, of no-self and of stream-entry. These three were not only real experiences, they were "seal" experiences, ones that resulted in permanent transformations in my perception, self-knowledge and phenomenological insight. They are also understandable as way-stations along a path of gradually developing, intuitive understanding of how consciousness works. I do not mean to imply that discerning sensorial pixels is either a necessary or sufficient condition for attaining stream-entry. It is clear from the literature that stream-entry can be attained without the previous realization of no-self having occurred. In those cases, the realization of no-self, if it has not occurred previously, is an inevitable consequence of stream-entry. What I can say from my own experiences is that, in my case, one realization followed the other in a sequence that, in retrospect, appears to have been the result of a maturation of introspective view. What does seem to be a necessary, but not a sufficient condition for stream-entry is the maturation of access concentration, for only in that state will the consciousness be able to let go into the experience of absorption without being hindered by anxiety or aversion.

My suspicion is that I came to realize sensorial pixels and no-self independently of attaining stream-entry because I was working as much from a neurophenomenological perspective as from Buddhist mindfulness (Laughlin, McManus and d'Aquili 1990). What I was doing was bracketing processes that were integral to perception. I also did this with respect to time-consciousness in a way that is not required in Buddhist mindfulness, but is fundamental to Husserlian phenomenology (Laughlin 1992; Laughlin and Throop 2008). Nonetheless, in retrospect, it is clear to me that one realization set me up for the next and continues to do so in a complex process of phenomenologically-oriented neurocognitive development.

Any subjective, "first-person" methodology is only useful for a science of consciousness if it produces reports that lead to further research. At the same time, and speaking in favor of radical empiricism, research based upon poor phenomenological descriptions will also produce poor science. As Dhananjay Chavan (2011: 248) notes:

> Whatever may be one's view of consciousness in the natural order, there is probably a need for systematic first-person methods to study our subjective mental states and correlate them to physical states (brain states) which can be empirically characterized. Given the bewildering variety and range of conscious mental states it seems unlikely that any methodical observation can be made of one's subjectivity without proper training and grounding in formalized first-person methods.

This said, it is hard for me to visualize a method for studying the neuropsychological underpinnings of the *sotāpatti* experience, for it is rare, it lasts but a moment, is unpredictable, and very likely cannot occur when the meditator is wired up or lying flat-out in an fMRI machine. But technological problems aside, this is no reason why the experience cannot be considered as scientifically relevant.

What can and has been researched is the interaction of meditation and dreaming. Indeed, in some traditions, dream awareness is considered essential to a contemplative's path. Hence, we will now turn our attention to dream contemplation and examine what, if anything, we can learn about how the brain and consciousness work by focusing upon our most common ASC—dreaming.

CHAPTER SIX

Meditation IV:
Dream Contemplation

*Your visions will become clear only when you can look
into your own heart. Who looks outside, dreams;
who looks inside, awakes.*

– C.G. Jung

People spend a fourth to a third of their lives asleep, and during sleep they dream. Most human societies on the planet pay close attention to their dreams and, in many cases, they include people who in one way or another specialize in contemplating their dream experiences. Also, in many cases, they share these experiences and the knowledge accrued from the dreams with the group. In traditional societies, people routinely share their dreams and discuss their meaning and import. They may seek guidance from ancestors or ghosts and may recount events had in dreams that seem to portend future events. Moreover, just as the natural functions of awareness in the normal waking state can be turned to self-discovery, so too may awareness while dreaming or entering other ASC provide the potential for a phenomenological attitude within that state—again, a "state-specific science." This is importantly the case for dream states, for dreaming is the premier state within which the unconscious most commonly reveals itself to the contemplative mind, especially for those capable of "lucid dreaming."

Phenomenology of Dreaming

What is it about dreaming that people in so many societies find compelling, informative and practical? The answer to that question must involve the neurophenomenology of dreaming. We can get a handle on this by first delimiting some aspects of dreaming that are universal to people everywhere.

Indiscernibility

If we bracket our very Western natural attitude about the "reality" of our waking life and the "unreality" of our dream life, we find that the two domains of experience are "indiscernible" (Globus 1987; see also Kirtsoglou 2010: 323). Both dreaming and waking worlds (both part of our brain world) are grounded in pure experience and, solely on that basis, one cannot tell them apart—they are equally domains of lived experience and must be studied as such. This phenomenological finding makes a lot of sense, neurophysiologically speaking, for both dream and waking experience are mediated by the same sensorium— that is, most of the brain systems that mediate waking experiences also mediate dream experiences (Pagel 2008: 63). This finding also makes ethnographic sense because so many of the groups we anthropologists have lived amongst and studied consider dreaming to be just as real as waking. Can we tell dreaming and waking apart on other grounds?

> The answer here is that the differences [our] reflection notes are not fundamental but related to sensory functions, which are highly restricted in sleep and open during waking. The dream life is like the wake life, except that there is no flowing array of sensory stimulation available to modulate it. As lived, the dream life is an authentic life, but reflection reveals that it is a peculiar unmodulated life because of the sensory restriction. (Globus 1987: 65)

While dreaming, we perceive "people," "plants," "animals" and "clouds" as being real. They are right there before the mind's eye. In the dream we react and interact with these images because they are real to us in that experiential moment (Craig 1987). What else can we discern about our dreams relative to our waking experiences? Globus suggests that there is a distinct "single-mindedness" about dreams. Dreams tend to proceed along a single train of thought, as opposed to waking life where there are many more distractions and alternative possibilities. Moreover, the sensory environment is less abuzz with endless distractions.

Apodicticity

Ethnologists often speak of a people's "beliefs" with respect to the culture's local knowledge. Under certain circumstances, this way of referring to local knowledge makes sense, for it allows the fieldworker to dodge any question of the truth-value of the hosts' ethnoepistemology—that is, a people's own theory of how they come to know what they claim to know (see Hongladarom 2002). Yet this approach to local knowledge also distorts the phenomenology of knowing, for the way we Western English-speakers use the word "belief" tends to imply a hedge on certainty of knowledge—as in, "well, I believe so," or "that was what she believes anyway." One thing that is lost in using the term "belief" to label local knowledge is the sense of *apodicticity* that may accompany an act of knowing among the people we are studying. For most peoples, there is no suggestion that dreams are fantasy or fiction. "...Rather, they take them to be literal experiences of the dreamer's soul—as [Edward B.] Tylor first proposed—the gripping reality of a dream while it is being experienced is certainly a powerful reinforcement of the idea in the waking afterthought" (Tuzin 1975: 563).

Jean-Guy Goulet (1987) takes up the distinction between belief and knowledge regarding Dene Tha ways of knowing:

> Among the Dene Tha, as among other Northern Athapaskans, knowledge that has been mediated is regarded with doubt. True knowledge is considered to be that which is derived from experience... . This view has profound implications for what Dene consider the proper way to teach or inform not only their children and each other, but also the inquisitive ethnographer approaching them to learn about their ways and their religion. (1987: 115-116)

In other words, the Dene Tha value knowledge from direct experience, regardless of the state of consciousness during which the knowledge is derived. Only through direct experience can one achieve that sense of the apodicticity of knowledge. In Dene terms, if I know something, I know it because I experienced it, and an ingredient of the experience is the immediate sense of apodicticity—the certainty that "this is the case," or "this is not the case." This is less a logical and more an existential certainty.

The Dene Tha are quite forthright about the dependence of true knowledge upon experience—namely, they choose not to share knowledge with anyone unprepared to understand it.

> Dene tend to exclude those who are not perceived as knowing from those among whom they discuss experiences of dreams, visions, and power. Such discussion occurs only between those who are 'in the know.' To one who 'knows' and understands, Dene offer a degree of explanation according to their estimation of his or her understanding. This estimation of the ethnographer's 'knowledge,' more than the investigator's own research agenda, determines the flow of information between the two, information that most often takes the form of stories, the significance of which at first simply escapes the ethnographer. (ibid: 114)

As Goulet puts it, "true knowledge is personal knowledge" and the only access to knowledge gleaned from dreaming is by way of learning the skills of the dreamer.

Speaking personally, there is no conceivable argument anyone could make that would dissuade me from the knowledge I attained via the experience of "stream-entry" (Chapter 5). That knowledge is not only grounded in direct experience but *was caused by that experience.* The experience and the knowledge are the same thing. In the Buddhist context, I know what is Path and what is non-Path. There is no confusion, no doubt and no possible alternative view. There is no pundit however charismatic that could confuse me as to what conditions will lead to stream-entry and what conditions will hinder stream-entry. This is apodicticity in the flesh.

Revealing the Hidden

When we bracket our belief in the unreality of our dreams, we are better able to appreciate one very significant and universal pattern in the phenomenology of dreaming cross-culturally—that in dreams, entities and forces that are normally invisible to waking life may become sensible, tangible and even palpable (see Sumegi 2008: 31). For example, Meggitt (1962) notes that among the Mae Enga of New Guinea, ghosts are invisible while one is awake, but may become visible in dreams. There are innumerable examples of societies in which dead ancestors, mere shades or shadows during the waking state, become significant characters and causal agents in dreams. Irving Hallowell, in reflecting upon the worldview of the Ojibwa Indians, speaks of "other-than-human persons" encountered within dreams. He notes that, "While in all cultures 'persons' comprise one of the major classes of objects to which the self must become oriented, this category of being is by no means limited to human beings. In Western culture, as in others, 'supernatural' beings are recognized as 'persons,' although belonging, at the same time, to the other than human category" (2002[1960]: 20).

We often find that in our hosts' world, they do not merely "believe" in other-than-human persons, they know them. They know them because they encounter them and interact with them in their dream life (perhaps also during drug trips and vision quests). This factor is of primary importance to cross-cultural dream research. It is what Goulet (1998: 254) is getting at when he writes:

I agree with [Clifford] Geertz that we can neither live other people's lives nor magically intrude on their consciousness, whether members of our own culture or of another. But to see the task of the ethnographer as Geertz defines it precludes some of what we can do and learn in the field, not only about others but also about ourselves in our interaction with them. Ethnographic work can – but does not need to – go hand in hand with the anthropologist's experience of dreams and visions. These often become part of interactions with others… . More than merely listen to what others say about their lives, then, anthropologists pay attention to their own lives, including their inner lives. They observe and listen to other people's responses to their accounts of their own dreams and/or visions experienced while living among these others. To do so is to become an experiential ethnographer.

Predicting the Future

Dreams are a ubiquitous source of information, not only about the self, but about future events (Goulet 1998: xxvii-xxix). People everywhere want to know what is going to happen before it does, thus removing a major source of uncertainty, anxiety and stress. We wake up in the morning and tune-in to the weather report so that we don't go out into foul weather unprepared. But everyone knows how inaccurate weather reports can be. So too may the precognition of events in a dream be questionable. Many peoples evaluate the accuracy of divinatory dreams by waiting to see if the predicted results happen—in other words, they use *post hoc* reasoning (Krippner 1994).

The Lacandon Maya take a "wait-and-see" attitude toward such dreams. Robert Bruce demonstrated this attitude by recording anticipatory dreams and then seeing how the people interpret the prediction relative to what happens later—whether the dream is confirmed as "predictive" or not. For instance (1975: 45):

Dream: Mateo (Sr.) of Najá dreamed of two domestic pigs, and later of *kitam* (collared peccary).

Interpretation: Foreigners are coming, and there will be two of them...

Confirmation: Not confirmed... unless (as is often the case) it was remembered long enough to be rationalized upon arrival of the next foreigners, weeks later.

Or again (ibid: 49):

Dream: [On June 7] Antonio (first son-in-law of Chan K'in of Najá) dreamed of Augusto de la Cruz, of a Tzeltal family living in El Carmen, coming to sell bread.

Interpretation: The person in question is thought to be of the deer Onen, so may foretell seeing a deer.

Confirmation: June 9, K'in Bol (son-in-law in service to Chan K'in of Najá) killed a deer.

Goulet (1998: 155-159) notes that the Dene Tha consider precognition in dreams as commonplace—what they call "knowing with the mind." "Dreaming in this manner, one knows where to go to kill a moose, discerns if a medicine fight has ended with the destruction of the power of the enemy, or learns that deceased relatives are well and happy in the other land." Goulet (ibid: 100) tells an interesting story about a Dene Tha woman who quite suddenly suffered insomnia for two nights. She told her sister about it and her sister sent her to a local healer. "The healer responded with the narration of a dream he had had two nights before. The dream was for a woman who was to visit him for help. In the dream the healer set his snares for beavers. Beavers came up to the snares but did not get caught. In his dream he had seen lots of clothes just scattered around; some were burnt, and others were still smoking. There was also a wolf around the area. When he woke up he wondered why he had had that dream. He told the sick woman that most people in the community looked after their things well." The patient then confessed that when her son had refurbished the attic of their house, he had thrown some of her old clothes downstairs. She was told to take care of them, but she didn't. Instead, some kids gathered them up and took them outside and burned them in the yard. The healer then told the patient that she had become ill because she should have done the proper thing, and not just what she felt like doing. In Dene Tha psychology, there is a close symbolic association between clothing and the self (ibid: 99).

The very idea that dreams may foretell future events flies in the face of our own Western materialistic and mechanistic conditioning about causation. The notion that one can "see into the future" violates our commonsense model in which event A causes event B, where A happens before B, and not vice versa. Yet, well-controlled scientific experiments have demonstrated both precognition ("future sight"), and causation at a distance as well as backwards causation. For instance, psychologist David Ryback (1988) investigated precognitive dreaming in college students. He administered a questionnaire to over 433 subjects and found that 290 (66.9%) reported some kind of paranormal dream. Although he ended up dropping many of these claims as unfounded, he did conclude that 8.8 % of the population did in fact have precognitive dreams (see also Rhine 1969).

In a series of ingenious experiments, Dean Radin and D.J. Bierman (Radin 1997, 2007: Chap. 10; Bierman and Radin 1997, 1999) have demonstrated a significant precognition or "presentiment" effect using physiological indicators of "precognitive information" when subjects act before they are presented with a random stimulus. Radin *et al.* (2011) have also shown experimentally that experienced meditators are more sensitive to "presentiment effects" than non-meditators.

Here's how the experiments work. The subject sits alone in a room in a comfortable chair and is wired-up to machines that measure the activity of their autonomic system, and hence their emotional state. When the subject is ready, they push a button and around 7 seconds later a random image is shown on a screen. The image may be of a calming nature or may be highly emotional (violent or erotic). A computer decides which picture to show after the subject pushes the button. Each subject does this a set number of times. Results showed that subjects tend to respond emotionally several seconds before the picture appears, and the correlation between measures of emotional reaction and highly emotional imagery is significant. Bierman and Scholte (2002) took this research even further by carrying it out on subjects while their brains were being scanned using a functional magnetic resonance imaging (fMRI) machine. Again, they showed that areas mediating the appropriate emotion (calm or intense feeling) became active before the randomized image was shown.

Keep in mind that this kind of research is by its very nature controversial among Western academics. Arguments rage over whether a "presentiment effect" exists or not. It would be interesting to know with absolute certainty that precognitive dreams happen or not in experimental situations. We must keep in mind in the meantime that among many traditions, the ability to "see" into the future is considered one of the attainments of advanced spiritual development (e.g, among Hindu yogis future sight is one of the *siddhis*, "magical powers"). In Buddhism such powers (Tibetan: *ngödrup*) arise spontaneously with spiritual advancement and are considered hindrances along the path to liberation.

But in the sense in which we speak of precognitive or "presentiment" dreams in anthropology, it is less important whether they foretell events, and more important that our informants and the societies we research experience presentiments as real and act upon them—an ethnographic reminder of W. I. Thomas' dictum: "It is not important whether or not the interpretation is correct—if men define situations as real, they are real in their consequences" (Thomas and Thomas 1928: 572). As we have seen, most polyphasic societies do believe in and experience precognitive dreaming, however empirical or skeptical they may be of any incidence of it.

The ethnographic information we have is commonly anecdotal descriptions and self-reports. Take for instance ethnographer Edith Turner's precognitive dream experiences while doing fieldwork among the Iñupiat people of northern Alaska. On October 5th she records a "waking" dream she had in which she, "...saw a man who was having to carry a whole pile of stuff like window glass—it had something to do with my house" (Turner 1996: 38). On November 26th, she had an intruder who broke into her basement by breaking a window (ibid: 80), and then on December 7th the trash man arrived. "I showed him the sheets of broken glass in the furnace room. He lifted them carefully and carried them out of the house to the truck. Immediately my waking dream of October 5 came back to me—a distinct picture of a man carrying a whole pile of stuff like window glass" (ibid: 83). For Turner, this break-in and glass removal were a "disturbance" that was presaged in her dream.

Special Dreams

Most polyphasic peoples distinguish between normal everyday dreaming, and the occasional special dream that has much greater significance. J. S. Lincoln in his classic book, *The Dream in Primitive Culture,* called the latter type a "culture pattern dream" (Lincoln 1935: 22), while others have referred to them as special, "big," archetypal, titanic, significant or memorable dreams.

> These dreams may be rare in the dream lives of most people, yet they surely occur to many as memorable exceptions. Some, like [C.G.] Jung and tribal shamans, seem to dream in an archetypal

style characteristically. The major defining feature of these dreams, part and parcel of their uncanny numinous quality and aesthetically rich structure, is the powerful sense of felt meaning and portent conveyed directly within the dream. (ibid: 129)

Benjamine Kilborne (1992) has suggested that the degree of elaboration of dream classification in a society may be proportional to the importance of dreaming in that society. Although there are no comparative cross-cultural data yet to support this assertion, it does make some sense, for that is the strong impression one has from the ethnographic literature on polyphasic peoples. In any event, Kilborne shows that modern Moroccans hold the distinction between true dreams that are divinely inspired, and false or deceitful dreams derived from other sources (ibid: 185). Dream categories vary with the informant, but may seem to consider dreams divisible into: (1) message dreams—divinatory dreams dreamt in holy places, (2) warning dreams—messages received from ancestors, etc. offering advice and cautions about the future, essentially divinatory dreams, (3) preoccupation dreams—dreams driven by internal positive or negative emotions, and (4) normal ("day residue") dreams—problem solving dreams, etc. Only the first category is considered true beyond question, for they derive from Allah and true dreams are associated with safety and harmony, while false dreams may derive from the *djinn* spirits who may be good or bad and may be harmful and destructive.

DREAM YOGAS

As most societies on the planet have polyphasic cultures, the importance of dreaming in peoples' lives is paramount. Therefore, it is valid to speak of each society's *dream culture*—that is, shared information about dreaming, dream symbols and dream happenings. This also includes, where applicable, dream-related mythology and ritual practices and sometimes full-blown dream yogas.

Dream Yoga Traditions

There are many dream yoga traditions among cultures across the planet. In each case one will find techniques of *warp control. Warps of consciousness* are the relatively short, rapid, and usually unconscious interludes between states of consciousness. Warps are the transformation points during which the neurophysiological system mediating one state of consciousness is altered to a new configuration mediating a subsequent state of consciousness. To the extent that one can control these warps by the application of concentrated awareness, one can control subsequent states of consciousness to some extent. Kelly Bulkeley offers several examples, including those of the ninth century Sufi mystic, al-Tirmidhi, who described the following hypnagogic dream or vision (2008:208):

> While praying one night, I was overtaken by deep weariness, and as I put my head on the prayer rug, I saw a huge and empty space, a wilderness unfamiliar to me. I saw a huge assembly with an embellished seat and a pitched canopy the clothing and covering of which I cannot describe. And as if it were conveyed to me: "You are taken to your lord." I entered through the veils and saw neither a person nor a form. But as I entered through the veils, awe descended upon my heart. And in my dream I knew with certitude that I was standing in front of Him. After a while I found myself outside the veil. I stood by the opening of the veil, exclaiming: "He has forgiven me!" And I saw that my breath relaxed of the fear.

It was the intense concentration of the trained meditator that facilitated such a dream. Lengthy periods of seclusion, dietary restrictions, ascetic practices and meditation may be used as methods of warp control. Naturally, the interpretation of the subsequent experience was couched in terms consistent with the Koran.

Many such shamanic traditions do involve a program of learning to control dreaming. One methodological problem we have in the anthropology of dreaming is that the details of these programs are frequently missing in the literature. Again, as I have noted, the common ethnographic situation involves the fieldworker asking questions about shamanism and shamanistic practices without being phenomenologically involved as an apprentice or student. Few ethnographers ever master the skills involved in shamanic dreaming, and thus have little appreciation for how difficult it is to carry ordinary dreaming to the shamanic level of proficiency. Accounts therefore are frequently perfunctory, and we are presented by the abilities of the trained shaman almost as a *fait accompli*.

Anthropologist Barbara Tedlock—who is herself a proficient lucid dreamer—has noted the similarity between Eastern practices and those of many Native American cultures, the latter being:

> ...a form [of dreaming] as self-conscious as Tibetan Buddhist dream yoga and the Hindu practice of "dream witnessing" found in Transcendental Meditation. Within both these Asian traditions initiates are taught techniques to enhance lucid dreaming as a form of meditation which is naturally available to a disciplined practitioner during sleep. Throughout the Americas shamans talk of experiencing conscious or "lucid" dreams in which they become aware of dreaming and then, while remaining in the dream state, direct the actions of their souls, shadows, selves, or doubles. (Tedlock 1999: 96)

These shamans not only may be "called" to their careers through dreaming, but they must then master the techniques by which they learn to control dream content and intentionality. It is the system of techniques, exercises and progression of realization of the mysteries that is one of the hallmarks of a dream yoga.

Dorothy Eggan described the process of learning that is behind the ease and lucidity with which the Hopi Indians access mythopoeic dreaming (1966: 240-241):

> We can now examine the hypotheses that are central to this discussion [of Hopi upbringing]: (a) that the conceptual universe of the Hopi ...was not delimited, as ours is, by notions of time and space which made of dreams an experience apart from reality; and (b) that much of the learning process among the Hopi, especially with reference to religion, involved perception through *imagery derived from dramatic rituals* enacted over and over again before learners, and that this imagery later, according to individual need patterns, could easily be, and frequently was, translated directly into dreams. For as memory, thought, and even perception can

be trained by repetitive response to needs through consistent opportunities to satisfy the needs by specific responses, it would seem that, as Murphy [1947:397] suggests, the richness and form of imagery available to a dreamer would depend in part "upon the specific way in which training and broader cultural emphasis have enriched, intensified, or inhibited the imaginal processes of the individual."

Methods for learning to control dream content vary from society to society. A remarkable account of developing this skill is to be found in the memoirs of a Cahuilla medicine woman named Ruby Modesto to be found in the book, *Not for Innocent Ears: Spiritual Traditions of a Desert Cahuilla Medicine Woman* (Modesto and Mount 1980). Ruby was born in 1913 to her Cahuilla family who lived in the Coachella Valley, the beautiful and arid valley that contains southern California's famous Salton Sea. When she was young, Ruby slept with her family and was told the sacred stories before she fell asleep each night. Her grandfather's Uncle Charlie was a *pul*, or shaman, and told her that shamans are born, not selected. One is chosen in the womb by *Umna'ah*, the Cahuilla's creator god. Each shaman has a dream helper which they contact in a dream that used to be incubated by ingesting the psychoactive plant, *datura* (Datura sp.), but more recently happens without herbal aids. Ruby's (ibid: 26):

> ...helper came spontaneously when I was about ten years old. I dreamed to the 13th level. The way you do that is by remembering to tell yourself to go to sleep in your first level ordinary dream. You consciously tell yourself to lay down and go to sleep. Then you dream a second dream [a dream within a dream]. This is the second level and the prerequisite for real Dreaming. Uncle Charlie called the process "setting up dreaming." You can tell yourself ahead of time where you want to go, or what you want to see, or what you want to learn. On the 3rd level you learn and see unusual things, not of this world. The hills and terrain are different. On both the 2nd and 3rd dream levels you can talk to people and ask questions about what you want to know. During Dreaming the soul goes out of the body, so you have to

be careful. ...When I dreamed to the 13th level, that first time, I was young and didn't know how to get back. Usually I dream to the 2nd or 3rd levels. But that time I kept having different dreams and falling asleep and going to another dream level. That was where I met my helper, *Ahswit*, the eagle. But I was in sort of a coma, asleep for several days. My father tried to bring me back, but couldn't. He had to call my Uncle Charlie who finally managed to bring my spirit back. That was one of his specialties, healing soul loss. When I woke up they made me promise not to Dream like that again, not until I knew how to get back by myself. The way you return is to tell yourself beforehand that you are going to come back (like self-hypnosis [auto suggestion]), later in the dream you have to remember.

Obviously, Ruby was exercising sufficient warp control in the ordinary dream and transformed the content into another dream (a "dream within a dream"), and so forth until she dreamed her way into a trance.[27] What is not clear by her description is whether by "ordinary" dream she was referring to sleep onset (hypnagogic) or the first REM period. In any event, by this point dreaming has become so lucid as to be virtually indistinguishable from a meditation trance—a point that Ruby appears to have stumbled upon early in her life.

The Shoshone Indian medicine man credited with revitalizing the Shoshone and Crow Sun Dance after it was outlawed in the 19th century was John Trehero, otherwise known as Rainbow (Fitzgerald 1991: Chap. 8). He received his calling, plus instruction, implements and power from the Chief of the Little People, Seven Arrows, during a three-day retreat in a cave. He was fasting and meditating, according to the traditions of his people. On the third day he heard drumming and singing and bells ringing from deeper in the cave. During a lucid dream he was joined by Seven Arrows, who invited Trehero to follow him back into the cave, so he could show Trehero some things. At first, they arrived at a place and saw men gambling on the hoop and arrow game. They wandered back further and came to a cavern where people

---

[27] I have many times been meditating in a dream and the dream turned into a normal, wakeful meditation session.

were betting on horse races. Still further into the cave they arrived at a place where people were betting on the hand game. Seven Arrows indicated that all these gambling games were no good.

They then walked back even further to a place where they could hear a drum beating and saw a tipi. The sides of the tipi were rolled up for ventilation and they could see a sick person who was barely "skin and bones" and a medicine man treating the patient. After the medicine man had completed his ministrations, Seven Arrows told Trehero, "This is what I am going to give you; this is what is good. I know you are sincere and will use your powers only for what is good. I want you to go back now; go back, take up your fasting. You should not use what I am going to give you to do any of the gambling things that you saw back there. Go back home now, and I will tell you later what things I want you to work with. You will be able to help people to get well when they are sick. Now take up your fast and go from the mountain down to that lake and wash up, take a swim" (ibid: 56). Seven Arrows led him back to the cave entrance where, as Trehero said to Fitzgerald (ibid: 220-221n), "...I saw my body lying there on the ground. I realized then that my vision had not been in the physical world. When I reached my body, I felt as though I was lying down on top of myself, and then I was awake." Trehero did as he was bidden and began his career as a healer and he was in touch with Seven Arrows the rest of his life.

It was through the intervention of Seven Arrows that Trehero stopped experimenting with the peyote religion and took up the Sun Dance fulltime. The rest, as they say, is history. "I was going only to the Sun Dances, and I was given more power. I was told what to do, given medicine things, and told how to use them. Seven Arrows gave me all the things I needed to work with. He also told me all the rules and how to run the Sun Dance in the Shoshone way so that our traditional way was restored. It was Seven Arrows and all the Medicine Fathers who gave me the authority to officiate the Sun Dances every summer among my people" (ibid: 59).

As the above examples illustrate, many dream yogas are designed to evoke transpersonal experiences and to acquire power by way of dream images. On the other hand, there are dream yogas the ultimate intent of which is to transcend perception altogether, whether in either the waking or dreaming states. These dream cultures conceive of transcendence as a state in which all sensorial activity ceases, leaving awareness with only itself as object—essentially "pure" awareness. Again, the purpose to which this transcendence is put depends upon the tradition. When one achieves this transcendent state, all the mental "chatter" has fallen away, and the mind is filled with bliss and tranquility—and more importantly, effortless single-mindedness or concentration. The advantage of this state is that the meditator can direct his/her concentration to any object at will without being distracted by competing objects.

Hindu yogas are all about realizing that waking/dreaming experience is an illusion created by the mind and misunderstood as reality. The whole point of Hindu practice is the realization of the true nature of consciousness. George Gillespie (1991: 225-226) tells us that according to the earliest Upanishadic tradition, there are four types of consciousness: (1) waking, (2) dreaming, (3) dreamless sleep, and (4) liberation. The first two categories are mundane ones alternately filled with sensory data about the body and the external world (being "awake") and the movie-like imagery of the inner world created and witnessed by the mind ("dreaming"). Both states are equally illusory. Far closer to the goal of liberation is the dreamless sleep state, which I read to be essentially access concentration in the Buddhist sense. We go into this state every night, but we Western-types are typically conditioned to lose consciousness when in dreamless sleep. The trick in Hindu dream yoga is to maintain lucid awareness after all sensory and dream-movie experience stops, for this produces the state of consciousness closest to the realization of liberation. To remain conscious in this state requires, of course, remaining attentive across the warp from dream to non-dream sleep stages. "To experience the fourth [liberation] is to experience the true nature of the Self and to be truly free from the other three states. ...The Self moves from dreamless sleep, its home, to dream and then to waking experience and then returns in reverse order, the way it came. Seen in another way, in dreamless sleep, the senses and mind do not function at all. When the mind works, dreams are created. When both mind and senses are active, it is the waking state" (ibid: 226).

A *yogin* (yoga practitioner) is taught certain techniques to transcend waking and dreaming phenomena (e.g., Radha 1994: Chap. 23; Eliade 1967: 493-527). The techniques boil down to learning to cultivate a mind-state that alternates between "choiceless awareness" (aka, access concentration; Chapter 3) and single-minded concentration upon one and only one object (usually the breath, but also the rise and fall of the belly, the heartbeat, visualizing a *bindu* (bubble), sacred images, etc.). Choiceless awareness is a state in which one watches whatever is happening in the "now" without clinging to, or dialoging with whatever is arising. Single-minded concentration is a state of observing the object of meditation without being distracted by any other object competing for attention. Ideally, these practices "pull the energy rug" out from under the chatter, and therefore, the chatter slows down, fades and eventually stops, just leaving the "watcher" and the object being watched. If the yogin uses dream yoga, this intense and disciplined lucidity continues into the dream states, and both waking and dreaming experiences are transcended, leaving the awareness of dreamless sleep. It is interesting that the Hindu take on dreaming and waking are the opposite of most traditional societies that, as we have seen, consider both equally real. Visualizing images at will and the use of mantra while dreaming are fundamental skills that are easier for some to master than for others (Radha 1994: 265).

My Own Dream Yoga Experiences

My own experience with dream yoga occurred during my exploration of Tibetan tantric Buddhism. I have described the techniques I used and some of the experiences that arose in my book, *Communing with the Gods: Consciousness, Culture and the Dreaming Brain* (Laughlin 2011: Chapter 13). I had already been a dream contemplative for about 15 years prior to being introduced to Tantric methods. The development of skill in exercising volition in dream states leads quite naturally to various forms of dream yoga. The key to any dream yoga is warp control (Laughlin 2011: 140-143, Laughlin, McManus and d'Aquili 1990: 140-145). Two of the most important warps from the view of dream yoga are the sleep onset warp (the *hypnagogic*) and the sleep offset warp (the *hypnopompic*). Maintaining consciousness through these warps was first noted as *yoga nidra* in the Upanishads and is a very ancient practice (see Desai 2017; Parker 2019). Maintaining a continuity of consciousness across a warp requires enough of the neural system mediating awareness be sustained across the warp. In this case, enough of "waking" consciousness (at least awareness and volition, plus core consciousness) must be maintained across the sleep onset warp for consciousness to continue into the "dream" state.

When I encountered Tibetan dream yoga, I changed my incubation practice to a more active meditation. My only instruction at the time came from my Buddhist teacher and what I could glean from the few books available at the time. I began my nightly meditation by going to bed before I was tired. I concentrated first upon a neon red English letter 'A' at the base of my throat (Tibetans use their letter corresponding to the "ah" phone in the "throat chakra"), and later simplified this image to a red *bindu* (Tib: *Tig Le*) or radiant bubble the size of a pea at the base of my throat. At the same time, I chanted "ahhhhhh" softly in my throat, and later learned to do this sublingually in my head. Using these simple techniques, I could enter sleep onset warp in an alert, energized and focused state of awareness, and eventually found that the warp, lasting but a few seconds in normal sleep onset, began to stretch out into minutes. I was eventually able to remain in the hypnagogic "hallucinogenic" state for up to a half hour, and experienced intense kaleidoscopic imagery which began as a kind of gorgeous two-dimensional slide show, but then deepened into dynamic, four dimensional experiences.

Many of the "signs" and "voices" I mentioned in Chapter 3 with respect to Kogi meditation arose. As I have intimated, meditation texts in the Buddhist tradition list many such images as lawfully associated "signs" of maturation in any meditation. Meditation on the breath produces one set of signs, meditation on water another set of signs, and so on. Because of the kind of meditation I was doing, mandala-like imagery arose. The rather two-dimensional mandalas I first encountered became dynamic tunnels down which I would travel and that led to various events, places and landscapes.

However, no matter how concentrated my mind-state entering the warp, I could not remain conscious more than about half an hour, when I would become fatigued and inevitably lose consciousness and enter normal sleep. My dream recall and rate of lucid dreaming increased markedly due to this more intense meditative practice—I recorded lucid experiences of some sort almost nightly—but I could not approximate the unbroken awareness throughout the sleep cycle that dream yogis have described. I finally decided to "up the ante" somewhat and stop trying to stay awake while lying in the prone position. It was obvious to me that I was struggling against a lifetime's conditioning to lose consciousness when I lay down, so I became determined not to lie down at all. So, I began sitting in half-lotus posture with my back in a corner and meditated my way into the hypnagogic. This worked to some extent in prolonging the onset warp and even entering deep lucid dreaming, but again, the conditioning was too strong, and I would wake up after a sleep cycle or two lying flat out realizing that I had lost consciousness. I even tried the Tibetan trick of using a meditation strap to keep myself in proper posture, but to no avail.

I finally decided to rig things so that it was impossible for me to lie down during the night. I built a box out of plywood approximately three feet square and higher than my shoulders when sitting in half-lotus (Figure 6.1). I lined the bottom and sides of the box with foam sheets thick enough that it made the inside rather round, soft and

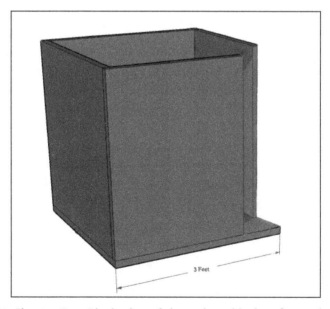

Figure 6.1. Sleeping Box. I built a box of plywood roughly three feet on the side with an opening at one corner. The sides were higher than my shoulders when sitting in half-lotus. The box was lined with foam. I slept sitting up in this box every night for months. Traditional monks would dig a hole in the ground and sleep sitting up.

snug. The corner facing me was open as the sides that would have met to form the corner extended only two-thirds the length of the sides of the bottom. This left a corner at my back and two angles on each side for my knees to fit in snugly, and an opening in front of me to enter the box and to lay things (water, tablet and pen, rosary, so forth) within easy reach on the floor. Thus, began a rather crazy time in my life and the most intense dream work I have ever undertaken. I slept sitting up for months, and though I was never able to remain conscious throughout the night, I spent much of my sleep in lucid dreaming, wafting in and out of the waking and dream states and recording experiences on paper as I could.

In accordance with Buddhist instructions, I began thinking of dreaming as reality and waking as dreaming—which, considering I was a university professor at the time with a full class-load, made my lectures rather strange I am sure. The goal from the Buddhist point of view is to realize that *all states of consciousness are illusory*, or products of the mind driven by karma, and the goal is the experience of Nirvana— that is, the realization of the essence of mind that projects or "builds" all these illusory "realities" (Chapter 5). True to the method's intent, my waking life really did take on the feeling and surreal qualities of the dream state, and the lucidity I attained in dream states was far more vivid and "real" than the waking state.

Throughout it all there was recognition that I was in and out of what the Tibetan teachers call *rigpa*, or non-dual awareness. I was acutely aware that whether "awake" or "dreaming," my mind was generating a movie which might or might not correspond with extramental reality. The experiences I had during and before using the sleeping box were not always pleasant ones—far from it in fact. Many were dark and disturbing, and some downright frightening. Because I was as much a Jungian as a Buddhist, I interpreted these ordeals as the result of my having tapped into the deeper levels of my unconscious self, which, because of my conditioned "neurotic" fear, took threatening forms. Different complexes warred with each other for control of consciousness—all of them affectively charged either positively (sometimes ecstatically) or negatively (fear, anxiety, revulsion, self-hate, rage).

Again, my Buddhist studies came in handy, for I took up another Tibetan practice; that being to consciously transform my dream-ego into a particular semi-fierce "deity" which I had been assigned by one of my teachers—my *yidam*, or personal protector, was called *Mahamaya*, the Great Sorcerer, who is depicted on Tibetan paintings (*thangka*) as a huge light blue figure dancing in flames with four multicolored heads, each with a mouth with fangs and two red eyes and a "third eye" just for good measure, two sets of arms with hands holding various implements, clothed in a tiger skin and wearing a necklace of human skulls. I cannot think of a better dreambody when encountering the demons of the depths. After some practice I was able to assume this dreambody, and this practice alone transformed encounters with the unconscious to a less terrifying tone.

During this period, I experienced "rebirthing," as some New Age folks like to call it. I spontaneously "recalled" and re-experienced my birth, which had been traumatic since my mother was drugged and I was apparently removed forcefully from the womb using forceps—all this compounded by anoxia. The sequence of dreamed birth experiences took many months to fully unfold and were very much involved with body witness and affect, especially hunger, anoxia and terror. During the sleeping box period, I kept a bowl of condensed milk on hand to bathe my mouth during the night, thus "feeding" the traumatized infant within my unconscious.

Many of the characters and objects I encountered during these years of intense dreaming were archetypal images. One of the hallmarks of encountering archetypes for the first time is that they often present as "pure" internal images with little, if any, cultural overlay. With repeated encounters the images begin to incorporate cultural and personal attributes, like hair-dos, Western clothing, Western gestures and mannerisms, so forth. Objects lose their universal form and become common everyday objects—pure bubbles may become wine glasses or milk bottles; geometric forms may become gem stones. In other words, the archetypal image shows development as it becomes more familiar, adapts to waking cultural expectations, and takes its place within the library of shared symbols and meanings available to both the waking/dreaming ego and the unconscious. One begins to recognize human images as being like people one has known. When they first present, archetypal human forms may take the appearance of "radiant" beings, whether positive (god/goddess) or negative (demonic). They are beings of light and no substance, perfect in every way (no flaws, blemishes, asymmetries, pores, etc.). Archetypal radiant beings are more complete, more beautiful, or repulsive, and way more numinous than anything in the waking "real" world could ever be. Moreover, when they first present they may be accompanied by a sense of power and the feeling of ecstatic bliss. These feelings too dissipate as the radiant being develops over time and takes its place in the library of internally shared symbols.

Being a heterosexual male, the goddess figures I encountered were lovelier than any real woman could ever be. They were perfect (as viewed with the sensitivities of my dream ego), garbed in veils of light, and able to morph into other forms before my mind's eye. Sometimes they would initially present as radiantly beautiful feminine forms and then morph into something bestial, repulsive and scary. I recall one dream in which such a lovely goddess figure came toward me and as she entered a gate in a picket fence that had been between us, she morphed into a demon of dull gray with leathery wings, fangs and threatening eyes. She spread her wings and flew at me and over my head. It was during many such dreams that I learned where traditional peoples get the notion that gods, goddesses and spirits are real. Had I not been as much a Jungian as a Buddhist, I might well have interpreted these encounters as communion with the gods, demons or ancestors dwelling "out there" somewhere. I also learned how people may get the notion that people and animals may be shape-shifters, morphing freely from form to form as the underlying archetype manifests its various visual and affective facets.

Coitus was another archetypal motif I encountered often, especially in the beginning before it got so utterly boring that the mind stopped producing the images. I dreamt of rocky landscapes with naked couples and groups made up of radiant figures making love in every conceivable position and using every possible technique. I learned that if I shifted my energies (*chi, prana,* or *tummo*) from my lower body and genital area up to my heart or head (Chapter 5), the imagery would likewise shift to some other symbolic motif. In other words, it was possible in these dreams to willfully modify how my libido presented from sexual arousal to the experience of non-sexual love and communion with whatever arose before my mind's eye.

Out-of-body experiences were commonplace in dreams during the sleeping box period. I could look down at my physical self in the box, and consciously leave my body to wander about and then return to it. I recall the first time I consciously left my body in this way. I was in my body at the beginning of an in-breath and was floating near the ceiling at the end of the in-breath. My first thought was, "How am I going to get down from here?"—immediately followed by an urge to test whether I was out of my body. I slipped my hand under my rear, and as I felt the padding under me, my dream ego was immediately back in my normal body awareness. I never tested the experience again, always interpreting that my out-of-body experience was another part of the movie unfolding between my ears. But I also became aware over time that many of my fellow Tantric practitioners uncritically assumed they were really out of their bodies and floating around "out there," not "in here" between the ears.

DREAMING AND THE CONTEMPLATIVE LIFE

I could go on and on describing the weird, quirky and even spooky experiences I had during this period of my life, but perhaps more important was that, as an anthropologist, I learned through direct participation how real the experiences described for other dream yoga traditions can be, and how very important the interpretive frame is to integrate these experiences into the rest of the practitioner's life. I should perhaps add that this is not a work that one should do without guidance. Driving consciousness the way I did can lead one into confusion about reality and self-identity. The more intense the meditative practice, the more important the role of the guru or guide becomes. The relationship with a guide grounds one in the "real" world of practical necessities. It is very significant that among that most meditative Catholic order, the Benedictines, one may be allowed to meditate in seclusion, but must be close enough to return to the monastery for the sacraments, where the Brothers will watch the contemplative to make sure he is alright.

Complexes: A Cautionary Tale

There are many "how to" books and videos purporting to teach one how to do dream yoga of one sort and another (see e.g., Duesbury

2016; Green 1968; Holecek 2016). As I am an unabashed Jungian, I recognize the crucial importance of dream work in developing the channel of communication between the ego and the vast unconscious, both personal and collective, especially once one has reached their middle age. But caution must be exercised in urging people to engage with their unconscious. One of the methods Jung used to introduce clients to depth work was active imagination, which we will discuss in Chapter 7. However, Jung himself was leery of publishing this method publicly because it can be dangerous if not used properly and under supervision. Again, the more intense the meditation, the more likely is the need for guidance. The trouble is that the unconscious is not merely a repository of random bits and pieces of data, not a dump site for the detritus of ego development. Rather, it is made up of alternative neural circuitry that can form alternative quasi-personalities—what Jung called "complexes."

I will have much more to say about Jungian complexes in Chapter 7, but for now let us say that a *complex* is an organization of psychologically active tissue that nucleates around a root archetype. A complex is either unconscious or partially conscious and can interfere with a conscious intention and act—indeed, this is how Jung discovered the complex in the first place. "Relatively stable patterns of complexes comprise the structure underlying both ordinary consciousness and neurosis. Those that are not well integrated into consciousness behave as 'part-personalities' in the psyche, each striving to become the model for conscious identity" (Singer 1994: 46). The hallmark of an encounter with a complex is awareness of an emotion (fear, anxiety, terror, lust, aversion) that is associated with an idea or image.

I freely admit that I am a neurotic and I have had to live with a neurotic complex my entire contemplative life. A *neurosis* is basically an anxiety disorder, mainly due to trauma experienced early in life, and *dissociated* from the conscious self (see Scaer 2014: 17). During my early years of meditation, the calmer and more centered I became, there was a growing awareness that some part of me was fighting against the calming trend. That part of myself was dissociated from awareness due to early childhood repression. It manifested at first as twitches and tightness in my left shoulder, a tightness that caused my left shoulder to be higher than my right shoulder, a very common phenomenon. As time went on, the complex underlying this tightness began to reveal itself during meditation and dreams. To make a long story short, there came a time when the aversive tension erupted in episodes of terror accompanied by a posture which might be best described as defensive with my neck and head twisted to my right, left arm straight out as if fending off a blow, right arm curled back over my head, left leg curled back with my left foot near my crotch and right leg stretched out below me—all this in extreme muscle tension while laying on my back. This occurred while a profound scream emitted from my lungs. As this occurred more and more freely, there were primitive utterances of "no! no! no!" and other meaningless sounds that verged upon glossolalia. As this work continued I came to learn via imagery that the root of this complex—this quasi-personality—was a terrified wee child who had been yanked out of the womb with forceps (images of a steel implement in my mouth in both dreams and during meditation sessions). Eventually this whole process became a classic *rebirthing* experience and is why I mentioned that I kept a saucer of condensed milk by my meditation box to bathe my mouth when Baby Denny (my name for the complex) became restive. Over many years Baby Denny became less dissociated and more integrated into my psyche, and its associated tensions, movements, images and emotions are familiar and well understood by me. Yet the complex still exists and presumably will to my dying day. Indeed, I doubt seriously that severe neurotic complexes ever "disappear." Rather, *re*-association (or what I like to call "relevation") is the only healing possible so far as I know.

Considering these experiences, you may forgive me if I am impatient with psychologists who, in their phenomenological ignorance, deny the existence of complexes—or neuroses for that matter.[28] Moreover, these experiences had under the tutelage of excellent teachers allowed me to appreciate how difficult the experiences would have been to endure without guidance. So, once again I suggest that, if one suspects they have a mental disorder, however slight it might be, that they seek

---

[28] In 1980, the *Diagnostic and Statistical Manual of Mental Disorders* (DSM) eliminated "neurosis" in its rush to allow only behavioral descriptions of disorders. Many health professionals still use the term, however, and frankly the move to drop the term was silly given the phenomenology of neurosis such as I have described here.

guidance from adepts or therapists who are familiar with neurotic blocks, as well as what meditation is all about. My impression after years of interacting with Tibetan teachers is that they commonly do not understand neuroses or the hindrances that anxiety-laden complexes can place in the way of students on the path. I benefitted from Western meditation teachers who had long experience with neurotics, and some of whom were themselves sufferers of anxiety and depression and knew a complex when they saw one. 'Nuff said.

Dreaming and the Call to the Contemplative Life

Most Westerners pay scant or no attention to their dreams, and hence their dreams are dim, vague phenomena that they may or may not remember when awake. When recalled, the dreams are often mysterious and devoid of any meaning to the waking mind. All it takes is a shift in attitude toward dreaming before dreaming may open-up to interested scrutiny. And that shift in attitude may be initiated by the unconscious. Indeed, it is not uncommon for shamans to be "called" to their career by poignant dreams. For instance, among the Tungus people of Siberia, "A dead shaman appears in a dream and summons the dreamer to become his successor. One who is to become a shaman appears shy, distrait, and is in a highly nervous condition" (Czaplicka 1914: 177). Novice shamans among the Chukchee are commonly isolated, either going off into the forest for days at a time, or remaining alone in a room. They will often sleep and dream a lot (ibid: 179). Among the Buryat, a child who is to become a shaman manifests these signs: "He is often absorbed in meditation, likes to be alone, has mysterious dreams, and sometimes has fits during which he is unconscious" (ibid: 185).

My Own Dream Calling

Though hardly a shaman, I myself was "called" to the contemplative life by curious dream phenomena, a few years before I learned how to meditate. It all began when I awoke early one morning in 1963 staring at the world through a mandala (in what I later would learn to be a hypnopompic experience; see Gillespie 1987). I don't mean mandala in a trivial metaphoric sense, but quite literally. I came out of sleep and into waking awareness in a state of intense bliss and looking at my bedroom filtered through an exquisitely complex and colorful mandala—like a filter of lace made of the most delicate, complex and multi-hued spider web (perhaps equivalent to Gillespie's "lattice imagery"). It was a living thing and pulsed in synchrony with the rhythm of bliss I felt coursing through my body. The experience lasted for only a few minutes and then subsided. The mandala image and intensity of bliss faded at the same time. It is hard to describe the complexity of the image, for no matter how proficient an artist I might have been, there is no way I could have ever rendered the image accurately on paper. It was made up of hundreds of thousands of fine, radiant colored lines, like a multicolored, pulsing curtain made of pure energy tendrils hanging in front of my eyes. The ambient light in my bedroom was dim, but I could discern the normal objects in the room through the gauze-like filter of the mandala. As the term implies, the mandala had a distinct center and radians from the center outward to the periphery.

This experience scared me. In fact, I became furious with a friend with whom I had coffee the night before, thinking that she had maliciously spiked my beverage with drugs. As absurd as it was, that was the only interpretive frame I had at the time to make sense of the experience. As it turned out, this was the first of many such experiences that I was to have over the years, and I quite naturally became very curious about my dream world. The experiences in those early days were always spontaneous, and I had no notion that I could willfully produce them. They were essentially hypnopompic images and they all shared a common structure:

The Visual Aspect. An intense, pulsing visual experience consisting of an intricate pattern of brightly colored, nearly infinitesimal lines – the total configuration corresponding to a classical mandala (i.e., manifests a definite center, is symmetrical about that center, is circular while at the same time "quaternary;" see Argüelles and Argüelles 1972). The pattern is so intense that it may be perceived for a few minutes or longer after awakening with the eyes open or closed, even in a lighted environment.

The Affective Aspect. An intense and active state of pulsing euphoria not associated with the ingestion of drugs. This affective state corresponds in intensity and decay rate with the visual aspect and is a similar state of bliss I later learned to that experienced under deep meditation or trance.

Over the years I have spoken with a few people who have had similar experiences of mandalas in their waking consciousness—usually during meditation sessions—and many more people who recall mandala motifs arising in their dreams. The direct experience of spontaneous mandala imagery while people are awake, however, appears to be a rare event.[29] I am still not clear as to whether this kind of mandala experience occurs in all persons during their dream life, or merely in a significant few. But that it is experienced by some people in all societies is quite likely, for the mandala motif in company with other images expressing the wholeness of the self is, as C.G. Jung (1951/1959) noted in *Aion*, a virtual cultural universal. The appearance of the mandala motif in religious and nonreligious symbolism is very wide-spread among the world's societies. It is present in the iconography of Buddhist sects, the Australian Aborigines, various Plains Indian groups, in Western Christianity, to mention but a few examples (see Krippner 1997a; TenHouten 1993).

Jung was, as it turned out, as fascinated with mandalas as I, and for very much the same reasons. But I was unaware of Jung or of his interest during those early years of spontaneous transpersonal episodes and later drug-assisted explorations of mandalas. My first encounter with Jung's study of mandala symbolism was both profound and significant. A decade after my own first mandala experience, I was browsing in a Philadelphia book store and found a copy of Jung's book, *Mandala Symbolism* (1969b). As I leafed through the book's plates, I was struck by the remarkable similarity between four of those images and my own mandala experiences (Figure 6.2). So, I bought the book, and only later did I discover in an editorial footnote that the four plates I had identified were the very four, and the only four, that Jung himself painted from his own dream recall. This remarkable correspondence naturally led me to study closely all Jung's writings pertaining to the mandala, and then everything else he wrote bearing on depth psychology and extraordinary dream experiences.

In several places, Jung (e.g., 1964) points to the scientific significance of the mandala motif in dreams and religious symbolism around the world. Jung (1969a: 3) described the phenomenon as follows:

---

[29] Other kinds of images arising in the hypnopompic are not uncommon; see Young (1994) who had similar "waking dream" images after waking.

Figure 6.2. One of Carl Jung's Own Mandalas. Jung presented many pictures of mandalas in his book *Mandala Symbolism* (Jung 1969b), but only four of them were painted by him.

The Sanskrit word mandala means "circle" in the ordinary sense of the word. In the sphere of religious practices and in psychology it denotes circular images, which are drawn, painted, modeled, or danced. Plastic structures of this kind are to be found, for instance, in Tibetan Buddhism, and as dance figures these circular patterns occur also in Dervish monasteries. As psychological phenomena they appear spontaneously in dreams, in certain states of conflict, and in cases of schizophrenia. Very frequently they contain a quaternity or a multiple of four, in form of a cross, a star, a square, an octagon, etc. In alchemy we encounter this motif in the form of *quadratura circuli* [quartered circle].

Jung firmly believed in the existence of the universal or "collective" unconscious, as well as in the fundamental tendency of humans to reason by constructing binary oppositions, or *antinomies*. Jung felt the mandala to be the key to human symbolism because it is a primal archetype, and as such it often represents both the self and the unification or nexus of all possible oppositions (Jung 1959[1951]:

31; see also Laughlin 2001).[30] Among other contexts, the mandala is encountered by the conscious ego through dreaming. The mandala symbol is a virtual cultural universal, appearing as it does in traditional art, iconography, myth and dreaming among peoples all over the planet (see e.g., Ridington and Ridington 1970: 51 on the mandala in Dunne-za cosmology).

So, Why Do We Dream?

Considering that virtually all animals with brains sleep and likely dream, there must be something terribly important about dreaming in maintaining life and the brain worlds of creatures. A few neuroscience dream researchers have begun to lodge their thinking within evolutionary theory, which makes them a lot more interesting to anthropologists and archaeologists. For instance, Antti Revonsuo (2000, 2006; Valli and Revonsuo 2007) has argued that dreaming is well organized and coherent, and operates as a simulation of the perceptual world, especially the simulation of threatening events. But these threats make more sense for people living in an ancient world than they do for people living today. He lodges this explanation within the context of *evolutionary*

---

[30] Selfscape Dream had while writing this chapter (3/25/11): I am a member of a group, one of four that were organized around a center and each to a quarter of the space. I have become the leader of my group and seem to have a special relationship with the group in the opposite quadrant to mine. I considered the leader of the opposite group to be a dull fellow and easily manipulated, so I fomented a plan to take over all the groups. But then the "boss" showed up whom I introduced jokingly as the "uber" something. I asked if I could speak to him alone, back in my own group, intending to communicate my plan to him, but the "uber" resisted going off with me as he was standing in the middle between all the groups. I told him my plan anyways, and he responded, "But what of art, of music...?" and some other finer things. Then he became abusive all of a sudden and I became angry, and I struck out at him and woke up. My immediate thought was of the obvious mandala-like spatial format of the groups and relations between groups, and the "special" complimentary relationship I had with my opposite in the other group. It seems that I, as spokesman for my group, was trying to usurp (was positively greedy for) the role of "uber," of leader of the whole -- in other words, my dream ego complex was trying to hog control of the whole self. I was reminded by the real "uber" that there was more to my Self than control by one unbalanced ego.

psychology as formulated by Barkow, Cosmides and Tooby (1992), Cosmides and Tooby (1995), Tooby and Cosmides (1995) and Buss (2004). Evolutionary psychologists argue that many of the adaptive processes of the human brain were developed and hardwired during the lengthy period of the Pleistocene (from 1.8 million years ago to around 12,000 years ago) and that adaptations that do not make much sense in today's environment do make sense when examined within the social contexts and physical environments typical of Paleolithic peoples.

Anthropologist Susan Parman (1979) has constructed an interesting theory linking dreaming and play, and as far as I know is the only scholar to have done so. She bases her reasoning upon the common view of dreaming among mammals as being a symbolically rich experience in which problem-solving in waking life is rehearsed. Dreaming has thus a long evolutionary history, as does play, during which the symbolic content of dreams no doubt increased along with the evolution of the neocortex. A complex brain is designed to operate upon interesting stimuli, while the total organism requires substantial down-time to conserve energy and carry out necessary developmental and metabolic activities. A complex brain does not do well under conditions of sensory deprivation; hence a major function of dreaming may be to keep an optimal amount of psychological activity going while somatic down-time is accomplished. Parman suggests that, "It is logical to extend this argument from the realm of sleep to the world of waking, and to suggest that play is analogous, if not homologous, to dreaming because it arises from the same neurophysiological need. The need for the disruption of synchrony, provided internally during sleep, is met during waking by institutionalized or noninstitutionalized forms of play" (ibid: 23-24). Just as play increased in complexity up to and including games (i.e., ritual play; see Laughlin and McManus 1982) during phylogenesis, it seems likely that dreams did as well. It also seems likely that dreaming and behavior only become fully integrated with the emergence of the hominin line. That is, only humans seem to exhibit the often elaborate behavioral consequences of dreams, including the acting-out of dreams, the ritual consequences of dreams and the performance of dreams.

One of the most intriguing explanations for why we dream while we sleep was suggested by the great English anthropologist, William H. R. Rivers, a participant in the famous Torres Straits Expedition in 1898, who wrote a good deal about dreaming (see e.g., Rivers 1917, 1923). He reasoned, as have many since, that the physiological requirement of sleep places animals at a competitive disadvantage. And as we know, environmental stimuli can and do penetrate the awareness of humans and other animals, so dreams will allow the most sensitive member of a herd to perceive and emotionally respond to dreamed dangers, reacting to them and waking the rest of the herd in the process (Rivers 1923: 183). Not bad reasoning I should say, considering the period in which he was writing.

Mental models, Neurognosis and Dreaming

As we have seen, brains build schemas of reality, and the schematic networks constructed by human brains are heavily influenced by both inheritance and culture. Schemas might better be termed *neural models* (Laughlin, McManus and d'Aquili 1990: Chap. 3). Think about a model for a moment. We usually use the term to label a simplified technical construction of some more complex construction. We build model airplanes that really fly like "real" airplanes. In a sense, the model airplane (car, boat, train, so forth) *represents* the "real" airplane in that it has some elements in common (wings, a motor, landing gear, control surfaces) and if we wish we can study the properties or behavior of the "real" airplane by studying the model. We might build a model of a car or plane and put the model in a wind tunnel to study its aerodynamics. An architect will build a model of a proposed shopping mall out of balsa and plastic to give the client a sense of what his project will end up looking like. Yet in many, many ways the model is not at all like the "real" thing it represents. The model plane is made of balsa or foam and not aluminum or titanium, can't carry heavy payloads or passengers, has no toilets or seats or hydraulic systems, no black boxes or transmitters. The model is thus a simplification of the real thing. Neural models are likewise simplifications. Anything in the real world modeled by the brain is always *transcendental* relative to a model, which is to say that there is always more to reality than is, or ever can be modeled by the brain. What does any of this have to do with dreaming?

Babies dream archetypal dreams. Well, for one thing, there are neuroscientists, cognitive scientists, anthropologists and other dream researchers who have claimed that fetuses in the womb and infants don't dream, even though they exhibit REM activity galore during sleep. Why? Well, they don't dream because they have nothing to dream about. My answer to that claim is that babies dream "archetypal" dreams because they have fully functioning brains at and before birth (Rakic 1995; Gazzaniga 1998: 2) and have a lot to dream about as their neural structures grow, "do their thing" during sleep and express themselves in dream imagery and feelings. They have a rich internal dream and waking world that just happens to be less conditioned by the external environment than it will increasingly become. Babies have an internal world full of faces and hands, nascent landscapes, geometric figures and other archetypal motifs, mediated by neurognostic models that are active and expressing themselves within the baby's sensorium as they develop I would wager that a fetus' dream life is richer and more interesting than its waking life, but there is no way as yet to know for sure. Psychiatrist Thomas Verny (1981) has hypothesized that the fetus and its mother may share dream content through extrasensory perception. It is hard to know if this is in fact true.

Dreaming has many functions. Understanding that human consciousness and dreaming are organized and active from early fetal days points us toward a better understanding of the biological and developmental functions of dreaming. There really is no single function of dreaming—the functions of dreaming are manifold and depend upon the state of the brain at the time of the dreaming (Kuiken and Sikora 1993; Hartmann 2011: Chap. 11). Dreaming is the expression within the sensorium of neural models that may be developing, readjusting and establishing connections among themselves or with other models, may be simulating or rehearsing waking experiences (Donald 1995), may be working to solve problems and seek information, may be consolidating memories (Stickgold and Wamsley 2011), may be expressing links between emotions and images (Hartmann 2011), may be working through "day residue" issues, may be expressing repressed desires and emotions, may be dominated by traumatized imagery-emotion structures that remain thwarted in their development (see Barrett 1996; Kalsched 1996; Hartmann 2011 on trauma and dreams), and so forth. Dreams are, in other words, the symbolic expression in consciousness of whatever the cognitive/emotional/imaginal parts of the brain are on-about at the moment. Dream imagery may be a synesthetic experience of activities going on unconsciously elsewhere in the nervous system and the body (see Hunt 1989 on this issue; Ramachandran 2004: Chap. 4). For instance, acid reflux in the digestive system might manifest itself as dreams of conflict and pain not logically associated with the ailment. If neurognostic models are being potentiated in development, corresponding dream imagery may be distinctly archetypal. An active and advanced Jungian dream worker can easily track the development of their psyche by recording dreams and carrying out active imagination in the waking state. The dream therefore is a stage upon which the brain portrays its ongoing activities (developmental, problem-solving, expression of repressed material, consolidation of memories, etc.) in often surrealistic plays.

Dream symbols may be pregnant with meaning. Dream symbols may be, like those in myths and fairy tales, "pregnant with meaning" (Cassirer 1957: 202; see also Laughlin, McManus and Stephens 1981; Kunzendorf 2007; Hall 1953). Images and other elements making up the manifest content of dreams are often *polysemic*—they have multiple meanings associated with them but hidden from view. Symbols are like a kid's toy magnet that is put under a piece of paper with iron filings sprinkled atop the paper, and then as the magnet is moved around under the paper, the pattern of iron filings is moved around as well. Only in this case the paper is turned over so all one may see is the magnet and the pattern of iron filings is hidden. The magnet is the symbol and the iron filings are the meanings attracted to and organized upon the symbol. As Ernest Hartmann (2011) notes, the amount of "condensation" found in polysemic dream symbols may be greater than symbols in the waking state. Dreams are the manifestation of the active and creative seeking of associations that may produce what he calls *central images* – images such as being caught-up and swept away by a gigantic tidal wave in the wake of trauma and associated "tidal" emotions (ibid: 12; see also Kunzendorf 2007). A pattern of neuro-perceptual activity mediating an image may become entangled with other, hidden associations in memory, emotion and behavioral networks. Thus it becomes pregnant with meaning and emotional associations. If you are like me, all I have to do to evoke an aversive response from my body is to imagine I have cut my finger.

Let me offer a personal example of a pregnant dream image. I was in a room with President Obama, who was sitting off to my left and slightly behind me. My role was as his advisor to evaluate a report being given by another man in front of me to my right (he was white). The report went on and on and it had to do with technical stuff that I do not remember. The overall tone of the dream was positive excitement. When I awoke and thought about the dream, several ideas suggested themselves to me. In my dreams black people (usually strange black females) almost always signal a message from the unconscious. They are often walking up a spiral staircase from below and are walking or standing to my left, my feminine side. But Mr. Obama is a male, was the President of the United States and is a known figure whom I associate with "high intellect," moral resolve and positive power—in other words, the unconscious is now "in charge." At the same time, the speaker was on my right, is also male and represents the masculine, conscious and rational-intellectual side of my being. So, for me, the dream is a reflection of the state of myself at the time during a period when I had turned away from my normally more balanced, retired way of life to a state of intense activity in researching and writing an earlier book. I (my waking ego) was essentially standing as mediator between unconscious intuitive processes which are "in charge" at the moment and the vast amount of material I was sifting through from the technical literature on dreaming and dream cultures. Mr. Obama appears as a single symbol condensing many meanings, including the King archetype, an active unconscious, being "in charge" of what is happening (I have more than once had the sense that the previous book was "writing itself"), an active engagement of the unconscious intuitive functions with the rational, and so forth.

Inter-state library of symbols. When one takes an interest in one's dream life over a lengthy period—as is often the case with shamans, seers, oneirocritics and others in polyphasic cultures—that dream life becomes more than a relatively passive reflection of what the brain and body are doing in the moment, and morphs into an interactive medium of communication between normally unconscious processes and the conscious dream ego. Indeed, as one becomes more and more involved in interpreting one's dream symbolism, a "library" of symbols and meanings develops (Hall 1953). In dream work, the brain's library of images becomes a shared language for both the conscious ego in different states of consciousness and the unconscious parts of the self. It is by means of this library of shared knowing that integration of the self, including consciousness, becomes possible. Achieving this intrapsychic integration is frequently *de rigueur* in polyphasic cultures; see e.g., Dorothy Eggan (1966) on Hopi dreaming and childhood immersion in religious symbolism, and Chidester (2003) on dream interpretation in Zulu religion.

The neurobiological functions of dreaming can vary depending upon the sophistication of conscious involvement in dream experiences, and the extent of development of the component neural structures mediating the dream content. The extent of the development of neural components mediating the dream will determine the content, complexity, qualities and significance of the dream. As we have shown, the more involved the prefrontal cortex is in the structures mediating the dream, the more organized, coherent and complex the material, and the more salient the meaning to the dreaming ego. The role of culture in developing or thwarting a sophisticated approach to dream phenomenology is paramount. It is probably true to say that cultural influence upon neural development leads to a patchwork of neurognostic models across cognitive domains that are highly developed, partially developed and under-developed, especially in situations where their development has been thwarted in waking life. Active dream work may operate to maximize development of neurognostic models, particularly those that are excluded from the montage of models that are recurrently active in waking life. In the same way that the neural systems mediating the movements of our fingers may vary in their development from learning to grasp tools and coffee cups to learning to play a Bach sonata, so too may the sophistication of the content of our dream experiences range from simple to complex. And for the same reason—in one case the development of the neural facility has remained minimally developed and in the other case development has been optimized. Always remember, the brain is a trophic system, and will consume its available energy doing what is necessary for adaptation. But adaptation has two poles: adaptation of the organism to the external environment (getting food without becoming food), and adaptation of neural subsystems to each other within the nervous system. One may to some extent influence the direction and extent of development in the latter sense by bringing conscious intention into the dreaming process.

SUMMARY AND SEGUE

One of the most important issues confronting the life-long contemplative is the role of dreaming in his or her self-exploration. We find that there is a voluminous literature on the neuropsychology of dreaming, both as a source of meditation and involving traditional methods for producing so-called "lucid dreams." To understand the role of contemplation in the spiritual life of peoples around the globe, we must rid ourselves of the technocratic bias that contemplation occurs only in what we call "normal waking consciousness." For many peoples, contemplation during ASC is important, for in ASC it is possible to assess otherwise invisible forces. Often, it is via dreaming that people negotiate with the normally hidden spiritual entities that cause events in everyday life. Contemplation of dreaming allows the isolation of the structures of dreams. We discussed some of the cross-culturally common attributes of dreaming characteristic of dreaming in polyphasic societies. It is critical to understand that, unlike most Westerners, in most societies on the planet, people routinely keep track of their dreams, for they find them informative and of great utility. Dream cultures often include some type of dream yoga—a set of practices utilized to incubate and assess dream material.

In practicing Tibetan Tantric Buddhist dream yoga, I had many adventures. I came to understand many things about dreaming and its role in self-discovery. I also learned that dreaming can become largely "lucid," and that dreaming for polyphasic peoples is likely more lucid than is normal for those raised in technocratic societies. We saw that the trick of maintaining lucidity in dreaming involves controlling the warp of consciousness across the point of transformation between waking and sleeping. Dream work is fundamental to my spiritual life, and, thus, I am aware of the importance of dream-calling found cross-culturally among shamans and healers. This realization of the importance of dream-awareness to self-discovery raises questions, of course, on why people and other animals dream in the first place. We considered this question from a neuroscience point of view.

Throughout the past chapters I have alluded to the fact that contemplation inevitably involves awareness that the self, or the psyche, is vast in scope compared to normal ego-bound consciousness. Indeed, contemplation *is* self-discovery. We will now turn our attention to addressing contemplation of the self, and the insights that may be gleaned from this effort.

PART THREE

Discovering the Self

CHAPTER SEVEN

The Brain and Its Self

Trying to define yourself is like trying to bite your own teeth.

– Alan Watts, *Life Magazine* (21 April 1961)

My brain and I are inseparable. I am who I am because my brain is what it is. Even so, I often think about my brain in terms different from those I use when thinking about myself. I think about my brain as that and about myself as me. I think about my brain as having neurons, but I think of me as having a memory. Still, I know that my memory is all about the neurons in my brain. Lately, I think about my brain in more intimate terms—as me.

– Patricia Churchland, *Touching a Nerve* (2013)

Thus far in the book I have mentioned the "self" in various contexts and connotations. There are the usual compound pronouns like "itself," "oneself," "herself," etc. which have the meaning of isolating an object or entity of reference. Then there have been the compound nouns and phrases that are used to denote mental acts that are directed inward toward an individual's being, and in particular the individual's psychological being; e.g., "self-awareness" and "self-reflection" (awareness directed towards one's own behavior, interactions, emotions, mental processes, etc.), "self-identification" (recognition of one's self in a mirror or other situation), "no-self" (in the Buddhist sense of the impermanence of the empirical ego), "sense of self" (awareness of one's being), "self-concept" (how one conceives of oneself, usually influenced by one's culture), and "neural self" (the neurophysiological structure of one's psyche, including consciousness and the unconscious).

I have implied that I am biased toward a Jungian understanding of the self—especially the contemplative process of understanding myself—but have yet to spell out what this self might consist of. Moreover, conscious, intentional engagement with the unconscious self is inevitable in the life of any contemplative, especially so if the contemplative utilizes meditative techniques to calm the mind and attain access concentration. I have already explained why this is so, for the relaxation techniques used eventually retune the ergotropic and trophotropic balance in the body, and in effect pull out the "energy rug" from under repression. And I have said that this can be particularly severe in the case of neurotics like myself. Because of the likelihood of engagement with the unconscious self, it behooves us to better understand what the "self" is all about. When we turn our gaze upon the heavens, eventually we come to understand astrophysical processes. In just the same way, when we turn our gaze inward toward the self, we eventually come to understand far more about ourselves than we did before. And this engagement goes beyond mere understanding, but it leads to a reorganization of one's personality and consciousness.

THE SELF

The word "self" is, of course, an English term which has its own distinct history of use and connotations. Etymological dictionaries tell us that the word comes from the Old English *self, seolf, sylf* (meaning "one's own person") and is related via Proto-Indo-European **selbaz* to the Old Norse *sjalfr*, Old Frisian *self*, Dutch *zelf*, Old High German *selb*, and Gothic *silba*. The Old English form was emphatic, expressing "(I) myself," "(he) himself," etc., an implied reference to both a physical-spatial distinction (self and not-self) and temporal continuity (same self through time; "I am the same person today as I was yesterday;" see Brockelman 1985: 81). Today we use the word self to refer to a person's essential being, that which distinguishes them from others, and is especially understood as the object of introspection or reflexive action. Implied in the term is the phenomenological "sense of self," self as directly experienced as distinct from the Other. Moreover, we can signal the continuity of self through time by such phrases as "back to his old self again." Conversely, we can signal that some change has occurred in a person by phrases like "he wasn't himself today." Hence, the connotation of self implies both physical and psychological boundaries, and both physical and mental continuity through time.

From ancient times, self has had an inherent ambiguity of meaning; what I will refer to hereafter as *self-as-being* and *self-as-psyche*. We use self to label the fact that our entire being, including our body, our physical existence, is present, is bounded, is distinct from the Other, and has remained so through some duration of time. We also use self to refer to our mental faculties and our entire psyche, including our personhood, ego, persona, feelings, and unconscious processes—perhaps also our soul—and so forth, which are distinct from the mental faculties of the Other, and that have remained the same "mind" through some appropriate duration of time. The degree of distinction between self-as-being and self-as-psyche depends upon the extent to which we are enculturated to believe that there exists a mind-body dualism; that is, the belief that mind and body are two different substances, levels, metaphysical planes, domains, or whatever. If I say, "I went there myself," I will usually mean that my entire physical being moved there, that I was there in both body and mind. However, an Australian Aborigine might say something in their language that is like "I went there myself," but mean that they traveled there in a dream state. For the Australian Aborigine the distinction between self-as-being and self-as-psyche is not as extreme as it is for most of us Westerners, yet she would certainly know that she had left her body behind while she traveled as her spirit-self, her "soul." Indeed, she may well report that she had met Others during her dream journey who had likewise left their physical forms behind, if they still had physical forms—were not perhaps ghosts of departed relatives (see Laughlin 2011). The distinction between self-as-being and self-as-psyche is sometimes subtle, and often muddled in anthropological writings, one reason being that although the self-concept (self-construal, self-representation) is a cultural universal—i.e., people everywhere make the distinction between self and not-self or Other—how different peoples understand the self can vary considerably (Spiro 1993). It is the task of ethnology to unpack differences and similarities among the ways people come to know what they claim to know about themselves, their society and their world. The thing to keep in mind is that anthropologists of whatever age have almost always been concerned with self-as-psyche, not self-as-being.

Anthropology of the Self

It is commonplace in anthropology to maintain that our Western (i.e., Euro-American-Aussie) cultural concept of the self is somewhat different, perhaps even aberrant, when compared with most non-Western peoples (Geertz 1984; Markus and Kitayama 1991a). We Westerners do tend to think of our self as an independent, distinct, separate and autonomous individual, while most peoples conceive of themselves as interdependent, as social actors whose identities derive from their position in a social network—as spokes in the social wheel. It is also the case that most people in all societies identify themselves with their culturally defined self-concept (social-self or empirical ego), rather than the self as it really is (see Spiro 1993). The Western vs. non-Western conception of the self is not a simple black and white contrast, for there are people in each type of society that may be found to exhibit the style of self-construal of the other (Hollan 1992; Mpofu 1994). Thus, any scientific definition of the self must be amenable to a range of sociocultural variation broader than is normal for Western psychology.

To one extent or another, ethnology has been interested in the social and cultural aspects of the self since the discipline's inception as a science. The reason for this is the obvious ubiquity of ethnopsychologies among the planet's peoples. As Paul Heelas has noted, "Indigenous psychologies are in fact necessary if three interrelated functions are to be fulfilled: sustaining the 'inner' self, sustaining the self with respect to the sociocultural, and enabling sociocultural institutions to operate" (1981a: 13). In other words, human beings everywhere are curious about themselves, and develop personal knowledge both through direct experience and through the internalization of the society's self-concepts and categories.

Ethnological interest in the self has burgeoned over the last three decades (e.g., see Battaglia 1995; Ben-Âmôş and Weissberg 1999; Cohen 1994; Erchak 1992; Heelas and Lock 1981; Hollan 1992; Lindholm 2007; Mageo 1995, 2002a, 2003; Morris 1994; Sökefeld 1999; Stromberg 1985; Throop 2000; Van Wolputte 2004; Whittaker

1992). The focus of this literature has been on the many ways that cultures construe the self, including identity, ego, the "I" and the "me," personhood, and the like. The principal interest is in understanding how the developing individual constructs his or her identity within the context of their physical and social environment. The ethnographic literature and ethnological analyses of enculturation thus have much to offer students of the transpersonal self. One fundamental impact of a cross-cultural view is that the definition of the self as used by psychology and interdisciplinary transpersonalists should conform to how it may be applied in other non-Western societies. In other words, the definition we use should reflect the fact that all societies have words for and concepts of the self, but that how the concept is instantiated in each culture may vary, as it will among different individuals with their different temperaments making up the group.

Factors in the Cross-Cultural Understanding of the Self

There are other factors that become evident in the cross-cultural literature, and I will discuss each of them in turn, offering examples from the ethnographic literature, and adding some relevant literature in case the reader wishes to follow-up. For the contemplative, these factors may suggest foci for phenomenological study, for each can be confirmed and explored using meditative methods discussed in previous chapters. Also, sensitivity to these factors will allow interdisciplinary transpersonalists to better utilize the ethnographic literature in their formulations. For instance, knowing that so-called lucid dreaming is quite common in many societies should temper discussions of lucid dreaming as an unusual experience among Western subjects, and how subjects construe their dream-selves (Laughlin 2011).

Self-as-being vs. self-as-psyche. Virtually all anthropological treatments pertain to the self-as-psyche, as opposed to the self-as-being. Perhaps as many as 95% or more of uses of the term in the anthropological literature are concerned with the psychological dimensions of personhood, identity, role, status, etc., rather than the greater existential sense of "being in the world" (i.e., existential existence or Heideggerian *dasein*; see Heidegger 1996[1953]). Keeping this distinction in mind may help in processing ethnographic data in the context of transpersonal studies wherein writers often imply self-as-being in their research methods and analyses. Indeed, transpersonal research often requires a developmental shift from a self-awareness locked into a culturally defined social identity to a transcendent awareness of being (e.g., Baruss 2003).

The people living on Saburl Island near New Guinea make a distinction typical of traditional peoples, and to some extent modern technocratic nations as well—that being the difference between someone who is physically human and someone who is morally human, the latter being defined as an individual who knows the "rules of sociality" (Battaglia 1990: 55-57). The process by which one becomes a moral human is a trick of memory in which the disparate experiences one has and stories one hears suddenly coalesce into a unitary understanding. The stories become one story, and one finds grounding for one's social self. By inculcating the lessons of experience and stories one realizes a self that is fully Saburl; that being one who can participate in a flowing, meaningful and unobstructed social discourse.

Self-as-experienced and self-as-reported. A close reading of the ethnographic literature makes one aware of a distinction that is often poorly operationalized. That is the distinction between self-as-experienced and self-as-reported; or to put it in other words, how I experience myself from moment to moment and how I talk about myself in public (Hallowell 1955; Hollan 1992). The ethnographic literature often seems to equate self with self-concept, self-knowledge and personhood—i.e., the self as described in language (e.g., Goddard 1996; Battaglia 1995). Limiting research to the ways that people talk about themselves and others: (1) slants the data in favor of the typical constructivist bias, for people are influenced by rules of appropriate linguistic production and etiquette and may be reporting in terms of cultural models as opposed to personal phenomenology (Throop 2000), and (2) leads to ethnographers ignoring or down-playing the vast depths of the *transcendental self*—the psyche each individual is culturally conditioned to model. Thus, ethnographic research that is limited to recording how people customarily talk about themselves is often psychodynamically shallow and of limited importance to transpersonal studies. Moreover, because different non-Western peoples talk about the self, personhood, social identity and consciousness in so many ways, it is difficult to compare cognitions across cultures, or to isolate those aspects of the transcendental self that may be universal to the species (Erchak 1992). It should be remembered that language hides as much or more than it reveals about experience (see Weiner 2001) and may easily gloss over non-linguistic factors involved in self-awareness and self-understanding which may be more fluid, universal, and developmental than self-reports may reveal. Another way to view this issue is to make a distinction between public and private self (see Heelas 1981b: 43). We all know there is more to ourselves than others know, or for that matter than we know. In fact, we often hear people say "nobody knows me." That means that we are not getting feedback about ourselves that match what we know about ourselves. Again, anthropology has most often focused upon the public self; the social identity, persona, public ego, and so forth.

The embodiment of self. Modern anthropological conceptions have insisted upon the embodied nature of the self. Following on from Hallowell's (1955) pioneering work, Thomas Csordas has argued that the only perspective that fits cross-cultural findings is an experiential-phenomenological one that recognizes the self as an amalgamation of "prereflective bodily experience, culturally constituted world or milieu, and situational specificity or habitus" (Csordas 1994: 5). The various somatic processes that orient the being to the world—processes mediating perception and action ("practice")—and that exist prior to self-reflection and cultural conditioning. The fundamental function of the self is orientational; that is, the embodied processes of the self operate to orient the being toward objects and events in the world, toward the social Other, and toward oneself as the center of an existential situation. In reflexively objectifying the self, one creates the fiction of personhood, an identity influenced by culture and projected outwards upon society.

I do not mean to imply that all non-Western societies exhibit the extreme mind-body dualism typical of technocratic societies. Far from it, for many cultures see the self as a physical entity. For instance, while the Muinane people of Colombia speak of themselves in much the same egoistic terms we do, their ontological assumptions about the self are as a physical substance; or, to put it in other words, they do not posit a clear distinction between thought and act, both being part of the same physical process (Londoño-Sulkin 2000). Muinane kids are enculturated to pursue a way of life they consider "cool," and remaining cool requires cool thoughts—like, loving their kinsmen, avoiding improper intentions, showing respect for others, working hard, and so forth. Evil is produced by people and other beings that are "hot," meaning egotistical, self-serving, angry, morally ignorant, and even violent. A hot person is transformed into a cool one by the ritual manipulation of the substances causing such anti-social and dangerous tendencies.

Nor should I leave the reader with the misconception that just because a people conceive of the self as a substance, that the substance equates to our category of physical "matter." Indeed, few non-Western peoples are materialistic in that way. One of the most common conceptions of self and body is that people, just like all other things in the world, are essentially made up of an *élan vital,* or vital force. As we saw in Chapter 4, Navajo folks speak of that force in terms of "wind," the Holy Wind that pervades everything in the world (McNeley 1981). Hence, everything (including people) is implicated in everything else. This is a common view among African peoples as well who conceive of this energy in each person which interpenetrates with all things (Morris 1994; Horton 1983). The African ontology is quite like that among Pacific peoples who hold to various conceptions of *mana* as a living, vital force in and between persons, and between persons and nature (Keesing 1984).

Egoistic vs. social self. Personhood never develops in a social vacuum. We all develop a self-concept in relation to others among whom we are raised, as well as the activities of others around us. All peoples everywhere experience themselves as both individuals and social actors (Mageo 1995, 1998). But in many societies, the sense of self develops so thoroughly bound to social relations that people have a difficult time considering the self apart from society, as in the case of the Muinane above. This also seems to be the case among the Cashinahua of Western Amazonia who make a distinction between a normal person who craves interaction with their kin, and a being they call a *yuxin* who has no fixed place in the world (Lagrou 2000: 159)—not a great place to be an introvert.

Moreover, all normal (i.e., non-psychopathic) individuals acknowledge the personhood of the Other in every encounter. As George Murdock (1945) noted, every culture on the planet demarcates encounters with the Other with ritual hellos and goodbyes (see also Gregor 1977 for a case in point among the Mehinaku of Brazil). Most societies encourage the developing person to conceive of themselves in socially pragmatic ways (Kitayama, Duffy and Uchida 2010; Markus and Kitayama 1991a). Who I conceive myself to be as a person, as an identity, as a self-image or ego, is coterminous with my social status, my role(s) in the social fabric, and my position in the family, lineage and clan. For instance, as Gerald Erchak (1992: 59-61) notes, all human societies exaggerate gender differences. Gender categories are often some of the most rigidly held in defining social identity. The cultures of the technocratic world are currently undergoing a profound LGBTQ revolution which reveals just how rigid traditional gender roles can be in our Western societies.

The role I play in the political and economic structure of the group is entirely entangled with my conception of social context. While knowing that I am distinct as an entity, a person, I nonetheless define myself in my relation to others. In a very real sense, we are all symbols to each other, and even symbols to ourselves (Stromberg 1985). When we encounter each other through the mediation of social categories (male vs. female, higher vs. lower status, authority vs. peer group member, etc.) we are conditioned to alter how we present ourselves in the encounter. We are often performing who we are on a socially appropriate stage (Battaglia 1990, 1995). This cross-culturally common situation involves self-construal; internalizing during development the historical narrative, social statuses and roles, and the system of reciprocal obligations and responsibilities in which the individual is embedded, as well as the projection of social categories and expectations upon the Other. These relations and reciprocal obligations may extend into cosmological domains, including backwards into my culture's cosmogony (Mageo 2001a: 4-6) and into my present or past interactions with other-than-human-persons, like ancestors, totemic spirits, gods, and so forth (Block and Parry 1982).

Martin Sökefeld (1999) makes the point that modern anthropology recognizes that traditional societies are made up of a *plurality of selves.*

Culture does influence the development of self-identity, but this does not mean that identities are stamped out by a cultural cookie-cutter. Indeed, as he illustrates among the people living in the town of Gilgit in Northern Pakistan, identities quite often come into conflict. Individuals under the stress of social involvement may be forced to embrace several identities, and some of these identities may even conflict with each other. **Sameness and duration of self.** A person's self-identity is almost always seen as an enduring process (Sökefeld 1999). Even though the self may change through time—may grow, develop, evolve, mature, transcend the limits of social categories, and eventually die—there is the sense that I remain the same enduring being over time. For instance, anthropologists will speak of "life-history" durations of selfhood (e.g., Cole and Knowles 2001; Thomas 2005), and again, the duration of the self may continue after death into ancestorhood (Royce 2011). Those societies that believe the person is reincarnated may consider aspects of the self to predate conception and to continue after death, perhaps lifetime after lifetime, if only as a bundle of karma (Block and Parry 1982).

In addition, the self not only has agency, it is the product of agency (Bourdieu 1977; Brockelman 1985; Sökefeld 1999). In either case, the human self is marked by the capacity to bind time in both its development and in its intentions (Piaget 1980). The self takes time to develop because it is the product of interaction between the individual and the social and physical world and may project its intentions into the distant future by way of planned actions that may take time to come to fruition. Hence, it is obvious that the role of memory in construing a social self or self-identity is fundamental to the process (Mageo 2001b: 15; Ben-Âmôş and Weissberg 1999). A clear example of this factor may be found in Marianne George's (1988) description of the importance of staging and participation in rituals that transform the status of people of power among the Barok living on the island of New Ireland off of Papua New Guinea. For Barok "big men," certain major rituals not only mark the transformation in personal power, the years-long effort in mounting the ritual produces the transformation. This is apparently typical of Melanesian rituals of exchange in that they operate to change egoistic motivations into social regard (Gow 2000: 48; Wagner 1967).

The lifetime process of self-development may be socially punctuated by phases of transformation demarked by ritual; so-called *rites of passage* (Turner 1967, 1969; Van Gennep 1960 [1909]). For example, transformation in a person's social status and power is often accomplished during such rituals (Burns and Laughlin 1979). Ritual transformations typically result in both public and self-referential changes in one's personhood. Male members of the Sambia tribe of the New Guinea highlands are forced through a series of brutal initiations which, according to Gilbert Herdt (1982), transforms each male's identity from a dependent, female dominated sense of self appropriate to early childhood to that of a fierce warrior who represses his feminine side and defines himself in opposition to women so that he may effectively fight wars and copulate with captured and presumably hostile women.

Self and emotion. The self includes emotional as well as perceptual, cognitive and behavioral attributes (Laughlin and Throop 1999; Marcus and Kitayama 2003; Throop 2000; Overing and Passes 2002b). Indeed, the control of emotion may be fundamental to how individuals are conditioned to present themselves in social situations. All too often anthropologists treat the building of self-construal as though it is strictly a cognitive-linguistic process. However, the self-as-psyche includes not only what I *think* about myself and the Other, but also what I *feel* about myself and the Other. C.G. Jung taught that we come to know ourselves by watching the emotionally-laden attributes we share with, and project upon, other people (Jung 1955: ¶318; 1976: ¶507). Emotions are contagious, as is inevitable in a social species. We tend to be drawn into the emotional tone of the group. Moreover, we tend to confound our own unconscious attributes with the perceived attributes of the Other. This quite natural empathy plays a significant role in the construction of a social self.

The role of emotion is fundamental to one's sense of self in all societies. Brian P. Farley (1998) has shown the role of anxiety in constructing a sense of self among the Nahuatl-speaking people living in the village of San Bartolomé Guahuixmatlac in the state of Tlaxcala, Mexico. "I argue that the sociocentric-oriented self as developed in San Bartolomé experiences deep emotional conflicts and strong resentment toward others. Individuals subordinate their own interests to collective purposes because they experience anxiety in association with their own drives and desires and fear retaliation from either social contemporaries or supernatural beings" (Farley 1998: 272). Indeed, for a person to exhibit willfulness in pursuit of their own desires may invite systematic and negative sanctions. Among Malayan peoples, there is pressure to deport oneself to not appear foolish or contrary, and thus avoid feeling shame (Goddard 1996). And in virtually all societies, the socially appropriate sense of self involves controlling the expression of negative feelings, especially anger (Overing and Passes 2000a: 22).[31] Indeed, so prevalent is this stricture on showing negative emotions that it has led Heine and associates to suggest there is a universal bias in cultural conditioning toward positive self-regard (Heine, Lehman, Markus and Kitayama 1999).

Self-system. There has been a gradual realization in anthropology that the self is less an entity than it is a complex psycho-physical system which may trend towards unity or fragmentation (e.g., Csordas 1994: 276) depending on personal, developmental, social and environmental pressures, especially during a person's formative years (Mageo 1995, 1998, 2002b). The *self-system* (as Jeannette Mageo aptly calls it) is organic and therefore it develops, grows and changes over time. When speaking of the self in this way—from the phenomenological point of view the only empirically accurate perspective—we are talking about arguably the most complex system in the known universe. As with any organic system, there are developmental factors that are all-important in understanding how the system comes to be structured and operate in its adult form (Bourguignon 1989; Mageo 1995).

Self-body dualism. Cross-cultural research has shown that virtually all societies on the planet conceive of the self and the body to be separable to some extent. In a research project some of my students and I carried out years ago, we asked some questions about mind-body relations of a standard holographic sample of societies from around the world (see full report at Laughlin n.d.). We found that although many societies hold a more unitary view of mind-body relations than

---

[31] Also see Gaffin (1995) for the Faeroe Islanders of the North Atlantic who recognize a type of person called a *rukkur*, "an easily angered fool;" Briggs (1970) for the Utku Inuit of the Arctic for whom reason is valued above all emotions, and those who show anger are ostracized; and Harris (1978) for the Taita people of Kenya who, recognizing the destructive effects of anger, have rituals for purifying negative emotions.

we Westerners tend to do, virtually all societies have some notion of mind being distinct from body, if nothing more than they experience leaving their body and traveling around in their dreams. In other words, mind-body dualism ranges from minimal to extreme, but is nonetheless a cultural universal. The importance of this finding for explanations of notions of immortality cannot be overemphasized. The phenomenological gap we discussed back in Chapter 1 suggests to a person's mind that their consciousness is somehow separate from their corporeal being, and that the mind, or some part of the mind, may continue to exist in some sense, "...long after the frail corporeal envelope which lodged it for a time has moldered in the dust" (Frazer 1966[1933]: 3).

Multi-state self. One of the most important findings in ethnology for transpersonal studies is that for most societies, people develop their identity from information they derive while in ASC; that is, experiences had while dreaming, having visions and mystical states, on drug trips, and experiences had while participating in rituals (Bourguignon 1973; Bourguignon and Evascu 1977; Laughlin 2011; Laughlin, McManus and d'Aquili 1990; Winkelman 2010). The distinction between these polyphasic societies and those monophasic technocratic societies where ASC are either not encountered or ignored in identity formation is critical, and for this reason we have defined two types of culture.

We know that certain states of consciousness are more permeable to unconscious processes than others. Our normal waking states tend to be focused upon experiencing the outer world. Our dream life is far more permeable to unconscious interactions, which is why dream work is vitally important in many types of psychotherapy and in advanced Jungian individuation work (Hillman 1987). Hence it follows that the construal of self among polyphasic peoples may be quite different—and some have argued potentially more productive of advanced, holistic self-development—than that among, say, modern Westerners whose protean ego development may thwart advanced self-realization. This factor is evident in the extent of control the dream ego may exercise in the dream life. For most Westerners and monophasic peoples generally, dreams just happen, usually without any exercise of will on the part of the ego. Among many polyphasic societies, however, people routinely travel at will in their very lucid dreams. This is a particularly important skill learned by certain shamans who may seek socially vital information and healing power in the dream world (Laughlin 2011; Laughlin and Rock 2014).

Transcendental vs. cognized self. Peoples vary in the extent to which they distinguish between culturally influenced self-construal and the recognition of the self as a transcendental object or field (Jung 1968b: ¶247). Some cultures hold that the culturally inculcated empirical ego is merely a reflection of the true, mysterious and mystical self that is either ultimately unknowable, or knowable by only a few advanced individuals (shamans, seers, mystics, etc.; see Winkelman 2010). Ethnographies will sometimes confound the term self with other terms such as identity, personhood, personality, ego, being, subjectivity, ethnicity and self-construal (Erchak 1992: 8). As I have said, what most anthropologists are referring to is the way a people talk about themselves relative to the Other (other persons or other groups), to their social position and status, or to their role with respect to their cosmology. There are some societies in which the development of the self is thought to pass through multiple stages, usually involving a person's comprehension of and participation in the society's spiritual life [e.g., see Jorgensen (1980) for the Telefolmin and Barth (1975) for the Baktaman, both peoples living in New Guinea].

Transpersonal self-construal. Mara, DeCicco and Stroink (2010) have suggested the term *metapersonal* self-construal for societies recognizing transpersonal development. Metapersonal self-construal "…is defined as a sense of one's identity that extends beyond the individual or personal to encompass wider aspects of humankind, life, psyche, or the cosmos" (DeCicco and Stroink 2007: 84). "The focus of an individual with this self-construal moves beyond personal and relational views of the self to a more universal view. In other words, the metapersonal self-construal is not simply defined by personal attributes or social relations, but instead defines the self as connected to all things. The metapersonal has a universal focus that includes all life and nature into the concept of the self" (Mara, DeCicco and Stroink 2010: 1-2). The ethnographic literature is rife with cultures that not only recognize a metapersonal dimension to the self, but actively encourage self-realization and peak experiences of self in relation to the world (LaHood 2007; Laughlin 1989, 1994a, 1994b, 2001; Laughlin,

McManus and Shearer 1993). In many of these cases, the distinction between self-as-being and self-as-psyche not only becomes blurred, it may well be culturally irrelevant (Bateson 1980).

Broadening the Definition of the Self

In summary, modern ethnology tends to encounter local conceptions of the self as an embodied system: (1) that perceptually orients the individual toward both the social and physical world and the inner being, and (2) that guides intentional action. The self is not an entity— not the product of a cultural cookie-cutter—but does develop a model of itself through adaptive development and some degree of self-reflection. The product is a self-concept or identity that may be pluralistic and even protean, that is inextricably linked to emotion, and that is strongly influenced by cultural categories (such as age, sex, status, role, spirit, soul, moral tone, etc.). Cultures generally recognize that the self is plastic and that it develops with age, sometimes passing through culturally recognized maturational stages that may be demarked or facilitated by rituals. Some societies also recognize higher, transpersonal dimensions of self-development which perhaps only a few individuals in the group ever actually attain.

THE BRAIN AND ITS SELF

What is emerging in the new anthropology of the self is the importance of grounding the cross-cultural study of the self in direct experience, rather than limiting the concept to cultural-linguistic categories, self-reporting and self-construal (Throop 2000, 2003). As anthropologist Clyde Kluckholn and psychologist Henry A. Murray noted decades ago, in some ways all human beings are alike, *in some ways some human beings are alike and in some ways no human beings are alike* (Kluckhohn and Murray 1948). All humans have selves (or psyches; in this respect everyone is alike) which may be experienced, thought about and talked about in different ways by different peoples (some people are alike), and individuals within any group will have their own subjective perspective on themselves (no one is alike). Anthropology has in the past specialized in the many wonderful and varied ways that some people are alike, but is now approaching an understanding that, with respect to the self, there are aspects that all peoples share.

Homo sapiens sapiens is a social primate with a very social brain (Dunbar, Gamble and Gowlett 2010), and as with any social primate the development of the self is first and foremost a social process. As we shall see, the orientation of self and consciousness for most people is towards the world, especially the social world. The universal aspects of the self are due primarily to the species-specific evolution of the human nervous system. At no point in the development of the pre- and perinatal brain is the organization of cells a "blank slate"—a random hodge-podge of neurons and support cells—patiently awaiting enculturation to provide socially meaningful order (see Pinker 2003). Yet this is the kind of developmental process often implied (never actually stated) by extreme cultural constructivist views of the self.

The Self and Its Brain

As we have seen in previous chapters (especially Chapter One), what we in fact know from developmental neuroscience is that the human brain is exquisitely ordered from its inception in neurogenesis (Johnson 2005; Laughlin 1991). Moreover, neural networks and processes are self-organizing—Humberto Maturana and Francisco Varela (1980) called this self-organizing function "autopoietic," organic systems operate upon universal mechanisms to "in-form" (Varela 1979) themselves in interaction with the world. The self-organization of neural structures is fundamental to neuropsychological accounts of learning such as *adaptive resonance theory* (ART; Carpenter and Grossberg 2003; Grossberg 2012; see also Laughlin and d'Aquili 1974 for our earliest discussion of this view) which holds that learning is a process by which internal perceptual (experiential) models operate as *expectations* that the brain evaluates relative to sensory input. Where a mismatch above a certain threshold (the "vigilance parameter") occurs, the model may change to conform to the input pattern. ART is like the earlier TOTE system proposed by Miller, Galanter and Pribram (1960; see also Pribram 1971) and our own modest "empirical modification cycle" (Laughlin and d'Aquili 1974: 84-86). The ART account has the advantage of being commensurate with the formation of fuzzy categories (Carpenter, Grossberg and Rosen 1991), a characteristic of the natural categories ethnographers encounter in the field all the time (Rosch 1977; Rosch, Mervis, Gray, Johnson and Boyes-Braem 1976).

Perception, categorization and other aspects of sensory experience are not automatic as they might be in robotic systems. Experience always involves the self in one way or another. In other words, the world is always experienced from within the context of the self. Neurophysiologically speaking, while the ART system may only involve sensory-cognitive networks, the act of perception propagates throughout the greater self-system so that objects are evaluated from a primarily subjective point of view (Baars, Ramsøy and Laureys 2003); namely the frontoparietal association areas and other networks that subserve consciousness (i.e., the "observing self"). This global neurophysiological involvement is dramatic when the object of perception is involved in self-referential plans and sub-plans, and projections of self chronesthetically into the past and the future—we might say the "temporal self" (Brockelman 1985; Buckner and Carroll 2007; Macrae, Moran et al. 2004; Gusnard, Akbudak, Shulman and Raichle 2001; Mitchell, Banaji and MacRae 2005).

Modern neuropsychology of the self makes it quite clear that the self is a distributed system that changes its internal organization moment by moment in interaction with the world and with the inner being (LeDoux 2003; Damasio 2010; Hood 2012; Gusnard, Akbudak, Shulman and Raichle 2001). Those readers familiar with the neuropsychological literature on the self will recall that philosopher Karl Popper and neuroscientist John Eccles wrote a book entitled *The Self and Its Brain* (1977) in which they posited aspects of conscious and unconscious mentation that transcend the physical constraints of the nervous system. Theirs was an interactional model which maintained the mind-body dualism that so many theorists before them found irresistible. Accordingly, I reversed the order of the terms in the title of this chapter, "The Brain and Its Self," for I wish to thoroughly repudiate any such dualism. There exists little evidence for treating consciousness as other than a function of the brain (Chapter 1) and every empirical reason to support an identity theory (see Rockwell 2005 for a review; see also MacDonald 1989).

As we have seen earlier, nowhere in the brain is there a wee homunculus peering at objects in the sensorium. Nor is the self a fixed, rigid, culturally imposed identity stored somewhere in memory. As we will appreciate later, it is the dynamic, organic systems nature of the self that may allow advanced development of self-awareness and self-construal of the sort that mature contemplatives undergo. The moment-by-moment sense of self changes with what is happening outside and inside the body. In extreme situations, people may experience their self-as-psyche departing their bodies (Alvarado 2000; Shields 1978). Sometimes they find themselves looking down on their physical body or flying around, unencumbered by their bodies. Out-of-body experiences (OBEs) are quite common during dreaming and are reported by folks in many cultures. Indeed, so-called "flying" shamans may specialize in OBE journeys and adventures in the aid of healing and conflict resolution (Winkelman 2010). These kinds of experience seem to be mediated by networks at the temporal-parietal junction, just below the inferior parietal lobule (Blanke, Landis, Spinelli and Seeck 2004; Blanke *et al.* 2005; Metzinger 2009: 82-98). It is this same area that mediates the more usual sense of self-body integration.

We know from studies of brain damage that lesions in various areas of the brain will result in different deficits in the sense of self (Feinberg and Keenan 2005b). Damasio makes the point that damage to cortical areas may leave deficits in self-awareness, but not to core consciousness or core-self (1999: 270-272). As we know, the neural areas most crucial to human self-awareness are in the frontal lobes—particularly in the prefrontal cortex (Blumer and Benson 1975; Gusnard, Akbudak, Shulman and Raichle 2001; Mitchell, Banaji and MacRae 2005; Saxe *et al.* 2006; Schmitz, Kawahara-Baccus and Johnson 2004). Depending on the location of a lesion, marked changes in personality may occur, including, bizarrely enough, denial of change by the patient (Stuss 1991). Lesions to the prefrontal lobe may result in change in the ability to make social judgments (D'Argembeau *et al.* 2007), while damage to the inferior parietal lobe may lead to deficits in body image (Joseph 1992: 40-43; Prigatano 1991: 121). Self-awareness of language production, including self-reports may be blocked by damage to the inferior parietal lobule.

Neuroimaging research is now adding to what we know about the brain and its self (see Northoff *et al.* 2006 for an excellent review). For instance, certain aspects of self-awareness involve lateral asymmetry of function (Geary 2005: 217-219; Joseph 1992; Feinberg and Keenan 2005a). Self-face perception involves a right hemisphere cortical network distributed over the inferior parietal lobule, inferior frontal gyrus, and inferior occipital gyrus. "[S]elf-face recognition appears to involve a simulation-like mechanism that recruits right hemisphere mirror neuron networks matching the face stimulus to an internal representation of the self, while other-face recognition recruits midline structures that have previously been implicated in social processing" (Uddin *et al.* 2005: 8).

Because we humans are social primates, by far the most important drive in the development of the self is the individual's social coordination—one's orientation to the social Other (Cacioppo, Berntson and Waytz 2005; Dunbar 2002; Dunbar, Gamble and Gowlett 2010; Heatherton *et al.* 2006; Macrae *et al.* 2004). Most of this development occurs early in the life of the child and involves the newer and more complex areas of the right hemisphere of the brain, particularly those prefrontal and inferior parietal portions of the right cortex that subserve how we mirror and interact with the Other and maintain a sense of agency (Decety and Chaminade 2003; Decety and Sommerville 2003; Mitchell, Banaji and MacRae 2005; Schmitz, Kawahara-Baccus and Johnson 2004). In addition, right hemisphere somatosensory cortices subserve the expression and the recognition of perceived emotions (Adolphs 2002).

The discovery of mirror neurons has provided a critical mechanism for many of the processes characteristic of the social self (Chapter 1). These types of cells are present in other social animals and birds, and presumably are fundamental to the organization of the brains of all social animals. Rochat, Serra, Fadiga and Gallese (2008) have carried out two experiments that seem to demonstrate the importance of "familiarity" of action patterns. The repetition of the actions of others impresses itself upon neural systems, and hence the understanding of those actions by the observer: "The results of both experiments seem to suggest that when an action performed by others becomes familiar, independently from the perceptual or motor source of its familiarization, it is nevertheless always mapped onto the motor representation of a similar goal (to take possession of an object) belonging to the observing individual..." (2008: 231).

Crucial to the sense of Other is the ability to empathize, and empathy requires mirror neuron entrainment. Among other things, empathy involves feeling the suffering of others (Jackson, Meltzoff and Decety 2005; Botvinick *et al.* 2005; Laughlin 2013a). Focusing on the apperception of pain in others, Singer *et al.* (2004) have shown using neural imaging that only a portion of the pain system is activated in the empathizing observer. The areas of the brain that light-up when either feeling pain oneself, or observing pain in a loved one, are areas in the anterior insula, rostral anterior cingulate cortex, areas in the brain stem and cerebellum. In other words, most people are wired from birth to recognize and to feel the pain of others.

Finally, establishing memories is fundamental to a person's sense of self, and involves memory of self-referential knowledge, judgments, evaluations, plans, intentions and actions (Gillihan and Farah 2005a, 2005b; Damasio 1999; Gallagher and Frith 2003). The laying down of memories pertaining to the self requires mediation by networks in the medial prefrontal cortex (Macrae *et al.* 2004). Indeed, memories about the self are easier and more likely to be laid down than memories about others (Rogers, Kuiper and Kirker 1977; Heatherton *et al.* 2006). The prefrontal cortex of the human brain is also involved in producing what has been called *autonoetic* consciousness, the ability to imagine ourselves in the past, future, and imaginary situations (Wheeler, Stuss and Tulving 1997; Gusnard, Akbudak, Shulman and Raichle 2001).[32]

Self from a Neuroanthropological Standpoint

Anthropological and neuropsychological approaches are not only compatible; they are mutually consistent and paint similar pictures of the self (see Kitayama and Park 2010). This is especially true when more introspective or experiential methods are used in ethnology. This is not surprising, for the structure(s) of the self are the neurophysiological networks that mediate awareness, personality, emotion, cognition, imagery, point of view, temporal perspective, planning, social identity, and all the other attributes of the self as described by ethnographers. Thus, a neuroanthropological perspective on the self is possibly the most

---

[32] Chronesthesia is a kind of autonoetic consciousness.

powerful window we have on human nature. So, let me finally define self in a way that is amenable to both neuroscience and anthropology. From the neuroanthropological standpoint, *the self is comprised of those neurophysiological structures that mediate the psyche, including those specialized networks that produce self-reflection.* Self is a distributed system of neural networks, some of which are more common to experience than others. Because it is made up of living cells, the self-system is organic and dynamic, and changes its organization from moment to moment depending upon the focus of consciousness. The biological function of the self is to orient mental functions to those aspects of the world that are of adaptive significance, including the physical environment, the social milieu and internal somatic and psychological states. All animals with brains have a self-system, however rudimentary. Primates, being social animals, are focused on social relations that play a major role in neuropsychological development. Most of the neural activities comprising the self at any given moment are unconscious, and some operations are either rarely or never conscious. Self-system states normally include elements of emotion and perhaps praxis, appropriate to the adaptational problem being faced.

One of the most important functions of the self is observing and modeling itself. As the great perceptual psychologist, James J. Gibson (1979; see also Neisser 1993) showed, self-perception is a special case of general perception in that *our being, our body, is part of the extramental world to which our brain must adapt.* The cognition of the self is no different in this respect than the cognition of any other object. Just how the self presents to self-awareness, and how we make sense of those presentations are heavily mediated by culture. As Larry Peters (1994) has shown, the "symptoms" of mental illness as interpreted by clinicians in a Western technocratic culture may be indications of the need for a rite of passage and self-transformation in a non-Western context.

Self-reflection, mediated primarily by cortical structures in the prefrontal lobes, is probably a more advanced facility among humans than any other animal on the planet. It is small wonder that we find anthropologists encountering such a varied range of customary self-construal represented in the ethnographic literature. Anthropologists have often emphasized the sociocultural factors influencing the development of personality, social identity, maturation of social role, alterations in consciousness, autobiographical narratives, behavior, and how people talk about themselves, etc. More recent studies (e.g., Hollan 1992; Mageo 1995; Throop 2000) have more fully recognized the systemic and reflexive nature of the self, but ethnologists so far have failed to ground the self-system in neurobiology. If we include neurophysiological grounding—if we acknowledge that the self is a distinct organization of the brain—it becomes obvious that there is always far more to the self-system than any cognitive model or self-concept, a factor rarely acknowledged in most anthropological studies. There is also a growing understanding that the self-system is not necessarily unitary, that self sub-systems may conflict with each other. There may exist recurrent contingencies that require a fragmented adaptation during the development of the self.

For phenomenological reasons (see Laughlin and Throop 2009), it is easy for peoples to ignore the embodied nature of mind, consciousness and even the self, and to conclude that there exists (to one extent or another) an ontological distinction between mind (psyche, self, soul, etc.) and the physical body (Chapter 1). In other words, local cultural epistemologies are hampered by the very structure and operations of the nervous system in reaching a complete identity theory of mind-body relations, or in understanding the full complexity of the self-system. Being a mature contemplative who is cognizant that the self-system is vastly complex, with most of its operations remaining unconscious to actors, allows one to realize that the self is transcendental relative to any possible knowledge we may accrue about it. It is also clear that there exists no cultural tradition that fully models the self-system in anything like the complexity of modern neuroscience. Unfortunately, there so far exists no widely accepted anthropological theory that can accommodate a transpersonal, transcultural or archetypal view of the self (cf., Daniels 2002 for a summary of theories in transpersonal psychology). For various reasons too arcane to go into here, psychological anthropology has historically been heavily influenced by Freudian psychoanalysis while virtually ignoring Jungian psychology (Laughlin and Tiberia 2012). Were anthropologists more aware of the Jungian concept of the complex, or of analytical psychology (Jung 1968a: ¶84), they would know that over a century ago Jung demonstrated that the psyche is a vast system of subsystems and sub-subsystems, termed "complexes," most of which remain unconscious to the person (Jung 1973: ¶1351), and which are redolent with emotional associations (Jung 1973: ¶733).

The self is merely a term that designates the whole personality. The whole personality of man is indescribable. His consciousness can be described, his unconscious cannot be described because the unconscious—and here I must repeat myself—is always unconscious. It is really unconscious, we really don't know it, so we don't know our unconscious personality. We have hints, we have certain ideas, but we don't know it really. ...The unconscious of man can go God knows where. There we are going to make discoveries. (McGuire and Hull, 1977: 301)

In other words, as Jung writes, "Every interpretation necessarily remains an 'as-if'" (Collected Works, Vol. 9i, p.265). And again:

An archetypal content expresses itself, first and foremost, in metaphors. If such a content should speak of the sun and identify with it the lion, the king, the hoard of gold guarded by the dragon, or the power that makes for the life and health of man, it is neither the one thing nor the other, but the unknown third thing that finds more or less adequate expression in all these similes, yet—to the perpetual vexation of the intellect—remains unknown and not to be fitted into a formula. (Jung, CW, V. 9i, p. 267; emphasis added)

Jung's view was that the empirical ego is but one complex out of a multitude, and it is entirely possible for the self to develop more than one ego-complex. Psychiatrist Robert Jay Lifton came close to the Jungian view when he described what he called *protean man* (Lifton 1971, 1999), a self-system with more than one ego-complex, each complex being adaptive in a specific set of circumstances. This type of fragmentation (e.g., emotional "splitting;" see Kernberg 1970) is characteristic of selves that develop under stressful conditions such as poverty, social conflict, domestic and social violence and so forth. Protean development is a significant hindrance to the natural tendency of the self toward totality or wholeness. In its extreme form, protean development may produce a consciousness so fragmented and dysfunctional that modern psychologists term it "dissociative identity disorder" (or "multiple personality disorder").

The empirical (i.e., the phenomenologically accessible) "hints" about the nature of the unconscious are derived from intuitive ideas, images, unintended actions (so-called "Freudian slips"), etc. that may be the objects of self-reflection. These indications may be expressions of quasi-egos, or complexes with distinct *psychoid* characteristics (Jung 1969e: 213-215)— that is, the complexes expressing themselves out of the unconscious may seem to have a will of their own, as well as other properties that resemble consciousness, but the complex itself is incapable of consciousness. This applies almost generally to all archetypes, as we shall see. Thanks to these psychoid characteristics, we may learn something of our unconscious selves via our dreams, visions, free associations, mythopoeic creativity, and other ASC. The unconscious is composed of endless archetypal structures which, although never observed directly, may be known to some extent from watching their operations (Laughlin and Tiberia 2012; Stevens 1982). For neuroanthropological purposes, the terms neural network and archetype may be treated as synonymous when and if the neural network mediates part of the personality. Everyone is born with a self-system, with an archetypal self.

The Transcendental Self

Once the transcendental nature of the self is understood by the contemplative, one of the most important attributes of self-reflection is that its operations may change one's self-construal, and thus potentially change the organization of the self. This process is what Harris L. Friedman (2013; Pappas and Friedman 2012) has called *self-expansiveness*, the transformation of the self-concept as a direct consequence of "consciousness raising," transpersonal experiences and explorations. This is a very useful concept for anthropology, as well as psychology, for it points to a common attribute of spiritual development among polyphasic peoples in which transpersonal experiences are incubated using meditation, ritual and psychoactive drugs. Again, the concept underscores the phenomenological fact that there is no little "me" floating around above the self, objectively watching what is happening. Self-reflection is a thoroughly subjective process by which the self-system monitors its own operations, even as it may be changing.

It is crucial to understand that, just as the self and world are transcendental relative to our knowledge, so too is our physical body. We never experience our body as it really is. Our extramental body is vastly complex, and yet we can be aware of the body only through exteroceptive (seeing, hearing, touching, etc.) and interoceptive sensations (pain, bliss, proprioception, etc.), and the self-model and self-image we form from those sensations. Our cognized body is a model of the real thing and is constructed by neural networks that are "wired-in"—by what Bermúdez, Marcel and Eilan (1995: 215-217) have called a "body-scheme-acquisition device" and a "body-image-acquisition device." Obviously, culture can impact this modeling process by varying the experiences one has of the body. For instance, an advanced practitioner of hatha yoga may develop a different model of their body than non-practitioners.

Most people in any culture will tend to project their self-concept and self–image onto their self, thereby mistaking, as Jung noted, the concept or image for the object itself (Jung 1969d: ¶516). Belief in a permanent "me" is a matter of self-deceptive attitude which is instilled in childhood (Hood 2012) and may be altered by culture, and potentially by experience. It seems likely that societies range along a continuum from those that discourage too much self-reflection to those that positively sanction, or even mandate more advanced self-reflection. The point is, from an empirical viewpoint, all that is required to realize the impermanence and illusion of the self-concept, or any mental function with which the self is identified, is a sufficient level of self-reflection (often during meditation; see Chapter 3). In a sense, the human brain is "wired" to see itself as it really is—that virtually all psychological functions of the brain are impermanent (Austin 1998; Flanagan 2011).

SELF CONTEMPLATING SELF

I have emphasized that sustained, disciplined meditation will bring the contemplative into engagement with the unconscious self, regardless of the culture or spiritual tradition the meditator belongs to. Also, to some extent at least, engagement with the unconscious will lead to a permanent reorganization of consciousness (Damasio 2003; Deshmukh 2006; Varela, Thompson and Rosch 1991; Varela and Shear 1999; Wilson 2004), in part because material in the unconscious will become deautomatized. A self-aware self is different both experientially and structurally than a non-aware self. Indeed, awareness of self is mediated differently than awareness of the Other (Decety and Sommerville 2003). The introspective mind-state is mediated by a discrete organization in the brain (Heatherton *et al.* 2006), and as that system of networks develops through disciplined application of self-awareness, it grows and reorganizes, incorporating previously automatized, habitual mental acts and behaviors (Goldberg and Malach 2006; Gusnard *et al.* 2001; Murphy and Donovan 1999; Deikman 1966). As we learn more about how the brain mediates its own self-reflection, there is a concomitant and growing realization among researchers of the value of introspective, phenomenological and meditative research in science (Tart 2001; Wallace 2007, 2009).

Yet disciplined self-awareness comes at a cost. There are reasons that most people do not jump at the chance to explore the inner self. It can be in fact frightening to do so. As the Trappist monk, Catholic priest and mystic, Thomas Merton wrote, no-doubt with Western contemplatives in mind:

> The external *self* fears and recoils from what is beyond it and above it. It dreads the seeming emptiness and darkness of the interior self. The whole tragedy of "diversion" is precisely that it is a flight from all that is most real and immediate and genuine in ourselves. It is a flight from life and from experience—an attempt to put a veil of objects between the mind and experience itself. It is therefore a matter of great courage and spiritual energy to turn away from diversion and prepare to meet, face-to-face, that *immediate* experience of life which is intolerable to the exterior man. This is only possible when, …we are able to see out inner selves not as a vacuum but as an infinite depth, not as emptiness but of fullness. This change is impossible as long as we are afraid of our own nothingness, as long as we are afraid of fear, afraid of poverty, afraid of boredom—as long as we run away from ourselves. (Merton 2008: 140)

Serious, disciplined contemplation of the unconscious self is inevitably a transpersonal project. Experiences will arise that bring the ego, the culturally-loaded self-concept into question. As we shall see later (Chapter 11), the best tool for encountering the unconscious is self-love—hence, the title of Merton's little book, *Choosing to Love the World*.

Guided Imagery Meditation

Perhaps one of the most popular, effective and creative methods of self-exploration is that of *guided imagery* (including *guided visualization*; see Trakhtenberg 2008; Gruzelier 2002). This is a method by which another person (teacher, therapist, book, audio tape, etc.) suggests imagery that you create in your own "inner theater of mind." The imagery can be from any of the sensory modes—picture, sound, taste, activity—and the task is to develop the images as clearly as possible:

> Mental imagery occurs when perceptual information is accessed from memory, giving rise to the experience of 'seeing with the mind's eye', 'hearing with the mind's ear' and so on. By contrast, perception occurs when information is registered directly from the senses. Mental images need not result simply from the recall of previously perceived objects or events; they can also be created by combining and modifying stored perceptual information in novel ways. (Kosslyn, Ganis and Thompson 2001: 635)

Perception and imagery are closely related, many of the same structures mediate both. But there are significant differences as well (Behrmann 2000). Imagery for instance is produced entirely in the higher cortical systems of the brain and does not require lower level processing, while perception does require lower level processing and does not require memory processing when the stimulus is not present. Guided imagery is a combination of both perception (listening to or reading the guide, looking at pictures, etc.) and imagery (images created and retained in memory). This is precisely the skill required for "arising yogas" of all sorts (see Chapter 3) where initial imagery is formed by perceived stimulus and then held in active memory as an object of concentration. This is a skill not commonly found among most people and must be developed if one is to use any form of arising yoga, including guided imagery.

When I have used guided imagery while teaching (perhaps you would like to follow along as well), I would invite students to sit with eyes closed and be as relaxed and thought-free as possible. Then I would suggest:

In the back of your closet is a secret door which opens to a set of ten steps descending into the dark. You take off your shoes and socks if any. By the door you will find a flashlight. You pick up the flashlight, turn it on and close the door behind you. Then you slowly walk down the stairs telling yourself to deepen your calm until at the tenth step, the bottom, you are totally relaxed and feeling comfortable. You see in front of you a wooden door with a ring in the middle. You take the ring in your hand and open the door outward, and as you do, bright sunshine pours in from the outside. You switch off the flashlight and place it by the stairs where you can find it on the way back. Then you pass through the door and find yourself on a warm sunny beach with palm trees and other plants growing. You look out at the water and it is a lagoon. You walk toward the water feeling the sand under your feet and see the patches of shadow and sunlight passing through the leaves of the palms. You come to the water and step into it a few inches and feel the coolness of the waves as they pass over your feet. You should look around and see what you can see, for this is your secret place and it will contain anything you want to be in it, and will not contain anything you do not want to be in it. What are the smells like? Can you feel the breeze on your skin? What odors if any do you smell? Look carefully into the water and see if you can find anything under the waves. Are there any living creatures there?

Look back over your left shoulder and notice a small cottage up on the beach, surrounded by gardens with a small brook flowing down out of the forest to the lagoon. What color is the cottage? What does it look like? What colors do you see in the garden? Walking out of the water, again feeling the sand underfoot, approach the cottage. Walk to the front door of the cottage and open it. It is bright inside, inviting, comfortable. You enter the hallway and notice there is a room on the left and a room on the right. You walk into the room on the right and look around. You find there are three old fashioned treasure chests sitting on the floor. You look into each chest and find out what if anything is inside. The first chest represents something from the past, the second chest something from the present and the third chest something from the future. What have you seen in each of the chests? Then you walk to the other room, the one on the left of the door, and find that inside are two comfortable armchairs facing each other. The room is well lit because of the large windows. You walk to one of the chairs and sit down and tell yourself that you are in your special safe place and that you are calm and happy and contented. You look around the sitting room and see what is there in addition to the two chairs. Are there paintings on the wall? What do they depict? Then, if you feel like it, invite someone to join you in the other armchair and enter into a conversation with your guest. Who do you invite? How do they look? Happy, sad, angry, elated? After you have finished talking to or listening to your guest, the guest vanishes and you rise from your chair and walk back to the hallway. You pause and look to your left. The hallway continues toward the back of the cottage. Are there more rooms? A back door? What else do you see or hear or feel? Then you leave the cottage by the front door, closing the door behind you, and then walk to the door with the ring in the middle, the door back to the stairs, and looking around at your special place, know that you can return at any time you want to. You now open the door, pick up and click on the flashlight and close the door behind you. There are the ten stairs. You begin to ascend and with each step you tell yourself that you are returning to full awareness of the real world and that you will remain calm, peaceful and happy. At the top of the stairs, you open the door at the back of the closet, switch off the flashlight and place it by the door, retrieve your shoes and socks if any, and leave the stairway, closing the door behind you.

There are of course, many variations of this kind of guided imagery, some simple and others quite elaborate. The one I describe here I learned from others. With this kind of practice however one sets up the practitioner to a series of autosuggestive processes to bring about deep calm and creative imagery. During the calming process several blank places are left for the practitioner to invite interaction with the unconscious self. What do they see in the water, what do they place on the beach, what are in the three chests, what do the paintings depict and who do they invite into the other armchair, what else is in the back of the cottage? The whole scenario incorporates calming meditation plus an invitation for the unconscious to enter dialogue with consciousness. I encouraged students to repeat this exercise over and over and record what pops up in the blank places. Those images (of whatever sensory mode) then become objects of meditation in themselves.

Jung's Active Imagination and Amplification

Jung had a term for psychological and spiritual development throughout one's lifetime. As we saw earlier, Jung called this individuation, a process that continued irrespective of the extent of an individual's awareness of the changes in his or her psyche. "In general, it is the process by which individual beings are formed and differentiated [from other human beings]; in particular, it is the development of the psychological individual as a being distinct from the general, collective psychology" (Jung 1971: ¶757). Conscious participation in one's own individuation (hereafter called *conscious individuation*) makes all the difference, and after years of conscious engagement with the unconscious produces a qualitatively different person. In Jung's theory this difference is because the self is made up of myriad antinomies, contradictions, complementarities and oppositions. In other words, Jung conceived of the self as a vast mandala with a center that unites all possible oppositions (Jung 1969b). In constructing an ego during childhood, we are conditioned to identify with one side of an opposition and relegate the other side to our unconscious. At the same time, our physical and psychical being strives for wholeness—a biologically driven process operating in all organisms. If we continue in life putting all our energies into propping up our conditioned ego, the process of individuation carries on, but the drive of the psyche toward wholeness—Jung called this the *transcendent function* (Miller 2004)—is thwarted, and one ends up with a rigid personality, fixed in its self-view, and incapable of change or incorporating change. If on the other hand one embraces a program of conscious individuation, a conversation between the conscious and unconscious self develops and gradually takes over one's life strategy. In the end the personality becomes "flexible but unshakable" (von Franz 1980: 264).

During Jung's long and very influential career as a contemplative and psychotherapist, he applied a closely related set of methods that combined he called *active imagination* (Hannah 2015[1981]; Chodorow 2006; von Franz 1997[1979]; Johnson 1986; Jung 1997a; Miller 2004: 23-24), which I have mentioned several times above. In some respects, his methods were new, in others they were age-old (see Hannah 2015[1981]: Chap. 5). Just as with classical contemplative traditions and with shamanic traditions before that, many of his practices were re-discovered and applied to his own project and his form of psychotherapy.[33] In a very real sense, Jung re-invented (re-discovered) the principles underlying arising yoga—but with some differences. One major difference is that Jung, understanding that visions, apparitions, journeys, mystical unions, etc. encountered in ASC are messages from one's own unconscious psyche, would develop methods different from traditions that interpret those experiences as deriving from the external world. Moreover, to feed the transcendent function, and thus guide conscious individuation toward integration of consciousness with the rest of the self, the contemplative needs data from the unconscious— both the personal unconscious (one's childhood history stored in memory) and the collective unconscious (the neurognostic structures of the evolving human brain). The quest for data is the essence of active imagination (Miller 2004: 23; for a detailed account of active imagination applied by one of Jung's clients, see Swan 2007). These data are acquired through conscious involvement with imagery in visions had during illness, drug trips, ritual procedures, as well as fantasies, hypnagogic/hypnopompic imagery and dreams. The blank spots in the guided imagery (treasure chests, paintings, hallway, etc.) just described above would be a source of unconscious imagery. Jung thought that dream imagery was of marginal

---

[33] Of the many different kinds of meditation used by the Buddha in his teaching, he only invented a few and most he learned from his own teachers.

importance to active imagination because of the "low energy" underlying most dreaming (Jung 1969c [1958]: 77). Of course, he was not referring to what we call "lucid dreaming" which is of much higher energy and is typical of polyphasic peoples for whom the dream life is very important (see Laughlin 2011). Indeed, as we saw in Chapter 6, high lucidity is characteristic of dreaming among many peoples, and is the domain of often intense interest and contemplation. Nonetheless, much of Jung's effort went into utilizing fantasies and visions derived from mythopoeic sources such as his beloved alchemy.

One application of the method that Jung explored in his own self-discovery and thereafter used with his patients was to focus on an affect (usually a negative one: anxiety, depression, anger) that seemingly had no clear cause, and then concentrate on any imagery that pops up in fantasy related to the affect. The imagery "behind" the affect is the real message from the depths (Jung 1965 [1961]: 177). When a fantasy arises, the contemplative allows the imagery to "do its thing," and let the fantasy run until it stops or repeats itself—follow the plot of the fantasy wherever it leads, without imposing any will upon it. It is crucial to neither shut the fantasy off (as we all do out of fear when we don't like where it is going), nor identify with the fantasy (this is "me"). In Buddhist terms, it helps the process if one cultivates bare attention in all active imagination sessions (Chapter 3). The object is to associate images and insights with the affect—the images become symbols of and for the affect which then may be used by the unconscious to communicate with the conscious ego. Gradually the practitioner develops a "library" of shared symbols that facilitate communication between ego and unconscious. This is one of the major factors differentiating Jung's use of symbols from Freud's earlier methods (Main 2006: 301). Where for Freud the task was to rationally interpret dream images—almost like translating Ancient Greek into English—Jung held, based largely upon his own direct experience, that each image-as-symbol has many meanings. Images from the unconscious are both *polysemic* and dynamic and may carry different information loads each time they are encountered, or when encountered in different contexts. For Jung (1956 [1912]), thinking of a sort goes on in the unconscious, and images and intuitive insights that burble up into consciousness are the products of that thought. Thus, the relationship between the conscious ego and the unconscious is one of reciprocity (a dialogue) rather than of the ego independently and rationally assigning meaning for unconscious materials.

This expansion of symbolic expression, and the increasing comprehension of the range of meanings carried by symbolic materials, is a process Jung called *amplification*. To amplify the images-as-symbols that are gleaned from active imagination experiences the practitioner burrows into the associations between the symbols and other materials found in myth, literature, art, stories and so forth. Jung himself discovered the relevance of alchemy to his project precisely through amplification. A person raised a Christian may find the amplification builds bridges between fantasy and hypnagogic imagery and scripture. In my Ezekiel dream experience (Chapter 5), I "amplified" the meaning of the dream by reading the indicated scripture, reflecting the while upon the psychodynamic implications of both the City of God, and the rather magical way that the unconscious "guru" knew to assign my reading.

The difference between Jungian amplification and working within an already elucidated meditation culture is that the amplification process may be cut short by ready-made culturally loaded hermeneutics. For example, some societies have "canned" dream interpretation frames in the form of dream dictionaries or *oneirocritics* who interpret the meanings and portends of one's reported dreams (see Laughlin 2011: 249)—yet another example of a society's cycle of meaning. Amplification, however, is primarily an individual process of dialogue with the unconscious, fleshing out the range of meanings that both the ego and the unconscious may draw upon for communication with each other. Its purpose is to forward self-discovery, not to vivify and verify the society's world view. From the point of view of individuation and amplification, it is irrelevant whether the dream image of Mr. Obama means the same for me as it does for you.

SUMMARY AND SEGUE

Combining ethnographic fieldwork with neuropsychological research underscores the systematic nature of the self. Traditional cultures exhibit myriad ways of conceiving, conceptualizing, imaging and talking about the self (Wexler, 2006). These ways of knowing are usually focused upon the socially active person, and emphasize the ways that societies have of encouraging self-identity (or the culturally conditioned model of the self). From an ecological point of view (Gibson, 1979; Neisser, 1993) we can best understand that self-construal is an adaptational process no different than adaptation to external reality. Enduring social relations require that there be a consensus, habitual and customary understanding of the social person, and everyone must more or less conform to social expectations in order to "go along to get along." But many cultures also recognize that such self-models are incomplete and changeable, at least implicitly reflecting the greater mystery of the true self which is largely unconscious to actors and transcendental relative to any knowledge of the true self.

It is reasonable to posit that the more pressure there is in a society for people to conform to a fixed and shared concept of the social (economic, political) self, the less the culture will recognize and encourage transpersonal explorations. On the other hand, one of the tipoffs that a society does encourage such explorations is that they will apply rituals to that end; e.g., the Sun Dance among Native Americans, ritualized meditations among Buddhist practitioners, the ritualized ingestion of psychoactive substances (entheogens) among shamanic cultures, the Sema dance among Sufis. The point of all such ritual practices is to set the stage for mind-states requisite to transcending ego-consciousness and accessing the depths of the true self. The ethnographic literature is rich with examples of transpersonal spiritual traditions that, as with modern anthropology and neuropsychology, acknowledge the transcendental nature of the self.

Finally, in terms of the evolution of the self, it is interesting that most of the higher processes of self and self-construal involve the most recent part of the cerebral cortex, the prefrontal lobes. This neurophysiological factor should be more important to anthropology than it heretofore has been (Laughlin, 2011; Laughlin, McManus and d'Aquili, 1990; Goldberg, 2009). For instance, it is the frontal executive functions that have made the social distribution of intelligence and complexity typical of our species possible (Huberman, 1995). What is intriguing here is that it is this same advanced cortical system of cognitive, imagining and emotion-modulating processes that produces the kind of complex self-construal typical of most people in all societies, and that also facilitates advanced self-awareness and dynamic self-models informing transpersonal phenomenological disciplines. The prefrontal lobes make the distinctly human cultural-self possible, as well as the self-actualizing mind-states of the few, if any, who transcend cultural models of the self in any society.

One of the aspects of self-contemplation that I have not discussed is the encounter with one's cross-gender self. This becomes increasingly important to a contemplative during their mid-life on into their old age. It is also quite difficult to address in any comprehensive way because the process is different for a male than for a female. As we shall see in the next chapter, I am only able to explore the topic from the male point of view.

CHAPTER EIGHT

Contemplating the Anima

*If we can stay with the tension of opposites long enough —
sustain it, be true to it—we can sometimes become vessels
within which the divine opposites come together and give
birth to a new reality.*

– Marie-Louise von Franz, *The Art of Original Thinking*

*Become a woman yourself, and you will be saved from
slavery to woman....*

– C. G. Jung, *The Red Book*

A major undertaking in conscious individuation in both males and females is the encounter with and integration of the cross-gender elements of one's psyche. This is a process that has preoccupied me for the last forty years, as it will for any mature contemplative who is dedicated to a lifetime project of self-discovery. We are each born into a social environment that interacts with us presuming we are a member of a gender (usually male or female, but in some cultures three and rarely four genders; see Nanda 1999). It is true that gender is fundamentally based upon our sexual biology, but gender is a blend of the biological and the cultural and includes numerous cultural overlays that operate as expectations about our social roles, personality, feelings, behaviors and cognitive/perceptual natures. Being raised as a male, female, or some other gender requires us to repress many of the factors that otherwise would make us a whole human being. The long-term contemplative life is thus in part taken up with engaging and re-integrating those elements of our cross-gender natures that have been relegated to the shadows during our upbringing.

But I am getting ahead of myself. Carl Jung's discovery of the *anima* (Latin for "breath," "soul," "shades") in males and the *animus* in females is one of the main distinguishing features of his view of psychodynamics. When I speak of the male or female version of all the stuff we left behind in the unconscious when we learned to be our male or female gender, I will speak of either the *anima* or the *animus* respectively. Otherwise I will refer to the phenomenon for both sexes as the *anima/animus*. The *anima/animus* is a:

> ...natural archetype that satisfactorily sums up all the statements of the unconscious, of the primitive mind, of the history of language and religion. It is a 'factor' in the proper sense of the word. Man cannot make [the *anima/us*]; on the contrary, it is always the a priori element in his moods, reactions, impulses, and whatever else is spontaneous in psychic life. It is something that lives of itself, that makes us live; it is a life behind consciousness that cannot be completely integrated with it, but from which, on the contrary, consciousness arises. For, in the last analysis, psychic life is for the greater part an unconscious life that surrounds consciousness on all sides—a notion that is sufficiently obvious when one considers how much unconscious preparation is needed, for instance, to register a sense-impression. (Jung 1940/1968a: 27)

The *anima/animus* performs as a bridge or mediator function between the ego and the collective unconscious (Jung 1930-1934/1997: 127; Steinberg 1993: 183)—that vast field of archetypal structures (neurognosis) that we inherit by having human brains (Jung 1940/1968a: 27-28). Jung noted that there were as many archetypes as there are species-wide, typical perceptions (1940/1968a: 48). Archetypes of the collective unconscious are in a certain sense indistinguishable from the instincts (1951/1959: 179), and it is from the archetypal structures that the more developed, differentiated and mature structures of experience grow (Steinberg 1993: 182-185). The archetypes are living tissue, and if they grow, they are alive and will at every opportunity "do their thing," usually outside the bounds of our ego consciousness.

The *anima/animus* is also one of the most controversial of Jung's notions, due primarily to: (1) the difficulty of operationalizing the term in the kind of crisp, inclusive-exclusive form that lab-oriented science prefers, and (2) the Western cultural stereotypes evident in Jung's definition of male and female attributes. Jung never intended the concepts to be other than phenomenological ones, covering as they so usefully do the very fuzzy natural categories of our experiences of the collective unconscious:

> The empirical reality summed up under the concept of the *anima* forms an extremely dramatic content of the unconscious. It is possible to describe this content in rational, scientific language, but in this way, one entirely fails to express its living character. Therefore, in describing the living processes of the psyche, I deliberately and consciously give preference to a dramatic, mythological way of thinking and speaking, because this is not only more expressive but also more exact than an abstract scientific terminology, which is wont to toy with the notion that its theoretic formulations may one fine day be resolved into algebraic equations. (Jung 1951/1959: 13)

The *anima/animus* cannot be pinned down to a crisp theoretical formulation, for to attempt to do so, as many "Jungian" systematists are wont to do, is to rob the term of its essentially phenomenological power. Indeed, natural categories of transpersonal experiences are by their very nature fuzzy (see Laughlin 1993 on this issue). As Jung (1961/1965) notes in his autobiography, *Memories, Dreams, Reflections*, the notion of *anima/animus* arose because of his experience of his parents, the experiences of his patients, and especially in his own internal process of individuation. Considering this rich symbolic material, Jung suspected at first that the *anima/animus* is in relation to the unconscious as the persona is in relation to the external world of objects (Jung 1928/1966: 304). But being open to his own experiences, he later came to see that the same-sex shadow performs that filtering process with the unconscious, and that the *anima/animus* involves the direct apprehension of the unconscious by the ego—a relationship that may nonetheless be distorted by shadow responses to contragender content. Indeed, it was Jung's view that it is through incorporating the shadow, or the personal unconscious that one comes into a more direct and effective interaction with the *anima/animus*. For this reason, he argued (Jung 1951/1959:

22) that the *anima/animus* should be encountered within the context of actual human relationships for the contragender elements of the psyche to be integrated into consciousness. As we shall see, while this is the most common course of integration of *anima/animus* materials, especially for individuals undergoing psychoanalysis, the enactment of the syzygies in actual relationships is neither necessary nor sufficient for individuation. Were this not true, then Eastern paths like Tantric Buddhism would be ineffectual.

Unfortunately, most people never come to understand that many of the attributes they project upon their contragender opposites derive from qualities of their very own psyches that their enculturation has caused to be alienated from their consciousness. In blind ignorance of their own psychodynamics, most people fail to perceive the many and varied ways they project their unconscious selves upon other people (Jung 1951/1959: 19; 1930-1934/1997: 4-5). Nonetheless, experience teaches those with the eyes to see that we frequently become ensnared by our own projected psychic materials:

> The *Anima* determines man's relationship to women, and in the encounter with a woman, man experiences and recognizes the essence of his own soul. Wherever he projects his soul upon a woman, a kind of magic identity is established. This expresses itself in the guise of overwhelming emotions, especially with the intense feeling of "falling-in-love." Thereby the *Anima* becomes fate-shaping. When one's own soul is projected, one feels unable to separate oneself any longer from the object of the projection. When one believes he has found, at long last, one's complement, one does not want to lose this "other half." Thus, the *Anima* drives the young man towards the realization of his yearnings. (Brunner 1963/1986: xxi-xxii)

We unconsciously yearn for unity with and within our self, but because we are outer-oriented, we project the contragender aspects of ourselves upon the Other and then feel compelled to interact with them in a manner Jung (1930-1934/1997: 6-7; after Lucien Levy-Bruhl 1923) called *participation mystique*, or the kind of magico-mystical involvement in which we can become trapped when possessed by unconscious materials. Such possession states are frequently highly charged with psychic energy (i.e., libido; see Jung 1912/1956: Part 2, Ch. 2) and the object of our obsession numinous, bordering on the sacred—"oh beloved, you are to me a goddess!" Because the state of participation mystique is a special kind of absorption state (see Laughlin, McManus and d'Aquili 1990: 118), the experience is of at least a partial dissolution of ego boundaries and a sense of union with the Other.

Culture and the *Anima*

It is my bias that it is possible for any of us to learn how our own psyches work. To accomplish this, however, requires that one develop the skills requisite to a contemplative frame of mind. Armed with contemplative skills (see Laughlin, McManus and d'Aquili 1990: Ch. 11), it is possible to understand the mechanisms of consciousness by studying one's own mental acts—even as they are operating upon objects and events in the world. And sooner or later this process of internal study brings us into contact with our *anima/animus*. As I mentioned above, Jung suggested the term *anima/animus* to cover the experiences we all have of the contragender archetypes buried in our own unconscious, the material appropriate to the opposite sex that we inherit as humans and suppress during our development. For me, as for other males, this relationship with the unconscious is often mediated by feminine imagery, as well as by reflection upon my relationships with real women.[34] That is, aspects of my unconscious self are frequently represented by female motifs in dreams, fantasies, episodes of active imagination, spontaneous visions (Skt: *nimitta*) during meditation, and in projections upon actual females with whom I am interacting (Meier 1995: 103). Those Eros qualities that during my own enculturation were considered female—qualities like nurture, emotion, sensitivity to nuances of relationship, mood, softness, intuition and spiritual awareness—were suppressed in my youthful quest for a male identity. But because that quest had drawn

---

[34] As with Jung before me, and with other Jungians wise enough to do so, I refrain from describing what the conscious individuation is like for females. There are significant differences in a male's encounter with their feminine parts, and a female's encounter with their male parts. I cannot describe a female's phenomenology for I cannot walk very far in their shoes.

my ego way off center from the self, the self began to call the ego back into its fold with imagery that hooked my attention and awareness—the first and foremost call being the mandala experiences I described before (Chapter 6). My path of individuation, as is perhaps the case with everyone, has been idiosyncratic—a reflection of my own distinct life-course (Ulanov and Ulanov 1994: 19). In addition, my path has also reflected both cultural and genetic elements—my childhood enculturation and the array of archetypal structures I inherited as a human with a very typical human nervous system.

Much has been made of Jung's presumed ignorance of the fact that his experiences as a contemplative and as a healer were culturally loaded—were in anthropological terms, *ethnocentric*. But this view is pretty much the result of a superficial reading of Jung. In fact, he was perfectly aware that the *anima/animus* experiences of people from other cultures would be different and conditioned by their upbringing. Moreover, as the archetypes themselves are never experienced directly, and are really structures, not contents, an infinite variety of images and themes may be mediated by the *anima/animus*, depending upon personal and cultural factors (see Ulanov and Ulanov 1994: 16-18 for a nice discussion of this issue). Keep in mind that Jung was as avid a reader of the ethnography of his day as was Freud. Indeed, his appreciation of cross-cultural variation was at the root of his suspicion of Eastern yogic and spiritual practices as appropriate for Westerners.

As for myself, because my masculine ego-ideal, as well as the field of underdeveloped archetypes comprising my unconscious was heavily impacted by my upbringing, it is clear to me that just what constellation of archetypes comprises the *anima* for me will vary from that of other males in my society, and is demonstrably influenced heavily by my culture. Culture clearly influences the extent to which a male identifies with the variety of functions of the psyche—with emotion, with intuition, and with other attributes of self. Thus, the path of self-discovery for each of us is as much an encounter with our cultural background and personal development as it is with the neurognostic collective unconscious. As is sometimes said in the Western mysteries, each knight must enter the forest at the place darkest to him (or her). This is St. John's "dark night of the soul" (Underhill 1955), and Chan and Zen Buddhism's *dai-gidan* (Hashi 2016). This is a necessary state in anyone's self-awakening.

Nixies, Goddesses and Succubi

Since the beginning of time man, with his wholesome
animal instinct, has been engaged in combat with his soul
and its demonism. If the soul were uniformly dark, it would
be a simple matter. Unfortunately, this is not so, for the
anima can appear also as an angel of light, a psychopomp
who points the way to the highest meaning....

— Jung (1940/1968a, p. 29)

When we males do enter that forest, we enter the domain of the Wild
Mother (i.e., the *chthonic* unconscious, the thoroughly chaotic and
undifferentiated domain of Eros). We encounter both mythical beasts
and domesticated animals, demons of every sort and description, and
eventually the positive and negative aspects of the contragender *anima*.
As we emerge from each encounter, we are impressed with the living
reality of the archetypes—entities in the depths of the psyche that
seem not only to be alive and enduring, but also marked by something
approaching consciousness.

Jung's writings appear at times to be ambiguous with respect to
whether the archetypes are conscious. He speaks at times as though the
anima only attains consciousness by interaction and integration with the
ego (e.g., Jung 1951/1959: 24-25), and at other times he speaks of the
anima as the ego's *psychopomp*[35] in its exploration of the unconscious,
and of having a personality of its own (e.g., Jung 1930-1934/1997: 1215-
1216). However, this apparent ambiguity is not actual. A closer reading
of Jung, accompanied by the requisite direct experience, may lead to a
better understanding of the subtle distinction between being conscious
of something in the normal ego sense, and the active, living presence and
intention of non-ego mediated archetypes. The archetypes do compete
for trophic resources, of course, because they are networks of living cells
within the central nervous system. Being organizations of millions of

---

[35] A *psychopomp* in Jungian psychology is an entity or image that mediates between
the unconscious and conscious parts of the psyche. In dreams, visions and fantasies,
the psychopomp may take the form of a wise man or woman, an animal helper, a spirit
guide, a shaman or guru.

cells, the archetypes will "do their thing," so to speak, in a very active way. But just because structures in the unconscious are living systems, compete for trophic resources, and may eventually become entrained to consciousness, this does not mean that the archetypes themselves are conscious. Rather, as Jung suggests: "It is as if you cut off a little finger and it continued to live quite independently; it would then be a little finger personality, it would be a he or a she, it would give itself a name and talk out of its own mind" (1930-1934/1997: 1216).

The struggle of "I-ness" among the complexes is achieved through the competition of organized networks of cells for entrainment to conscious network—in this respect I come down heavily on Jung's side rather than James Hillman's more metaphysical views (Hillman 1989: 31; Collins 1994: 13). So far as I can tell from my own explorations, the archetypes are not conscious in the commonsense way we all mean by the term—a term defined primarily upon the qualities of awareness and intentionality that we experience in ourselves every day. But when the archetypes engage consciousness by way of imagery, they do become involved to some extent in consciousness, and in a certain sense "become conscious." As Jung repeatedly emphasized, however, the archetypes are autonomous, and cannot be known directly, but only by way of their imaginary productions. So, causation from consciousness back to the archetypes (so to speak) is constrained by the fact of the unconscious nature of archetypal processing (1928/1966: 97). The unconscious, and especially the collective unconscious, is largely free from the intentionality of consciousness. Yet, at the same time, the process of assimilation of archetypal materials by the ego does exercise a certain limiting effect upon subsequent transformations produced by the archetypes, and the role of the ego in generating distinctions and discriminations among archetypal elements arising in consciousness is fundamental to the effect of the archetypes on our experience.

The most common medium for encountering the *anima/animus* is in our most intimate contragender relationships, beginning of course with our contragender parent or caregiver (Ulanov and Ulanov 1994; Schwartz-Salant 1998).[36] There is fascinating evidence from pre- and perinatal psychology that we are born as social beings, cognizing and

---

[36] Roughly half of the traditional cultures we know about have caregivers other than parents (see Laughlin 1991).

participating in social events, and knowing our mothers. Not only is the world of physical objects archetypally "already there" to neonatal perception at, or before birth, so too is the world of socially significant objects and interactions—objects that include speech sounds or vocal vibrations, interactive gestures, emotional expressions, and especially the face, gestures, feelings, smell, physical touch, breasts and speech of the mother (Field 1985; Murray and Trevarthen 1985; Butterworth and Grover 1988; Lagercrantz 2016). In other words, we are born with certain neurognostic proclivities to project socially relevant meaning upon significant others.

As I have argued elsewhere (Laughlin 1990b), the psychological attributes projected upon the feminine are non-arbitrary and are grounded in our pre- and perinatal experiences of both the woman *as the world*, and the mother or female caregiver as a powerful mediator between the perinatal child and the world. Because of this heavy archetypal loading, followed by early experiential identification of the feminine with Eros, the Logos faculties of the higher cortical functions that generally develop later than the experiential-emotional faculties become invested in the masculine. Of course, the extent of opposition between feminine and masculine attributes in the adult will depend upon the personality, enculturation and age of the individual. Nonetheless, there exists a recognizable cross-cultural and non-arbitrary regularity to gender projections.

The whole of the self is never projected upon the Other, nor can we rely solely upon tracking our projections onto Others in the outer world to learn the full breadth and depth of our *anima/animus* manifestations (Jung 1951/1959: 19; cf. Schwartz-Salant 1998: Ch. 10). This is because living people often evoke projections that they resemble relative to our *anima/animus* imagery. The classic example is when a person is drawn to a contragender Other who reminds them, either consciously, or more often unconsciously, of their mother or father. But no one person can resemble our entire *anima/animus*. In my case, my *anima* will generate one set of attributions upon a small, dark, compact and moody woman who becomes for me a *chthonic* nixie—a woman vaguely resembling my mother in her youth, and a creature of the oceanic depths, inarticulate and seductive in her ways, emotionally chaotic and often destructive. If my gaze were to become trapped by her, I would be led into a tumultuous and chaotic roller coaster ride which would inevitably end in torment and self-denigration—for me, a siren of monumental proportions.

But also, my *anima* will project another set of attributions upon a taller, fairer, slenderer and more intelligent woman—a female Other of radiance and loving countenance who may act as both nurturing lover, fellow spiritual companion, and even psychopomp. The *anima* qualities that I "recognize" in the Other will be somewhat different, depending upon the archetypal category to which the woman's image penetrates. And of course, no living person can live up to these projections entirely, if at all—be they positive or negative. There is an interesting difference here in that when men make love to a woman in dreams, the females tend to be generic *anima* figures, while when women make love to a man in a dream, he tends to be some positive male figure that they know in waking life, either romantic figures, heroic ones, or spiritual teachers (Garfield 1988: 36-37, 335). If one holds tenaciously to these projections while awake and attempts to ignore or explain away the anomalous qualities of the real person, then the relationship, so long as it lasts, is doomed to acted-out psychopathology and/or oblivion. In extreme form, a person could become so ensnared by negative projections upon women as to possibly become a malignant psychopath, whether he acts out his projections of not.

When it comes to relationships with the opposite sex, we are caught between the horns of the proverbial dilemma—a dilemma wired into our neurophysiology. On the one hand we are designed to track and model reality in a veridical way. Psychotic hunters would not last long in the jungle. On the other hand, we are propelled by an inner urge to organic unity—to organize the bits and pieces of our psyche into a coherent whole. When we become engaged in tracking our *anima/animus*, we find out that the same person in the real world—our significant Other—is the object of the drive both for verity and for, as it were, an *anima/animus* "projection device." The same person becomes both a real object in the world, and a mirror of our own unconscious processes. Obviously, a relationship that is born of mutual projections may fail miserably unless the couple grow to transcend those projections and ground their relationship in the real natures of their respective selves.

As I have mentioned already, much is made in the literature about real relationships being the principal locus for the *anima/animus* work (e.g., Schwartz-Salant 1998). While this is probably true for most people who work within a Jungian frame, full engagement with the *anima/animus* requires neither a real person, nor is a real relationship sufficient for completing the work. Indeed, there are dangers attendant to using other people in this kind of exercise. However, those familiar with Tibetan Tantric meditation techniques may be aware that while most Tibetan practitioners may use pictures to visualize the male and female deities (the *yab* and the *yum*), advanced Tantric practitioners have practiced with a cross-sex consort in the flesh (Child 2016). As far as I know, this practice is now virtually dead among Tantric meditators. However, there are modern practitioners of what might be called *mystical sex* who combine meditation and *coitus reservatus* (reserving ejaculation) to prolong sexual union and to incubate a mystical experience (see Meldman 1990: Chap. 2).

To optimize our encounters with our *anima/animus*, we must learn to track our dream, fantasy and other imagery directly—we must learn to quiet the mind and contemplate spontaneous visions and explore themes and scenarios in active imagination (Chapter 7). In so doing we may come to explore our *anima* materials freed-up from projection upon real people and contain the projections to images evoked within the internal field of our own "theater of mind." In this way we accumulate the data necessary to discern patterns in the imagery, and thus begin to make cognitive distinctions based upon the recurrent form of the imagery, recurrent context of presentation and typical emotional and intuitive loading.

The *Coniunctio*

I have described for you one of my own *anima* experiences in Chapter 4, the one involving the image of that beautiful blond female figure dressed in a red shift. Let me remind you of the details: The figure of the lovely woman appeared to my left walking away from me. I sent her a blast of loving feeling visualized as a laser beam of rose light emanating from my heart. As the laser beam of light connected with the image, both the image of the woman and my bodily self-awareness instantly exploded into a rapidly expanding sphere of rose energy. Within a split second, my consciousness was in a state of intense absorption upon boundless space filled with pulsing, shimmering rose particles and ecstatic bliss.

There then followed the eruption of a soundless scream and another energy explosion from the depths of my being that culminated in the awareness of the visual image of a tunnel or birth canal. When corporeal awareness gradually returned, I spent a couple of hours in complete tranquility, either contemplating the essential attributes of mind, or in absorption upon this or that symbol as it arose before the mind's eye.

Several elements of this experience are significant to our discussion of pure *anima* visions and contemplation:

Perfection of the image. Contemplatives come to understand that images freed from the imposition of external perception tend to perfect themselves. From my point of view, the female form was utterly perfect. The sense is that no living human being could ever be that flawlessly beautiful. Or if it is a negative *anima* image, nothing in the world could be that totally repulsive or terrible. In both Eastern and Western meditation training, an external object like a bowl of water or a flower or the painting of a deity or guru is frequently used to activate an image that is then internalized in the "mind's eye" and meditated upon as an internalized image. Those who do this work notice that the internalized image or "visualization" tends to perfect itself. It will lose any flaws present in the external stimulus and will perfect the ideal geometry of relations in the form. A roughly rounded bowl will become perfectly round, a picture with flaws or scratches will become flawless. The deity may become translucent and even radiant as though it were backlit. In this manner one may learn that no object in the real world could ever completely match the perfection of the inner imagery. As a matter of fact, there exist Tantric texts in the East describing the physical qualities to be looked for in finding the ideal Tantric consort (a *lekyi chagya*). These instructions are a guide for finding a lover who simulates as close to the perfect *dakini* (female spirit consort of the *Yab*) on the inner plane as is possible. And with such an experience, one may learn where our notions of gods and goddesses derive—from the projections onto our sensorium, and from our sensorium onto the world of the perfect productions of our unconscious.

Intense affective charge. Pure *anima* images may be entrained to intense psychic (libidinous) energies. Indeed, the affective charge may become so intense as to constitute a warp driving the consciousness into an altered state—perhaps an intense state of absorption. This pairing of the *anima* image and intense affect may confirm and animate our interpretation of the feminine principle. In the East, this energetic principle is associated with images of the *dakinis*, young naked females dancing in the flames of transformation. The image of the blond woman in the red shift was my very Western vision of the *dakini*.

The *coniunctio*. With the amount of love that had been generated doing the loving-kindness visualization and mantra work, there transpired the explosive dissolution of both ego consciousness and alienation from the Other, thus producing, for a few moments at least, what Jung called the *coniunctio oppositorum* (Jung 1951/1959: 31; 1940/1968a: 175-177; von Franz 1980: 268), the mystical resolution of the tension of *syzygistic*[37] duality. Loving or positive blissful psychic energy is the alchemical *alkahest*, the universal solvent which, when it fills the crucible containing the opposites, dissolves the boundaries and creates a union (Chapter 11 for more on this). I suspect that the closest most people come to this experience is during orgasm, a relatively brief state which is mediated by the simultaneous discharge of both the sympathetic and parasympathetic nervous systems (see Chapter 4). The meditative *coniunctio* experience is probably energized in a similar fashion, but without the involvement of the sexual organs. I should note that for me the *coniunctio* experience was many times as intense as any orgasm I have ever experienced, thus adding to the sense of the sacredness and numinosity of the joining.

Girls, Girls, and Not a Drop to Drink!

The woman in a red shift experience proved to be a profound one for my development but was by no means a solitary event. In fact, many hundreds of images have emerged out of the mist in dreams and visions that have provided information about the breadth, depth, and various attributes of the *anima*. Often these images reflected the positive and negative (ego-shadow) ambiguities relative to the feminine. As I described in Chapter 5, there was one period during which numerous visions and dreams were replete with more than the usual sexual imagery. Also, I have already described how I learned to direct psychic energy either outward as sexual energy or up the central channel to

---

[37] A *syzygy* is a perfect pairing of the male and female principles forming a whole.

the various chakras. If for example one is focused upon a radiant female deity as the object of meditation, the psychic energy directed from the heart may lead to ecstatic union, whereas if the energy is directed outwards through the genitals, the imagery may shift to coitus. A central point to make here is, so far as my phenomenology shows, as goes the structure of psychic energy (or libido), so goes the imagery. The image and the affect appear to be two aspects of the same underlying archetypal expression. As an aside, my hunch is that male Tantric practitioners who used actual coitus with a female were using this "switch" to transform the sexual energy they stimulated at the genitals to the central channel, thus energizing their heart chakras. As we shall see in Chapter 11, it is intense mystical love that can produce the antithesis of fear and aversion.

With respect to the shadow and its impact upon experiencing the *anima* and its productions, one must keep in mind that we are dealing with the interplay between two levels in the development of the brain—one being the conditioned "personal" unconscious and the other being the deeper, more primordial and relatively unconditioned "collective" unconscious—the latter in my view being the nascent, genetically inherited organization of the human nervous system, while the former are the more developed, antinomous adaptations that have emerged during enculturation and ego-identity formation of the individual. In my case, during my youth there existed a strong draw towards, complemented by a fear of, anger at, and aversion to the female Other. This ambiguity was laid down in my infancy and was acted out in the world for years by a neurotic alternating attraction and aversion to the same woman. In the experience of *anima* imagery, the positive-negative duality expressed itself at times as female figures that would morph from sexually attractive forms into repulsive, fearsome forms, and vice versa. This ambiguity expressed itself in such meditative visions as the shape-shifting woman coming through the picket fence described before. The affect during this episode was revealing and typical of many of my encounters with *anima* figures. The affect was ambivalent—of sexual attraction or interest on the one hand and anxiety on the other, the ego/persona associating itself with the positive attraction to the feminine, while the shadow was in fear of engulfment and possession by the Terrible Mother. To the shadow, woman takes on the aspect of the *succubus*, one of "Kali's minions" as my late friend John McManus used to say.

Obviously, the *anima* may be experienced both positively and negatively, as both good and evil, as radiant light and order, or darkness and all engulfing chaos, depending upon the filter of affect and attitude intervening between consciousness and the archetypal material (Jung 1940/1968a: 28-36). Of course, the normal state of consciousness of one encountering the *anima* is primarily that of ego involvement with imagery while repressing the various shadow elements. Hence, for most of us, we are conscious primarily of positive affect relative to our cross-gender Other. Our shadow attributions and affect remain in the subconscious and act out their feelings, values and intents in devious ways, including projection upon people often more distant from us than loved ones, and "passive aggression" upon those closer to us. But in meditation states the shadow may become far more conscious such that one is aware of both complexes simultaneously. As Jung himself put it:

> The relative autonomy of the *anima-* and *animus-*figures expresses itself in these qualities. In order of affective rank, they stand to the shadow very much as the shadow stands in relation to ego-consciousness. The main affective emphasis seems to lie on the latter; at any rate it [the ego] is able, by means of a considerable expenditure of energy, to repress the shadow, at least temporarily. *But if for any reason the unconscious gains the upper hand, then the valency of the shadow and of the other figures increases proportionately,* so the scale of values is reversed. (1951/1959: 28; emphasis added)

Of course, in meditation work, the unconscious may well gain the upper hand, at least for a while, for the deepening tranquility that develops in mature contemplation, as it were, withholds energy for repressions. Arising *anima* figures may be greeted by ambiguous feelings and conflicting attitudes, depending of course on the distinct pattern of enculturation and personal development of the individual psyche— that is, depending upon the ego-shadow configuration and its limbic and cognitive-perceptual associations.

Anima possession can no doubt be dangerous to the stability of an individual's daily adaptation. But possession does have its lighter side. The funniest encounter with *anima* possession I ever experienced occurred during that lengthy retreat in Scotland I mentioned in Chapter 5. During that retreat I was working on the symbolism of the Tibetan tantric deity Demchog (in Tibetan Buddhist terms, the *yab*). Demchog's consort is Dorje Pakmo (the *yum*). The two are depicted in the text and in pictures as dancing in flames while in sexual union—that is, in so-called *yab-yum* posture. One of the techniques used in this practice is to imagine oneself alternately as the male deity embracing the female, then as the female deity embracing the male. Naturally it was far easier for me to identify with Demchog than with Dorje Pakmo, so I spent a lot of time working on visualizing myself as a young, vivacious, red-skinned female. While identifying with the *yum*, I would take on a certain submissive relationship to the *yab*, and would imagine quite successfully being entered by "his" phallus. Meanwhile, during this retreat I was wearing the long flowing red robes of the Tibetan monk, and I would daily take long walks out on the moor where all I ever saw were herds of sheep in the distance and the occasional shepherd. There came a point in these meditations when the female image penetrated deeply into my unconscious and I began to act out the part, and on several occasions found myself dancing lightly across the moor singing tunes like "I'm a girl! I'm a girl!" at the top of my lungs. Part of my observing mind was fascinated with these acted-out transformations, while another part drew amusing associations with Julie Andrews in the movie, *The Sound of Music*.

Less entertaining, but of equal importance were the *anima*-related imagery that emerged during the *yab-yum* work. I have already mentioned back in Chapter 5 that the *yab* and the *yum* simplified into a blue and red *bindu*. I learned several things from this relative to doing a kind of active imagination using these images:

Bindus may represent the *anima.* The interaction of the *bindus* represents to some extent the general state of consciousness at the moment, even during more ordinary states, and the interaction between the watcher, the shadow and the feminine *anima*. The vastness of the self often crops up as a red mist surrounding the dynamic *yab* and *yum bindus*, the red sphere representing the *anima*-bridge between the ego identified with Logos and the vastness of the unconscious.

Simplification increases symbolic universality. As internal images *qua* symbols become naturally simplified, they also become more universal. Symbols like Demchog and Dorje Pakmo, as with Jesus and Mary, or with the Navajo's First Man and First Woman, are heavily loaded with cultural attributes. But as they simplify before the mind's eye, they take on increasingly universal forms—forms like flowing water, colored mist, spheres, lightning bolts, rocks, etc. This includes the naked human form as well.

THE *ANIMA* AND CULTURE

Thus, the anima *and life itself are meaningless in so far as they offer no interpretation. Yet they have a nature that can be interpreted, for in all chaos there is a cosmos, in all disorder a secret order, in all caprice a fixed law, for everything that works is grounded on its opposite. It takes man's discriminating understanding, which breaks everything down into antinomial judgements, to recognize this.*

— Jung (1940/1968a: 66)

Coming to terms with one's *anima* is a hermeneutic process (Jung 1940/1968a: 32-41). Meanings do not adhere to the contents of the unconscious but are attributed by conscious reflection to contents. Yet there is an ordered—one might even say lawful—regularity to these contents. It is the task of the engaged ego to apply meaning that as closely as possible approximates the hidden order expressed by the *anima*, and to do so in a dynamic, growing and non-ideological manner. For, as I have said, the *anima* is not the unconscious itself, but only the expression of processes forever hidden from our sight. As a northward flying wedge of geese is the harbinger of spring, so too is *anima* imagery the harbinger of processes in the self revealing themselves. The sight of a flight of geese is only a harbinger to the mind that associates this phenomenon with a much-welcomed change of seasons. In other words, the phenomenon is interpreted as a sign, and as it happens is naturally associated with seasonal changes.

In the same way, we learn to interpret our own *anima* imagery in a way that both accurately reflects the underlying processes of the psyche and builds a shared repository of meaning by means of which the conscious and unconscious parts of our psyche may communicate with each other. It is as though there is room for only one library of symbols within memory, a repertoire of images that both the conscious and unconscious parts of the psyche may use to communicate. The problem is that the grammar of the communication differs drastically between the two, and it is the task of the conscious mind to learn to read the unfamiliar rules of the unconscious, for the unconscious cannot and will not adapt to the grammar of the higher cortical functions of the brain. In time, there develops a corpus of shared meanings by which the unconscious may express its deepest processes, and the conscious mind may use to penetrate and engage unconscious processes. For example, if I close my eyes and focus my attention upon the spontaneous dance of the *bindus*, I will be better able to interpret what is going on in my psyche. In that way I am privileging the communication from the unconscious. But alternatively, I can use visualization techniques to trigger desired activities normally outside the direct control of consciousness. For example, suppose that I am feeling stressed. If I focus my attention upon a radiant cool blue, pea-sized *bindu* in my "third eye" region and then suddenly drop the sphere into my navel region, my body will almost instantaneously calm. In this way I am privileging the executive function of the conscious ego over the unconscious (see Rubia 2009 on the effects of meditation upon stress).

The Traditional Cycle of Meaning

For my conscious ego and for my unconscious, the meaning of the *bindu* and other *anima*-related images (nixies, goddesses, succubae) has developed out of their nascent, relatively undifferentiated forms into a virtual dictionary of symbols, based upon a lifetime of experiences associated with them in memory. If I had been born and raised in a traditional society with an intact mystical world view, and had I undergone many of these experiences, I no doubt would have interpreted them within the local cosmological context—within their cycle of meaning. The cosmology, which people mainly carry around in their heads, is imagined and expressed by way of their culture's stock of symbolic material in such a way that people can participate intimately in their version of a symbolically pregnant mythic reality. As Alfonso Ortiz (1972, p. 135) noted, the associations, principles and assumptions upon which a traditional cosmology are founded are rarely, if ever, created anew by individuals. Rather, most people accept and participate in accordance with the world view they inherit from their culture. This participation results in real life experiences that are in turn interpreted in terms of the cosmology, thus completing a negative feedback loop which instantiates the cosmology in individual experiences and which also confirms the truth of the people's system of knowledge.

Let me suggest a good example of an intact traditional cycle of meaning from the culture of the Navajo people of the American Southwest—a people amongst whom I lived and researched on and off for years. While it is true that many Navajo people today do not entirely subscribe to the traditional world view and may in fact know little about their traditional roots, traditional Navajo cosmology exhibits many of the features common to such cosmologies worldwide (see Laughlin and Throop 2001). Moreover, the cosmology is thoroughly syzygistic, both in religious iconography and in its appreciation of the antinomous, yet unitary nature of reality. Much of Navajo philosophy is organized around the postulate that all perceivable things in the world have invisible aspects that may be imagined as "Holy People"—for example, the Mountain People, the Star People, the River People, the Rain People, the Corn People, and so forth. Most of the humanoid Holy People have a male and a female representation; that is, Blue Corn Boy, Blue Corn Girl, and so forth. For more philosophically inclined Navajo thinkers, these Holy People are thought of as anthropomorphized symbols for the normally hidden and vital element within all things, which traditional Navajo philosophy equates with "Wind" (*nilch'i*; see McNeley 1981). As real people, we also have such a hidden dimension called "the Wind within one" (*nilch'i hwii'siziinii*). All these Winds are really part of the one all-pervasive and all-encompassing Holy Wind. Winds are never understood to be distinct entities, since energy is thought to be flowing in and out of even the most apparently enduring objects. It is the coming and going of wind that accounts for the tapestry of reciprocal causation typical of this understanding of the cosmos. The choice of "wind" as the central metaphor is an explicit recognition—common among many cultures on the planet—that there are forces that normally cannot be observed, save by inference from their effects (Chapter 4).

At the root of the sacredness of Navajo cosmology, and of the Holy People who represent the essence of reality, are the many myths recounted down through the generations. It is very much the function of myth in societies like Navajo to reveal and explicate the hidden dimensions of the world. The hidden energies that are the essence of the world are given a face—a countenance that may be contemplated, that is "pleasing to the mind," that may be enacted in ritual (e.g., in the elaborate and ingenious Navajo system of *hitaal*, or healing ceremonies), and that may be imagined in daily life as the efficient cause of significant phenomena and events. For those members who are well versed in their society's mythopoetic system, the core myths and their various symbolic extrusions are often understood to be all-of-a-piece. They form a single, ramified "cognitive map" (Wallace 1966) within the context of which events in their everyday lives make sense and are easily related to both other events in the contemporary world, and archetypal events that unfold in the context of mythological narratives.

As I said, Navajo cosmology is essentially syzygistic. The main tension and complementarity characteristic of the world is attributed to the interplay of the male and female principles. Complementarity is emphasized, each pole requiring the other to maintain viability. There are even myths that tell the story of what happens when the male and female principles get out of synch (see Matthews 1897/1994: 71-74). Even the famous Navajo ceremonials are divided into complementary sets, the Blessingway ceremonies, given female attribution and concerned with harmony, and the Enemyway ceremonies (given male attribution and concerned with protection; see Griffin-Pierce 1992: 40-41). Within each of these sets, there are male and female elements—like the male *bindu* in the female field and the female *bindu* in the male field in the yin-yang symbol. Hence anyone reared under the influence of these stories and ceremonies would come to interpret relationships as characterized by both polarized tension and unity of complements. Moreover, both men and women are conditioned to think of themselves as both embodying male and female principles and being essentially whole and spiritually empowered by the one all-pervasive Holy Wind. The most important concept in Navajo philosophy is *hozho*, which is usually translated as "beauty" or "blessing," but which also connotes harmony, health, unity, good, and so forth (Farella 1984). Men who have knowledge about and participate in the traditional ways will explicitly interpret their state of *hozho* in terms of the male and female principles being in harmony within their being. Their *anima* (they would not speak in Jungian terms of course) would be related to the female Holy

People and specially to Changing Woman, the Navajo's most revered goddess and beloved Earth Mother (Schwarz 1997).

My Own Transpersonal Cycle of Meaning

Many of us in modern Euro-American-Aussie society do not have such an intact syzygistic cosmological tradition into which we have been nurtured and enculturated, and to which we can have recourse when interpreting our inner imaginings. We do have elements of a long past world view of traditional structure—we attribute feminine qualities to the moon and male qualities to the sun, Earth is feminine, and Mars is masculine. But there is no commonly accepted story that integrates all these "survivals" of a past age to provide a transpersonal interpretive frame. Thus, part of the spiritual path for many of us requires that we discover some sensible context within which to lodge and integrate these meanings. It was not mere happenstance that led Jung to embrace latter-day alchemy as his base for interpreting his experiences (1944/1968b; 1955-1956/1970). And the remarkable irony is that his psychology allows many of us to ground our conscious individuation in an interpretive frame. Traditional peoples usually have this feature built-in as it were to their cosmology.

Moreover, this quest for an integrated context of meaning is required by the "holistic operator" of the brain (d'Aquili and Newberg 1999), or what Jung called the archetype of wholeness, which he held was indistinguishable from the image of the divine (Jung 1951/1959: 40; 1940/1968a: 388). I, on the other hand, like so many these days, have borrowed extensively from Eastern mystical teachings and have combined them with various aspects of modern science, including knowledge about how the human brain works. Still others have found the required context in charismatic Christianity, Sufism, or in shamanism, Wicca and other so-called "New Age" religions. The result is that I, like many who spend years tracking their inner psyche, have developed a quite personal, and essentially transpersonal cycle of meaning. Recall the mandala experience I previously mentioned. The first time I encountered this experience, the only context of interpretation I had in my head was that a friend had dosed me with a psychotropic drug. In other words, I had no appropriate cycle of meaning within which these transpersonal experiences made any sense. But later—much later—my life course had led me through various avenues and adventures, and I ended up thinking about things out of an essentially transpersonal world view in which not only mandala experiences, but ecstatic union with ladies in red shifts and dancing *bindus* make perfect sense. The major difference between both mine and Carl Jung's paths on the one hand, and those of people raised in traditional cosmological cycles of meaning on the other, is that mine (and I read Jung's as well) is relatively dynamic and plastic, while most traditional systems tend to be extremely conservative of meaning. In fact, adepts in traditional systems tend to place strict controls on the types of experiences that can occur and the range of interpretations available for those experiences. For instance, professional Moroccan oneirocritics always interpret the more important dreams of their clients in terms of the symbolism and teaching of the Koran, whereas a proper Jungian approach to dream interpretation is appropriately individual and dynamic (see e.g., Jung 1930-1934/1997; see also Maidenbaum 1998).

SUMMARY AND SEGUE

These reflections upon the *anima* have been all too brief. But a few salient points have, I think, been brought out with respect to our engagement with the *anima*. Let me close by briefly outlining the more important points, and then note the relevance of *anima* to transpersonal studies:

Anima **and gender.** Although we most commonly encounter our *anima* in the image of the female person—especially in the intimate relationship with our significant Other—not all *anima* imagery is explicitly female. Nor need it be, either when it spontaneously arises or when we use imagery to penetrate to and potentiate unconscious processes. Images like mandalas, animals, geographical features like simulacra, tunnels and streams may all represent or penetrate to the *anima*. A symbol as simple as a *bindu* may suffice. Thus, whether or not a symbol represents the *anima* is an interpretive act, easy enough to accomplish with projections upon actual females, but a much more creative operation with tunnels and *bindus*. We need always to keep in mind that Jung never intended the concept to be crisply defined upon any distinct form. The *anima* is a function of the psyche. Whatever imagery occurs to express those unconscious and archetypal aspects of the nonmale self that we have suppressed in our development as males may be reasonably supposed to be activities of the *anima*. In any event, this forms a good working hypothesis from which to begin discriminating *anima* and non-*anima* imagery.

Anima as structure and as content. There is a natural ambiguity between thinking of the *anima* as an innate function of the nervous system which, until active in producing imagery in the sensorium, remains essentially content-less. This is like saying that until the hand does its thing, there is no grasping. *Anima* may refer to the underlying structure of communication between the conscious and unconscious mental faculties, and it may refer to the dream and fantasy imagery that expresses activities in the unconscious. This distinction is far from trivial when we place the issue in cross-cultural perspective, for while there is such a phenomenon as a relatively pure archetypal experience, most *anima* imagery is culturally loaded. I seriously doubt that a black citizen of Zimbabwe, or a Micronesian from the Marshall Islands would encounter a radiant white blond in a shift during a meditation retreat. More than likely, their positive *anima* ideal would resemble their own culture's goddesses. But to say that the content of *anima* imagery is culturally influenced is not to deny the universal, archetypal basis of the structures within the nervous system that mediate them.

Anima and affect. While it is natural to focus upon dream imagery and meditation symbols, it is often the affect associated with these phenomena that provides the tipoff to *anima* eruptions. This is especially true with shadow-*anima* interactions. My impression for years has been that the symbolism in a vision or dream may be produced by the affect, rather than the affect tagging along after the imagery. Often the imagery would seem to provide a scenario that makes sense of the feelings we have going on now. Conflicting emotions may well produce a scenario of conflicting relations among images. Thus, not only may archetypal images be influenced by culture, so too will the emotion that is associated with the imagery, for emotion as it is commonly understood in our culture is mediated by cognitive as well as affective structures (Laughlin and Throop, 1999).

Anima and interpretation. The main point I wish to stress here is that working with the *anima*, in any cultural setting, is an interpretive process. The *anima* must be involved in some form of cycle of meaning that integrates knowledge—often social ways of knowing—with the individual's direct experiences. Most traditional cultures will provide an interpretive context within which *anima* imagery and affect will make sense within the context of their system of local knowledge. It is very unlikely that such systems will interpret *anima*-like experiences as psychodynamic. Rather, they will tend to be interpreted in terms of visitation by ancestors, spirits, goddesses or demons, depending upon whether they are affectively positive or negative. *Anima* possession may be viewed as soul-loss, or possession by some spirit for healing or killing (Boddy, 1994; Bourguignon, 1976; Prince, 1968). If they are considered bothersome, sometimes *anima* states may be due to witchcraft or sorcery. The positive aspect of *anima* manifestation may involve interpretations of "divine intervention" when manifestations include intuitive inspiration—the word "inspiration" being used advisedly here, for it originally meant the divine breathing wisdom into one. Intuition in many cultures is considered intervention from the external domain of spirit, rather than as an internal and largely unconscious function of the psyche.

It is very important from the anthropological point of view to understand that a "Jungian" hermeneutic is just as culturally loaded as any other. It is the purpose to which the interpretation is put that matters. From the standpoint of individuation, the Jungian approach will probably carry one to higher states of maturity than will many traditional cycles of meaning. The latter are normally more concerned with social integration of meaning than with aiding the individual to optimize his or her own individuation.

Transpersonal anthropology takes as a fundamental tenet that the extraordinary experiences encountered by people everywhere are to be considered relevant and appropriate to science—thus reinforcing the arguments made by William James in support of a radical empiricism (James 1912/1976; see also Laughlin and McManus 1995). The range of experiences that may be considered *anima*-related will vary from culture to culture. I am emphasizing the cross-cultural aspect to *anima* experiences, not because ethnography is the stock-in-trade of the professional anthropologist, but because of the apparent ignorance of cross-cultural factors often found in the Jungian literature today. During the years that I worked with meditators of all ideological stripes and cultural backgrounds, I was impressed with the extent to which people can uncritically accept the interpretations most amenable to their world view. To my reading at least, the failure to take into consideration the relativity of interpretation is not only antithetical to what Jung taught, but is also a blind-spot in the development of transpersonal studies.

The study of the *anima/us* function of the human psyche might provide an auspicious focus for the integration of transpersonal psychology and transpersonal anthropology. This for several reasons: First, *anima/us* experiences are almost by definition transpersonal, in whatever the cultural setting. Because of the bridging function of the *anima/us*, the ego, of whatever configuration, is brought into direct communion with the unknown, the mysterious and the numinous. Second, *anima/us* imagery would appear to be a cultural universal, usually related to the aspect of culture we in the West recognize as religion. As such, there must be a genetic and psychophysical basis for such universal psychological properties which produce some of the core elements of traditional world views. And third, *anima/us* related experiences would seem to arise in many folks as spontaneous and ineluctable callings from the spiritual domain–though how people interpret such encounters will vary with their cultural background. Thus *anima/us* imagery may provide valuable clues to the etiology and psychological significance of shamanistic and other spiritual conversion experiences. In short, the transpersonal study of the *anima/us* function and *anima/us*-related experiences would seem to be pregnant with possibilities for research, whether that research be based upon contemplative, clinical, experimental, ethnographic, or psychophysiological approaches.

Syzygistic experiences sometimes lead to mystical experiences, a range of often experienced ecstatic union with the Other, or with the All. As we saw from Roland Fischer's cartography of states of consciousness, mystical experiences form one "color band" along the spectrum of ASC (Figure 4.1). The next chapter will focus upon the mystical experiences had by contemplatives all over the planet and will again relate them to neuropsychological processes.

PART FOUR

The Mystical Brain

CHAPTER NINE

The Mystical Brain I:
At One with the Cosmos

*One day I was walking over a bit of marshy ground close to
Inchy Wood when I felt, all a sudden, and only for a second,
an emotion which I said to myself was the root of Christian
mysticism. There had swept over me a sense of weakness,
of dependence on a great personal Being somewhere far off
yet near at hand. No thought of mine had prepared me for
this emotion, for I had been pre-occupied with Aengus and
Edain, and with Mannanan, son of the sea.*

– William Butler Yeats,
"The Voice"

*The overcoming of all the usual barriers between
individual and the Absolute is the great mystic
achievement; in mystic states we both become one with
the Absolute and we become aware of our oneness.*

– William James, *Varieties of
Religious Experience* (1902: 419)

O
ur exploration of the neurobiology, phenomenology and
cultural interpretations of ASC would be incomplete without
addressing what is called in English "mysticism" and "mystical
experience." Meditators are frequently called "mystics," especially if they
are devoted to spiritual practices—practices that have in many cases
been used for thousands of years, and in some traditions, have been
negatively sanctioned by organized religious institutions as "heresy,"
"improper," "evil," and so on. Moreover, "mystical" experiences do

not require meditative practices of any kind, for they may happen spontaneously, as the quote from Yeats testifies, and are usually life-changing. However they occur, such experiences are mediated by neuropsychological processes and may result in different treatments and interpretations in different cultures.

What Is Mysticism?

Mysticism is the quest for the hidden dimensions of spiritual reality. The word *mystic* has an old and venerable history among Indo-European languages; e.g., the Old French *mistique* meaning "mysterious, full of mystery," the Latin *mysticus* meaning "mystical, mystic, of secret rites" leading to the Italian and Spanish *mistico*, the Greek *mystikos* meaning "secret, mystic, connected with the mysteries." These terms refer to the hidden, the occult (also meaning unknown) and the invisible aspects of reality. The root meaning is carried into a variety of words in modern English: we may speak of a "mystic," a "mystery," to "mystify," something is "mysterious," all which refer to something that may be knowable but is not immediately apparent.

But this is our Western way of referring to things mysterious. The fact is that most human cultures and languages *do not* provide words that precisely gloss to our English word "mystical." For instance, as we have seen (Chapter 4), the religion of the Navajo revolves around what we would recognize as mystical insights and spiritual practices, but there is no way to refer specifically to "mysticism" in their language. Rather, they will refer metaphorically to experiences of *nilch'i* or "Holy Wind" (McNeley, 1981). Thus, we may interpret an experience had by a non-Western person as "mystical" in nature, although the person themselves may interpret the experience according to their own cultural lights. Yet, even here in the West, different scholars define mystical experience, and categorize such experiences, quite differently. For instance, Robert Forman (1999: 5) reserves the term "mystical" for those experiences had along the less energetic, more peaceful scale of experiences, while Eugene d'Aquili and Andrew Newberg consider any experience, however attained, as mystical if it allows the practitioner "to enter into the realm of God or ultimate reality" (1999: 14). For a review of definitions of mysticism, see Paper (2004).

MYSTICAL EXPERIENCES

There is an enormous range of experiences that may be considered mystical (e.g., George 1995: 186-188), although many are classed by anthropologists as "extraordinary," "shamanic," "possession," or "transpersonal" (see Bourguignon 1973; Cardena, Lynn and Krippner 2000; Goulet and Miller 2007; Young and Goulet 1994). Mystical experiences may occur spontaneously while a person is involved in other activities such as long-distance running (Jones 2004), or merely walking somewhere (Merrell-Wolff 1973). They may also arise spontaneously during dreaming (Laughlin 2011: Chap. 13), illness (Wallace 1969), or brain injury (Vaitl et al. 2013; Fenwick et al. 1985). More often mystical experiences are intentionally evoked by ritual and meditation practices (d'Aquili, Laughlin and McManus 1979; Franco 2009; Laughlin, McManus and d'Aquili 1990), by imbibing psychotropic drugs (Dobkin de Rios 1984; Furst 1976; Ruck et al. 1979), by vision quests (Irwin 1994), etc. Mystical experiences may take the form of near death experiences (NDE; Newberg and d'Aquili 1994; Alexander 2012), sensory deprivation hallucinations (Zubek 1969), "shamanic" journeys (Winkelman 2010), absorption states (Ott 2007), meditation states (Davidson 1976), lucid dream states (Laughlin 2011), trance states (Winkelman 1986), psychiatric conditions (psychosis, dissociation; Lewis-Fernández et al. 2007), possession states (Bourguignon 1976; Edge 1996), and so forth.

Let us begin with a textbook spontaneous mystical experience to give us a flavor for the kind of experience we might label "mystical." Researcher and comparative religion specialist, Professor Jordan Paper, has given us a description of his own life-changing experience he had while laying peacefully under a tree one sunny day at a music festival in 1972:

I was lying on my side and directly in my vision across a sunlit, mown field I perceived an attractive woman. Without moving my head or eyes, I focused on her, enjoying the vision with little or no thought, save a pleasant erotic feeling. At first, she slowly filled my vision, as if I were floating toward her or her toward me. Then with increasing speed she came closer and closer, followed by trees. Rocks, the field, then the entire universe, whirling in a giant vortex that funneled into me. As everything literally become one with me, I perceived a bright light inside rather than outside of me. This light can best be described as white, but it was all colors simultaneously, and it was bright beyond the brightest light imaginable. I, the universe, began to fly faster and faster toward this light. At that moment, I comprehended that I had to make an instantaneous decision: I could enter the light into which I would merge and be gone or stop and end the experience. Somehow, I recognized what was happening; I sped into the light and dissolved in an immense flood tide of joy. ...Later—it could have been a quarter of an hour or an hour or more—I regained awareness. At first, I was but aware of a blissful nothingness; that is, the first awareness was simply of being aware while awash in the afterglow of bliss. Then there was an awareness of somethingness, which I began to perceive as composed of things: sensations of sights and sounds. Slowly these components took on specific qualities, took on names and meanings. The world was again around me; there was an "I" that was again in a remembered world. But it was not the same "I" as before. It was an "I" that knew with absolute certitude that the state of being an "I" was less true than the state of being not "I," that the only reality is a blissful, utterly undifferentiated nothingness in which there is no "I." (Paper 2004: 1-2).

As we shall see, Professor Paper's experience exhibits many of the features that we in the West recognize as typical of mystical experiences, including vortexes and tunnels, movement into bright lights, ecstatic bliss, undifferentiated unity and subsequent apodictic knowledge of the oneness of everything.

Qualities of the Mystical Experience

While the field of ASC is vast, especially when considered in a cross-cultural perspective (Bourguignon 1973; Bourguignon and Evascu 1977; Locke and Kelly 1985), mystical experiences tend to be defined more narrowly within that range in accordance with a finite set of characteristics (Figure 4.1). Here we run smack into one of those post-structuralist, constructivist debates that arose in the wake of the publication of Steven T. Katz's anthology, *Mysticism and Philosophical Analysis*. The book is full of articles extoling the virtues of a constructivist view of mystical experience, namely that there is no one single mystical experience, that there are no universal properties of mystical experience, and hence the labelling of an experience as mystical is meaningless. Katz summarized his opposition to the universalist or structuralist account of mystical experience by stating that "descriptions of mystic experience out of their total context... severs all grounds of their intelligibility" (Katz 1978a: 47). In other words, to claim cross-culturally universal attributes of mystical experience is tantamount to ripping the experience out of its cultural context and interpretive frame. The debate carried on for years with positions taken on all the various sides. I will not waste space on this issue, for as I have made my position clear from the beginning: There are always universal aspects to experiences since the same human brain is mediating every experience (d'Aquili and Newberg 1999: 109-110). Besides that, Samuel Brainard (1996) put the period to the argument by simply showing that most of the post-structuralist arguments were at the level of language, texts and semantics, not on the level of the actual phenomenology of mystical experiences—what Brainard labeled the "nominal" vs, the "real" levels of discourse.

> Although I conclude that the term "mystical experience" both presumes and, in fact, signifies a set of universal "core" characteristics that are indeed "real," it also shows that the nature of this core—and the nature of "realness" in general—is involved with language and concept formation. The problem is that the essential defining traits of all objective phenomena appear to have, paradoxically, two foundations, one nominal and one real, without there being any clear sense of how the two are mediated. (Brainard 1996: 362)

A more accurate depiction of the universal aspects of mysticism is also available in a couple of books edited by Robert K. Forman (1997, 1998; see the Introduction for a discussion of constructivism). Although a long way from a "perennialist" in Aldous Huxley's sense (2004), my hunch, in company with Forman (1999: 1) and others, is that those who are stuck at the nominal level of analysis have never themselves enjoyed a mystical experience. Their narratives are distinctly different than those who clearly have experienced transcendence. Take the description offered by the great theologist, Rudolf Otto as recorded in his classic book *The Idea of the Holy*:

> The feeling of it may at times come sweeping like a gentle tide pervading the mind with a tranquil mood of deepest worship. It may pass over into a more set and lasting attitude of the soul, continuing, as it were, thrillingly vibrant and resonant, until at last it dies away and the soul resumes its "profane," non-religious mood of everyday experience. ...It has its crude, barbaric antecedents and early manifestations, and again it may be developed into something beautiful and pure and glorious. It may become the hushed, trembling, and speechless humility of the creature in the presence of—whom or what? In the presence of that which is a Mystery inexpressible and above all creatures. (1923: 12-13)

In my experience and in the phenomenological descriptions available reporting mystical experiences, this type of ASC is characterized by:

Absorption into the Void. The primary quality of a mystical experience would seem, as the quote above from William James indicates, to be an ultimate absorption state which in extreme may be an example of what Eugene d'Aquili liked to call absolute unitary being or AUB (Chapter 1)—the dissolution of "all boundaries of discrete being" (d'Aquili and Newberg 1999: 95). As we saw in Professor Paper's experience, this is an experience of ego-loss, or the dissolution of apparent boundaries between the ego and the universe (Void, Godhead, etc., depending upon interpretation). If the union is with nature, and nature is experienced as a totality, then it may be called a *panenhenic state* ("all-in-one" state; Zaehner 1961). An experience of AUB is very likely to be profoundly transpersonal; so profound in fact that it leaves a person fundamentally changed. In his classic discussion of mysticism, Walter T. Stace (1960a: 14-15) wrote:

> The most important, the central characteristic in which all fully developed mystical experiences agree, and which in the last analysis

is definitive of them and serves to mark them off from other kinds of experiences, is that they involve the apprehension of an ultimate nonsensuous unity in all things, a oneness or a One to which neither the senses nor the reason can penetrate. In other words, it entirely transcends our sensory-intellectual consciousness.

The mystical experience may be accompanied by the intuitive certainty (or "apodicticity"; see Laughlin 1994a) that everything interacts with everything else, and that reality is a single, vast monad or totality of existence.

Just as with mystical experiences, questions have been raised over whether AUB is a single experience, or whether it is an umbrella term for the advanced absorption experience in each spiritual path, sect or teaching (see e.g., Brainhard 1996, 2000; Katz 1982; Miller 2009; Runehov 2007: 141; Austin 2006: Chap. 77). Gene d'Aquili was convinced that AUB was a single experience that was interpreted differently in different traditions, and that it was tantamount to a union with God.[38] However, Buddhist mystics make a crucial distinction between absorption into a Godhead (considered a hindrance or sidetrack to awakening) and the intuitive knowing of the essence of mind, or *Nirvana* (the ultimate goal of Buddhist meditation; see e.g., Nyanaponika Mahatera 1962). Absorption has also been implicated in varieties of Christian devotion and ritual (Luhrmann, Nusbaum and Thisted 2010). A major problem here is that it is impossible to put someone into an MRI machine and have them enter an AUB on command. We can and do have people meditate while they are in the machine, but there is no guarantee they will enter a peak experience while doing so. We just do not have the kind of neuropsychological

---

[38] Gene d'Aquili and I were close friends and colleagues for many years, and co-authored papers and books together. D'Aquili, a devout Catholic, was convinced that all mystical experiences were fundamentally a union with the Godhead, regardless of how that Godhead was labeled. I, being a Buddhist, was equally convinced that the attribution of divinity to a mystical experience was an interpretive act conditioned by the mystic's cultural and religious background. We discussed the difference between what d'Aquili meant by AUB and the experience of absorption into *suññatā*, or "emptiness," "voidness." We had great arguments over this, but never came to an agreement on this issue.

data that can prove that the same neural network mediates AUB had by different people from different cultures.

Time-consciousness and space-consciousness distortion. A profound absorption state will usually collapse time consciousness into a "now" state characterized by loss of what Husserl called "retention" (memory of what has gone on before) and protention (anticipation of what is about to occur), two aspects in of the normal apprehension of the naïve "present" (Chapter 2; see Husserl 1964; Laughlin and Throop 2008). In other words, the experience is "timeless." Awareness of past and present falls away, and the cause and effect, and cyclic interpretation of time ceases altogether (Ott 2007, 2013). Consciousness is solely involved in the pure, ongoing "now" moment. Likewise, the sense of position in space—of here and there—disappears, and in its place, is the awareness of the All (or *samadhi*), an undifferentiated extension (bounded or unbounded) inseparable from consciousness. Very often distinct forms distributed in and bounded by space have dropped away. This is a type of absorption Buddhist meditators would call "formless," or *arūpajhāna* (Shankman 2008).

Spontaneous vs. intentional. Again, as we saw with Professor Paper's experience, many anecdotal descriptions of mystical experiences appear to occur spontaneously while the person is involved in some other activity, or no activity at all. Peter Jones has described AUB-like experiences had by "ultrarunners"—that is, long distance running that "consists of a group of people (sometimes the truly crazy go solo) who run along a semi-marked 'course' through rain, sleet, snow, hail, wind, and sunshine over hills, rivers, valleys, mountains, and various other sundry terrain to complete the 'course' within the allotted time, usually 24 hours for the century [100 mile] races" (2005: 40). Ultrarunners "regularly report a feeling of 'unitary connection,' 'flow,' boundless energy and a cessation of time" (ibid: 41)—that is to say, a spontaneous, unsought-after encounter with AUB.

Many of these experiences are, of course, driven by practices like running, swimming, fasting, etc. that are undertaken for other reasons. Most often, however, mystical experiences arise because of ritual or spiritual practices, such as contemplative prayer (Merton 2008), meditation (Davidson 1976), ritual dancing (Friedlander and Uzel 1992), the use of entheogens (Furst 1976), physical ordeal (Voget 1984), and so forth. But even when they are a product of active participation in religious practices, the mystical experience itself comes unbidden and uncontrolled or controllable by the practitioner. As any mature contemplative can attest, it is relatively straightforward to enter a mind-state conducive to absorption experiences, but impossible to willfully cause them.

Flow, ecstasy, bliss and numinosity. Mystical states are frequently accompanied by blisses that can range from body rushes to full-blown ecstasy. These feelings of bliss in the body give one the sense of the body being composed of flowing energy, rather than solid tissue or matter (Csikszentmihalyi 2008; Chapter 4). Intense ecstasy may be experienced as the dissolution of the material body and consciousness being transported to another "level" or "dimension" of reality (Eliade 1964). These feelings impart to the experience a sense of *numinosity*—a rapturous presence of a spiritual being which is beyond the will of the ego, and that accompanies a state of surrender or "letting go" (Otto 1928: 74; Jung, 1960[1947]: ¶ 383). The intensity of numinosity may be accompanied by a sense of awe, fascination and even terror because the experience is beyond ego control (Harding 1963: 337). Ecstatic states can be ritually driven by use of psychotropic drugs and painful ordeals.

Gnosis, or esoteric knowledge. Mystical experiences almost always are accompanied by attainment of intuitive knowledge, or *gnosis* (Merkur 1993). The dawning of knowing is often of a revelatory nature, the sudden seeing of things in a new light. Something about reality or the self has been revealed in the experiencer, and the knowing leads to a permanent transformation of consciousness. Hence, mystical experiences are usually transpersonal experiences in the literal sense—the experiences take one's understanding beyond the boundaries of ego. The term gnosis derives from the ancient Greeks and was used in the Christian tradition to label direct knowledge of God, hence considered by the early church as a heresy. From my own point of view, gnosis is intuitive knowing that permanently alters one's self-view. As Jung noted in *Aion*, "…gnosis is undoubtedly a psychological knowledge whose contents derive from the unconscious" (Jung 1959 [1951]: 223). In a sense we already know, but it takes the right experience to trigger awareness of that knowing, potentiate the development of that knowledge, and integrate the knowledge into our consciousness.

Other writers will suggest additional characteristics and make other distinctions. For instance, Stace (1960b: 78-79) would include such characteristics as ineffability (mystical experiences defy description or expression), the sense of the sacred, the sense that everything in the world is conscious, etc. Moreover, he insisted that mystical experiences come in two varieties across cultures, "extravertive" (meaning through external perception of the unity of all things) and "introvertive" (meaning the esoteric absorption into unity without sensory content). In a similar vein, Moshe Idel (1990: xii-xiii), addressing the Kabbalistic tradition of mysticism, makes the distinction between "theosophical-theurgical" (or exoteric) mysticism and "ecstatic" (or esoteric) mysticism, the latter as practiced by the famous Kabbalistic mystic, Abraham Abulafia (Idel 1988). Ken Wilber (1998) has made a clear distinction between "transcendent" mystical experience and "immanent" mystical experience; the former being an act of devotion to the divine and the latter being an absorption into the divine in which the sense of self and other disappears. And Robert Formen (1999: 5) would like to restrict the term "mystical experience" to those associated with what Gellhorn and Kiely (1972) termed "trophotropic" neuroendocrine activity, and "visionary experiences" for more ergotropic activity (see below). It is our contention that these distinctions are of secondary importance, for although they may make sense when dealing with Indo-European traditions of mysticism, they are not of much use when dealing with non-Indo-European traditions.

Mystical Experiences and Culture

The attributes of a mystical experience and its cognitive sequelae may be heavily impacted by cultural material and by one's theory of mind. As Professor Paper recounts, his mind eventually connected his experience with literature he had read in the Buddhist tradition, and his interpretation of the experience followed suit. As I noted before, my own tendency is to interpret images and experiences from a Buddhist, Jungian and Husserlian phenomenological point of view. I will inevitably interpret experiences had in alternative states in terms that make sense to me; namely, archetypal structures representing meanings in the collective unconscious, or experiences that crop-up because of entering the transcendental epoché. Again, it is crucial to parse out the interpretive

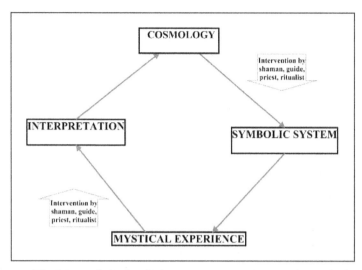

Figure 9.1. The Mystical Cycle of Meaning. A society's cosmology which includes its local theory of religion and consciousness, gives rise to symbolic representations of knowledge in the form of a myth-ritual complex (perhaps including taking entheogens), stories, art, drama, texts and drivers. Participation in the "mysteries" may lead to direct mystical experiences that are then interpreted, perhaps with the aid of a shaman, priest, elder, etc., in such a way that the experience instantiates, enlivens and verifies the individual's or group's world view.

aspect from the sensory aspect of experience (Paper 2004). It is also important to isolate those phenomenological characteristics that are impacted by cultural conditioning.

Because of the blending of phenomenological and interpretive actions in mystical experiences, it is obviously crucial to consider reports of mystical experiences from a wide variety of cultures (Eliade 1964, 1967). Any person having a mystical experience will likely comprehend their experience within a culturally patterned cycle of meaning (Figure 9.1; see Chapter 3).

Every society on the planet enculturates ("passes down") its world view—including its metaphysical assumptions—to subsequent generations. Where the knowledge inherent in a mystical experience— the knowledge of the unity of opposites and of totality—comes into conflict with, say, a fragmented materialist world view, the mystic may be faced with a cultural conundrum fraught with cognitive dissonance. The culture is saying that things are distinct and unrelated while the mystical experience is phenomenological proof of the entanglement of all things. The mystic is then confronted with the problem of finding an alternative frame that conforms to his or her experience of totality and embeddedness. Intact traditional cultures almost always have a world view that emphasizes entanglement, and they do so because of experiences had by individuals in their midst or their history that have "seen" the truth.

Mystics are often forced to lodge their intuitive knowledge of totality and causality in one of three alternative frames: (1) a self-generated frame, (2) a revitalized frame from their society's distant historical past, or (3) a frame borrowed from another culture:

Self-generated frame. An individual undergoing a mystical experience may have recourse to inventing their own interpretive frame. If so, the frame will rarely be produced from whole cloth, but rather from elements already in place in their society's world view. For example, Anthony F. C. Wallace (1969) reconstructed the history of the Handsome Lake (*Sganyodaiyo*) cult among the Seneca Indians of the northeastern United States. Handsome Lake was a man born during a period of cultural florescence (the 18th century) among the Iroquois tribes, but witnessed the gradual decline and deprivation of Iroquois way of life because of European incursions. The decline was due in part to rampant alcoholism, a depravity that Handsome Lake embraced. Toward the end of the 18th century, Handsome Lake became very ill due to his alcohol consumption, and in 1799 had prophetic visions that featured three spirits who taught him how to revitalize his people. He shared these teachings (the *Gaiwiio*, or "Good Word"), formulating a new way of life that became the Code of Handsome Lake—the code that became today's Longhouse Religion.

Revitalized frame from the society's distant past. It is interesting that perhaps the classic example of this option was Carl Jung's discovery of latter-day alchemy. For most of us, an alchemist was a pre-scientific character who was busy in his laboratory replete with bubbling caldrons and steaming retorts, trying to fashion gold out of lead. It was Jung who came to realize that the procedures—the "experiments"—of the latter-day alchemists (say, the 16th century or thereabouts) were in fact rituals having to do with dissolving the mental oppositions within the self (see e.g., Jung 1965 [1961]; Marlan 2006; von Franz 1980). Prior to his discovery of the spiritual nature of alchemy, Jung was hard-pressed to understand his own dreams and visions. For those interested in

Jungian psychology, a comparison of Jung's writings at the time of the *Red Book: Liber Novus* (2009), finished before his discovery of alchemy as an explanatory frame, but published way after his death, with some of his alchemical writings will illustrate the changes in his thinking (e.g., Jung 1967). It is also interesting that Jung considered many of the procedures used by the alchemists to resemble his own method of active imagination (Chapter 7).

Frame borrowed from another culture. My own journey through spiritual practices and experiences illustrates how one may make use of interpretive materials from another culture—in my case Buddhist teachings. This option is of course common in today's New Age cultures with gurus, temples, meditation centers and esoteric practices being derived from Japanese (Zen, Shingon), Indian (Theravada Buddhism, Hindu yoga), Chinese (Chán Buddhism, Qigong), Korea (Mahayana Buddhism) and Tibet (Vajrayana Buddhism). These sources provide practices, guidance and interpretive frames for making sense of one's experience. Some of these frames are more amenable to consolidation with modern neuropsychology than others, but as far as I know, there is no such thing as an ASC that is not amenable to a modern scientific account.

MYSTICAL EXPERIENCES ACROSS CULTURES

The variety of mystical experiences reported by people from world religion-type cultures and cults is considerable (see e.g., Katz 1982; Zagano 2013; Eliade 1967). All I can do here is give a small sample of the kinds of experiences considered by these cultures as "mystical."

Islamic Mysticism

> *Your heart is the size of an ocean.*
> *Go find yourself in its hidden depths.*

> – Rumi

Mysticism has been fundamental to Islam since its inception (Knysh 2000). Arthur Saniotis (2001, 2004) describes the way of life and methods (*tariqah*) of the Indian Islamic *faqīr*, or holy man. Central to that way of life is the mystical union between *faqīrs* and their personal saint (*hal*, plural *ahwal*). This is a union that is experienced directly via a "trance or ecstatic state." Unfortunately, Saniotis appears not to have participated in *faqīr* practices or have experienced the state of *hal* but finds himself in accordance with the definition Vincent Crapanzano (1973: 195) gave for the same term used among Moroccan *Hamadsha* practitioners as a "… complete or partial dissociation, characterized by changes in such functions as identity, memory, the sensory modalities, and thought. It may involve the loss of voluntary control over movement and may be accompanied by hallucinations and visions which are often forgotten." Saniotis expresses the relationship between a *faqīr* and his *hal* thus:

> Probably nowhere is a *faqīr's* involvement with *tariqah* more aptly expressed than by his mystical tie with a saint, referred to as *hukm*, meaning 'order' or 'command.' *Hukm* contours and informs a *faqīr's* engagement with the spirit world, and is a source of creative and emotional expression. *Faqīrs* stress that it is *hukm* which binds them to the saints, and which informs their mystical beliefs and practices. *Faqīr* often speak of their *hukm* as being acquired through a special vision or sacred dream (*basharat*), or during spiritually aroused states. This may entail the *faqīr* either seeing or hearing the voice of a specific saint calling him to become his servant. Indeed, a *faqīr's* initial *hukm* sets the tone for *hukm* in the future, and is almost always engaged in during non-ordinary or spiritually aroused states of awareness. *Hukm* is enshrouded in ambiguity; a *faqīr* does not know when he will receive a saint's command and where, or what kind of duty he will be obliged to perform. Moreover, a saint's command is non-negotiable; a *faqīr* must adjust to the conditions that a saint requires of him. Each *faqīr's* *hukm* is unique and individualized, reflecting his emotional and mental proclivities, and level of mystical awareness (*maqam*). (Saniotis 2001: 360)

Faqīrs express their experiences in the form of poetic speech. In both cases, the experience itself appears to be that of an ecstatic absorption state of union ("intimacy") with the saint which is driven by various practices including celibacy, fasting, breathing exercises, praying, chanting, solitude and smoking hash oil. According to Saniotis (2008: 19), these practices are necessary and are carried on for years, for they are "...believed to be central to controlling the *nafs* (animal ego, lower self). Sufis insist that taming the *nafs* is crucial for attaining mystical mastery, which includes communion with the spirit world." Again, "[i]n other words, the *nafs* which is not controlled gives way to sinful acts. Mastery over bodily urges is mandatory if a Sufi is to achieve mystical mastery. 'You cannot get power unless you know how to control the mind. The *nafs* is always distracting the mind, always leading it astray. It doesn't want you to be in control', I was told. However, to control the *nafs* requires vigilance and constant effort" (Saniotis 2012: 72). This relating of control over the body-mind is like the Buddhist contention that body-mind conditioning must be brought to heel (*samatha*) before advanced insight practice (*vipassana*) will bear fruit.

It is quite telling, I believe, that I can find no ethnographic account of *faqīr* esoteric practices by an anthropologist who has undergone the rigors of the practices themselves and are able to report on their own phenomenology first hand. Yet the quest for ecstatic union with the divine has been fundamental to Sufi asceticism from its inception (Schimmel 1975). Sufis use many techniques for moving individuals out of their ego-centered comfort zones and open the possibility to mystical experiences (Eliade 1967: 514-527). One of the most effective is the whirling dance (Turkish: *semazen*) of the Mevlevi and other sects of Sufism (Figure 9.2). Practitioners are known as *dervishes* or *semazens*, Sufi ascetics who use various active techniques (*sama*)— including chanting, singing, standing and walking meditations, etc.— to undermine the ego and attain oneness with God.

I once had the opportunity to practice the Mevlevi dance to special music composed for the purpose. My instructions were to spin around backwards while visualizing colored lights streaming from my palms. The music is scored so that it increases in rhythm so that one is spinning faster and faster, and then slower and slower and finally stop. At one point I realized that I was no longer spinning and that the world was spinning around me. I felt totally at peace and blissful and at one with everything. Then I thought about the experience and fell flat on the floor.

Figure 9.2. Whirling Sufi Dancers. One of the most effective and beautiful meditation techniques, the *dervish* spins to appropriate music while clearing his or her mind and visualizing light. With eyes open or closed, the *dervish* becomes the center of the universe into which he becomes absorbed. (Photo by diaz - Flickr, CC BY-SA 2.0, https://commons.wikimedia.org/w/index.php?curid=4285188).

Kabbalah (Judaic Mysticism)

> *Ultimately, our questions must emerge not from mental categories, but from deep within the heart. They must rise to the surface of our beings as we sit in silence, so that they are not just the old questions which we raise whenever we have nothing else to talk about or just for the sake of argument. They need to be the questions which make a difference in our lives.*
>
> – Zalman Schachter-Shalomi

The point of all Judaic meditation practices is to experience and have direct intuitive knowledge of the Divine (Chapter 3). The Kabbalah is one of the ancient Judaic esoteric teachings about how the Divine (*Ein Sof*) became matter, and how by following that process in reverse, humans can re-unite with the Eternal (Figure 9.3; see Matt 2009).

This mystical nothingness is neither empty nor barren; it is fertile and overflowing, engendering the myriad forms of life. The mystics teach that the universe emanated from divine nothingness. Similarly, …cosmologists speak of the quantum vacuum, teeming with potential, engendering the cosmic seed. This vacuum is anything but empty—a seething froth of virtual particles, constantly appearing and disappearing. (Matt 2005: 134)

Each of the *sefirah* (see Figure 9.3) represents one or more aspects of the psychology of spiritual enlightenment (Ginsburgh 2006), and each is associated with specific qualities of consciousness. For instance,

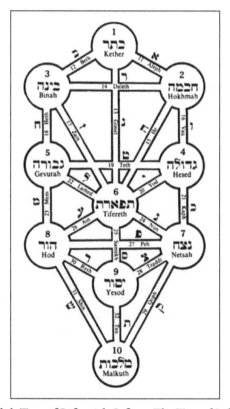

Figure 9.3. Kabbalah Tree of Life with Sefirot. The Tree of Life depicts in stylized form the stages by which the Divine (*ein soph*) becomes matter. Imagined as a tree with its roots upward to Heaven and downward toward Earth, each of the circles (*sefirah*) are stages during the transmission of Divine energy into the material world of our senses. The *sefirot* are also associated with aspects of the spiritually awakening psychology of reunion with the Godhead.

the middle *sefirah*, *Tifereth* (or "beauty"), is the equivalent of access concentration (Chapter 3). The esoteric Tarot became associated with the Kabbalah back in the 18th century (Decker 2013). A card game dating back for millennia took on esoteric meanings when merged with the Tree of Life model. Each of the *sefirah* is associated with one of the cards of the major arcana and further spells out the esoteric attributes of the stages leading to mystical union with the godhead.

Back when I taught anthropology of religion courses, I would sometimes allow a small group to do their term project working with the esoteric Tarot. We ordered copies of the black and white major arcana deck known as the Builders of the Adytum Tarot (BOTA) set,[39] and used colored pencils. We colored in each card and meditated upon it for one week. By meditation I mean we used the coloring of the card as a means of internalizing the picture on the card, and then meditating upon the internal image, and then writing down whatever happened during sits and in dreams. That work, plus discussions of the meanings of esoteric symbols led many to have a deeper understanding of the role of ritual, symbolism, visualization and contemplation in spiritual traditions.

Christian Mysticism

> *The journey is a simple one. It requires a certain vision of its importance, a certain humility to begin, and a certain fidelity and courage to persevere. It needs above all, perhaps, the willingness to be led into fullness. These are all essential human qualities that are needed for any fruitful contact with life. And the journey is an ordinary one. We don't follow it in order to sensationalize life but to see every aspect of life as the mystery it is.*

> —Father John Main OSB

---

[39] The BOTA deck is an updated version of what is called the Rider-Waite Tarot (aka, Rider Tarot, Waite Tarot, and Waite-Smith Tarot). The deck is also available in full color and both versions can be ordered through Amazon and other online book stores, as well as from the BOTA Online Store. Disclaimer: I have no connection whatever with this organization or its products. There are also posters of these Tarot cards interposed atop the Tree of Life.

Mysticism, including instructions for proper meditation, among Christians dates to the time of Jesus (see MacGinn 2006; Egan 1991; Keating 1994, 2002; Del Monte 1996). Quoting from the 5th century writings of St. John Cassian who witnessed and described the teachings of the Abbot Nesteros on attaining spiritual knowledge:

> For this continual meditation will bring us a twofold fruit: first, that while the attention of the mind is taken up in reading and preparing the lessons it cannot possibly be taken captive in any snares of bad thoughts: next that those things which were conned over and frequently repeated and which while we were trying to commit them to memory we could not understand as the mind was at that time taken up, we can afterward see more clearly, when we are free from the distraction of all acts and visions, and especially when we reflect on them in silence in our meditation by night. *So that when we are at rest, and as it were plunged in the stupor of sleep, there is revealed to us the understanding of the most secret meanings, of which in our waking hours we had not the remotest conception.* (Cassian 2015:248, emphasis added)

Cassian was steeped in the teachings of the Desert Fathers and Mothers of Egypt who advocated (beginning in the 3rd century CE) a process of purification, dedication and meditative realization fueled by love. This process unfolded in three phases of a monk's life, the *purgatio*, the *illuminatio* and the *unitio*. The *purgatio* involved various methods for eliminating the desires of the body, including lust for sexual partners, rich foods and possessions. Resistance to the various kinds of greed was considered a matter of grace gifted by God. This first ascetic phase could last years, depending upon the tenacity of pollution of the monk. Once the monk gained control over his desires, the phase of the *illuminatio* began, which was essentially an increased identification with Christ and Christ's teachings and way of life. Monks were encouraged to give to others in whatever way they could—in other words, supplant greed of self with love, selfless giving and caring for others before self. The third phase, grounded upon the love fostered by *selfless service* (unrestrained giving and self-denial), was the *unitio*, or the uniting of the individual consciousness (or soul) with the Spirit of God. If a monk reached this phase of the practice, they would often leave the Brothers and seek solitude in the deserts or forests of the wilderness (Figure 9.4).

One of the methods advocated by the Desert Fathers and Mothers was known as the *hesychasm* (Greek for "stillness," "tranquility" and "silence;" see Ward 1975). This involved the use of prayer as a continuous meditation upon the totality of God. Later, during the 14th century CE when the formal methods, such as repeating the Jesus Prayer of the Heart,[40] were formalized. This and other prayers were repeated as mantra while resting in silence with the eyes closed (Ware 2000).

Cassian's writings, as well as other Christian mystics, influenced St. Benedict whose order of ascetic monks specialize in a meditative life not unlike that of the Desert Fathers of old. Father John Main, whom I had the opportunity to know, modernized and taught the meditation practices of the Desert Fathers for the Benedictine order (Main 2011). Again, notice how similar methods are used in the interests of controlling the normal conditioning of the body-mind, a control that is necessary for more advanced insight and absorption experiences leading to the ultimate mystical experience—to be at one with the All. Father Laurence Freeman has continued the work of his teacher, Father John, and instructs Christian meditators and communities in the meditation upon the oldest Christian mantra:

> The word I would recommend is the word, *"Maranatha."* It's a beautiful prayer word, a beautiful mantra. It's in the language that Jesus spoke, Aramaic, and it means, "Come, Lord." You're not thinking about the meaning as we say it. And St. Paul ends the First Letters to the Corinthians with it. So, it's a scriptural word of great sacredness, the oldest Christian prayer. If you choose that word, say it with just four syllables: "Ma-ra-na-tha." Listen to the word as you say it. Don't visualize it. Just listen to it as you say it. As thoughts come, let them drop, let them go, and keep returning to your word. So, this is how you meditate. You sit down. You sit still. Sit with your back straight so that you are alert and awake. Meditation is about being awake. Close your eyes lightly.

---

[40] One version of the Jesus Prayer reads: "Jesus Christ, Son of God, have mercy on me, a sinner" repeated over and over as a mantra.

Sit relaxed. Breathe normally. And then silently, in your mind and heart, begin to say your word, your mantra. The word again I would suggest is "Maranatha, Ma-ra-na-tha." That's the simple way of meditation. It's very simple, not easy, but you can meditate at any point in your life. You start to meditate from where you are. You can teach a child of six to meditate. You could meditate on your death bed. The important thing is to start where you are, to accept yourself where you are, and begin to deepen your spiritual journey from the place you find yourself to be. (Freeman 2017)

Other Christian meditators choose to augment the silent prayer/mantra with visualizations, perhaps of the image of the Sacred Heart (of Jesus), a practice associated with the visions of the 17th century Catholic mystic, Saint Margaret Mary Alacoque (1647–1690; Croiset 2007). I have myself done this meditation while at the late John Main's priory in Montreal, Quebec, and its effects in terms of signs and ecstatic bliss are inseparable from those of the Eastern loving-kindness meditations I have practiced. The interpretive frame is, of course, quite different.

Figure 9.4. St. John of Egypt. This drawing depicts John of Egypt (305 – 395 CE) who walled himself into a cell in the Nitrian Desert where he remained for 40 years as an ascetic and contemplative. The cell had a small window through which he received food and spoke with people on pilgrimage.

Hindu Mysticism

*The moment I have realized God sitting in the
temple of every human body, the moment I stand
in reverence before every human being and see God
in him – that moment I am free from bondage,
everything that binds vanishes, and I am free.*

— Swami Vivekananda

Probably the oldest recorded system of teachings and practices leading
to mystical experiences are the early forms of yoga in India that may
go back as far as 3300 BCE or before (Flood 1996). These are practices
of mind and body control intended to prepare ascetics for liberation
(*moksha*) from the cycle of death and rebirth into the material world
(*saṃsāra*). These practices combined ascetic renunciation of ego-based
greed and hatred with body postures and movements (*asana*), breathing
exercises (*pranayama*) and single-minded concentration (*dhyana*) and
absorption (*samadhi*). These yogas later came to influence Buddhist,
Jain, Sikh and Hindu mysticism. Among Hindus, yoga practices are
fundamental to self-directed awareness and the process by which the
yogi realizes the real self (*atman*), one's relationship with other living
beings and divine reality.

As I have already mentioned in Chapter 4, sustained, dedicated
meditation will inevitably result in (sometimes profound) psychic energy
experiences—energy experiences termed *Kundalini* (Arundale 1938). As
we saw in Chapter 4, *Kundalini* is the single source of psychic energy
necessary for life and for consciousness. Alterations in consciousness
are mediated by alterations in the flow, centering and propagation of
Kundalini. As the great yogi Vivekananda remarked, "Wherever there
has been any manifestation of what is ordinarily called supernatural
power or wisdom, there a little current of the Kundalini must have
found its way into the *Sushumna* [central channel]" (1956: 58). In
Kundalini yoga, the goal is not merely to stimulate the production
and rising of psychic energy, it is rather to gain sufficient control
over the source and channeling of that energy such as to produce
states of higher consciousness in which loving-kindness, wisdom,

and eventually the experience of *moksha* may occur (Figure 9.5). In days long ago, yogis drank a psychotropic substance known as soma, which in modern days has been associated almost certainly with a plant called *haoma* (Jay 1999; Houben 2003). The botanical name for *haoma* is *Ephedra sp.*, a non-hallucinogenic plant that grows all over central Asia.

Kundalini is associated with the feminine and with the serpent. Melanie Takahashi, herself both a Ph.D. anthropologist specializing in religion and an advanced *Kundalini* yogi writes:

> *Kundalini* refers to a divine feminine cosmic energy that lies dormant at the base of the spine as a serpent coiled three and half times. The three coils represent the states of consciousness—waking, sleeping, and dreaming—and the last half symbolizes cosmic consciousness through union with the divine. The three coils can also signify the past, present, and future with the remaining half being the transcendence of time. The root meaning of the Sanskrit

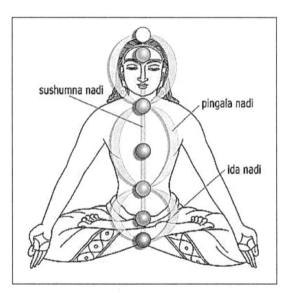

Figure 9.5. The Mystical Chakras of Indian Yoga. The tubes (*nadis*) and centers (*chakras*) of the energy body as experienced by an advanced yogi. This is not just a theory, but a descriptive model of direct experiences of psychic energy movement in the body. To center psychic energy in any one of the centers, all that is necessary is to imagine a small colored marble (*bindu*) in that center.

words offers a clue as to the way in which *Kundalini* unfolds: the feminine creative force is said to lay dormant at the base of the spine in a bowl or womb, and when ignited, this forceful energy is unleashed up the spine.... Just like a snake, this energetic fire can prove dangerous if unprepared, however if harnessed in the correct way, it can be a vehicle for transformation and an evolution in consciousness. (Takahashi 2018)

Kundalini, psychic energy, is thus no small matter in Hindu mysticism. In fact, everything depends upon it. As Takahashi notes, however, the awakening of psychic energy can have both positive and negative effects. The eruption of this energy may result in the kind of explosion of consciousness I described in the Lady in the Red Shift experience, or it can produce troublesome symptoms that Western psychology may mistake as psychosis (Sannela 1987).

Let me give you an example from my own experience of a negative effect: I was in a retreat at a Buddhist center and was working on the Tibetan *tummo* heat (*Kundalini*) yoga (see Chang 1986, 1991[1963]). This practice involves vigorous breathing exercises (known in Sanskrit as *pranayama*) that the novice can easily over-do. I over-did and fell unconscious where I sat. I gradually came back to consciousness feeling dazed, anxious and confused. A wonderful female monk named Wangchuk was right there to hold my hand and help me reorient myself. That was the last time I ever over-did a breathing exercise. I also came to better understand how important it is to work with others when doing risky intense practices.

One of the most common drivers leading to mystical experiences worldwide is the intentional production of painful ordeals, whether that be in rites of passage (Morinis 1985) or in bondage and SM sex (Baker 2016). Ordeals are also incorporated in religious rituals, as among Tamils in Malaysia and other countries who annually celebrate the festival of Thaipusam, dedicated to the Hindu lord of war, Lord Murugan. Many folks will offer prayers and libations to Murugan during the festival, but often a greater commitment is called for in the form of *kavadi*-bearing (Figure 9.6), "...where devotees allow their bodies to be pierced and decorated with needles, hooks and skewers in an expression of faith and loyalty. Despite extensive piercing, most

Figure 9.6. A *Kavadi*-Bearer Participating in the *Kavadi Attam* Dance in Celebration of the Hindu Festival of Thaipusam. The devotee prepares for the ordeal by participating in ritual procedures that involve intense contemplation, chanting, fasting, hyperventilating and other drivers.

devotees rely on ritual control of pain and bleeding and can complete the pilgrimage to Murugan's temple, carrying *kavadis* weighing up to 40lbs. to fulfill vows and offer thanksgiving" (Ward 1984: 307). Before taking on the burden of the *kavadi*, practitioners engage in temple rituals interlaced with drivers like intense meditation, fasting, hyperventilation, repetitive sounds (chanting), continuous and fervent prayer and breathing incense to enter an ecstatic trance—that is, a dissociative state that keeps the pain at bay. "All in all, repetitive rhythms, contemplative meditation, expectations, and past learning experiences play a part in trance induction" (ibid: 321).

Mystical Alchemy

Alchemy in its broadest and most historical sense was primitive chemistry blended with mysticism, religion and astrology. It has been practiced all over the world for four thousand years, beginning in ancient Egypt, and evolved in one form or another in Europe, Asia and Africa (Linden 2003). In Europe, alchemy played a major role in the development of modern science (Eddy, Mauskopf and Newman 2014). However, it is beyond the scope of this book to trace the history of alchemy. What interests us here is the emergence of a form of alchemy in 13th century Europe which blends the material and spiritual dimensions into a microcosmic-macrocosmic mystical philosophy and practice (Burckhardt 1967), a merger of exoteric and esoteric aspects that some see as inherent in alchemy throughout the Christian era (Martelli 2014). Certainly, by the 13th century, European alchemists believed that the exoteric physical and esoteric mystical were at least complementary—two sides of the alchemical coin (von Franz 1997[1979]).

As the development of modern science took hold in the 18th century, alchemy went into decline as chemists desired to separate their physical experimentation from the "pseudo-science" of alchemical practices. Yet, interest in alchemy increased again during the Victorian period of the 19th century, but almost entirely due to its esoteric interpretations of alchemical procedures as rituals intended to incubate mystical experiences and eventually spiritual enlightenment (Eliade 1994).

Figure 9.7. The Squared Circle in Alchemy. The squared circle represents the perfect alignment of the four elements, fire, air, earth and water, into the philosopher's stone, as well as the perfection of the circle.

In Hermetic alchemy, the ritual procedures involve the transmutation of "base metals" like lead into the "noble metals" like gold by use of a universal solvent (*alkahest*) known as the "philosopher's stone," the "elixir of life," or the "elixir of immortality" (Figure 9.7; see Linden 2003: 16-18). Production of the philosopher's stone was known as the *magnum opus*, or "great work." The focus in the transmutation was in the change of color of the "metals." These transmutations symbolized the process of individuation in which the body and spirit of the adept are purified, and the adept can access *gnosis*, or direct divine knowledge. Clearly, the transmutation process—the alchemical *magnum opus*—is a transformation of consciousness to a mystical ASC, one of meditation upon symbols and contemplation of the self or soul. The *magnum opus* is a form of insight meditation in which the alchemical apparatus is essentially a *kasina*, a tool to be used in an arising yoga (Chapter 3). As Barbara Obrist has noted, latter-day alchemists relied heavily upon visualization practices to incubate this mind-state, utilizing the various drawings found in latter-day alchemical texts as meditation objects:

> Visualization in medieval alchemy is a relatively late phenomenon. Documents dating from the introduction of alchemy into the Latin West around 1140 up to the mid-thirteenth century are almost devoid of pictorial elements. During the next century and a half, the primary mode of representation remained linguistic and propositional; pictorial forms developed neither rapidly nor in any continuous way. This state of affairs changed in the early fifteenth century when illustrations no longer merely punctuated alchemical texts but were organized into whole series and into synthetic pictorial representations of the principles governing the discipline. (Obrist 2003: 131)

Alchemy, or at least latter-day alchemy was not about the material transformation of base metals into gold, but rather the healing of the fragmented self (soul) and reunification of the self with the godhead, utilizing metals and chemical properties, as well as laboratory devices as meditation objects (Burckhardt 1967). This is what Carl Jung discovered and why alchemy became the central interpretive frame for his psychodynamics and his personal hermeneutics (Jung 1965

[1961], 1967). Indeed, it was in the heart center that Jung located the transcendent function, the coming together of the opposites, the conscious and unconscious, and the dissolution of all antimonies fragmenting the psyche (Odorisio 2014).

Mystical Experience and the Physics of Totality

Let us take a moment to look back at some of the properties, characteristics and interpretations of mystical experiences across cultures. The preparations for prayer and meditation advocated by the different traditions lead to esoteric knowledge, or gnosis. Transformation of self-view is fundamental to establishing the proper mind-state for realization of the mysteries—direct apprehension of the divine or spiritual ultimate. Each in their own way, traditions encourage activities and lifestyles that take the mind away from those things that nurture ego-centeredness and toward selflessness, be the lifestyle that of solitude or monastic community and selfless service to others. All these traditions lead an initiate toward the direct realization of totality and causal entanglement of all things. The knowledge that arises and matures is along the lines of gnosis (Merkur 1993) rather than intellectual, linguistic or logical knowing, and the knowledge is of the sort d'Aquili called AUB, whether it be interpreted as god-consciousness, void-consciousness, or Totality. This points to the fact that this unitary knowing is grounded in neurognosis which is triggered in its development by requisite experiences. In other words, the brain is wired to know wholeness, embeddedness and entanglement (Miller et al. 2018). The truth of that intuitive grasp of systemic reality has been confirmed scientifically by modern astrophysics (Longair 2006: 236) and quantum physics (Bohm 1980).

SUMMARY AND SEGUE

We have explored one of the major types of contemplation. We discussed some of the issues around defining "mysticism" and "mystical experience" which has been made more difficult because of constructivist accounts that deny that any such thing as a universal mystical experience exists. I take the side of the universalists, not out of mere preference, but because I have experienced mystical states and know better. We noted several properties of these states, including absorption into the void, distortion of time and space, spontaneous vs. intentional, and bliss and numinosity. Culture has a lot to do with the ritual circumstances and interpretation of these experiences. These factors, as discussed earlier in the book, involve a cycle of meaning that will link the world view, the ritual practices and interpretive frame to ASC. Mystics usually lodge their intuitive knowledge of totality and causality in one of three alternative frames: (1) a self-generated frame, (2) a revitalized frame from their society's distant historical past, or (3) a frame borrowed from another culture. Several examples of mystical experiences within their respective cultural context are described.

One of the interesting results of having a mystical experience and the inherent encounter with totality is that one's comprehension of reality comes very close to the realization that modern physics teaches us about the entangled nature of physical reality. Both astrophysics and quantum physics hold that reality is essentially a single system in which everything, including our body and mind, is embedded and causally entangled. Far from being a modern realization, however, mystical experiences are probably as old as human spiritual traditions. Evidence for this conclusion is to be found in shamanic traditions all over the world. In the next chapter we will expand on this point in the interests of showing that the brain world generally finds a way to model the real world as veridically as possible.

CHAPTER TEN

The Mystical Brain II: Shamanic Mysticism

*Life lived in the absence of the psychedelic experience that
primordial shamanism is based on is life trivialized, life
denied, life enslaved to the ego.*

– Terence McKenna, *The Evolutionary Mind*

*Shamanism is a path of knowledge, not of faith, and that
knowledge cannot come from me or anyone else in this
reality. To acquire that knowledge, including the knowledge
of the reality of the spirits, it is necessary to step through the
shaman's doorway and acquire empirical evidence.*

– Michael Harner

As I noted early in this book when I discussed constructivism vs. deconstructivism (see the Introduction), there are many overlaps, indeed near universal structural features, to contemplative traditions all over the world. We have seen last chapter that meditative techniques leading to mystical experiences share many of these features. So far, we have looked at classical mysticism from Asian and Western religious traditions. In anthropology we often group mystical practices found in more traditional societies with relatively simple socioeconomic, technological and political systems under the rubric of "shamanism." The role of a ritual specialist or shaman may be significant in a culture in which forms of meditation and contemplation are practiced. Thus, shamanic meditation cultures are important to us for at least two reasons: (1) The shaman is very likely to be the most advanced meditator in the society and indeed may depend for his or her reputation on the ability to enter ASC and utilize their skill for the benefit of the people (Price-Williams and Hughes 1994; Rock and Krippner 2011), and (2) contemporary shamanic traditions are as close as we can come to the original meditation cultures of the Upper Paleolithic, and hence the role of the ritual specialist, and of meditation, in the origins of religion (Lewis-Williams 2002; Ridington and Ridington 1970; Whitley 2004; Winkelman 2010; McClenon 1997).

It is important to keep in mind that all shamanic meditation cultures are found in polyphasic societies. In virtually all such systems, reality consists of the visible (mundane) and the invisible (spiritual). The spiritual world becomes visible during dreams, trances, drug trips and other ASC during which spiritual forces may be perceived, approached, communicated with and appealed to for help and information. Meditation states are one avenue for making the normally invisible forces visible. A shaman is a specialist, skilled in the procedures for accessing the invisible (Townsend, 2004)—very often the invisible, supernatural causes of illness and misfortune (Murdock 1980: 26-27). Very often his or her encounter with the invisible is in the form of a journey to a spirit realm, perhaps an underworld or the city of the dead to confer with ancestors and seek intelligence as to the invisible causes of calamity.

The Shaman and the Shamanic Principle

As the reader may know, the term "shaman" was lifted out of its context among peoples living in Siberia. The term became elevated to a technical term in the writings of Eliade (1964) and although it has been criticized as "cultural appropriation" by some latter-day scholars, it will do as well as any other term for a global range of traditional practices which have many aspects in common, not the least being the methods of incubating, evoking and interpreting mystical experiences (Vitebsky 1995; Krippner 2002). Not all ASC experienced by shamans are mystical experiences, and we are interested here in those traditions that value mystical experiences. So, a *shaman* for our purposes here is any specialist in entering mystical experiences among non-technocratic societies. Such specialists can be found on every continent of the planet. And they stand out from the rest of the crowd by directly experiencing multiple realities that most others only conceptualize about:

In the archaic cultures communication between sky and earth is ordinarily used to send offerings to the celestial gods and not for a concrete and personal ascent; the latter remains the prerogative of shamans. Only they know how to make an ascent through the "central opening;" only they transform a cosmo-theological concept into a *concrete mystical experience.* This point is important. It explains the difference between, for example, the religious life of a North Asian people and the religious experience of its shamans; the latter is a *personal and ecstatic experience.* In other words, what for the rest of the community remains a cosmological ideogram, for the shamans …becomes a mystical itinerary. For the former, the "Center of the World" is a site that permits them to send their prayers and offerings to the celestial gods, whereas for the latter it is the place for beginning a flight in the strictest sense of the word. Only for the latter is *real communication* among the three cosmic zones [overworld, world, underworld] a possibility. (Eliade 1964: 265)

Naturally enough, my own emphasis has been upon the neuropsychological processes exhibited by those who seek insights, knowledge and power from direct encounters with the sublime. In order to emphasize this, Gene d'Aquili, John McManus and I liked to speak of the *shamanic principle* that may be found operating at all levels of institutional complexity: "From the transpersonal perspective, the many discussions of shamanism, like those which focus on social status, initiatory rites, healing techniques, cosmological sources of power, historical change, and cross-cultural influences upon traits, frequently overlook a fundamental experiential and structural principle: there is an almost universal drive among humans to seek and explore [ASC]…, and *those who become adept at attaining valued [ASC] are expected to help others attain such experiences…*" (Laughlin, McManus and d'Aquili 1990: 149-150; see also Laughlin and Rock 2014; Krippner 2000).

It is true that shamans, in the strict sense of the term, are typical of simpler societies where the social organization and the polity are not structured beyond the local community (Czaplicka 1914: 197-198; Figure 10.1). However, the principles of contemplation, with or without the aid of entheogens are very similar to those used by practitioners in more complex societies, including our own (see Eliade 1967: 423).

The techniques I described in the last chapter for *kavadi*-bearing in the Hindu Thaipusam festival is an example of shamanic techniques used in a more advanced and complicated religious setting.

When we analyze contemplative practices among such folk and compare them with practices used in more technologically advanced societies, we find that the methods used, as well as the experiences described are quite similar. As Larry Peters, an authority on shamanistic religions, states:

> The descriptions given by shamans, yogins, meditators, or Western mystics about transpersonal states of mind are equivalent in many ways. The cultural context in which shamanism occurs, its techniques for inducing trance, and the explanations given these experiences are relative. However, this cultural relativity should not obstruct the view of the deep underlying experiential features shamanism has in common with other spiritual disciplines. The basis of these is an endogenous transformation process with an identifiable structure that guides the shamans' and other mystics' trances through a psychic death and rebirth. (1989: 116)

Figure 10.1. Pacific Northwest Kwakiutl Hamatsa society shaman. "Hamatsa [member of secret society] emerging from the woods… seated on ground in front of tree, facing front, possessed by supernatural power after having spent several days in the woods as part of an initiation ritual." Photo in 1914 by Edward S. Curtis.

Anthropologist Michael Winkelman (2010), another authority on traditional religions, has made a career of studying the neurobiology, evolution and phenomenology of shamanism. He has argued persuasively that the form of religious practice of a people will reflect the organization of society in general:

> The relevant socioeconomic conditions underlying the evolution of shamanic healers involve: (1) the absence/presence of hunting and gathering versus agriculture as the major source of subsistence; (2) fixity of residence (nomadic versus sedentary lifestyle); (3) political integration beyond the level of the local community; and (4) social stratification (classes and castes/hereditary slavery). These relationships of socioeconomic conditions to forms of magico-religious practice were established as being independent of diffusion..." (2010: 63).

By "diffusion" Winkelman means the spreading of cultural traits and practices from one group to another through time. Here in the United States we borrowed pizza from Italy, *manga* art from Japan, and the *bindi* from India. Methods of contemplation can of course also diffuse. Just look around us where people are practicing all kinds of meditation techniques borrowed from other societies (Buddhism, Sufism, Brazilian martial arts, sweat lodges, etc.). But the important point here is that when the brain begins contemplating its own nature, for whatever the provocation or culturally valued purpose, the same or similar neurobiological and neurochemical processes will involve:

> ...the psychobiological bases of human consciousness and its adaptation to social and ecological conditions of hunter-gatherer societies. This is possible because the alterations of consciousness basic to selection, training, and professional activities occur spontaneously under a wide variety of circumstances – injury, extreme fatigue, near starvation, and as a consequence of a wide variety of deliberate procedures... Consequently, shamanism was reinvented or rediscovered in diverse cultures because these experiences provide important adaptive capabilities. These are derived from their usefulness in meeting challenges to survival,

including healing through stress reduction and other physiological changes that enhance systemic integration of the information processing strata of the brain.... (Winkelman 2010: 64-65)

INDUCING SHAMANIC MYSTICAL EXPERIENCES

There are numerous ways of attaining ASC. We have looked at many of these along the way. The most natural way is by attaining lucidity in dreams (Laughlin 2011: Chap. 9; Laughlin and Rock 2013). Journeying is very common among shamans during dreams (Harner 2010; Kracke 2006) and shamans in the past have commonly used entheogens and empathogens to alter their minds during ritual enactments (Schurr 1995; Bourguignon and Evascu 1977; Guerra-Doce 2015; Ruck et al. 1979; Rush 2013; Richards 2015; McKenna and McKenna 1975; Dobkin de Rios 1984; Dobkin de Rios and Winkelman 1989; Harner 1990[1980]; St John 2018). We earlier also mentioned that the brain itself can synthesize entheogens—for example the hallucinogenic substance DMT can be created by the pineal gland under certain circumstances and might be sufficient to alter consciousness (Bradley 2010; Newberg and Iversen 2003; Strassman 2000; but cf. Nichols 2018). In addition, many other stimuli are slotted into rituals as neuroendocrine drivers, including visualizations, drumming, chanting, music, meditation, fasting, dieting, painful ordeals, vision quests, sensory deprivation, use of sweat lodges and so forth (see Peters and Price-Williams 1980 for a review). Of course, these drivers may be used to produce ASC without any requisite increase in concentration or contemplation. Young people in our modern society imbibe psychotropics to get high and have a good time, usually without learning anything about themselves in the process. It was never so among traditional peoples, unless we are referring to alcohol and weed (Metzner 1998). Each of these drivers may be considered as discrete stimuli to enhance certain kinds of contemplation, and the results of discretely or collectively driven mystical experiences always occurred within a cultural cycle of meaning. With respect to the use of entheogens, herbal concoctions used in some societies were mixed in different ways to produce distinct effects (Rodd 2006; Rodd and Sumabila 2011; Dobkin de Rios 1984; Dobkin de Rios and Winkelman 1989).

The Orang Rimba live in a forest environment on the island of Sumatra. For them, their forest is a "sentient lifeworld" (Elkholy 2016: Chap. 8). The forest is a living being that interacts with the human and non-human beings dwelling within it. It is the responsibility of people to maintain this interaction by being aware of the state of things as they go about their hunting and gathering activities. This includes maintaining a dialog with the forest spirits. It is the special duty of shamans (*dukon*) to mediate between people, deities and forest. Through their ritual practices the shaman enters an ASC characterized as a union with the forest and all the beings and forces within it. Thus, the shaman becomes absorbed into the totality of relations within the forest and operates as a conduit of communion and communication between the everyday world of the people and the supernatural world of normally unseen sentient forces operating within their forest world—the latter world being "more real" than the everyday world of people. Shamanic "trance" visions are interpreted as relevant to, and mediators of tensions between the people of the forest and the reality of conditions in the outside world.

Alas, many shamanic traditions like that of the Orang Rimba have been lost or attenuated due to acculturation from imperialistic nation states. Such a case was the shamanism of the Ainu people, the largest aboriginal group in the Japanese islands. Prior to World War II, shamans were involved in healing and within ritual contexts, shamans were possessed by spirit beings from whom they sought diagnostically relevant information about sickness (Ohnuki-Tierney 1973).

The Ainu discern two stages in what we call spirit possession. The first is *tamuy maw toro*, which means "to acquire the power of a deity." A spirit helper is here referred to as a deity, although, as discussed later, the spirits are not considered to be real deities. This stage of spirit possession may be identified by observers, since a shaman's facial expression and voice change at this time, and his normal voice and expression are replaced by strange ones. Both voice and expression alter from time to time depending upon which spirit is possessing the shaman. The second stage is when the spirit enters the body of the shaman, referred to in Ainu as *kamuy ko ahun* (the deity, i.e., spirit, enters).

Unlike other possession traditions, the Ainu recall everything that happens when possessed. The spirits that possess people are animals of various kinds, never the higher deities from whom information is sought with the possessing spirit as mediator. As is so common in the ethnographic literature, we have no information about what the shaman experiences during their "trance."

There is a literature in psychology and anthropology going way back that fosters the opinion that shamans are essentially sick in the head, burdened with one kind of psychopathology or another. I will not go into this issue, for in my opinion it has been put to rest by authorities who have studied shamanic phenomena closely (e.g., Winkelman 2010; Peters 1989; Vitebsky 1995; Walsh 2007). Suffice to say that the hallmark of the shaman in any traditional society is his or her mastery of mind-states—control of ASC. For instance, one of the more interesting phenomena in shamanic traditions is the so-called "shaman's journey" (aka, "magical flight," "soul journey;" Eliade 1964; Walsh 2007: Chap. 20). In many societies, shamans may leave their bodies at will and travel to other places while in "trance" (read ASC, and often a mystical experience or "ecstatic" state; Peters and Price-Williams 1980).

In traditional societies whose world view divides reality into three or more levels, the shaman will often travel to the overworld or underworld layers to carry out some task or to seek intelligence about some matter. Among the Tungus people of Siberia, the shaman travels to both the upper and lower worlds to answer questions directed at him by his audience, who he in turn depends upon to make music and share in his "ecstasy" (read excitement and "high;" Shirokogoroff 1935). This is a dangerous journey and the shaman will recount the many perils he encountered during the journey. Among the ancient Turkmen shamans, the initiate had to learn his way along various roads that access the gods and other supernatural beings. "Shamans possessed the secret knowledge about the roads leading to all kinds of supernatural beings. They regularly traveled to the other, secret reality, hidden away from normal perception, in search of solutions to a range of practical and existence-related problems their communities were beset by" (Zeranska-Kominek 1998: 266). And among the Baniva people of Amazonia, spiritual journeys are facilitated by the entheogen termed *piriká*, a powdered snuff extracted from the inner bark of the *Virolatheidora* and *Anandenathera peregrine* trees that grow in northern South America (Wright 1992). During their journeys, the shamans protect the cosmos, return it to a state of beauty and retrieve lost souls that make people sick. The journey is:

...seen to consist of five phases identifiable as the following: (1) ascent and transformation on *piriká*, (2) going beyond death, (3) remaking the world, (4) curing in the sky world, (5) descent, reentry to this world, curing in this world. In every one of these phases, the shaman's quest is conceptualized in terms of the protective and beneficial: to make the world beautiful; to make this world and people better and more content; to not let this world fall or end; to retrieve a lost soul and make a sick person well. In fact, it is as though the specific intent of the shaman's journey—to retrieve and revive a lost soul—were so interconnected with the larger, cosmic drama of making the world better that it is impossible to separate them. In all phases, the beauty, goodness, unity, order, and truth of the primordial world stand in contrast with this world, Maatchikwe, the place of multiple pain and evil. The shaman's quest, we might say, in one sense is to beautify (*rualiapikwe*) this world. The beautifying of this world through the creation of order is essential to its salvation and healing.... (ibid: 135)

I have had some interesting experiences that relate to the "shaman's journey" motif. I have mentioned elsewhere that one type of meditation in Buddhist and other traditions is done while walking. During *walking meditation*, one may be instructed to pay attention to the sensations on the bottom of the feet while slowly pacing back and forth in a room, hallway or outside. In this specific meditation, I was instructed to walk very slowly, concentrating on the changing sensation as one foot began to lift, heel first, then bottom, then toes leaving the ground and heel planting, bottom planting, toes planting, then the other heel rising, bottom rising, toes rising, moving foot forward, heel planting, bottom planting, toes planting, then the other heel lifting..., and so forth. Doing that work, one may feel very unstable at first, but when one adjusts to the novel practice, it begins to flow and becomes both stable and slower all the time. Eventually one no longer must label each movement, but just intensify the concentration upon first one foot and then the other.

The process can become so slow it takes one thirty minutes to cross a large room. After doing this on and off for hours, I began to have an unbidden vision of floating atop white fluffy clouds on a sunny day, and through the clouds I was looking down upon a landscape as though I were traveling in a hot air balloon. There were roads and houses and trees and people. The people were often looking up at me, shading their eyes as if to see better, some pointing and chatting with others (I could not hear what they were saying). My feelings were mild, but non-stop bliss. I felt as though I was smiling down upon the people and the beauty of such an idyllic, constantly unfolding scene. There was no sense of going anywhere—no destination—just traveling. I repeated this meditation during lengthy meditation retreats to take a break from sitting meditation, and every time I did so, the same scenes arose.

There is another type of meditation that I participated in on a weekly basis for two years. This time it was a group meditation involving at least five advanced meditators. The practice is known as *star group meditation*,[41] and was practiced by fellow students of one of my teachers, Namgyal Rinpoche. The technique is deceptively simple. A group (ideally five individuals, and if more, only an odd number) sits in a circle holding hands and meditating for 50 minutes upon an imagined blue light hanging above the center of the group (we found that an actual blue light was unnecessary). It is okay to shift the awareness to any images and watch them unfold with bare attention. If the images disappear, one returns to the blue light. At the end of the time, without speaking to anyone, each participant writes down with as much detail as possible all the imagery and other experiences had during meditation. After that, individuals share what they experienced with the group. What is fascinating about this work is that: (1) most people have visual and other experiences to relate, (2) there is often a correspondence between experiences had by two or more members, and (3) experiences are commonly out-of-body trips taken into outer space involving revolving planets, moving through star systems, planetary landscapes, sometimes even spaceships. Upon occasion I found it a rude shock to return to my body and the group setting when the timer went off.

---

[41] Detailed instructions for carrying out a star group meditation may be found at http://www.wangapeka.org/star-group-meditation-instructions/.

The point I am making here is that it is quite normal for the mind to take itself on trips and journeys, be they in fantasies, visions or dreams, and that it does not take much effort to incubate and evoke journeys using simple meditation techniques (see Noll 1985 on the shamanic use of visualization practices). Augmented by hallucinogenic entheogens, and intense ritual events, these journeys may be vivid and of lasting duration.

Possession by Spirits

One of the classic forms of mystical experience is often termed a *possession trance* in the anthropological literature. This is a shorthand way of referring to an ASC in which one's consciousness is "taken over" by a spirit being—in other words, the ego bonds with, or perhaps is absorbed into a spirit, or an other-than-human person. Possession states are of interest to us in the present context for three reasons: (1) possession-related ASC are widespread in the world (Bourguignon 1976; Oohashi *et al.* 2002), (2) possession states involve absorption into some facet or entity of the supernatural (Krippner 2008), and (3) the actual experience of possession/absorption mystical experiences are poorly understood due largely to the seeming inability of ethnographers to embrace and evoke those experiences for themselves. With respect to number three, while there are numerous articles and books about possession in the anthropological literature, they are almost always either social analyses focused upon the institutions and social roles of mediums, or psychological diagnoses suggesting that possession states are some form of dissociative pathology (see Seligman 2005; Hageman *et al.* 2009; Cardeña *et al.* 2010). As I mentioned in the introduction to this book, this kind of analysis will not do. It will not do because: (1) most shamanic ASC are not possession states (Wright 1989), and (2) there are different kinds of possession trance (Rapaport 1951, 1967), and the type that incorporates "reflexive awareness" constitutes a mystical experience. There are data to suggest that mediumship is accompanied by a marked incongruity between the phenomenological report of a medium and bioenergetic measurement of what is happening in their body. Hageman, Krippner and Wickramasekera (2011: 19) have studied Brazilian mediums and found what others have reported:

Wickramasekera… proposed that spiritual practitioners often are at risk for stress-related symptoms because of the noted incongruence. Among the most common incongruence are verbal reports of low negative affect while ANS [measured by EEG and EMG] data indicate otherwise: (a) profound temperature differences between the right and the left sides of the body (e.g., IR specificity), (b) "flip-flops" between a repressive cognitive style, and (c) easy access to cognitive processing ….

Before expanding on this, let me introduce you further to the possession mysticism group I mentioned as an example back in the Introduction. The Candomblé cult is practiced in Salvador, the capital city of Brazil's Bahia state, as well as other South American countries (Seligman 2005, 2016; van de Port 2005). Candomblé is a syncretic religion, an admixture of West African and New World beliefs and practices, including rituals intended to unite the adept with their *orisha* or "saint:"

The Candomblé community in Salvador is comprised of approximately 1500 different centers, or *terreiros*, each of which has between 30 and 300 members. Candomblé cosmology involves the belief that a pantheon of deities and lesser spirits occupy the universe along with humans, and that *the gods and spirits may take physical form within the bodies of chosen individuals,* who act as their mediums. Within each *terreiro* membership is divided among several different religious roles: the *Mae* or *Pai de Santo* (mother or father of saint) is the spiritual leader of the group; initiated mediums, known as *Filhos de Santo* (sons and daughters of saint), are vehicles for the deities; *Ogas* and *Ekedes* are male and female initiates who occupy important ritual roles but do not become possessed by deities; and finally, *frequentadors* are the lay people of the religion. (Seligman 2005: 274; emphasis added)

The community holds that specific individuals are susceptible to trance states (ASC) during which an *orisha* may enter and possess "their head," after which the person is initiated into mediumship, a role that is defined as a healing shaman (Seligman 2010; 304). Very often the potential initiate will seek healing from the community and is directed to a diagnostician who uses patterns made by thrown cowrie shells to divine the malady. The diagnosis may be to undergo initiation into mediumship, a long and arduous process, which results in the "incorporation" of the *orisha* into the body and mind of the medium.

By cultural expectation, Candomblé possession is supposed to produce complete amnesia after the trance state—probably not true in many cases. We know that possession states can occur with or without dissociative elements (Krippner 1997a). Moreover, most possession states in traditional settings are therapeutic, not pathological (Money 2000). In Candomblé the trance is induced by many of the ritual drivers we have already discussed, including "...seclusion from the everyday world, immersion in a different setting and living conditions, participation in novel and elaborate rituals, and learning of trance induction techniques involving intense focus of attention away from self-consciousness and onto rhythmic and repetitive stimuli like dance, singing–chanting, and drumming" (Seligman 2010: 306). Mattijs van de Port (2005: 150) offers us a description of one of the community's trance rituals:

Ceremonies of Candomblé can be powerful performances, and this particular one, in a small neighborhood temple (*terreiro*), packed with locals rubbing shoulders, certainly was. After an introductory round dance had been danced, the drums started calling the orixas, the spiritual entities that are worshipped in Bahian candomble. They seemed to arrive in large numbers. The daughters-of-saints (*filhas-de-santo*; initiates) who had been dancing for hours, circling round and round the central pillar, started bending forward and backward, quivering their shoulders and "grunting like a Vitrola needle at the end of record".... Many of the locals who had been watching the scene became possessed as well: a plump lady on high heels, a middle-aged man, a somewhat grayish looking woman wearing an apron, they all started to stagger on their feet and turned up their eyeballs. Contrary to the initiates, they took off silently, as if sneaking out of their bodies. Soon, two of the adolescent boys who had been busy displaying a "cool" and unaffected posture amidst the general effervescence, entered into trance. I clearly remember the nervous expression on the face of the third one after "departure" of his mates. A young girl, who had been chatting and giggling with a friend as if this was a schoolyard rather than a place of worship, all a sudden fell into a rigorous spasm, and rolled over the dance floor, stiff as a broomstick. She was covered with a white sheet and for over an hour lay motionless on the floor.

Wonderful, but what are the daughters-of-saints experiencing? Let me quote van de Port (2005: 151) again, as I did in the introduction:

> I'm certainly not the only anthropologist to have observed that no matter how possession trance is tackled theoretically, its most immediate experience escapes our understanding. Janice Bodd, Paul Stoller and Michael Taussig, to name but a few, all have remarked that whereas the Otherness of the phenomenon (its uncanny inexplicability, its screaming incompatibility with Western notions of personhood, its seeming disdain for self-control, its radical otherness) demands explanation, and this explanation highlights the inadequacy of our conceptual categories rather than the phenomenon itself.

To get behind the appearances and gain some appreciation of what these folks are experiencing, we must look further afield. Etzel Cardeña *et al.* (2010: 173-174) defined three types of possession trance phenomenon (PTP):

> [T]ransitional states (e.g., *saoulé* or inebriation in Haitian Vodou, *irradiación* in Afro-Brazilian religions…) where individuals are in a cognitively disorganized state as they move from their usual state of consciousness to an alternate state or identity…; (2) in the prototypical type of PTP, the person adopts an alternative identity (e.g., a culturally recognized spirit or an ancestor [as is the case for Candomblé]; and (3) spirit possession involving a transcendent, non-ego state in which the person experiences a union with everything or a Godhead rather than a different, discrete identity [as is the case with d'Aquili's AUB].

The latter two types are really absorption states (Chapter 3); in the case of Candomblé-type possession an absorption into a specific inner image, and in the case of AUB, an absorption into the All. The importance of absorption in possession states is not missed by Etzel Cardeña *et al.* (2010: 176):

> Absorption, the ability to fully deploy one's attention toward internal or external stimuli, is a construct related to dissociation and hypnotizability, and it shows substantial heritability (Tellegen *et al.* 1988). Individuals with high levels of absorption, dissociation, and/or hypnotizability tend to report unusual experiences, including reputed psychic phenomena and an openness to experiencing altered states (Cardeña, Lynn and Krippner 2000). This is consistent with Laria's (1998) finding that mediums had "thinner mental boundaries" (e.g., greater fluidity between states of consciousness).

The ability to "let go" into an absorption state is fundamental to all types of meditation (Pagano and Warrenburg 1983: 188). Contemplative projects require the ASC involve concentration, or "reflexive awareness" (Rapaport 1951). I would suggest that many of the cases of possession trance which are accompanied by real amnesia, rather than the cultural expectation of amnesia, are due to the absence of concentration across the warp between the states, much like forgetting dreams we had when we wake. We now know that people range in their susceptibility to entering absorption trance states (Tellegen and Atkinson 1974; Barrett 1992). We also know that trance can happen with a range of concentration from none to hyperawareness. What we do not know in the case of Candomblé adepts is the extent to which their explorations of this interesting ASC occur with the awareness of a contemplative. Be that as it may—it is an empirical question yet to be answered—because the orientation of Candomblé is toward healing, they are an excellent example of the shamanic principle.

SUMMARY AND SEGUE

This chapter carried-on with the discussion of mystical experiences by exploring these experiences among various shamanic traditions.

We anthropologists tend to lump spiritual traditions, especially those involving ASC, among societies with simpler socioeconomic systems under the umbrella term "shamanism." It is often the case that there exists a role of ritual specialist in those societies that practice some form of meditation. Thus, shamanic meditation cultures are important to us for at least two reasons: (1) The shaman is usually the most advanced meditator in the society and indeed may depend for his or her reputation on the ability to enter ASC and utilize their skill for the benefit of the people, and (2) contemporary shamanic traditions are as close as we can come to the original meditation cultures of the Upper Paleolithic, and hence the role of the ritual specialist, and of meditation, in the origins of religion. The knotty problem of defining what constitutes a "shaman" was addressed. I differ slightly from other anthropologists in that I suggest that there is a "shamanic principle" underlying most religions, regardless of the complexity of their political and economic systems. This principle was illustrated by several examples of shamanic contemplative traditions.

One of the phenomenological and neuropsychological ingredients of mystical experiences has awaited its own elaboration, and that is the role of love in facilitating mystical experiences. Many of the contemplative traditions we have explored emphasize the importance of eliminating ego-bound states of consciousness in favor of selfless service, empathy and compassion for others. Indeed, love is the natural antidote to greed, anxiety and hatred, these being major hindrances to absorption states of all kinds. We will next take up this element of the contemplative life—the cultivation of mystical love.

CHAPTER ELEVEN

The Mystical Brain III:
Love, the Universal Solvent

*But your vision will become clear only when you look into
your own heart. Without, everything seems discordant; only
within does it coalesce into unity. Who looks outside dreams;
who looks inside awakens.*

– C. G. Jung (1973)

*Love is patient, love is kind. It does not envy, it does not
boast, it is not proud. It does not dishonor others, it is
not self-seeking, it is not easily angered, it keeps no record
of wrongs. Love does not delight in evil but rejoices with
the truth. It always protects, always trusts, always hopes,
always perseveres.*

– 1 Corinthians 13

*...phenomenological investigations indicate that the
playground of freedom is love.*

– William Sadler (1969:219)

There are two key elements to any mystical experience, unity (non-duality) and love—the former refers to the dissolution of all distinctions, and the latter to the positive psychic energy facilitating the experience. For instance, Christian mystics consider love to be fundamental to mystical experiences (Johnston 1978). Indeed, love may be considered a *universal solvent* in the alchemical sense, for it fuels the mystical brain, it is the binding of conceptual and affective opposites, and the glue that cements union. Love is the antithesis of anxiety, greed, anger and hatred, the latter four being the major hindrances to absorption states.

Naturally, the English word "love" is extremely fuzzy in its meanings. In sloppy usage love can range from the love of God, the love of a mother for her child, the love of your sweetie, the love of ballet, to the love of pizza—essentially labeling any pleasurable feeling whatever. This is not the kind of love that I am talking about. In the distant past, Ancient Greeks found it necessary to distinguish four kinds of love (Oord 2010): romantic love (*eros*), familial love (*storge*), friendly love (*philia*), and divine love (*agape*). *Eros* of course is the root of "erotic," and signals the sexual aspect to pleasurable feelings one has toward another. From *philia* we derive our phrase "filial affection," "brotherly love," and in this age of political correctness, "sibling love." *Storge* refers to familial love, the love that parents have for their offspring and boys and girls have for their parents and each other—which in modern technocratic society would seem to be less frequent than in ages past. *Agape* is the form of love the Ancient Greeks reserved for the highest form of affection, as between people and their gods and *vice versa*. *Agape* refers to the universal, unconditional and continuous feeling of positive regard for everything. *Agape* refers to "altruistic love," "affirmative affection," and other phrases that attempt to label a mind that is feeling nothing save affection for the other beings, or the entire world and everything in it (Post 2002). It is the love that both produces boundless compassion and kindness towards all beings and allows mystical experiences to arise. Using the modern Buddhist convention, I will henceforth call this form of love, *loving-kindness* (see Kornfield 2009; Salzberg 1995).

When we say that we love something or someone, what this means is we have an affection or positive regard for some person or object, and we will tend to interact with that person or thing in a kindly manner. After all, *altruism* derives from the Latin for "somebody else." Most distinctions we make with respect to love are tied to the object of our affection. If I were to get specific, I might say that I am feeling Luke-love (Luke is my pet dog), Kate-love (Kate is my daughter) and Danny-love (Danny is my best friend). I could go on to discriminate my love of Beethoven, of pizza, of Sherlock Holmes stories, of shopping and of soccer. But we do not do that in everyday life. We are satisfied with fuzzy categories of things like birds, SUVs, trees, berries, clouds and so on. So it is with love. But development often confounds our feelings of love. Early failure of nurture, psychological, physical and sexual abuse, abandonment and other issues can produce what is called "affective splitting"—ambivalent positive and negative affect directed at the same object. In extreme form, such splitting of feelings can produce psychopathology (Kernberg 1970; Fischer and Ayoub 1994). Full-on, global loving-kindness is all but impossible in a consciousness conditioned to affective splitting.

Neuropsychological studies of the brain's loving-kindness processing have been thin on the ground. There are several reasons for this paucity of information. Neuroscientist and psychiatrist Thomas Insel mentions a couple of the main reasons:

> The relative absence of neuroscience research on love can be attributed to two fairly obvious and related limitations. One is definitional. Love, whether considered as attachment, such as pair bond, or viewed as a form of self-sacrificing altruism, is difficult to define operationally. ...The second major problem is one of measurement. Although most of us may recognize love as the most powerful psychological and biological experience of our lives, how do we quantify this experience? (Insel 2002: 254-255).

With respect to the kind of contemplation-related loving-kindness we are discussing here, I would add another problem, and that is the limitations of personal experience with mystical-level love—or *mystical love*—on the part of researchers.

There is of course some interesting research on pair bonding among monogamous animals that, at least in an evolutionary sense, bears looking at—for instance among prairie voles (*Microtus ochrogaster*; see Figure 11.1), a species of rodent that mates for life (Young and Wang 2004).

This kind of bonding and attendant feelings are linked to mate selection and reproduction. One of the problems that animals have is that to approach and interact sufficiently to reproduce, there must be some mechanism to decrease "social space" to facilitate intimacy. Monogamous pair bonding is one solution to this problem. Research on voles has confirmed that males experience distinct pleasure when

Figure 11.1. A Pair of Prairie Voles Tend to Their Young. Prairie voles are a species of rodent living in North America who bond for life to one mate. They are the subjects of research into the neurobiology of bonding.

interacting with their mate, a feeling that does not occur when interacting with other females. This pleasure is mediated by the biochemical properties of the so-called agonist[42] oxytocin stimulating cells in the basal forebrain called the *nucleus accumbens* (Figure 11.2). There is a *nucleus accumbens* to be found in the lower reaches of each side of the frontal lobes, which is involved in mediating pleasure from sports, sex, music, etc., as well as mediating humor/laughter, and fear. It is the site of the activity of dopamine-activating drugs like the opiates, cocaine, amphetamines, nicotine, etc.

So, it would seem with humans as well, for when we look through the long lens of evolution, it is apparent that hundreds of thousands of years have gone into developing a single *caregiving system*, including the requisite neurophysiological structures to mediate different aspects of the system (De Waal 2008; Brown, Brown and Penner 2011; Swain *et al.* 2012).

[T]he insula and oxytocin emerge as prominent anatomical and hormonal mechanisms, respectively, underlying both parenting

---

[42] An *agonist* is a chemical that binds to a specific receptor in an area of the brain and causes that structure to "do its thing."

and non-kin caring. Hence, it is suggested that the insula and oxytocin are key players in a general Caregiving System ...which may regulate compassion in any of its forms.... This system can be formulated as having a tripartite structure starting with (1) perception of an individual's need for assistance, which can elicit (2) a caring motivational or feeling state, and consequently (3) helping responses to the individual in need are made—for the child in the instance of parenting in response to baby-cry.... (Swain *et al.* 2012)

Of course, this generalized caregiving system must have evolved in tandem with neural functions that bring members of the opposite sex together for reproduction. Among humans, *romantic love* is a near cultural universal, although just how these feelings are acted-out varies considerably across cultures. Romantic love is presumably mediated by the same neurobiological processes in all people everywhere (Jankowiak and Fischer 1992; De Munck 1998). Romantic love is essentially the pairing of thoughts and perceptions of a significant Other with areas of

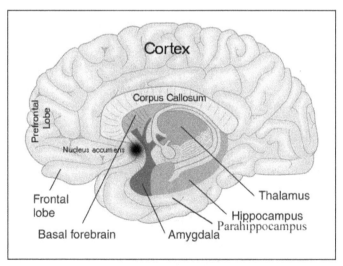

Figure 11.2. A side-on view of the midbrain. This is the brain sliced down the middle (sagittal diagram) and exposing some of the areas most implicated in mediating loving-kindness, mate selection and social bonding. Important are the structures of the basal forebrain, including the *nucleus accumbens*, ventral and dorsal striatum, *nucleus basalis*, diagonal band of Broca, *substantia innominata*, and the medial septal nucleus.

the brain that mediate both pleasure and sexual arousal, thus producing the experience of attraction—even obsession. Studies of people deeply in love using functional magnetic resonance imaging (fMRI) techniques have shown that romantic love is mediated by dopaminergic pleasure centers, specifically in the brainstem right ventral tegmental area and areas of the right caudate nucleus (Fisher, Aron and Brown 2006; Figure 11.3). This area is heavily connected to the prefrontal cortex (see Figures 1.2 and 1.3), which among other things is known as the "social brain." This connectivity mediates pleasurable feelings in the presence of others, and specifically generates attraction to potential mates and bonding between mother and child.

Of course, one may be sexually attracted to another person whom one does not love. Indeed, there are those who are sexually aroused by people they hate, as is the case with sexual sadists and other paraphilics

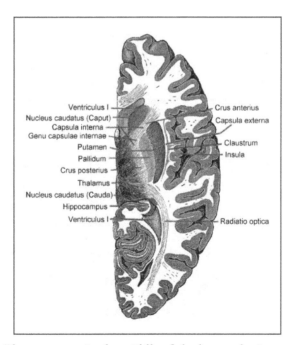

Figure 11.3. The structures in the middle of the human brain, one hemisphere sliced side-to-side. Buried underneath the cortex lies the core area of the brain that contains a group of structures called the *basal ganglia*, one of which is the caudate nucleus (or *nucleus caudatus*) which mediates pleasurable feelings including joy and ecstasy. These structures are intimately interconnected to cortical areas, especially the prefrontal cortex (PFC), the so-called "social brain."

(see e.g., Segarra-Echebarría *et al.* 2015). But if we more nearly normal folk get turned on by someone—view them as a potential mate—we call that "jonesing," "horny," "ardor," "passion," "have a thing for," or "lusting after." The problem of moving from sexual arousal to mating is a social problem, not just for humans, but for any bisexual animal as well. That gap is typically dissolved by one kind of ritual or another. Among humans reciprocated love helps. In societies where there is greater anxiety about mating, "love magic" may be used (see Shirley and Romney 1962) to bridge the gap.

What begins as ardor may develop into romantic love, or it may not. It is very possible for a naïve person to imagine that what they are feeling is "love," but the feeling does not produce the dissolution of personal boundaries, nor does it lead to altruistic behavior. Lust is self-fulfilling, love is other-directed. And those persons who are not capable of love, such as extreme narcissists and psychopaths, may feel horny, but their arousal is always associated with the "will to power" (desire for control). Carl Jung showed that power over another and love are antithetical. As he put it, "Where love rules, there is no will to power, and where power predominates, love is lacking. The one is the shadow of the other" (Jung 1991: 87). In other words, the twisted psyche of a psychopath has a snowball's chance in a microwave of experiencing ecstatic union with the All.

LOVING-KINDNESS MEDITATION

Love, or perhaps more accurately, love-infused social cognitions, relations, and interactions, are fundamental to producing and maintaining a "convivial" group dynamic. However, any of you living your life in a technocratic society will realize that we are relatively alienated from this, perhaps more natural, social environment. Alienation, and especially social alienation, is the cost we bear for the kind of bureaucratic capitalist society we have inherited (Marcuse 2013[1964]). People around us seem to act out the persona of Ayn Rand's character John Galt in her novel *Atlas Shrugged*. Quoting Galt, "By the grace of reality and the nature of life, man—every man—is an end in himself, he exists for his own sake, and the achievement of his own happiness is his highest moral purpose" (1957: 1014). This "every man is an island," "every man for himself" alienation includes a fractured network of loving relationships. Depending on who you are, people tend to be alienated from nature, from family and community, from the love of fulfilling work, from a sense of justice, and even from ourselves. Neal and Collas (2013: 114) emphasize the centrality of social isolation in the modern world: "While social isolation is typically experienced as a form of personal stress, its sources are deeply embedded in the social organization of the modern world. With increased isolation and atomization, much of our daily interactions are with those who are strangers to us and with whom we lack any ongoing social relationships." As William Kornhauser wrote: "Mass society is objectively the atomized society, and subjectively the alienated population. Therefore, mass society is a system in which there is high availability of a population for mobilization by elites... [p]eople who are atomized readily become mobilized. ...[B]oth elites and non-elites lack social insulation; that is, when elites are accessible to direct intervention by non-elites, and when non-elites are available for direct mobilization by elites" (Kornhauser 1959: 33, 43). By and large, and save perhaps for interactions with our family and close friends, our everyday lives of work and travel are not charged with love and caring for the strangers around us.

By way of comparison—and without in any way evoking the "noble savage" mystique—traditional peoples more typically conceive of the group as the bulwark against a dangerous world, and they work towards creating a necessary spirit of loving-kindness and conviviality to maintain group cohesion. Peter Gow describes this kind of zeitgeist among the Piro people of the Madre de Dios Region in Peru:

> The flatness of everyday life turns out to be fully intentional, it is an achievement. It is won from a cosmos that is governed by other kinds of reason . . . Piro people know themselves to be virtually powerless to change the given structure of a cosmos which was not created for their benefit and which is totally indifferent to their fate. Knowing this, Piro people know they must help each other, Piro people know that they have been and will be helpless. They

see the helplessness of others, and this compassion leads them to heighten their social regard for them, in specific acts of consolation. In everyday life, when things are going well, this "thinking beautifully" transforms into the sustained plateau of kindness and companionship that Piro people call "living well." (Gow 2000: 61)

I suspect that cultural recognition of loving-kindness (or *agape* love) is as much a near-universal as romantic love, although I do not have the data to confirm it. Most of the literature on love across cultures focuses upon romantic love. Cross-cultural psychologists have tested various types of love across a wide variety of countries and have found that strong feelings of love of various types, including romantic love and *agape*, seem to be relatively independent of cultural conditioning (Neto *et al.* 2000). Loving-kindness is equivalent to the Buddhist concept of *metta*, Hindu and Jainism's *priti* and *maitri*, and Judaism's *chesed* (Salzberg 1995). Studies have now shown that very little practice of loving-kindness and compassion meditation is required to have the effects of increasing positive regard and decreasing negative regard for self and others (Hofmann, Grossman and Hinton 2011)—in other words, *the practice of loving-kindness may well diminish the social isolation conditioned by alienating technocracy*. Indeed, certain modern social rituals seem to be designed to do just that, often incorporating the use of psychotropic drugs to attain the requisite level of social distance dissolving loving-kindness. As my friend and colleague, and authority on the ethnography of raves, Melanie Takahashi, notes:

MDMA[43] falls under the unique class of psychoactive substances known as empathogens. When ingested, it induces feelings of connectedness, empathy, and oneness. During the height of the rave scene, ecstasy (a pressed pill combining MDMA and speed) and Molly (pure MDMA in powder form) were the substances of choice that complimented the movement's ethos of PLUR (Peace, Love, Unity and Respect), and simultaneously became emblematic of the movement itself. These substances continue to have a strong

---

[43] MDMA is the drug 3,4-Methylenedioxymethamphetamine, otherwise called "Molly," or "ecstasy."

presence in the post-rave electronic dance music communities that later emerged. Participants describe the experience as a drug induced heart opener that can be felt emotionally, energetically and physically. A popular combination of drugs among the more spiritual oriented dance communities is mixing MDMA with magic mushrooms or LSD. This process is referred to as "candy-flipping" and it involves taking the MDMA first, allow the often-associated nausea to pass, wait for the state of love and connectedness to kick in, then LSD or mushrooms are ingested. This process ensures a positive experience and tends to most often occur at outdoor music festivals as LSD can be very overwhelming in the club environment. Participants also regard the outdoor events as inherently more spiritual with some of the most transcendent and memorable experiences taking place in these environments. (Personal communication, September 6, 2017)

My own experience with MDMA allows me to confirm the increased sense of loving-kindness and connection with others had with this drug. I also took LSD (obtained from Owsley Stanley himself, I am proud to say) six times in the later 1960s, and each time I found that the drug produced states of ecstasy, well-being, loving-kindness and unity. The feeling of unconditional love was so intense that I recall weeping about how wonderful my electric coffeepot was to me for producing such a heavenly beverage. More seriously, I found it very easy to enter a state of absorption into anything toward which I turned my attention. Even now I recall observing a small spider for an hour or more moving about on its web between several leaves of grass. I felt totally at one with that tiny being and am to this day an avid arachnophile.

Loving-Kindness Meditation

For those of you who have not tried loving-kindness meditation (LKM), here are three examples to illustrate what loving-kindness meditation is like. Each is started only after you reach a level of maximum relaxation in a quiet place.

Breathe with a leaf. The fastest method I know of for getting a feel for what elevating your loving-kindness and perhaps even compassion through meditation might be like was taught to me by my friend Tarchin Hearn, a meditation master and teacher who runs the Wangapeka Study and Retreat Centre in New Zealand. I will just call the method "breathe with a leaf." Sit comfortably in front of a plant, preferably in the outdoors—best of all out in nature—where it is quiet and with no distractions. Focus on a leaf or leaves and as you breathe in say to yourself "the leaf (plant) is breathing for me," and as you breathe out say to yourself "I am breathing for the leaf (plant)." The focus of your consciousness is upon the breathing in and out, but the reciprocity between yourself and the plant-being is part of the awareness. After a while you are just aware of the reciprocity without saying anything, even in your head.

A rose in your heart. One of my students came to me and told me what a god-awful job she had as a checkout clerk at a supermarket. She said she had come to the point of despising customers, many of whom were rude and disgruntled. I suggested that she try an experiment— that every time a customer passed through her station, that she imagine picking a red rose from a bush in her heart and handing it to the customer. She later reported that this simple practice turned her head around and that she was enjoying going to work. I have no idea how long this lasted, but this is an example of the kind of loving-kindness visualization practice that goes back thousands of years. It can be a very simple technique. While sitting and relaxing as much as possible you imagine—create an image as clear as you can—whatever flower you associate with love (red or pink rose if you are a Westerner, an utpala or lotus flower if you are an Easterner, and place the image in your heart center. You can accompany this with a mantra: *"om mani padme hum,"* the Jesus Prayer, or repeat the seed syllable "hum" or "hung" making sure the vibration occurs in the heart region. Such visualizations can be simple or complex. As I have described in Chapter 5, even when you begin with a complex visualized image, eventually it will simplify itself to perhaps one or more colored spheres. One of my own pet visualizations is to imagine an inner image of a red marble (*bindu*) sitting on a rose in the heart. I have found this especially effective.

Friends, strangers, enemies. This is another age-old method in which you sit relaxed and then conjure up images of people you love, avoiding anyone for whom you feel lust. Imagine each person's face as clearly as you can and feel the love generated by this parade of beloved faces. You want the heart level psychic energy radiating, not lust. As soon as you feel the warm loving-kindness feeling, switch to imaging the faces of people you neither love nor dislike, people you are neutral about. Try to keep the loving feeling going while running through the neutral faces. When you lose the loving feeling, then go back to imagining the faces of those you love until the feeling is again active, and then move on to neutral faces. When you can maintain loving-kindness toward ordinarily neutral faces, then begin imagining the faces of people you normally dislike or are afraid of. This is the hardest part of the work. Keep going back to the loved ones to get the feeling going and then move to first neutral and then disliked faces. The object of course is to keep the loving-kindness feeling going strongly enough that it does not matter who's face you imagine. This is the feeling of "unconditional positive regard" the literature speaks about. An alternative to the "friends, strangers, enemies" string you can also practice on categories of animals. Imagine those animals you love, then animals you have no positive or negative feelings about and finally animals you detest or are afraid of.

It is well to note that the role of the hormone oxytocin is significant in activating systems involved in positive affect, bonding, child birth and child-caring. Oxytocin is manufactured in the hypothalamus and stored in the pituitary. When released into the bloodstream the chemical will activate cells in the *nucleus accumbens* (see Figure 11.2). Barraza and Zak (2009) have shown that increased oxytocin is correlated with both an increase in felt empathy toward strangers, and generosity.

Those of you who have followed a disciplined, long-term practice of LKM can attest to the fact that such work does increase the feelings of love and decreasing anxiety and other stress-related problems in one's life. Clinicians are now frequently turning to LKM techniques with clients to reduce stress and increase self-love and wellbeing— using loving-kindness as a solvent for dissolving anxiety, reducing depression and other stress-related problems (Hofmann, Grossman, and Hinton 2011; Hutcherson, Seppala, and Gross 2008; Sears and Kraus 2009). In other words, as with other kinds of meditation, LKM leads to a permanent change in consciousness that is reflected in measurable changes in the brain. Moreover, the changes that are produced by LKM are somewhat different than the changes resulting from other kinds of meditation; for example, meditation upon the breath. Leung *et al.* (2013) have indicated that the volume of gray matter in the right angular and posterior parahippocampal gyri increased in long-term loving-kindness meditators compared with novices. Furthermore:

> …LKM experts had significantly more gray matter volume in the right angular gyrus, which may be unique to the effect of LKM training. Neuroscience studies have linked the right angular gyrus (a part of the right [temporo-parietal junction]) with empathy for others during meditation. Our LKM experts also had more gray matter volume in the right posterior parahippocampal gyrus. It is part of the paralimbic system, which works with the limbic and neocortical regions to regulate emotional or empathic responses…. (ibid: 34)

And as Lee *et al.* (2012: 10) note:

> … [R]esponses of LKM experts to sad pictures were more in line with differentiating emotional contagion from compassion/emotional regulation processes. These observations contribute to the literature on neuroplasticity by adding evidence that practice is associated with specific effects on brain activity. Meditation does influence emotion processing, regardless of whether the practice focuses on cognition (*anapanasati*) or emotion (*metta*). Finally, the neural pathways underlying emotion processing associated with [loving-kindness meditation] are likely to be different from those associated with [focused attention meditation].

At this point, let me remind you of the interesting experience of psychic energy flipping I described in Chapter 4. You will recall that I was doing the Tibetan Tantric *tummo* work by means of which practitioners learn to activate and marshal their psychic energy for use in other practices, such as mindfulness and loving-kindness.

Figure 11.4. Dorje Pakmo Dancing in Flames. A nearly-naked and fierce young woman dancing in fire is associated with the arousal of psychic energy in both Tibetan and Hindu Tantric traditions. This black and white picture does not do her justice, for she is a fire-engine red color and dancing in yellow flames. Notice she wears a tiger skin around her waist, symbolizing, among other things, natural energy and fearlessness. As with all anthropomorphic Tantric figures, what the goddess holds in her hands depicts aspects of awakening consciousness, a code to the precise occult meaning of the picture.

The work is associated with a Goddess of Heat—in my case, the Tibetan goddess *Dorje Pakmo* (*Vajravārāhī*), often pictured as a naked red teenage female dancing in flames (Figure 11.4). I noted that when I learned to activate and direct psychic energy from my "root *chakra*" (the *muladhara* in *Kundalini* yoga), I could will the energy outward into my genitals or upward through the central channel to the various centers, including my heart center (the *anahata*). This was significant to my understanding of Eastern phenomenology, not only because the descriptions of these experiences we have from ages past are so accurate, but because Tibetan and Hindu writings associate the rising of psychic energy up the central channel as "semen" and "fire." Moreover, this discovery—at least phenomenologically, if not physiologically—ties the energy experienced as sexual arousal with the energy emitted by the heart center experienced as *metta* or loving-kindness.

Compassion Meditation (CM)

You may have noticed that I have not mentioned compassion. This is because if there is any term fuzzier than love it is compassion, the connotations of which range from pity and sympathy through to wisdom-imbued empathy. One problem is that the English word "compassion" is derived from the Greeks and Romans, and as usually understood means pity and sympathy for others. The term that is usually translated into English as compassion is from the Pali word *karuṇā*, a term used in Buddhism and Jainism and which specifically excludes pity (which has a connotation of selfishness about it), and is more than sympathy and empathy (which can both refer to an emotion). Compassion is a higher-order—indeed *the highest* order—of caring for beings.

So-called *compassion meditation* (CM) is related to LKM. I say "so-called" because to my mind what some researchers consider to be "compassion" is little more than positive empathy and altruism. In some research designs compassion is defined as the desire to alleviate the suffering of others. For instance, Lutz *et al.* (2008) measured activation of neural structures using an fMRI among two groups of people, one being expert meditators and the other being novices. They instructed the experts to do an exercise like the friends-strangers-enemies meditation I described above as a classic LKM. Their protocol showed that the insular cortex (Figure 2.4) is involved in loving-kindness and compassion as they define the term. It is known that the insula becomes thicker among long-term meditators than among normal folks (Lazar *et al.* 2005). The trouble with their research is that they seem to equate positive empathy with compassion and confound empathy and loving-kindness. In fact, compassion can be experienced in the absence of emotion—indeed, this is the type of compassion described for highly enlightened contemplatives (i.e., those endowed with the *bodhicitta*; see e.g., Buddhaghosa 1976). What is missing from this research *is the wisdom aspect of compassion*, which is more a cognitive than and emotional function—by cognitive I do not mean thought, but rather intuitive knowledge of the causes of suffering and its alleviation applied to specific instances.

In comparison, Kim *et al.* (2009) carried out similar research upon compassion where the term is defined *as an attitude* toward perceived suffering, in this case, pictures of sad faces. The researchers defined compassion in this way:

> Compassion is an essential human quality that allows one to feel, *understand, and respond to the suffering of others.* Compassion is one of the essential components which enable individuals to enter into and maintain caring relationships. Most of the world's major religions hold compassion as one of the highest spiritual virtues. It means a feeling of being moved by another's suffering, the deep feeling for and *understanding of the misery of suffering and the concomitant motivation to alleviate such suffering....* (ibid: 2073; emphasis added)

Their research protocol was thus oriented more toward the cognitive and motivational aspect of compassion. While still including the loving-kindness element, they have shown that the neural systems involved in compassionate *understanding and action* are more diverse, involving several areas of the cortex and midbrain (Figure 11.5):

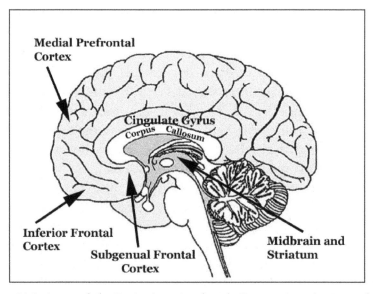

Figure 11.5. Areas of the Brain Associated with Compassion. Again, we have a drawing of the brain sliced down the middle (sagittal view) showing the approximate location of the medial prefrontal, inferior frontal and subgenual areas of the right cortex, as well as the cingulate gyrus and midbrain/striatal areas.

[O]ur results suggest that taking a compassionate attitude may enhance the activities of brain regions involved in the cognitive and experiential understanding of another's state and thereby enables *deep understanding* for others. Particularly, the results of this study support our hypothesis that a compassionate attitude towards another's sad expression modulates the activities of the fronto-midbrain–ventral striatum/septal region network that is known to be implicated in the prosocial/social approach motivation and the accompanied rewarding feeling. (Kim 2009: 2080)

The attitudinal definition of compassion implies that the compassionate person be operating upon what has been called a *theory of mind* comprehension of the other being. This means that inside the compassionate person's mind is a representation of the other being's mental state which would include the other's intentions, desires, feelings, behaviors and beliefs (Premack and Woodruff 1978; Frith and Frith 2005). The importance of including the theory of mind and attitudinal orientation toward defining compassion allows for *development of the attitude (the cognitive understanding) at the core of compassion over the course of a contemplative's career.* It is entirely possible for my theory of mind understanding of why you are suffering to be entirely inaccurate, thus leading to inappropriate action on my part. This is often the case with "enablers" who make a situation worse by their caring, but inappropriate interactions. Over the course of life, the theory of mind element in compassion can grow and develop and become more sophisticated and realistic in understanding.

It is important to understand that compassion begins at home. That is, *self-compassion* is as important to the development of a mature contemplative as compassion for others. Kristen Neff (2003) has defined self-compassion as incorporating three elements: "…(a) **self-kindness**—extending kindness and understanding to oneself rather than harsh judgment and self-criticism, (b) **common humanity**—seeing one's experiences as part of the larger human experience rather than seeing them as separating and isolating, and (c) **mindfulness**—holding one's painful thoughts and feelings in balanced awareness rather than over-identifying with them" (ibid: 89; emphasis added). Self-compassion is crucial for contemplations involving intercommunication with the unconscious self (Chapters 7 and 8). Keep in mind that the enemies of self-realization are fear, self-loathing and self-criticism. Compassion is the antithesis of these conditioned reactions, and in a full-on state of self-compassion, there is no hindrance to engagement with unconscious materials (Germer and Neff 2013; Neff and Davidson 2016). Mindfulness and self-compassion go hand-in-hand. Research has shown that long-term mindfulness meditation produces an increase in self-compassion and well-being (Baer, Lykins and Peters 2012; Hölzel *et al.* 2011) and thus is an excellent entrée into the skills required for in depth self-exploration (in the Jungian sense; see Leary *et al.* 2007).

Research on the functions of the temporal pole of the temporal lobe have also implicated this region in theory of mind functions related to compassion (Olson, Plotzker and Ezzyat 2007). More specifically, this region forms a part of the paralimbic cortical system which also includes the piriform cortex, entorhinal cortex and the cingulate cortex just above the corpus callosum. The temporal pole seems to integrate highly processed theory of mind related information with affect, self-control and emotionally linked goal setting. So, we can see that the elements of compassion, at least in the Eastern connotations of the term *karuṇā*,

Mystical Love

There is a myriad of ways to evoke and nurture loving-kindness to counter the anti-mystical emotional reactions spawned from angst, fear, aversion, greed, anger and hatred. We have explored some of these ways in the last three chapters and have shown that the brain is physiologically prepared to mediate full-on love, both in the social and reproductive sense, and in the mystical sense. Rituals have enormous power to alter people's emotional states. Early Roman peoples grouped together to perform rites and meditations in attendance to their gods. Religion, or *religio*, was equated with *cultus deorum*, "worship of the gods" (Cicero 1997[45 BCE]). Ignoring the negative connotations of our English word "cult," the intent of the term *cultus* is devotion, adoration, and thus cultivation—that is, an active giving of love through emotional outpourings and material gifts—to establish a relationship of reciprocity with the deity (see Mauss 1969 [1924]; Laughlin 1985).

This is very likely the intent of many of the early Roman Dionysian (Bacchic) practices leading to the ecstatic communion with the god (Warrior 2006: 86).

As we saw in Chapter 3, monastic traditions all over the globe have structured lifestyles for male and female monks to decrease those feelings and activities that bolster ego-centered consciousness, and to promote those that lead to loving-kindness toward all beings and selfless service to all. This program in every case sets the stage for more advanced contemplation, which must be energized by unconditional positive regard for all experiences. Again, as Thomas Merton wrote:

> The important thing in contemplation is not enjoyment, not pleasure, not happiness, not peace, but the transcendent experience of reality and truth in the act of supreme and liberated spiritual love. The important thing in contemplation is not gratification and rest, but awareness, life, creativity, and freedom. In fact, contemplation is man's highest and most essential spiritual activity. (Merton 2008:132)

How the mystical experience is triggered, whether it be by ritual procedures, by illness or injury, because of contemplation, or by some other stimulus, love (whether coded as "devotion," "adoration," "adulation," "affection," or any of the other synonyms for love) is always a part of the experience. Neurosurgeon, Dr. Eben Alexander, author of the book *Proof of Heaven* (2012), contracted a severe brain disease and slipped into a seven-day coma during which he was out of touch with material reality. When he woke, he recalled having a remarkable and lucid experience of heaven, bright lights, divine orbs, lovely landscapes and a beautiful woman sitting on a butterfly wing broadcasting unconditional love and assuring him that he had nothing whatever to fear.

In Buddhism, there is no clearer image of mystical love than the various manifestations of Avalokiteśvara (Tib.: Chenrezig), the deity of compassion. One of the most popular images of Avalokiteśvara is the peaceful, four-armed male figure. Usually found on Tibetan scroll paintings or *tankas*, the objects held in Chenrezig's hands signify attributes of the mind-state being depicted. In Figure 11.6, the deity has an *utpala* flower in his left hand, a crystal rosary in his right hand, and a *chintamani*, or "wish fulfilling jewel," in his inner two hands. There is some confusion about just what plant is referred to by "*utpala* flower" but most authorities hold that it refers to the water lily, *Nymphaea caerulea*, which contains a natural alkaloid called *apomorphine* which has tranquilizing and other psychoactive effects when imbibed, and which has been used as an entheogen for its psychodysleptic effects in many cultures since at least the time of the ancient Egyptians and Mayans (Emboden 1978). Thus, one may understand the *utpala* on the surface as symbolic of unfolding purity and beauty—after all, the water lily grows out of the muck at the bottom of dirty ponds and rivers, much as the dung beetle with its gorgeous carapace grows out of manure; hence, the origins of the Ancient Egyptian's sacred *scarab*. Or, one may take the flower as symbolic of a more esoteric level of

Figure 11.6. *Chenrezig* **(Skt: Avalokiteśvara), the God of Compassion.** This image is the Tibetan version of the bodhisattva of compassion. This version has the god with four hands, one outside hand holding a flower symbolizing loving-kindness, the other outside hand holding a crystal rosary (*mala*) symbolizing one clear moment of consciousness after another, and the two inner hands holding a *Cintāmaṇi* (wish-fulfilling jewel) symbolizing the wisdom of compassion.

significance, that being the calm, centered and sensation-rich mind-state much like that induced by the entheogen.

The crystal *mala* (rosary) in his right hand presumably is being used to count the deity's repetition of the mantra, OM MANI PADME HUM. But the clear crystal beads are also symbolic of the dynamic movement of one clear moment of consciousness after another—each temporal epoch after another—each moment in a state of access concentration. The "wish fulfilling jewel" cupped in his inner two hands is a symbol of ancient standing in the East, often equated with the alchemical "philosopher's stone." Some authorities simply consider this to be a symbol of the nature of mind, the ability of the mind to conjure up anything the being desires—this being the root of suffering. It should be noted that none of the attributes represented by objects in the hands of deities should be considered alone, for they all represent aspects of the one mind-state being depicted symbolically by the entire image. In other words, Tibetan Tantric *tanka* imagery is intended to be a language of images that describe better than words the state of consciousness being represented by the whole painting. By meditating upon the image in the way I described for arising yoga practices (Chapter 3), one may eventually *become* that mind-state, and in this case, *become* Chinrezig.

SUMMARY AND SEGUE

We have seen that the most important ingredient of mystical experiences is mystical love—loving-kindness in the sense of selfless service and global positive affect. Mystical love may be considered as a "universal solvent" in the sense that love, and only love, is the natural emotional counter to anxiety, greed and hatred, all which pose major hindrances to absorption states. Many of the mystical traditions we encounter in this book have developed techniques for eliminating ego-centered mind-states in preparation for the experiences and sequelae of mystical realization. We examined the affective processes involved in empathy and bonding, including pair-bonding among non-human monogamous animals. The parts of the brain that mediate empathy and love were distinguished, and their cognitive-affective operations traced, including the pairing of love with sexual attraction and the drive toward reproduction, and the evolution of the social brain. We focused on loving-kindness meditation techniques used to counter negative aversion to absorption. We saw that those who practice loving-kindness become less anxious (particularly about death). Also covered were types of compassion meditation which operate to enhance the wisdom aspect of loving-kindness. I finished the chapter by discussing one of the most representative symbols of compassion, and one of the most powerful meditation traditions, that being the Tibetan Tantric Buddhist meditation on Chenrezig, the deity of compassion.

Not only is mystical love, and loving-kindness generally the critical ingredient in evoking mystical experiences, but it is also the preferred affective state for contemplating the inevitability of one's own death. A compassionate view of life surely must incorporate an encounter with the fact of one's own death. We will now turn to death contemplation, perhaps one of the most potentially transpersonal and life-changing practices one may undertake.

CHAPTER TWELVE

The Mystical Brain IV: Death Contemplation

The irony of man's condition is that the deepest need is to be free of the anxiety of death and annihilation; but it is life itself which awakens it, and so we must shrink from being fully alive.

– Ernest Becker, *The Denial of Death*

Even death is not to be feared by one who has lived wisely.

– Jack Kornfield, *Buddha's Little Instruction Book*

Death is a fact of life, no matter where you live.

– Kent Haruf

Death is the mother of spiritual life.

– Erasmus, *De praeparatione ad morte*m, 1534

Death is a fact of life—perhaps *the* fact of life. Every living being consisting of more than a single cell must die. Many big-brained animals perceive death as troubling, and human beings face a profound existential dilemma when they confront and attempt to understand the fact of death. People in every society on the planet naturally become self-aware and recognize death as both a life cycle end-state or liminal phase, and as a process that everyone must eventually experience (Palgi and Abramovitch 1984: 385; Sheikh and Sheikh 2003). Death is one of the great life crises, taking its place among the other significant points of life—birth, puberty, adulthood, marriage, and sickness—that most societies will demarcate with ceremony and lore. Like birth, death presents the human mind with an existential dilemma. People confront material evidence of the cessation of life, sometimes daily, and yet I know of no society on Earth that accepts the fact of death at face value—e.g., as being also the end of consciousness, spirit or being. In other words, people everywhere find death a mystery, and consequently, every culture provides an account of death that explains—some might say "explains away"—the phenomenon as a transcendental event, thus avoiding the more painful repercussions of our very mortal, biological nature.

In my opinion, virtually all full-on paths of contemplation lead inevitably to an encounter with death anxiety (or nonbeing anxiety). I am at heart an existentialist in this respect, not because I prefer existentialism to other forms of philosophy, or gravitate to any favorite philosopher, but rather because my experiences as a contemplative have provided sufficient evidence of the fact that behind all forms of fear lies a stratum of anxiety derived from a wired-in, neurognostic recognition of non-being. On top of that, as we shall see, there are tons of evidence now supporting an innate death anxiety. As the great theologian, Paul Tillich wrote:

> The first assertion about the nature of anxiety is this: *anxiety is the state in which a being is aware of its possible nonbeing.* The same statement, in a shorter form, would read: anxiety is the existential awareness of nonbeing. "Existential" in this sentence means that it is not the abstract knowledge of nonbeing which produces anxiety but the awareness that nonbeing is a part of one's own being. It is not the realization of universal transitoriness, not even the experience of the death of others, but *the impression of these events on the always latent awareness of our own having to die that produces anxiety.* Anxiety is finitude, experienced as one's own finitude. This is the natural anxiety of man as man, and in some way of all living beings. It is the anxiety of nonbeing, the awareness of one's finitude as finitude. (Tillich 1952: 35-36; emphasis added)

Here we have an essential tension between awareness of being and non-being that works its way out in everyone's awareness during their lifetime, with or without the aid and comfort supplied by their culture. We can see that an essential tension lies beneath and energizes much of what we in the West call "religion"—the kinds of spiritual knowledge and ritual activity that ethnographers routinely encounter when they do extended fieldwork among peoples, be those people traditional or technocratic. The essential tension is between the perceptual fact of death and the meaning of death, usually as mediated by culture. While every normal human being on the planet experiences loss and grief at the death of loved ones, how those emotions are expressed depends upon cultural background (Kagawa-Singer 1995: 101).

The Denial of Death

One of the most profound books I have ever read is anthropologist Ernest Becker's *The Denial of Death* (1973). In that book and elaborated in a couple of his other works (1971, 1975), Becker argued that the knowledge of our death permeates the way we live our lives. We are animals and like other species, we are biologically wired to preserve our existence. Unlike other animals, however, we can think about our existential plight, and develop systems of meaning that stand between us and reality. But rather than facing this tension between meaning and reality head-on, we build cultural barriers to protect us from the terror of our own demise. Like Tillich before him, he realized that there is a stratum of anxiety in all people everywhere about the nature of our "creatureliness." Despite our best efforts to avoid the issue, to elevate our consciousness to some transcendental level, we intuit that we "…have emerged from nothing, to have a name, consciousness of self, deep feelings, an excruciating inner yearning for life and self-expression—and with all this, yet to die" (Becker 1973: 87). Much of this angst is unconscious to most people because we are born into cultural systems that operate to buffer us from the repercussions of the fact of our own death. So effective are these cultural constructs that we can, in effect, deny our death and repress our terror. Yet in our daily lives, our very biological bodies intervene to remind us of our creatureliness: We must eat and drink water, defecate, feel pain, crave sex, and breathe. The effect is a constant reminder by the body, "Here I am, and I'm mortal."

Because we operate cognitively upon a symbolic world of our own making, and remain mortal biological beings, a tension exists that leads to all sorts of fictions woven into our cultural world views. Every culture deals with death in some way, usually with a theory of how the consciousness or soul miraculously survives the death of the physical body—Becker's "immortality project." Bolstering this view, we construct "hero" myths that elevate humanity to a status far above our creatureliness. Contemplative traditions are not immune to this illusory vision of human transcendence. Far from it. Most such traditions, except for Husserlian transcendental phenomenology, are wired-in to a cycle of meaning that offers interpretive accounts of experiences that arise in accordance with the techniques used. Even Buddhism which emphasizes the realization of no-self offers an ontological/psychological explanation of how consciousness survives death—our lifelong karma leads to a summary bundle that passes on to the next lifetime.

Becker's influence upon my thinking and, perhaps more importantly, upon my interpretive frame with respect to experiences had during meditation, has been considerable. From early on, I have been automatically skeptical of ontological claims grounded solely upon transpersonal experiences. Just because I experience something to be true, even apodictically true, does not mean that it really is true (see Katz 1978b on this issue).

Terror Management Theory and the Anxious Brain

I am of course not the only scientist to be influenced by Becker's thought—far from it. Becker's work eventually led to a large body of research and psychological theory that came to be known as Terror Management Theory (TMT; see Pyszczynski, Solomon and Greenberg 2003; Pyszczynski et al. 2006; Harvell and Nisbett 2016). The TMT project has been summarized nicely by Sandra L. Bloom (2010):

> Terror Management Theory hypothesizes that human awareness
> of the inevitability and possible finality of death creates the

potential for existential terror, which is controlled largely in two ways: (a) faith in an internalized cultural world view, and (b) self-esteem, which is attained by living up to the standards of value prescribed by one's world view. Research has in fact demonstrated that when the fear of death—or *mortality salience*—is triggered, even outside of conscious awareness—people tend to become more fearful, intolerant of difference, more prejudiced, more socially conservative, more supportive of leaders who support their world view, more fundamentalist, and more punitive towards those who are disrupting or who threatened to disrupt their world view.... To date, over 300 experiments, conducted in 15 different countries, have provided support for Terror Management Theory hypotheses.... (emphasis added)

Death anxiety, or "mortality salience," is rarely confronted directly, but rather fuels occasional fears of specific objects: fear of pain, fear of spiders, fear of driving, fear of another person, etc. Indeed, the neuropsychology suggests that there are two systems of death anxiety at work, one at the unconscious level and the other at the conscious level (LeDoux 2008). The neurophysiological systems that mediate death anxiety are found in the limbic system, including the amygdala and linked structures involved in the development of unconscious fear-related memories, and the hippocampus and cortical areas involved in the development of conscious fear-related memories (Figure 12.1). The amygdala is located inside the temporal lobe on each side of the brain and has the job of evaluating the emotional salience of stimuli in the environment. For instance, Schwartz *et al.* (2003) found that infants who had their natural temperament inhibited, relative to those with uninhibited temperaments, experienced greater amygdala activation, and thus experienced more anxiety, when faced with novelty. If the amygdala is injured, there may be a disruption of the development of appropriate emotional salience, and the person may not feel fear when it is appropriate to do so (LeDoux 2003).

Death anxiety is sometimes conscious, but most often is unconscious, and encounter with the raw existential anxiety is buffered by two cultural factors, (1) a commonly accepted world view that explains away the reality of death, and (2) self-esteem, which is to say that one believes they are living their lives in accordance with his or her world view (Pyszczynski, Greenberg and Solomon 1999). Here the TMT people introduce a crucial distinction (at least from our point of view): lower level neuro-sensory systems are designed to reproduce reality as veridically as possible, whereas higher level perceptual and cognitive systems are designed to create a meaningful brain world. Here we see the difference between the "effort after truth" and "effort after meaning" (see Introduction) in action. There are two layers of defense against death anxiety. One is the lower level *proximal defense system* and the other is the higher level *distal defense system*:

> ... whereas proximal defenses are activated only when the problem of death enters current focal attention, distal defenses, involving the pursuit of self-esteem and faith in one's cultural world view, are active whenever the individual is awake and conscious. Activation of distal world view defense increases with increasing accessibility of death-related thought, up to the point at which these thoughts enter consciousness. At this point, proximal defenses to remove these thoughts from consciousness

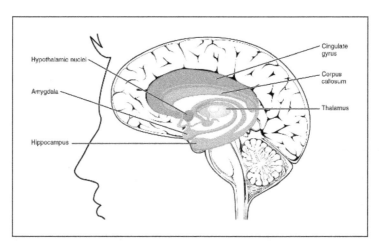

Figure 12.1. The Human Limbic System. The brain is cut down the middle (sagittal view) showing the limbic structures involved in death anxiety: the cingulate gyrus, thalamus, hypothalamus, hippocampus and amygdala. Illustration from Anatomy and Physiology, Connexions Web site. http://cnx.org/content/col11496/1.6/, accessed September 28, 2017.

are initiated. Once this is achieved, distal defenses are activated in the service of reducing the accessibility of death-related thoughts, thereby keeping the potential for terror in check... (Pyszczynski, Greenberg and Solomon 1999).

Distal defenses are activated when we are face to face with death, and involve those defenses that are most automatic and furthest from the center of consciousness:

The initial line of defense against conscious death-related thoughts are proximal, relatively rational, threat-focused cognitive maneuvers that push these thoughts out of consciousness, often by simply seeking distractions. For example, after passing a gruesome accident scene, a person might turn up the radio or intensify the attention being focused on plans for the evening. (Pyszczynski, Greenberg and Solomon 1999)

While proximal defenses are those involving the conscious meaning (or symbolic) system itself:

Distal defenses are activated to defend against death-related thoughts that are outside of current consciousness or focal attention. They address the problem of death in a more indirect symbolic manner by providing a sense that one is a valuable contributor to a meaningful, eternal universe. Rather than pushing the problem of death out of consciousness or rationalizing it away into the distant future, distal defenses provide security by making one's life seem meaningful, valuable, and enduring. This attempt to deal with threats indirectly, by embedding oneself in a meaningful enduring cultural reality that is hierarchically connected to the threatening material, is the essence of distal defense.

Either way, people are equipped to keep death at bay by various defense mechanisms, thus reducing the level of terror. From the TMT vantage point, the role of culture looms large in inculcating the symbolic and meaningful level of world view and a sense of self-worth that protects us from the consequences of direct encounter with death anxiety.

Death Cultures

As Becker demonstrated, and TMT research has empirically shown, albeit usually with samples of Westerners, how people are taught to think and feel about death, and how they respond to death and dying is very much determined by culture. It has no doubt been thus since at least the time of the Neanderthals who show the first archaeological evidence of a death culture (Rendu *et al.* 2014). How people view death varies widely across cultures. For instance, while we tend to view death as an event or state, many peoples see death as a lengthier process. Let me offer a not uncommon example from my own experience in the field. While doing fieldwork among the So, a group of farming and herding people living in Northeastern Uganda (Laughlin and Allgeier 1979), I happened to wander into a compound one day early-on in my fieldwork and witnessed a woman howling and running around with her hands on top her head, obviously distraught about something. I asked someone why she was in such pain and was told that her baby had just died. Where is the baby? I asked. In her hut, was the reply. I went over to the woman's hut and, peeking inside, saw an infant crying quietly and wiggling around. Without thinking things through, I grabbed the baby and then told the mother to come with me. She followed dutifully, and we ran to my truck and drove mother and baby to the local hospital. There a nurse tried various methods to save the child, but she soon died. I returned to the So compound with the mother and turned the dead baby over to her grandmother. The grandmother soon took the baby's body and left to walk up into the forest. I followed her and watched as the grandmother lovingly removed the child's adornments and propped the little one up against a tree, and then turned and walked back to the compound where she and others did what they could to console the distraught mother.

For me this was a profound lesson, for I was then a very young and inexperienced ethnographer, and my immediate reaction to the situation into which I had wandered was totally ethnocentric and inappropriate. I thought to myself, these people can't tell the difference between someone who is sick and needing treatment and someone who is dead. My reaction was pure Americana—I sought help from medical professionals at a Western-oriented hospital. I failed to see the evidence, plainly visible on the baby's body, of the So healer's previous attempts to treat her sickness. I later understood that because the So only have recourse to the district hospital as a last resort, if at all, most people who are taken to the hospital end up dying there. Hence, for the So, a hospital is conceived to be a place one goes to die. Thus, what I had managed to do was reinforce in everybody's mind that this view of hospitals was indeed true. Moreover, I also learned that *there is no distinction in the local language between dying as a process and death as a state.* For the So, to say that someone is dead also may mean they are in the process of dying. The people knew perfectly well that the baby was still breathing, but they had released hold of her as a living family member and were in the process of accepting her death—a family process I impertinently interrupted by interfering. Needless to say, I never made that mistake ever again, either among the So, or among any of the other peoples I have lived amongst.

These misunderstandings across cultural and linguistic lines are quite common. Nigel Barley tells a story in his book, *Dancing on the Grave,* about one of his encounters with death among the Dowayo people of Cameroon. He saw his friend Pascal on the road and asked after his wife. Pascal nonchalantly replied, "She died last night." Barley was dumbstruck for a moment and then asked, "What happened?" Pascal said, "She was just walking about, felt dizzy and died."

> I stammered out consolation and as I did so Pascal looked over my head, waved and grinned. Looking up, I saw his wife walking slowly down the road, pulling idly at leaves on either side, dressed in cloth and heading for town. I felt a flash of anger that he had played such a silly trick. Then I remembered. Amongst the Dowayos, anyone who faints or goes into a coma is described as "dead;" death is a much less cut-and-dried affair than amongst ourselves. (Barley 1995:46-47)

Because of this, as I mentioned above, I hold that *thanatophobia,* "death anxiety," is another universal response to the existential dilemma posed by the fact of death. While the evidence supporting this view is sound for modern societies (see Kastenbaum 2006: 17), the ultimate answer to this question is an empirical one and requires anthropological analysis to solve. Death psychology does set us many interesting questions, for some of their research findings have been counterintuitive. For instance, it might be assumed that the closer we get to death, the more we would fear it, but research on the elderly show either no difference or slightly less anxiety. In addition, fear of death is greater among children and adolescents than later in adulthood (ibid: 18). Also, intense religious belief does not seem to alleviate the fear of death among Americans (Wink and Scott 2005; Emerick 2000). Even a high exposure to death does not seem to increase the acceptance of the inevitability of death and reduce fear (Fernandez, Castano and Singh 2010). One also must be aware that many people who would claim they are not afraid of death eventually discover they have been suppressing their anxiety, as modeled by TMT, which reveals itself (fear may be *sublimated* to use a psychiatric term) in dreams and other indirect ways (various phobias like fear of crowds, heights, snakes, etc.). There are data suggesting that fear of premature death and fear of the dead are the death factors most related to anxiety states (Hoelter and Hoelter 1978).

Fear of death and dying can take bizarre forms. People have long harbored anxiety about being prematurely pronounced dead, and thus buried, burned, cut open or embalmed before their time:

Safeguards to prevent premature burial date back to antiquity with the Thracians, Romans, and Greeks, who each waited [three] days for putrefaction to begin before burying their dead. The Romans took a more extreme approach by cutting off a finger to see if the stump bled (spilling blood would imply circulation) in addition to calling out the person's name three times while on the funeral pyre. It is clear that premature burial was a concern, although it did not reach a fevered pitch until the 18th century; this was largely facilitated by the intellectual climate. (Whetstine 2008: 66)

Many people in 18th and 19th century England became obsessed with the possibility of being buried alive (Bondeson 2001; Quigley 1996: 183-188). It was a period during which Edgar Allan Poe used "premature burial" as a motif in some of his more horrific stories. All sorts of presumably "true" stories circulated about mistakes by physicians and others leading to the burial of comatose patients before their time. Some of the most lurid accounts were collected by William Tebb and Edward Perry Vollum in their 1905 book, *Premature Burial and How It May Be Prevented*. They list some 160-plus people either buried, or dissected and embalmed, and over 200 cases of people who barely escaped that fate. As entrepreneurs always will, all sorts of *safety coffins* were designed during the period— Figure 12.2 illustrates one such contrivance designed in the latter 1800s. The (hopefully dead) corpse was to be buried in a standard coffin, but with a long tube extending up and out of the grave with a box on top, the door to which would swing open if the person comes back to his senses and pulls a rope. The rope also rings a bell and fresh air descends via the tube while the person awaits rescue. There were many such designs, most of which never got past the drawing board (Tebb and Vollum 1905; Dittrick 1948; Bondeson 2001: Chap. 6).

Among Tibetans, it is commonplace to let a corpse sit or lay "in state" until it demonstrates definite signs of putrefaction. Tibetan Buddhist lamas routinely instruct those around them that they will be found "dead" and that they are not to be disturbed for three days, or until their bodies begin to decompose (often signaled by fluids running out of their nose). According to my friends and fellow monks, this was the pattern followed by my own Tibetan preceptor and meditation master, Chogye Trichen Rinpoche, when he died in January 2007, and sat in that state for 16 days. I myself witnessed this pattern when I was

Figure 12.2. The Lindquist Safety Coffin. Designed in the latter 19th century by August Lindquist, this arrangement was equipped with an air tube and a bell to summon help.

staying in Rinpoche's monastery in Lumbini, Nepal, and a well-known and beloved annual pilgrim died at the monastery. He passed away in meditation posture and was left to sit that way for some days before another monk and I cremated him with due ceremony.

What death psychology tells us is that death and dying are not simply matters of the end of life, but rather are a complex phenomenon indeed:

> Fear of death is not a unitary or monolithic variable. Various subcomponents are evident, for example, fear of going to hell, loss of identity, loneliness. For a good number of persons, negative connotations of death are associated substantially with feelings of rootlessness and having to face the "unknown" with minimal mastery. These features appear to be more prominent than even such aspects as "I may not have lived completely," or "My family may suffer." For many, death no longer signals the possibility of atonement and salvation, or a point in time on the road to eternity, but isolation and loss of self... (Feifel 1990: 539).

Far from being a unitary emotion, the fear of death varies along several dimensions, both among members of the same society and among people in different societies. Psychologists have developed several methods for measuring death anxiety along various lines, the foremost being the Collett-Lester Fear of Death Scale (CL-FODS; Collett and Lester 1969). This instrument is essentially a questionnaire used to assess attitudes toward death and does so by distinguishing between death as an end state and the process of dying both for oneself and for others. The instrument is organized into four separate subscales: *Fear of death of self, fear of dying of self, fear of death of others, and fear of dying of others* (Lester 1990; Lester and Abdel-Khalek 2003). This fear of death scale has been used effectively among populations living in several modern societies, including Turkey (Zeyrek and Lester 2008), Spain (Tomás-Sábado, Limonero and Abdel-Khalek 2007), Nigeria (Kolawole and Olusegun 2008) and various Arabic speaking societies (Abdel-Khalek and Lester 2004). Whichever instrument is used, cross-cultural studies of death and dying tend to confirm the common assertion that the fear of death is a cultural universal (e.g., Abdel-Khalek 1986).

Summarizing the empirical findings of death psychology, Herman Feifel (1990: 539-540) lists the following (but in my words):

1. Death is a factor in consciousness throughout life.
2. Fear of death may be and often is cloaked by various symptoms, such as insomnia, depression, enhanced fear of loss and psychosomatic and psychotic eruptions.
3. There are subcomponents of the fear of death as a variable; for instance, fear of going to hell after death, fear of loss of self or identity, fear of isolation and loneliness.
4. Many people fear death at an unconscious level while at the conscious level they may appear to accept death with a positive attitude, or deny they fear death. Accepting people's claim that they do not fear death must be taken critically in doing research.
5. The coping strategies of individuals facing life-threatening illnesses and death threats will vary not only among groups, but also among different situations.
6. Most dying [modern Western] people do not expect "miracles" and are concerned mostly with obtaining proper care.
7. The experience of grief is not considered a weakness or self-indulgence. It is a need we have in reaction to the loss of loved ones. It arises in all ages, occurs in all kinds of loss, and manifests in a variety of ways, including: "anticipatory grief, high-low grief, self-grief, survival grief, or anniversary grief."
8. Just as there are numerous ways of living, there are numerous ways of dying and grieving. Fixed stage models of grieving are not supported by the data.
9. Those working with dying patients and mourners need to be able to recognize the signs of denial of, avoidance of, and antipathy toward death, both in themselves and in others.
10. When a cure for what ails the dying patient is no longer possible, extending care and comfort is just as valid and important in meeting the real needs of the dying patient.

There are, of course, several factors that differ among more modern populations: the role of professionals and bureaucratic institutions in caring for the dying (e.g., hospice care) and commercialization of handling the dead (funeral industry). In addition, there has been a historical decline in the ritualization of bereavement (expression of grief and expressing mourning) when compared with either our own preindustrial culture or more traditional societies (Parkes, Laungani and Young 1997b: 4; Homans 2000b).

Death among Big-Brained Animals

There are scientists and philosophers who persist in thinking that only humans have a psychological life and culture. There are still those that would treat our responses to death and dying as unique and exclusively human. They cry "anthropomorphism" every time they hear someone refer to animals "loving," in pain, as moody, having intentions or depressed—and yes, grieving. However, I am not one of these overly restrictive and anthropocentric scientists, preferring (with King 2013 and Anderson 2011, among many others) to spread the widest possible net for insights on the significance of death and dying, and how responses to death have evolved. In addition, the fields of ethology (the study of social animals) and neuroethology (the study of the brains and social behavior of animals) have developed evidence in support of the broader perspective (see e.g., Cavalieri and Singer 1993; DeWaal 2001; Wrangham et al. 1994; Bekoff 2002).

The interesting thing is, mammals with big brains (primates, dolphins, elephants, etc.) are also able to recognize death when it occurs and are disturbed by the death of their own. Prosimian mothers will attempt to nurture their offspring, even if they are stillborn or have died. Nakamichi, Koyama and Jolly (1996: 505) reported on maternal response to dead infants among ring-tailed lemurs (*Lemur catta*) at the Berenty Reserve in Madagascar. In contrast to mothers in simian species, ring-tailed lemur mothers rarely carried their dying, immobile or dead infants. However, they sniffed, licked, and touched them even after they had died. While the dying infants were still peeping, their mothers remained near them, and 15 to 76 minutes after the infants ceased to peep, they were left by their mothers. Six of the seven mothers returned to their dead infants several times within the first few hours after they had left them. All seven mothers gave repeated calls, such as "mew" and "pyaa," when they were separated from either their dead infants or other troop members or both. Thus, each mother exhibited some form of maternal behavior toward her dead infant for hours after its death.

Baboons have larger brains and are cognitively more complex than prosimians, and their behavior toward the dead reflects this evolutionary advance. A mother whose infant dies will hang onto, protect, nurture and clean the body for days, even after the infant has mummified (Cheney and Seyfarth 2007: 195; see also Fashing et al. 2011 for similar behavior among wild gelada monkeys, *Theropithecus gelada*). Meanwhile, other members of the group, including members of the mother's family, cease to respond to the infant as if it were alive, but will guard the dead infant if the mother leaves it on the ground. Even after the mother leaves the corpse behind, group members will continue to attack any human that tries to touch the body. The loss of a relative to predation or some other form of death is distinctly stressful for female baboons (ibid: 86). Such females cope by seeking grooming and extending their social network. Bereavement—often leaving the animal visibly despondent (ibid: 87)—leads to enhanced social contact which, just as it does among humans, alleviates the stress of loss.

When I was doing some field research in 1976 preparatory to writing a chapter for our *Spectrum of Ritual* book (d'Aquili, Laughlin and McManus 1979), I visited my friend and colleague Donald Stone Sade at the Caribbean Primate Research Center on Cayo Santiago just off the island of Puerto Rico. The little island is home to a population of free-ranging rhesus macaques (*Macaca mulatta*) that have been closely observed for years. Although I was interested in mother-infant interactions at the time, I chanced to observe troops of monkeys responding to a dead infant that had been dropped by its mother. First one troop and then another would pass through and each would stop for a while and form a circle around the infant's body. They seemed to purposely look away, while one animal after another approached the body cautiously, sniffed it, sometimes plucked at it, and then returned to their circle. They were obviously disturbed by the corpse. Eventually a troop moved away to be replaced a while later by another group. What I took to be cognitive dissonance was very apparent in the monkeys' behavior. Their demeanor and behavior seemed quite different than any other circumstance I observed.

Our closest biological relatives are the chimpanzees and bonobos of Africa, the common ancestors having lived perhaps 5-7 million years ago. When chimps die from old age or through violence, their family members behave in distinctive ways that seem to signal intense emotional conflict, dissonance, sadness and grief. Teleki (1973) reported one incident at the Gombe reserve in Tanzania during which an adult male chimp died suddenly when he fell from a tree. The others in his group evidenced aggressive display behavior, alarm calls, and a lot of mutual touching and holding. They would approach and sniff at the corpse but would not touch it. Four decades later, Stewart, Piel and O'Malley (2012) also reported on chimp response to a dead adult female at the Gombe reserve. Male juveniles and adults showed aggressive behavior toward the corpse—a not uncommon response which has been interpreted by Anderson, Gillies and Lock (2010) as attempts to resuscitate the body. Some animals formed a circle around the body and individuals would occasionally sniff the body and caress it. When the corpse was removed by scientists, group members made calls and displays indicating distress.

Anderson, Gillies and Lock (2010) videotaped and described the behavior of a group of captive chimps around an old female as she died. The animals showed all sorts of solicitous and succoring behavior toward their ailing friend during her dying, including grooming and stroking her. This behavior stopped when she died in the evening, but her daughter remained with her corpse for the rest of the night, and others in the group showed restlessness during sleep. After the corpse was removed, the group were "profoundly subdued" throughout the next day. There are several other observations of chimpanzee response to death in the literature (Kooriyama 2009; Matsuzawa 1997; Biro et al. 2010), but we have seen enough to illustrate that the responses to a dead conspecific is both special and varies from group to group (Hosaka et al. 2000; Zeller 1991). What responses do seem to indicate is that, just as with other primates, chimpanzees find death troubling, and the cause of confusion, distress, cognitive dissonance and grief. Many of the behaviors described would seem to be attempts to revive or animate the dead body, or guard it for a period.

Primates are by no means the only mammals that seem to be troubled by the death of their own kind. African elephants—whose common ancestor with us lived roughly 105 million years ago—are known to exhibit great interest in, and caregiving (technically called "epimeletic behavior") for ailing and dying members of their own species, whether of the same group or from another group (Douglas-Hamilton 1972; Douglas-Hamilton *et al.* 2006; Moss 2000). In one study, Iain Douglas-Hamilton (2006) documented the death of a matriarch named Eleanor and showed that over the next while both her relatives and elephants unrelated to her showed concern. GPS tracking technologies allowed the scientists to track the movement of many of the elephants in the study area. "This allowed us to analyze the behavior surrounding her death. Combined with earlier work and the data of other scientists it leads to the conclusion that elephants have a generalized response to suffering and death of conspecifics and that this is not restricted to kin. It is an example of how elephants and humans may share emotions, such as compassion, and have an awareness and interest about death" (ibid: 101). A major result of this kind of fieldwork is summed up by Douglas Hamilton in these terms: "The conclusion must be that elephants are interested in the sick, dying or dead elephants irrespective of genetic relationship. There seems to be a generalized response to elephants in distress, rather than help or interest only being restricted to close kin" (ibid: 99).

It is also clear that elephants grieve their lost ones. Joyce Poole (1996) witnessed the death of infants and watched mothers grieving over their dead offspring for days on end, first trying to bring them back to life and then just caressing the corpse. "As I watched Tonie's vigil over her dead newborn, I got my first very strong feeling that elephants grieve…. Every part of her spelled grief" wrote Poole of one such infant death (ibid: 95). Cynthia Moss reports on the response of one family of elephants to the death of one of their matriarchs named Emily whose bones were visited and revisited months and even years later:

The animal[s] stopped and reached their trunks out. They stepped closer and very gently began to touch the remains with the tips of their trunks, first light taps, smelling and feeling, then strokes around and along the larger bones. Eudora and Elspeth, Emily's daughter and granddaughter, pushed through and began to examine the bones. And soon after Echo and her two daughters arrived. All elephants were quiet now and there was a palpable tension among them. Eudora concentrated on Emily's skull caressing the smooth cranium and slipping her trunk into the hollows in the skull. Echo was feeling the lower jaw running her trunk along the teeth—the area used in greeting when elephants place their trunks in each other's mouth. The younger animals were picking up the smaller bones and placing them in their mouths before dropping them again.... Several years before, I had also seen the [members of the EB family] start to bury the carcass of a young female from another family who had died of natural causes. (Moss 1992: 61)

Folklore is rife with stories of elephants returning to "elephant graveyards" to die, and descriptions of elephant's remarkable treatment of the dead go back to Aristotle (Meredith 2001: 30-31). Although the graveyard story is apparently not true, it is the case that elephants show considerable interest in the bones, tusks and skulls of their own kind (Moss 2000: 270-271). Reports suggest that the animals will take time to examine bones, skulls and tusks when they run across them. They will sniff the bones, stroke them and pass them around the group, and eventually may bury or cover them with branches and earth (Meredith 2001: Chap. 22). On one occasion, when some park rangers and scientists had culled elephants in Uganda, they stored the ears and feet of the dead animals in a shed for later sale. Elephants later broke into the shed, carried off the grisly souvenirs and buried them (Moss 1976: 33). McComb, Baker and Moss (2005) set up an experiment to explore elephant responses to elephant remains. They concluded that elephants spend more time examining elephant carcasses than either novel material objects or the remains of other species. Because the scientists knew all the elephants involved, the living and the dead, as well as their relationships to each other, they were able to conclude that elephant interest in carcasses was no different for dead relatives, or the dead of non-relatives.

Dolphins—large-brained members of the Cetacean order of sea mammals, and whose common ancestor with us humans lived roughly 95 million years ago—also recognize the death and dying of their own kind and are obviously troubled by death. The nurturing and succoring behavior of dolphins toward the young and the sick is well known (Caldwell and Caldwell 1966). This behavior apparently does not extend to dead dolphins. Dudzinski *et al.* (2003) observed the responses of dolphins to two different dolphin carcasses. In neither case did attending animals attempt to succor or lift the dead conspecific to the surface, but rather seemed to hang around the corpse, "point" at it and communicate with each other, perhaps about the phenomenon they were investigating. Males would also carry out "guarding" behavior, acting somewhat aggressively toward others. This behavior was considered by the investigators to be unique and significant. Like various primate species, mothers will carry around their dead infants for some time, sometimes with adult escorts seemingly protecting the mother and infant (King 2013: 98-99).

I am inclined to the view that the fact of death for large brained mammals presents an existential dilemma, however short may be the duration of dissonance. What dissonance? Why, the mismatch between my experience of myself as a continuous, conscious being, and the evidence of my senses that tells me that other beings I viewed as having the same quality cease to be. There they are, and yet they aren't there anymore. I doubt elephants, chimps or dolphins wander around pondering the inevitability of their own and others' deaths the way we humans do. At the same time, we can see in these very different animals the evolutionary anlage (precursor form) of the human condition (Archer 1999: 57). The often-devastating effects of bereavement, especially evident in infants who have sustained loss of their mother, stand as grim testimony to the similarities between animal and human bereavement (Zeller 1991; King 2013; Archer 1999: 54-57).

CONTEMPLATING DEATH

As reasoned by Becker, and subsequently empirically demonstrated by TMT researchers and other psychologists, death poses an existential problem for people everywhere, regardless of their cultural background. The most common defenses against the full comprehension of death involve explaining it away, distracting the mind, bolstering one's self-esteem and other cultural and psychological "tricks" designed to lessen the angst of realizing our creatureliness. Research has shown that a variety of situations and experiences can reduce death anxiety. One of those is the *near death experience* (NDE), the reports and details of which vary considerably cross-culturally (Belanti, Perera and Jagadheesan 2008). People who have had NDEs demonstrate several significant changes in their emotional and attitudinal responses:

> Specific areas of change included increased concern for others, reduced death anxiety with a strengthened belief in an afterlife, increased transcendental experience, reduced interest in material possessions, increased self-worth, increased appreciation for natural phenomenon, and an enhanced awareness of paranormal phenomenon. Analysis of the depth of the experience indicated that the depth and the extent of change were positively correlated. Collectively, this information strongly suggests that it is the actual NDE itself, rather than some other factor such as merely being exposed to a life-threatening situation, that is crucial in facilitating change. (Groth-Marnat and Summers 1998: 110)

There is ample evidence that various types of meditation practice may reduce death anxiety and increase quality of life (Austin 2006: 400). Part of this effect involves direct engagement with death and the supplanting of old beliefs and other cultural "tricks" to avoid or deny death. Another part is that there is a natural decrease in death anxiety among people who score high in mindfulness, whether meditators or not (Grevenstein and Bluemke 2016: 26), as well as humility (the ability to take what comes without the need to control things; Kesebir 2014). Park *et al.* (2016) showed that what they call *insight-based death meditation* (derived from *vipassana* and Zen) among Korean adults did have these effects. A 30-day program of self-study and meditation carried out among a sample of Indian women demonstrated the same reduction of death anxiety (Kulshrestha 2012).

It should come as no surprise, therefore, that the contemplation of death finds its way into virtually all contemplative traditions (Sheikh and Sheikh 2003), for the contemplation of anything shifts the balance away from the effort after meaning and toward the effort after truth. It should also be obvious that how one contemplates death and dying has a lot to do with how one is raised and what world view influences our naïve, "natural attitude" understanding of death. At its most intense, death contemplation shuts down the automatic and culturally-loaded defenses and allows the consciousness to engage death and whatever angst is present directly—ideally with no buffers, but usually with some alternative frame of reference.

Buddhist Death Contemplation

Probably the best-known technique of *death contemplation* is that of Theravada Buddhist corpse meditation (*maranasati*, "death awareness;" see Rosenberg 2001; Bond 1980). Of the forty classic Buddhist meditations (Pali: *kammaṭṭhāna*), ten of them are meditations upon decaying corpses (*asubha*, "objects of repulsion"). Buddhist scholars of the past loved to count things, and the ten "objects of repulsion" are just ten different stages in the decomposition of a corpse from bloated yucky to skeletonized (Buddhaghosa 1976). Figure 12.3 illustrates the meditation upon corpses at the skeletal end of the spectrum. In olden days when bodies were laid out in carnal grounds, monks from nearby monasteries might be assigned to stake out "their" corpse and spend hours daily meditating upon the form, and how it decomposed over time. The intent of these meditations was to counteract lust for sensual pleasures. A teacher, having divined that a student was addicted to sensual desires and was perhaps of an intellectual disposition might assign this kind of meditation as a corrective. I have known fellow meditators who collected animal skeletons and road kill to use in this kind of work.

Rather than being a peripheral or exotic meditation, death awareness is fundamental to Buddhist practice, and the *maranasati* meditation is one of the most important, right up there with LKM (Conze 1999; see Chapter 11).

Larry Rosenberg, a meditation master and founder of the Cambridge Insight Meditation Center in Cambridge, Massachusetts, has summarized one of the classic *maranasati* methods used in Theravada Buddhism. The method involves shifting attention from whatever calming meditation one uses to center and stop discursive thought and image chatter. Ideally, one will do a basic *samatha* meditation such as the air passing in and out of the nostrils until the state of access concentration arises (Chapter 5). The focus of the meditation then shifts to some aspect of death and dying. Alternatively, one can take up *maranasati* directly and that may lead to access concentration. The previous method is easier for most meditators. The contemplation outlined by Rosenberg (1994) is very simple and straightforward, and involves three mindfulness steps, each with three sub-steps (what did I say about Buddhists loving to count things?):

1. Reflecting on the inevitability of death
    a. Everybody dies
    b. We get ever closer to death
    c. Death will happen whether we practice awareness or not
2. Reflect upon the uncertainty of the time of death
    a. Life expectancy is uncertain
    b. There are many causes of death
    c. The body is fragile
3. Reflect upon how only awareness can help us at the time of our death.
    a. Our wealth cannot help us at the time of our death
    b. Our loved ones cannot help us at the time of our death
    c. Our own body cannot help us at the time of our death

Figure 12.3. Thai Buddhist Monks Meditating on Corpses. Monks meditate upon "repulsive objects" in order to counteract their desires for sensual pleasures.

In the *vipassana* state, one brings each of the three reflections to mind, and focuses on the insight, not the words themselves. The texts warn against thinking about loved ones who have died, for that will stimulate sadness, nor the death of enemies, for that might stimulate glee. Focus of attention is upon the impermanence of one's being, or all beings. Eventually, the reflection upon death becomes one contemplation, and as with all meditation objects, the reflection upon death has its specific "countersigns" (*patibhaganimitta*; see Chapter 5). In this case the fruits of realization spread out throughout life as a stratum of realization:

> Those disciples who devote themselves to this meditation are always vigilant and take no delight in phenomenal existence. They give up hankering after life. They avoid evil-doing. They are free from craving as regards the requisites of life. Their perception of impermanence (*anicca*) becomes established. As a result of these things, they realize the suffering (*dukkha*) and selfless (*anatta*) nature of existence. At the time of death, they are devoid of fear and remain mindful and self-possessed. If, in this present life, they fail to attain to deathlessness (*nibbana*), upon the dissolution of the body, they are bound for a happy destiny. (Paravahera 1987)

Notice once again that the contemplative practice steers one away from ego and toward the truth of impermanence and entanglement with the cosmos.

There are of course other schools of Buddhism. Each of them use death contemplation in some fashion to gain similar ends. In the *Vajrayana* school of Buddhism, including Tibetan Tantric Buddhism, the practice of death contemplation is carried further to prepare the practitioner for the passage of their consciousness from this life to the next, in order to assure an auspicious rebirth (Carr 1993). The epitome of this teaching is found in the various translations into English of *The Tibetan Book of the Dead*. This is not the real title of the work, as Buddhist scholar Robert Therman makes clear in his commentaries upon the work (Thurman 1994: xx). The complete title of the work in Tibetan is *Bardo thos grol chen mo*, or *The Great Book of Natural Liberation Through Understanding in the Between*. The most common title used by

Tibetans today is the *Bardo Thodol.* To avoid the mistranslation, I will use the common Tibetan title.

The texts comprising the *Bardo Thodol* are extremely complex and, for the average Westerner, extremely esoteric. The word *bardo* means "between," so the essence of the *Bardo Thodol* is about preparing the contemplative (or "yogi") to pass through the "between" that is situated at the end of this life and mediates entry into the next life. The process of moving from death through the between to rebirth is developed in four stages: preliminary stage, mentor/initiation stage, creation stage and perfection stage (ibid: 58-81). The *preparatory stage* is comprised of beginner meditations such as the "four hundred-thousands"—doing a hundred-thousand repetitions of (1) prostrations to the guru, or the Buddha, (2) the hundred-syllable mantra of *Vajrasattva,* a purification visualization practice, (3) mandala offerings, and (4) loving-kindness mantra OM MANI PADME HUM accompanied by visualization of Chenrezig, the deity of compassion. These constitute the "foundation" practices for any Tantric aspirant. These various practices introduce the initiate into mantra and visualization skills requisite to more advanced practices. These practices also steer the beginner away from ego gratification to consideration for the wellbeing of others, and towards renunciation of the shortsighted and earthly pleasures that feed egocentric awareness and the clinging to the world of appearances (*samsara*).

The *mentor/initiation stage* is again a period of discipline and practice fundamental to all Tibetan Buddhist Tantric yogas. One seeks a teacher (guru) to guide one's path. This is necessary because Tantra is a "fast path" and is fraught with potential stumbling blocks, dead ends and dangers (see the Conclusion). From that teacher, usually a *tulku lama* (reincarnated *bodhisattva*) who is presumably an advanced Tantric practitioner, one receives initiations (*wang*, "empowerment") that demonstrate for the initiate how to perform various arising yogas (Chapter 3). The nature of the work will be determined in part by the school of Tibetan Buddhism to which the teacher belongs. One practices the Tantric exercises by following the instructions accompanying the empowerment—a *sādhanā*, or manual of practice. Central to the *sādhanā* work are appropriate visualizations of deities, mandalas, and various symbolic items (see Figure 11.4 for an example of a visualization image).

It is at the *creation stage* that Tantric death contemplation becomes specifically about death. Every aspect of the ordinary world that one tends to cling to is mentally transformed into energy and reimagined as part of a vastly complex mandala. One does this repeatedly until it becomes second nature.

The basic goal of the practice is to harness the imagination to transform the perception and conception of ordinariness into the vision and experience of enlightenment. All the elements of the ordinary world—the ordinary subject and the ordinary object— are imaginatively reenvisioned as pure wisdom energy. Death, the between, and life are imaginatively converted into the Three Buddha Bodies, Truth, Beatitude, and Emanation, respectively. The five body-mind aggregates [matter, sensation, conception, creation, consciousness] are envisioned as the five Buddhas, and the five poisons [hate, pride, lust, envy, delusion] are the five wisdoms. Every other being is imagined to be a Buddha-deity. Every subtle instinct is imagined a micro Buddha-deity. Every form is imagined as part of the mandala jewel palace. (ibid: 68-69)

During practice (over months, even years) one ideally comes to the point where one can imagine the entire mandala or Buddha Palace in exquisite detail and located into a pea-sized drop which one can hold for hours and can place in any of the energy centers of the body. The creation stage merges with the *perfection stage* in which the work uses the skills in imaginative transformation of the ordinary into the Buddha Palace or mandala. The intent is to gradually untie all the knots in the energy body, especially those in the heart center, so that psychic energy can be gathered and moved effortlessly from the root to the crown and back again without hindrance. All this preparation is designed to take the place of fear, confusion, clinging and reacting that most dead folks supposedly experience in the between. "This is why the between-traveler can become instantly liberated just by understanding where he or she is in the between, what the reality is, where the allies are, and where the dangers" (ibid: 80).

There is no way that I can give justice to the enormously elaborate and convoluted practice described in the *Bardo Thodol*. What perhaps I can do however is put this type of image-based death contemplation into perspective. And this can be done by underscoring a single fact: *None of the experiences described for the death bardo are unique to that between.* Indeed, Tibetan Buddhist psychology recognizes six *bardos*: between birth and death, sleep and waking, waking and trance, and three "betweens" during the death-rebirth *bardo* (ibid: xxi). During my period practicing dream yoga, I repeatedly experienced the "betweens" we in the West call the hypnagogic (sleep onset) and hypnopompic (wake onset). By exercising conscious warp control, one can have greater influence over the subsequent state. Indeed, the most direct route to remaining lucid during dream states is to not lose consciousness falling asleep (Chapter 6). And many of the techniques one uses to practice dream yoga are the same as described in the *Bardo Thodol.* This would naturally lead a sceptic to suggest that the practices devised to prepare a person for their post-death adventures derived from experiences had during other types of "betweens."

Death Contemplation in Islam

Like Buddhism, Islam has produced mystics and ascetics who have carried out death contemplation and have left us accounts of their teachings. The most famous of these was the academic turned Sufi ascetic, Abū Ḥāmid Muḥammad ibn Muḥammad al-Ghazālī (Al Ghazali for short), who lived between 1056-1111 CE (Al Ghazali 1994). Author of some 70 books, Al Ghazali enjoyed great success and material comfort (Figure 12.4). But during his midlife, he began to take stock of his life, and of his egoistic attachment to status and wealth. This self-criticism reached a crisis point when he stood to give a lecture one day and found he could not speak. This led to a full-on anxiety attack that eventually led to him putting all his wealth into a trust for his family and heading into a life of ascetic renunciation (Perreira 2010: 251).

He spent years in solitary seclusion, ridding himself of all thoughts and feelings supporting attachment to life. Eventually he developed a series of methods in aid of this end. Central to his practice was focusing the mind upon the inevitability of death, and considering death, the pointlessness of worldly pursuits. Virtually all his methods involve visualization, practices that are quite like methods used in Buddhism. For instance, he carried out a bedtime ritual:

When you want to go to sleep, lay out your bed pointing to Mecca, and sleep on your right side, the side on which the corpse reclines in the tomb. Sleep is the similitude of death and waking of the resurrection…. Remember that in like manner you will lie in the tomb, completely alone; only your works will be with you, only the effort you have made will be rewarded… As you go to sleep say: "In Thy name, Lord, I live and die and with Thee, O God, do I take refuge…. (Quoted from Perreira 2010: 252)

He even suggested that one dig a hole in one's floor to sleep in, reminding oneself of the inevitability of the grave.

One should also make a prayer of death, recalling the inevitability of death, the death of those who have gone before us, and those who will die after us. This should be ritualized, requiring one to remember death at least 20 times a day (Perreira 2010: 252), using visualizations of the decay and corruption of the body as a focus of one's practice, accompanied by devotional prayers repeated as a mantra.

Figure 12.4. The Muslim Academic Turned Sufi Ascetic, Al Ghazali (1058-1111).
Al Ghazali gave up his prestigious post as a professor and noted philosopher to follow the ascetic life of a Sufi. He advocated the contemplation of death to put life into its proper perspective.

Could you but see me three days after having been set in my grave, when the pupils of my eyes have come forth and flowed across my checks, when my lips have shriveled back over my teeth, when my mouth has opened and the pus run out, when my belly is inflated and rises above my chest, when my spine protrudes from my rear, and when the worms and the pus have emerged from my nostrils; then you would behold something far more remarkable than that which you see now. (ibid: 255)

The similarities between Al Ghazali's death contemplation and the practices described above for Theravada Buddhist practices are remarkable. As Todd LeRoy Perreira (2010: 255: emphasis added) notes in his perceptive comparison of Muslim and Buddhist practices, "These are clearly not the words of someone who simply imagines dying. The intimate level of detail given here bears the unmistakable traces of a keen observer: *putrefaction of the human body was a process the Caliph witnessed first-hand, indeed studied, in situ.*"

SUMMARY AND SEGUE

In this chapter we extended the discussion of loving-kindness into the domain of death contemplation. Sooner or later, a contemplative will inevitably confront the fact of their own mortality. This awareness of "mortality salience," as psychologists like to call it, peels back layers of self-illusion and delusory compensation, as well as cultural conditioning and ideology to reveal a stratum of death anxiety. Ernest Becker's analysis of the human "immortality project" and the influence upon our everyday lives of the existential dilemma posed by our "creatureliness" led to considerable research upon how culture and inherent neuropsychological processes operate to buffer people from fully acknowledging the fact of their own inevitable death. Indeed, Becker's writings gave rise to three decades or more of what is called Terror Management Theory which we explored for insights into the reasons why loving-kindness and other types of meditative techniques work so effectively to counter "denial of death" mind-states.

All cultures on the planet recognize in various ways the salience of death—the existential dilemma of encountering being and non-being. We examined death cultures and isolate some of the ways human societies have come to grips with the fact of death and dying. Of course, we are not the only social animals that die, and we have shown that non-human animals also recognize death as special, perhaps even salient, for they demonstrate distinct behaviors when perceiving the death of their own. We completed the chapter by examining a few traditions of formal death contemplation, and how these practices are used by people to alter the salience of mortality, as well as to expose the culturally conditioned states of mind and behavior that buffer people from fully confronting their own inevitable demise. We have also emphasized that when one is freed from the burden of unconscious death anxiety, the contemplative's mind-states open-up to an enormous range of experiences, unfettered by existential angst.

In the next and concluding chapter I will summarize the central narrative of the book, focusing upon the contemplative brain; that is, that our brain evolved in such a way that exploration of its own internal processes became possible. In addition, several issues that relate to contemplation, but that heretofore have received less attention will be addressed, including health-related research on meditation, stumbling blocks that may arise in a contemplative's path, and the relationship between contemplation and language.

CONCLUSION

The Narrative, Plus Odds and Ends

*In the consciousness of the infinite, the conscious subject
has for his object the infinity of his own nature.*

– Ludwig Feuerbach,
Das Wesen des Christentums

All men by nature desire to know.

– Aristotle, *Metaphysics*

I would like to summarize the central narrative developed over the course of this book, giving full emphasis upon the fact that in the real world it is our brain that is exploring and cognizing its own nature. I then would like to briefly discuss several residual issues that are both germane to contemplative science now and of relevance to those readers who may wish to take up the contemplative life. These include the health benefits of the contemplative path, some of the traps that lie in waiting for neophyte contemplatives, and the role and limitations of language in learning and expressing contemplative insights.

THE CENTRAL NARRATIVE

The effort after truth about the nature of the real world must be grounded in science, while the effort after truth about the nature of our inner being must be grounded in contemplation. Both science and contemplation overlap in privileging the quest for truth. Both science and contemplation at their best privilege experience of the scope of inquiry over theories. Both reconsider anomalous experiences as positive feedback into points of view, knowledge and theory. As we have seen, explorations of the inner nature of the human psyche are imperfect at best without the inclusion of a phenomenological discipline. This is as true for ethnographic fieldwork as it is for laboratory experimentation. When one realizes that conscious and unconscious mental acts are mediated by neurophysiological structures, and that these structures have evolved over hundreds of millennia, then the combination of phenomenology with evolutionary biology and neuroscience becomes essential to any modern account of psychological states.

Based upon these understandings, I have argued that the ability to contemplate our own nature is an exaptation derived from our ability to explore and understand (make meaningful) the external world. The "prime directive" of all brains, human or otherwise, is to detect patterns in sensory data displayed in the sensorium and use these patterns to construct an internal brain world—a dynamic world of experience—in the service of adaptation to an ecological niche. This adaptive mechanism in its primordial form allowed animals to move around in the environment, and to find food without becoming food. The veridicality of an animal's brain world is tested daily by being able to find shelter and sustenance sufficient to live long enough to reproduce. We do not know if any other animals, save us humans, can turn this system inward to explore and model the inner being. That we humans can do so has been evidenced by thousands of years of contemplative traditions and has probably been the case since sometime in the Upper Paleolithic. Animals with brains are conscious, but the question is what they can be conscious of, given the limitations of their neurobiology. Can they introspect to some extent? Certainly. Are they, at whatever level of sophistication, able to watch and conceptualize their own mental acts? Probably not.

In Chapter 1, I argued that the ability of higher animals to introspect is the anlagen of phenomenology. Put another way, contemplation is an exaptation (Gould 1991) derived from introspection. To make exaptation clearer, consider the part of the brain responsible for rendering shapes on a page into words: circuits in the inferior parietal lobule (the angular and supramarginal gyri; Figure 1.11). These circuits did not evolve to make sense of writing, but rather to make sense of visible patterns, like animal spoor, leaf shape and the like (Kagan 2013: 8). Moreover, an illiterate person still has a fully functioning inferior parietal lobule. Reading is thus an exaptation based upon the earlier selective pressure for visual pattern recognition.

When a meditator begins a disciplined path of self-discovery, it is especially his prefrontal lobes that are being exercisised and eventually his brain will be significantly different than that of non-meditators (Cardoso et al. 2007; Davidson 2003; Fox et al. 2014; Hasenkamp and Barsalou 2012; Kang et al. 2012; Lazar et al. 2005). As I have said, I assume—and may well be proved wrong—that all big-brained vertebrates, and perhaps some big-brained invertebrates, are capable of introspection, but not phenomenology. The isolation of introspection as a set of distinct ASC is likely a human ability. Moreover, there are probably societies where no one meditates and hence no one is an advanced phenomenologist, while other societies contain many such. The role of culture in encouraging and supporting an institutionalized form of phenomenology is crucial.

In any event, we do know that we humans are able to contemplate our own internal processes. Indeed, we all do so all the time. We sense when we are hungry, when we are sleepy, or when we hurt. We do something about these internal states. But this rudimentary introspective ability can be extended, structured, disciplined and pursued to the extent that our entire lifestyle can become focused upon and dedicated to our own self-discovery. This is what I choose to call the path of contemplation—again, the brain using its own natural empirical faculties to observe and model its own processes. Depending upon one's culture, the pursuit of self-discovery may be somewhat antithetical to the demands of quotidian social existence. One is conditioned (enculturated) to value certain activities over others, perhaps to become skilled in an occupation, to carry out the expectations of social roles, and to produce and support a family. The stresses of doing all that is required of one as a member of a group may be unproductive of the states of consciousness requisite for the contemplative life. The demands of daily life may hinder the ability to chill-out and concentrate upon our inner nature. For instance, one of the earliest hurdles a neophyte meditator faces is finding the time and space each day to do meditation exercises.

SPEED BUMPS ON THE CONTEMPLATIVE PATH

*An idea is something you have; an ideology is
something that has you.*

— Morris Berman

Human beings are social primates and we have evolved a decidedly social brain (Graziano 2013; Gazzaniga 1985). Our brain did not evolve solely to process information about the physical environment, but also to facilitate complex social relationships to take advantage of social adaptation strategies (Dunbar 2003; Dunbar and Shultz 2007). As our brains became larger, it became necessary for birth to occur before the skull became too large to pass through the birth canal (Trevathan 1987). Relative to other social animals, our newborns are helpless and require intense nurture to survive. Among modern humans, a major percentage of our cognitive power is given over to social and cultural matters that concern the group (Fiske and Taylor 2013). Thus, it is that the neurocognitive power of the human brain facilitates both highly complex social lives and adaptive strategies, as well as mature contemplation, the latter ironically often leading practitioners away from the group and toward solitude—an interesting exaptation.

Looking more closely, however, one finds that in most cases contemplatives, no matter how reclusive and ascetic they may at first blush appear, depend upon the community to support their solitary way of life (Fracchia 1979). You will recall our mentioning the 4th century ascetic John of Egypt who lived in a cell in the Nitrian Desert for 40 years contemplating God. But perhaps you missed the fact that for all those decades, and for all his solitude, he was being fed, clothed and watered by his community through a small hole in his walled-up cave. One of the rules of the Benedictine Order requires that monks living in solitude be within reach of a monastery to receive the sacraments once a week—thus allowing the brothers to keep an eye on the ascetic's mental and physical health. Indeed, it is very rare for a contemplative to totally separate themselves from their sociocultural environment. Furthermore, as we saw in Chapter 9, institutional religions will frequently coopt contemplatives or their subcultures so that some measure of control may be exercised over who and how contemplation takes place. Another way to say this is that most contemplative traditions operate within the greater society's cycle of meaning. The rituals used by the contemplative, the conditions under which they live, and the interpretations of their experiences are normally provided by the group. So powerful may the cooptation be that the initial inner focus of asceticism can be reversed, and monastically organized asceticism can become in service to the everyday world of economic and political rationalization. This is what happened to Church-dominated monasticism in the Middle Ages (see Kaelber 1998: Chap. 2).

As I made plain back in Chapter 2, the closest thing we have to a culture-free (or social-free) contemplative tradition is Husserlian transcendental phenomenology. This school of phenomenology specifically teaches that one must learn to "bracket" (set-aside) one's "natural attitude" (enculturated interpretive frame) to study the essential processes of consciousness. Students who wish to study Husserlian methods may attend the Institute of Philosophy in Leuven, Belgium, which holds most of Husserl's writings, but this is no monastery, and as far as I know, no such Husserlian monastic institution has ever been built. Still, here we have a spiritual and phenomenological tradition with teachers, texts and methods that others avidly follow. I have never heard of a Husserlian ascetic, and the very idea of one boggles the mind. Yet, it is doubtful if anyone could invent a contemplative path that was totally devoid of historical and cultural influences. It is in our nature to share with and to guide, and be guided by others.

In addition, the personal transformations that inevitably follow in the wake of contemplation-evoked experiences have social and cultural consequences. Typically, a newbie meditator discovers that he or she must drop some activities to make time for the inner work, and like tapping a wedge into a log to split it, the more time taken for meditation, the more space opens for this new occupation. Moving from our naïve, conditioned, outer-directed, daily existence to one of mature contemplation requires more than a sustained act of will. The contemplative path is nothing less than metanoia (Chapter 3)—a fundamental transformation of the mind (Avanessian and Hennig 2017: 2). For most folks, metanoia requires a training procedure of some kind—what we in the West call a *meditative discipline*. As I have used the term, meditation is training to become a contemplative. This training—nothing less than the systematic deautomatization of one's mind—may take months, usually years to come to fruition. Most people who take on this kind of spiritual path do so by seeking others of like-mind for support. More than likely the discipline taken up will be one of the traditions associated with one of the world religions: Judaic Kabbalah, Buddhist mindfulness training, Tantric practice, or Zen, Hindu yoga, Christian meditation, etc.

Ideologies and Ideologues

There are all sorts of bumps and hurdles along the road to mature contemplation. Two of the most pernicious are ideologies and charlatans. Ideologies are ready-made explanations for what you are experiencing. Charlatans are people who claim to know what it's all about, but really don't. Ideological systems are a very conservative form of the cycle of meaning (Chapter 3). They radically privilege the effort after meaning over the effort after truth, and experiences encouraged by ideological social systems are pre-interpreted to reinforce the "party line"—a set of relatively rigid beliefs and attitudes that are valued by the group (society, institution, movement, cult, etc.). Ideological systems tend to ignore, explain away, or otherwise devalue anomalous experiences that in a less rigid system might produce positive feedback into the system. In other words, ideologies stop the state of questioning, of curiosity and of epistemological freedom that mature contemplation requires.

Theories about ideologies usually focus upon the politico-economic aspects of life. Whereas there may be politico-economic influences upon contemplatives, we are more interested here in experiential, epistemological and spiritual ideologies, those that operate in groups to structure the experiences and interpretations of contemplatives. Ideology can be a two-edged sword, slicing into the individual's process of exploration and understanding. "Ideology, defined as a set of consensually shared beliefs and doctrines that provide the moral and intellectual basis for a political, economic, or social system, imbues human existence with meaning and inspiration, but it also fosters illusion and threatens individual freedom" (Jost, Fitzsimons and Kay 2004: 269). Experimental work by psychologist John Jost and his colleagues "…suggests that two classes of motivation, namely epistemic motives to reduce uncertainty and existential motives to minimize threat, are capable of influencing ideological outcomes…. Next, we propose that there is also a third, relational motivation that underpins ideological opinions. From this perspective, ideology is linked to processes of social influence and the motivation to achieve and maintain 'shared reality' with others…" (Jost, Ledgerwood and Hardin 2008: 2). Humans are, after all, a species of social primate, and there have been strong evolutionary pressures on brains to develop "system-justifying" world views that bring local knowledge into coherence with individual experience (Jost and Hunyady 2005; Jost, Nosek and Gosling 2008; see also Geertz 1983 and Laughlin and d'Aquili 1974).

One of the most common ways that groups have of evoking and integrating potentially anomalous, extraordinary experiences within an ideological interpretive frame is by prescribing rituals. Rituals are very powerful procedures because: (1) they are valued by the group at large, (2) they express the mythopoeic world view of the group, (3) they dominate the behavior, and thus the mind-states of participants, and (4) they typically incorporate within their tapestry very effective drivers (Davis-Floyd and Laughlin 2016: Chapter 3). Rituals may be so efficacious at influencing mind-states that Belgian anthropologist, Pierre Smith considered them as "mind traps" (Smith 1984; see Halloy 2015).[44] Rituals operate as "mind traps" by ensnaring mental processes through *practice*—that is, because the mind is a property of the body (no mind-body dualism here), the mind can be moved and transformed by moving the body. Indeed, all physical yogas are based upon this factor—that moving the body "moves" perception, cognition, emotion and psychic energy. Mind traps:

[E]mphasize the importance of the form of action in ritual efficacy and describe what ritual action potentially does to the mind. Mind traps literally entrap the mind; they confuse it by generating uncertainty and ambiguity—uncertainty about

---

[44] We are greatly indebted to Belgian anthropologist Arnaud Halloy (2015) of the University of Nice Sophia-Antipolis in France for making Pierre Smith's work available in English.

incompatible…interpretations and ambiguity about one's own attitude towards them, some kind of a consented entrapment. At the very heart of Pierre Smith's characterization of mind traps, form and content, action and reference, cause and representation, performance and identity tend to be merged, revealing their *autotelic* (ritual action referring back to itself) and *conflationist* nature. (Halloy 2015: 369-70)

The ethnographer working in polyphasic cultures is frequently confronted by the necessity of deciding whether to engage in mind-altering practices to better understand what his or her hosts are talking about. We touched upon this in Chapter 5 when we mentioned Ken Wilber's (2005[1983]: 156) injunction "If you want to know this, do this." One does "this" (i.e., meditate, dance, take the magic herb, carry out the ritual), then certain experiences consequently arise, and then perhaps a conversation ensues with one's hosts or guides, and one learns what those experiences mean both for oneself and for the hosts' culture.

The *Disputatio* and the Enlightenment

Divorcing the effort after truth from ideological interpretive frames can be an arduous, even deadly affair. Our own cultural history is rife with examples. An obvious historical instance is the 14th century movement that came to be called *the enlightenment*, a process that accelerated through the Renaissance and into the Enlightenment Period (Ferrone 2015). In a very real sense, science grew out of a movement in natural philosophy that rejected appeal to history and authority as a basis for true knowledge. What I like to call the *enlightenment urge* was the empowerment of an individual's effort after truth, his freedom to pursue the truth, and a rejection of epistemological authority at every level of inquiry. This was especially torturous with respect to what has been called the *Aristotelian disputatio* and its ultimate appeal to *endoxa* (Grk: ἔνδοξα), or "the authority of the opinions of the wise" (see Frede 2012). There was also a turning away from scholasticism and the overweening concern with the divine. The rise of humanism, a system of thought attaching prime importance to human, rather than divine or supernatural matters, came to hold sway. This system stressed the value and goodness of human beings. The focus was upon common everyday human needs, and upon discovering rational ways to solve human problems. This led eventually to the value placed on education for the elite and the middle class in the 16th century.

The *disputatio* did not go quietly, of course. Indeed, it has never disappeared altogether, popping up repeatedly in today's conflicts and "political correctness" sensitivities. The 17th century was a century of continuous conflict and war in Europe, and during this period universities continued to teach (in Latin, of course) Aristotelian dialectics and physics, expounding on received wisdom and fundamental disputational methods while ignoring contemporary developments in enlightenment natural philosophy (i.e., "experimental" philosophy and eventually "science"), the latter being carried out in concert within various societies (e.g., the Royal Societies) that operated independently of the universities. Rooted in the empiricism of Bacon, the societies insisted that knowledge about the world must be grounded in careful observation, empirical generalization and mathematics, not in appeal to authority, scripture or ideology. Knowledge about the world unsupported by direct, individual observation became suspect. Each rational and natural philosopher of the Enlightenment age— including Francis Bacon (1561-1626), Kepler (1571-1630), Kant (1724 -1804), Descartes (1596 -1650), Hobbs (1588 - 1679)—emphasized that by application of individual rational reflection, the stage may be set for ascertaining the truth of things and thereby improving the human condition. All in one way or the other found that the first order of business was to quash the influence of *endoxa* upon human conceptions of both what is (ontology) and how we come to know what is (epistemology). The *disputatio*, the Church privileging received wisdom and appeal to authority, had to go. In its place there must be an appeal to either individual deductive reasoning (Kant, Descartes), or induction from direct observation of reality and matter-in-motion (Bacon, Galileo).

It is ironic that the typical way of teaching the "hard" sciences (biology, physics, chemistry) is by pairing lectures with "labs," the latter being ritual enactments of experiments that are interpreted as supportive of the views propounded in lectures (Feyerabend 2010).

Chemistry labs are not designed so that the neophyte chemist can pursue an effort after truth. Nothing new is learned in the exercises set for the labs except how to do science in prescribed ways. Suppose we are being taught the nature of diffusing gases. In the lab we stick one cotton ball soaked in ammonia in one end of a glass tube, and another cotton ball soaked with hydrochloric acid in the other end of the tube. We count the number of seconds it takes for a white ring to form on the glass as the two chemicals meet after diffusing through air. And we measure the distance travelled by each chemical from their initial position at their respective cotton balls. Voila! We get a solution in time and distance. Hundreds of thousands of students have done this experiment in labs and if they did it right, they always get more or less the same answer. What has this taught the student? What is learned is nothing new about diffusion of gasses, but how to behave, how to approach the effort to know, a way of viewing the world and its nature. The student learns little by little to enter the mind-states known as "being a chemist." In this case, it is an effort after meaning, not truth. In the same way, spiritual ideologies ritually set-up experiences for neophytes so that the world according to the ideology and its proponents is confirmed.

With the long history of freeing the minds of individual contemplatives, it is also ironic that so many aspiring contemplatives today give themselves over holus-bolus to what we might call the *contemplative industry*—organizations, companies and entrepreneurs that sell better health and better living through meditation and other spiritual products (Bush 2011). Tibetan Buddhist teacher Chögyam Trungpa Rinpoche (2002) called this peculiar Western tendency "spiritual materialism." As my cynical friend and one-time yoga instructor Patricia Kolarik used to say, "If you want to get Americans to do anything spiritual, you have to provide them with supplies." Hence, there are stores online and off that cater to the needs of the aspiring contemplative, where one can buy the requisite clothing, incense, cushions, pads, altar symbols, crystals, bells, icons, beads, music and instructional CDs, and on and on. A remarkable feature of modern life to embellish the simple process of turning the mind inward upon itself and exploring its own nature.

Ideologues

A proponent of an ideology is an *ideologue*—often a charismatic person who expresses adamant, rigid, uncompromising and dogmatic attitudes and beliefs. They may also be incessantly proselytizing. If their advocacy is within the political arena, they might be called a *demagogue*. They are also what sociologist Eric Hoffer (2002[1951]) called the *true believer*, a fanatical advocate of a political, economic, religious or other point of view who may be perceived as being perspicacious. The hallmark of an ideologue is that no matter what potentially anomalous evidence is adduced to contradict his point of view, the evidence is either ignored or explained away. For dastardly government conspiracy theorists, trips to the moon may be a hoax, and pictures of astronauts walking on the moon may be faked; for holocaust deniers, pictures of concentration camps and eyewitness accounts are all faked. No evidence whatsoever is admissible into the discussion. Ideologists energetically wish to stop question and impose their rhetoric on one and all. Fanatic religious sects are full of people like this, many of whom become leaders and teachers, and many who are aggressively intolerant of alternative points of view. World history is rife with death and destruction wrought by ideologues and religious zealots.

Guru, Or No Guru, That's the Question

Apropos to ideologies and ideologues, there is a perennial question among meditators and those thinking about becoming a meditator: "Do I need a guru?" The answer is, yes and no. It all depends upon circumstances. Specifically, the answer depends upon: (1) the level of one's spiritual maturity, (2) how skillful one is in looking at themselves, acknowledging the negative aspects of themselves, (3) how supportive are one's family and community of one's intentions, (4) how intensely one wishes to follow a path, and (5) the extent to which there is a physical aspect to the practice (yoga, tai chi, Sufi dancing, etc.). My own practice sometimes involved yoga and tai chi, and once doing Sufi dancing (Chapter 5), and I benefited from having expert teachers in each case. As I mentioned earlier, one of my professors taught me to meditate for the first time, but because of the practice I was doing, little guidance was required. It is only later when I took up meditation full-time that I required a teacher.

My answer to the question about whether a teacher is necessary or not is this: If you are mentally healthy and are relatively amenable to looking inward at yourself without feeling overwhelming anxiety, and you intend to do some simple meditation (breathing, Husserlian phenomenology, loving-kindness meditation) once or twice a day, then you are probably safe to carry on without a teacher. However, if you are a neurotic like I am, then more intense meditation (sitting hours per day, undertaking long meditation retreats, doing intense dream yoga) might benefit from expert guidance. Certainly, if you intend to take up a spiritual path that results in a massive change in your lifestyle and support structure, you surely need a guru and probably also a *sangha* (community of like-minded practitioners). And if your practice involves either complex meditation practices (like Tantric Buddhist work) or intricate physical activities, then having a teacher is fundamental to success.

That said, where do you find a teacher? Most especially, where do you find a teacher who is the real-McCoy and not a charlatan or an ideologue? Bogus gurus abound these days and thrive upon naïve spiritually questing people who have no yardstick to measure genuine guidance from manipulation (especially financial manipulation). When asked how to distinguish true teachers, Jesus said it well: "By their fruits you will know them. Do you gather grapes from thorns, or figs from thistles?" (Matthew 7: 16). As I am writing this, a famous guru calling himself Saint Dr. Gurmeet Ram Rahim Singh Ji Insaan has been convicted in India of raping two of his female followers in his ashram. Thousands of his supporters have violently clashed with police and now 38 people are dead. I imagine Jesus shaking his head and saying that the followers of this charlatan are picking berries in a briar patch.

There are many such examples of this sort of guru-ish will-to-power rather than compassionate guidance. India also gave us Bhagwan Shree Rajneesh (Figure 13.1), a global guru with a thirst for luxury (he is famous for owning dozens of Rolls Royce automobiles) who moved to America after reputedly filling Indian emergency rooms with followers with psychological problems. When he arrived in the United States he established a community in Oregon which ran into political problems and ended up with his Rajneeshees trying to poison local political leaders. Americans are particularly gullible when it comes to selecting spiritual guides. To demonstrate this, a New Jersey-born film maker named Vikram Gandhi set out to do a documentary on false-gurus, and during the process set himself up as a spiritual leader named Kumare just to see what would happen. He ended up with hundreds of followers. His adventure is recorded in his movie, *Kumaré: The True Story of a False Prophet*. Another example of doubtful guru-competence is the cult following of Franklin Albert Jones (1939-2008), who later became known as Adi Da. He set up an ashram in Fiji and a community called Adidam. Jones was always a wacky and controversial figure, and as time went on he drew criticism and even lawsuits because of his sexual adventures with the wives of his followers (Lowe and Lane 1996). Again, by their fruits shall ye know them.

My suggestion—*only a suggestion, mind*—is that you avoid any guru that manifests greed for possessions, drug highs, and sex with nubile young followers. Teachings centered on "end of times," imminent apocalypse, giving up all you own to the "teacher," or absolute obedience to the will of the leader. There are literally hundreds of these narcissistic, manipulative and controlling men and women who revel in gaining control over "followers" who become the victims of "brainwashing," loss of identity and will (Stein 2016; Singer and Lalich 1995; Robbins and Palmer 1997). *Prima facie*, these people are not spiritually advanced,

Figure 13.1. Bhagwan Shree Rajneesh and One of His Many Rolls Royce Automobiles.

cognitively enlightened, and they do not have a private channel to God. I would also suggest that you avoid cults with closed and secretive organizations, practices, rules and venues, such as Scientology and Transcendental Meditation, each posing as a meditation method, but which through a labyrinth of increasingly expensive courses, draw you into a full-blown cult—and you may find it the very devil to get out of them once inside (Jennings 2016). Perhaps it would be useful for me to share one of the principles I taught in university for years—what I call the *Principle of Inevitable Perversion*, to wit: *Any occupation that can be interpreted as fulfilling perverted desires will draw perverts like flies to a cow pie.* This applies to sadists seeking jobs as police officers and soldiers, pedophiles seeking jobs in childcare centers, as priests and Scouting organizations, serial killers with their bottles of poison to the nursing profession and so on. This also applies to narcissists with a lust for power over others promoting themselves as gurus. Positions of power and control over others draw narcissists like sweet flowers draw bees. *Caveat emptor* applies here, don't you think? 'Nuff said.

Seeking the Inner Guru

One final matter deserves mentioning with respect to gurus, and that is the function of the Inner Guru. Mature contemplatives learn that there comes the time when guidance shifts to one's own inner guide. To put this another way, one gradually, or perhaps even abruptly, retrieves the projection of guide from the external guru (the priest, the meditation master, yoga teacher, the sage, etc.) and lodges it in one's greater self. Jung was particularly astute in this respect, for being a contemplative, he had tracked his own process of individuation, past the point where he required little external guidance, and recognized that his maturation was guided by his greater self, by what he called "the archetype of transcendent wholeness" (Jung 1956 [1912]: ¶297). He used the metaphor of the "inner sun" which illuminates our way toward wholeness and integration.

I do not mean to suggest that the mature contemplative cannot or does not learn from others after transitioning to the inner "transcendent function." Far from it, for new directions may be triggered by novel experiences, literature, masters of new disciplines, teachers of one sort or another. Remember Ken Wilber's injunction: "If you want to know this, do this." Each new contemplation may lead to novel encounters with the world and self, and conversations about these new psychological venues with others who have been there, done that, may extend one's self-realization. Yet ultimately, the realizations become integrated into the self by way of the transcendent function and one's own internal "solar" guide. I recall one of my teachers telling us that "Your job is to get rid of the need for me as soon as possible." I found the profound truth of his statement in time.

CONTEMPLATION AND HEALTH

The latter 20th century and into the 21st century has seen, not only a popular demand for contemplative teachers and movements (see Bush 2011), but also an integration of meditation and contemplation into education (Miller 2013) and an opening of scientific disciplines to contemplative methods as an epistemologically valid source of data (see Komjathy 2018; Karna 2013). There are efforts along a number of lines to teach scientists to contemplate as a way to broaden their insights and observational skills in their respective fields—this is especially gratifying among neuroscientists (Desbordes and Negi 2013). More sophisticated research in the neurosciences has led to a gradual amalgamation of brain and meditation studies (see Hanson 2009; Austin 1998). Indeed, Harold D. Roth (2006: 1787) has defined a new multidisciplinary field of *contemplative studies* in this way:

> We have reached a moment in history when it is time to reenvision certain basic aspects of the existing models of teaching and research in higher education in order to foster a deeper knowledge of the nature of our existence as human beings in a world that is intricately interrelated on many levels. This article suggests that one way to accomplish this is to develop a new field of academic endeavor that takes account of the emerging scientific work on the neurological foundations of the concentrated and relaxed states of mind attained by meditation and by a variety of other human endeavors and applies them directly to our lives. It is important that we do not

study them only as objects divorced from our own experience but bring our own subjectivities directly into the equation. The field I am proposing, "contemplative studies," would bridge the humanities, the sciences, and the creative arts in an effort to identify the varieties of contemplative experiences, to find meaningful scientific explanations for them, to cultivate firsthand knowledge of them, and to critically assess their nature and significance.

Healthy Benefits of Contemplation

Perhaps of even greater importance is that health-related psychological research has now turned considerable attention to techniques of meditation (Walsh and Shapiro 2006). There is now an expanding body of scientific research indicating that meditation is correlated with significant psychological and physiological benefits (see Hölzel *et al.* 2011, Mathers, Miller and Ando 2009, and various articles in Haruki, Ishii and Suzuki 1996). Studies have shown that meditation is associated with alterations in neurotransmitter activation, changes and increases in cognitive abilities, decrease in severity of affective disorders, decrease in age-related nervous system atrophy, and perhaps most importantly, the alleviation of distress. In fact, meditation is thought to reset what Brewer *et al.* (2011: 20254) term the "default mode" of consciousness in technocratic societies. The default mode "appears to be that of mind-wandering, which correlates with unhappiness, and with activation in a network of brain areas associated with self-referential processing" (see also Killingsworth and Gilbert 2010 on mind-wandering and unhappiness). Mindfulness and loving-kindness meditation training shows marked effects upon the connectivity and activity of those parts of the brain associated with both mind-wandering and self-absorption. These and other studies show that life in technocratic societies is so unnatural as to condition people into stress, anxiety, worry, and anger/hatred.

Stress researchers will say, after Hans Selye (1956, 1974), that some stress is necessary for the healthy and optimal functioning of the human body and mind. Good stress is called *eustress*, while bad, destructive stress is called *distress*. Chiesa and Serretti (2009) carried out a meta-analysis of studies of the effects of mindfulness meditations upon stress and concluded that such activities do indeed seem to reduce distress in healthy people (see also Rubia 2009 on effectiveness of meditation upon psychiatric disorders and stress and Newberg and Iversen 2003 on the use of meditation in stress management). Vestergaard-Poulsen *et al.* (2009) using fMRI scans studied the effects of meditation on lower brain stem structures associated with cardiorespiratory control: "This could account for some of the cardiorespiratory parasympathetic effects and traits, as well as the cognitive, emotional, and immunoreactive impact reported in several studies of different meditation practices." Marchand (2012) discusses Buddhist practices that have been successfully used in various clinical interventions, including stress-reduction, depression, anxiety and pain.

With respect to specific clinical applications, numerous studies have pointed to healing effects of various kinds of meditation upon specific mental and physical complaints. Grant *et al.* (2010) have shown that Zen meditators indicate a lowering of pain sensitivity. With equivalent findings, Zeidan *et al.* (2011: 1) discovered that:

> Meditation-induced reductions in pain intensity ratings were associated with increased activity in the anterior cingulate cortex and anterior insula [Figures 2.4 and 3.5], areas involved in the cognitive regulation of nociceptive processing. Reductions in pain unpleasantness ratings were associated with orbitofrontal cortex [Figure 3.4] activation, an area implicated in reframing the contextual evaluation of sensory events. Moreover, reductions in pain unpleasantness also were associated with thalamic [Figure 12.1] deactivation, which may reflect a limbic gating mechanism involved in modifying interactions between afferent input and executive-order brain areas. Together, these data indicate that meditation engages multiple brain mechanisms that alter the construction of the subjectively available pain experience from afferent information.

Meditation has been found to ameliorate the effects of mood disorders, including depression which is rampant in today's technocratic societies. Aftanas and Golocheikine (2001) show that long-term meditators have an enhanced ability to modulate intense emotions, and Barnhofer *et al.* (2007) indicate that meditation may decrease the severity of depression in previously suicidally depressed patients. Yu *et al.* (2011) found that the practice of Zen meditation virtually eliminates negative moods. Williams *et al.* (2014) and Piet and Hougaard (2011) report that mindfulness-based cognitive therapies are effective in preventing relapse into deep depression after clinical treatment.

There are also some studies that indicate that meditation may slow certain aspects of the aging process. Newberg *et al.* (2010) report that meditation increases memory retention for some Alzheimer's patients. Luders (2014) and Luders, Toga, Lepore and Gaser (2009) present evidence that meditation may decrease age-related brain atrophy. All-in-all, the bulk of research on health-related effects of meditation indicate nothing but positive outcomes. In a word, meditation makes one a healthier person. Of course, meditation techniques of the sort most psychologists use in their protocols do not necessarily involve contemplation, other than the rudimentary focusing of attention upon some single object. As I have illustrated using my own early meditation experience (Chapter 5), one may reap the calming, distress-reducing effects of meditation without a single question in mind (practicing "frozen ice" samadhi). Most of the research I have cited here involves the pragmatic and clinical utility of meditation traditions without getting directly into the self-transforming process that constitutes the contemplative way of life.

LANGUAGE AND CONTEMPLATION

It is fitting, bhikkhus, that you—who are young men from good families who have gone forth from home to homelessness out of faith—are seated together talking about the dhamma. *When you are gathered together, bhikkhus, there are two things to be done: discuss* dhamma *or maintain the noble silence.*

— The Buddha, *Ariyapariyesana Sutta*

I began this book by pointing up language as an imperfect medium for communicating with those who do not share one's experiences and cannot grasp the precise meaning one wishes to communicate through metaphors and other linguistic devices. Some readers may have noticed when I presented Ken Wilber's injunction method back in Chapter 5, I mentioned that conversations may ensue from realization of "this." Let me remind you of what I wrote:

> As Ken Wilber suggests in his book, *A Sociable God* (2005[1983]: 156), one begins the process of inquiry with the injunction "If you want to know this, do this." When one does "this" (i.e., meditate, dance, take the magic herb, carry out the ritual) then certain experiences consequently arise, and *then perhaps a conversation ensues with one's hosts or guide, one learns what those experiences mean both for oneself and for one's host culture.* (emphasis added)

As Wilber implies, there is a social dimension to the injunction. I have also emphasized that contemplatives usually carry out their efforts within at least a minimum of social interaction. Very few contemplatives end up as total hermits. On the other hand, many monastic traditions (Christian, Buddhist and Jain traditions included) forbid talking for much of the day, except where practically necessary. These prohibitions against speaking perhaps emphasize the importance of speech and language to the contemplative's path. As my late friend John McManus used to say, "Ninety-five percent of what most people talk about is solely social ritual and transmits very little or no information." But that leaves the five percent of conversation that is information rich, as the Buddha taught in the epigraphy above.

Because I am an anthropologist and was trained in linguistics, I am sensitive to the evolutionary and phenomenological aspects of *natural language*.[45] Thus, I simply cannot complete a book on the contemplative brain without at least a brief reflection on the role played by language in transmitting knowledge about the contemplative path to others, the sharing of experiences, and the description of experiences. There are many books out there that theorize about the biological evolution and functions of natural language (see Deacon 1997; Fitch 2010; Hurford,

---

[45] I define natural language broadly as any naturally evolved communication system including both all of the languages spoken by the 4000+ cultures on the planet and communication systems among social birds and mammals (e.g., honey bee dance, dolphin vocalizations, whale "songs," etc.).

Studdert-Kennedy and Knight 1998), as well as the rather neglected field of the phenomenology of language (Azzouni 2013; Inkpin 2016), and so I have no intention to survey and analyze the pros and cons of these perspectives. After all, this is not a book about communication *per se*. What I need to do is consider the pragmatic, everyday use of language to highlight the relationship between language and experience, the limitations of conversation and text relative to communicating experiences, and the use of language to evoke experiences.

The Evolution of Language and Experience

Some 45 years ago, Gene d'Aquili and I wrote a book entitled *Biogenetic Structuralism* in which we reasoned that language evolved to synchronize the cognitive maps of individuals within local groups of our hominin ancestors (Laughlin and d'Aquili 1974: 90-98). Alas, our theorizing was in the context of the times, and was marred by a dialog with structuralism and with the "protolanguage" debates. But our reasoning went essentially like this: There reached a point in the evolution of the hominins at which the cognitive maps of group members became so complex in spatial and temporal memories that social cohesion would be diminished, and the value of social adaptive strategies lessened. For members of a group to share a consensus brain world, a more complex way to share information was required, given that the hominin brain world increasingly expanded beyond the limits of direct perception. Prior to this expansive evolution of cognitive processes, the hominin cognitive map was like that of other animals, fairly determined by ongoing experience. After the hominin cognitive map became more complex in both time and space, the interpretive frame of experience among group members could potentially become maladaptively discrepant. Hypothetically, we reasoned, without some mechanism to share information and interpretation of experiences each group member could be so different in their understanding of the world that social adaptive strategies would become seriously hampered, and biological fitness decreased.

Fortunately, like all other social primates (and other social animals as well), hominins already had gestural and vocal communication, the former allowing augmentation of information about events between conspecifics within visual range of each other, and the latter allowing such augmentation whether in sight of each other, or only within sound of each other. I presently think, along with Arbib, Liebal and Pika (2008), McNeill (2005) and others, that gestural and vocal communication were equally important in early hominin communication, and have remained so ever since:

> In looking for the evolutionary roots of human speech, many researchers turned to the vocal signals of nonhuman primates … as opposed to a "gestural origins" view of how language might have evolved. However, children use gestures for communication before their first spoken words, and adult speakers normally accompany all their speech with expressive manual gestures…, while human signed languages are full-blown languages that do not use speech. Thus, any theory of language origins must address the fact that gestures form a crucial part of the human "language performance system." (ibid: 1053)

Face-to-face communication in the real world, both back in the Paleolithic and in modern times, is a whole-body process involving gestures, facial expressions, movements, posture and speech. Essentially, what evolved is communication faculties sufficient to maintain synchronization of cognitive maps that over the ages became more and more complex and less and less tied directly to perception. In time, the inner brain worlds of hominins became capable of cognizing and imagining aspects of realty that were unperceivable, save perhaps in dreams. Maps of "supernatural" realities could only be transmitted and synchronized by way of communication, as in initiations, stories, songs, performances and art. Accounts of the evolution of language divorced from the pragmatic and performance aspects of communication are most often wrong.

Meditation and Language as Performance

As J. L. Austin argued in his little book *How to Do Things with Words* and elsewhere, many natural utterances are not merely descriptions or statements of fact, but are acts, or as he said, *performative sentences* (1975: 6). People in fact *do things* with speech. It is this pragmatic aspect of language that is so relevant to the contemplative path. Language has several performative functions with respect to the exploration of the inner being. This is implied by Wilber's "If you want to know this, do this" injunction, as well as subsequent communications after experiences arise. An injunction is not merely a description of procedures or a statement of fact about what needs to be done to "know this." It is more a command; "if you want to know this, then you bloody well must do this." This sort of language use is virtually universal to initiation traditions around the globe. The injunctions embedded in the ritual procedures in initiations are intended to make change happen.

Esoteric texts, either transmitted by spoken words or in writing, may merely be descriptions when taken out of context. But when used in rituals, the intent of which is to incubate or evoke ASC or intuitive insights, they have the force of injunctions. Let me offer a couple of examples from my own experiences. First, I once did a meditation retreat for a month, during which one of the practices I explored was to read *The Sutra of Hui-Neng* (Cleary 1998) from cover to cover repeatedly in bouts of 20 minutes of reading followed by a lengthy period of mindfulness meditation. I found that the reading operated as a driver—as an injunction—that resulted in the emergence of a deep intuitive realization of the meaning of the text. The text *penetrated* (see Laughlin, McManus and d'Aquili 1990: Chap. 7) to the depths of my unconscious psyche and became for me the meaning of the text. In our book, *Brain, Symbol and Experience*, my colleagues John McManus, Gene d'Aquili and I wrote:

> Penetration... means the effect exercised by the activities of one neural system upon another neural system. By *symbolic penetration* we wish to refer specifically to the effects exercised by the neural system mediating a symbolic percept (or the entire perceptual field) upon other neural, endocrine, and physiological systems within the being. We are speaking of the pattern of evocation and entrainment of neural and other physiological systems produced in the wake of activating a perceptual network. (ibid: 190)

Penetration in this sense is very useful to us here, for it underscores the physiological process by which symbolically *pregnant* (Cassirer 1957) percepts evoke a series of entrainments of neural processes that become, for the individual experiencing the percept, all or part of the meaning of the percept. Thus, it is that one may hear or read of a grisly event and feel an intense revulsion, aversion or excitement. In this case the networks processing the audio or visual stimuli penetrate to the circuits that mediate emotional and behavioral aversion. Alternatively, one may read an erotic story and become sexually aroused. The magic involves how perceptual networks interpreting the spoken or written words can penetrate to (activate, propagate to) the circuits mediating visceral reactions, as if the individual were directly experiencing the event.

We can understand then that words, sentences and texts can evoke essentially non-linguistic events in the brain and body. In our specific focus, hearing or reading texts can penetrate to, evoke, potentiate for future development and realization of the wisdom that is the intention of the author of the text. A second example of the power of symbolic penetration for the maturation of a contemplative is the use among Zen practitioners of the *koan* (Chapter 3; see Heine and Wright 2000). As we have mentioned elsewhere, the *koan* is often a word or phrase that becomes the focus of meditation until the countersigns arise that indicate the *koan* has penetrated to its intended realization. The realization is *never* another word or phrase, but rather an experience that may then be communicated to others (usually the teacher) by some symbolic means (gesture, posture, sentences, etc.). The same for Sufi stories and many of the stories told by shamans and other traditional spiritual teachers in cultures around the globe.

The intimate association of speech and music, the former providing denotation and the latter rhythm, tone and frequency landscape, combine to produce powerful drivers that may trigger penetration to experiences, realizations, and intuitive insights (see Fitch 2006). My third example is how, in Tibetan Buddhist *pujas* (meditation ceremonies), chanting of textual materials is often punctuated by instrumental and vocal music. Chanting and the repetition of mantras are performative textual acts (again, J. L. Austin here) intended to "do something;" in this case, to penetrate the participant's psyche and evoke the experiences and realizations that are both the intentions of the text and, for each individual practitioner, the meaning of the text. It was my impression while living and talking with my fellow Buddhist monks in Nepal that very few had any real understanding of the words they had memorized and chanted on a daily basis. My fourth example is the experience had while working with meditations involving mantras. The meditator may or may not know the meanings of the words of a mantra. More than likely the practitioner may retain only an overall sense of the meaning of the utterance relative to the intent of the specific meditation being practiced. Over the months when I was completing the 100,000 repetitions of the Tibetan Vajrasattva visualization practice, each iteration of the visualization of certain images was accompanied by the "100 syllable mantra" in Sanskrit, which goes something like:[46]

> *oṃ vajrasattva samayam anupālaya vajrasattva tvenopatiṣṭha dṛḍho me bhava sutoṣyo me bhava supoṣyo me bhava anurakto me bhava sarvasiddhiṃ me prayaccha sarvakarmasu ca me cittaṃ śreyaḥ kuru hūṃ ha ha ha ha hoḥ bhagavan sarvatathāgatavajra mā me muñca vajrī bhava mahāsamayasattva āḥ*

Which roughly translated into English means:

Oṃ. Vajrasattva, keep your samaya [vows]. As Vajrasattva, remain near me. Be steadfast towards me. Be very pleased with me. Be completely satisfied with me. Be loving to me. Grant me all accomplishments. In all actions, make my mind pure and virtuous. Hūṃ. Ha ha ha ha hoḥ. O Blessed One, Vajra-nature of all the Tathāgatas [enlightened beings], do not abandon me. Be of vajra-nature, O great Samaya-being, āḥ.

When I began the work, I read the translation of the Sanskrit and promptly forgot what the words meant but carried with me (to this day) the sense of the meaning of "taking refuge in the performance of purification"—as in Buddhaghosa's (1976) *The Path of Purification (Visuddhimagga)*. I have already discussed the phenomenology of seed syllables like *oṃ, hūṃ, ha, hoḥ,* and *āḥ,* in Chapter 4. They may or may

---

[46] The Tibetan and English versions of the 100 syllable mantra was copied on February 14, 2018, with great appreciation, from the Bodhicitta Sangha website: https://www.bodhicittasangha.org/100-syllable-mantra/.

not have a denotative meaning to the meditator, but usually not. Their principal effect is due to the frequency of their respective vibrations on energy centers in the body.

I am emphasizing the performative functions of speech and text in part because of the mistaken Western bias that language produces no physical effects, as in: "Sticks and stones may break my bones, but words can never hurt me." This attitude is of course silly, because we all know that we can hurt others with our words, and be hurt by the words of others. Most cultures on the planet recognize the causal efficacy of words, hence the force of incantations in magic and sorcery. Words and utterances have psychosomatic power. Speech can very much injure us by penetrating to our visceral selves; i.e., utterances may influence the tuning of the ergotropic-trophotropic balance of the body, a factor that Barbara Lex (1974) once suggested as an explanation for the "voodoo death" phenomenon (see also Cannon 1942; Sternberg 2002).

I have been focusing upon the phenomenology of language in its injunction sense. There is of course the opposite process by which speech and text have an expressive power. This is inherent in Wilber's protocol in that the contemplative may enter conversation or write about experiences and insights had during contemplative work. A classic example of a text written by a contemplative with the power of injunction is *The Cloud of Unknowing* (Johnson 2012) penned by an anonymous 14th century monk. In that work, the contemplative describes the process by which the novice may come into direct union with God through prayer and meditation. With respect to conversation, it is by way of communication of experiences to others in the group or society that the cycle of meaning (Chapter 3) is completed, and interpretations of experiences return full circle to either confirm or alter the world view of a people.

THE FUTURE OF CONTEMPLATION

A couple of decades ago, I gave a lot of thought to the future of artificial intelligence (AI) and cyborg technologies and their impact upon human consciousness (Laughlin 1997b, 2000). One implication that occurred to me was that once a brain-computer interface had been developed to a sufficient degree to produce a human brain-AI cyborg, what I called at the time a Stage IV cyborg, there would be the potential for optimizing human consciousness and psychological development:

> A neurocognitive model of the evolution of cyborg consciousness was presented showing a probable bidirectional penetration of technology outwards from the body into the world, and inwards from the world into the body. The model posits four stages in the evolution of the cyborg, with Stage IV cyborgs emerging as a consequence of direct CNS-AI interfacing. I have argued that Stage IV cyborg technologies will likely be implemented in children, thus opening up profound implications for psychological development. (Laughlin 2000)

One of those developments would naturally be the production of both "ideology chips" and "guru programs," the former used to indoctrinate the young in accord with group and society values, skills and knowledge—basically what school classrooms do in technocratic societies—and the latter being essentially an interactional guide to optimal neurocognitive development. Great strides have been made in the development of wearable computers (Mann and Niedzviecki 2001), "transhuman" augmentations (O'Connell 2017), neural interfacing (i.e., brain-machine interfacing; Dornhege 2007; Nair 2013; Machchhar, Koticha and Aysan 2014), and ethical and legal considerations pertaining to cyborg enhancements (Greguric 2014; Carvalko 2013). There are now literally hundreds of research projects seeking to develop operating brain-computer interfaces by means of which various medical conditions (blindness, para- and quadriplegia) and rapid military applications (thought-controlling fighter planes) may be solved.

In any event, the rather science fiction-ish notion of a cyborg guru program becomes gradually less fiction and more science with every passing year. Such a technology might operate along Wilber's line by setting contemplative goals for the developing brain, monitoring progress, guiding away from wrong turns, correcting for mistaken interpretations (such as belief in a permanent ego), and so forth. There would thus be an inner dialog with the guru program that directs the developing brain away from conservative efforts after meaning and toward the effort after truth, away from negative feedback between experience and interpretation and toward positive feedback that optimizes growth. How the future scenario unfolds, whether by brain-computer interfacing or by introduction of nanobot technologies into the body, cyborg technologies will almost certainly accelerate *neuro-emergence*, "emergence" in biology meaning "biological systems increase in their level of self organization and complexity" (Saniotis 2009: 482; see also Maturana and Varela 1987). One of the likely properties of technologically enhanced neural emergence in the future will be the ability of the technology to alter the biochemical activity within specific neural processes (Saniotis and Henneberg 2011). Part of the injunction process may be along the lines of "what you need to do to know this is introduce this psychotropic drug (entheogen)." The interface then provides the requisite drug and the guru program guides the experience, as it were, from the inside.

Another possible application for neural interfacing would be to facilitate mind-to-mind communication. This has yet to be accomplished, but it is clear from studies of twins joined at the head and sharing neural connections between their brains that sharing feelings, imagery, thoughts, insights, etc. directly between individual brains is quite possible (see Langland-Hassan 2015 on the Hogan twins). This technology could allow the human guru direct access to the chela's (disciple's) direct experiences and interpretations. This could optimize the injunction type of teaching and guidance. Alas, however, the potential for abuse in the interests of political and economic brainwashing is alarming.

A LAST WORD

It is my overwhelming sense that we human beings must optimize our wisdom-factor before we destroy ourselves and our vulnerable ecosystem. As the historian Timothy Snyder in his book *On Tyranny* (2017) makes clear, the idea that history unfolds in a straight line from a primitive past to a transcendentally hopeful future is nothing more than a cultural fiction. In the real world, history is a dynamic process of cycles within cycles. At the moment we are in danger of returning to autocratic, nationalistic and involuted nation states in which the gap between the rich and poor continues to widen. At a subtler level, we are in danger of losing the psychological and cultural foundations of both science and democracy—in short, the basis for the kind of creativity that will allow us to advance beyond national technocratic "tribalism." Meanwhile, we are polluting our planet—our precious "pale blue dot"—daily and thereby endangering the wellbeing and future of both humans and all other species, the latter becoming extinct at an alarming rate.

The most direct and optimal route to wisdom is by the contemplative path. Hence, so far as I can see, our only hope is to encourage the contemplative way as early as primary school—build meditative techniques and contemplative inquiry into the curriculum of our public and private school systems as completely as we can do so without dragging along institutional religious ideologies. In other words, what we need to break the cyclical return to autocracy and ideologically driven curricula is to teach the methods necessary for children and young adults to recognize the "natural attitude" (culturally-conditioned) mind-states that may quash questioning about the world, skepticism and creative cognitive abilities. Only the routes leading to self-awareness and self-realization are productive of the level of wisdom and compassion necessary to reduce the mind-boggling level of human suffering that we as social primates have brought upon ourselves, our fellow creatures and our planet.

BIBLIOGRAPHY

Abdel-Khalek, Ahmed, 1986. "Death Anxiety in Egyptian Samples." Personality and Individual Differences 7(4): 479-483.

Abdel-Khalek, Ahmed and David Lester, 2004. "The Factorial Structure of the Arabic Version of the Revised Collett-Lester Fear of Death Scale." Death Studies 28:787-793.

Abramson, A., 2005. "Drinking to Mana and Ethnicity: Trajectories of Yaqona Practice and Symbolism in Eastern Fiji." Oceania 75 (4): 325-341.

Adam, Barbara, 1990. Time and Social Theory. Philadelphia: Temple University Press.

Adolphs, R., 2002. Neural Systems for Recognizing Emotion. Current Opinion in Neurobiology 12: 169–177.

Aftanas, L. I. and S. A. Golocheikine, 2001. "Human Anterior and Frontal Midline Theta and Lower Alpha Reflect Emotionally Positive State and Internalized Attention: High-Resolution EEG Investigation of Meditation." Neuroscience Letters 310: 57-60.

Alexander, Eben, 2012. Proof of Heaven: A Neurosurgeon's Near-Death Experience and Journey into the Afterlife. New York: Simon and Schuster.

Al Ghazali, A. H. M., 1994. The Faith and Practice of Al-Ghazali, trans. by W. M. Watt. Oxford: Oneworld.

Allen, M., 2012. "Cognitive-Affective Neural Plasticity Following Active-Controlled Mindfulness Intervention." The Journal of Neuroscience 32: 15601-15610.

Alvarado, Carlos S., 1987. "Observations of Luminous Phenomena around the Human Body: A Review." Journal of the Society for Psychical Research 54(806): 38-60.

Alvarado, Carlos S., 1994. Individual Differences in Aura Vision: Relationship To Visual Imagery and Imaginative-Fantasy Experiences. European Journal of Parapsychology 10: 1-30.

Alvarado, Carlos S., 2000. "Out-of-Body Experiences." In Varieties of Anomalous Experience: Examining the Scientific Evidence, ed. by E. Cardeña, S. J. Lynn and S. Krippner. Washington, DC: American Psychological Association, 183-218.

Amaro, B. and B. Pasanno, 2009. The Island. An Anthology of the Buddha's Teachings on Nibbāna. Redwood Valley, CA: Abhayagiri Monastic Foundation.

Amodio, D. M. and C. D. Frith, 2006. "Meeting of Minds: The Medial Frontal Cortex and Social Cognition." Nature Reviews Neuroscience 7: 268-277.

Anderson, James R., 2011. "A Primatological Perspective on Death." American Journal of Primatology 73: 410–414.

Anderson, James R., Alasdair Gillies and Louise C. Lock, 2010. "Pan Thanatology." Current Biology 20(8): R349-R351.

Anonymous, 1871. St. Gertrude the Great: Herald of Divine Love (1994 edition). Gastonia, NC: TAN Books.

Applegarth, A., 1971. "Comments on Aspects of the Theory of Psychic Energy." Journal of the American Psychoanalytic Association 19 (3): 379-416.

Arbib, M. A., K. Liebal and S. Pika, 2008. Primate Vocalization, Gesture, and the Evolution of Human Language. Current Anthropology 49(6): 1053–76.

Archer, John, 1999. The Nature of Grief: The Evolution and Psychology of Reaction to Loss. London: Routledge.

Argüelles, J. and M. Argüelles, 1972. Mandala. Berkeley: Shambhala.

Arundale, G. S., 1938. Kundalini: An Occult Experience. Adyar, India: Theosophical Publishing House.

Assagioli, R., 2007. Transpersonal Development. Forres, Scotland: Smiling Wisdom.

Atkinson, Anthony P., Michael S. C. Thomas and Axel Cleeremans, 2000. "Consciousness: Mapping the Theoretical Landscape." Trends in Cognitive Sciences 4(10): 372-382.

Austin, James H., 1998. Zen and the Brain: Toward an Understanding of Meditation and Consciousness. Cambridge, MA: MIT Press.

Austin, James H., 2006. Zen-Brain Reflections. Cambridge, MA: MIT Press.

Austin, James H., 2009. "Our Ordinary Sense of Self: Different Aspects of 'No-Self' during States of Absorption and Kensho." In Self and No-Self: Continuing the Dialogue Between Buddhism and Psychotherapy, ed. by Dale Mathers, Melvin E. Miller and Osamu Ando. London: Routledge, pp. 59-65.

Austin, John L., 1975. How to Do Things with Words: Second Edition (The William James Lectures; 2nd edition), ed. by J. O. Urmson and Marina Sbisà. Cambridge, MA: Harvard University Press.

Avanessian, Armen and Anke Hennig, 2017. Metanoia: A Speculative Ontology of Language, Thinking, and the Brain. London: Bloomsbury Publishing.

Avarguès-Weber, Aurore, Theo Mota and Martin Giurfa, 2012. "New Vistas on Honey Bee Vision." Apidologie 43(3): 244-268.

Azzouni, Jody, 2013. Semantic Perception: How the Illusion of a Common Language Arises and Persists. New York: Oxford University Press.

Baars, B. J., T. Z. Ramsøy and S. Laureys, 2003. Brain, Conscious Experience and the Observing Self. TRENDS in Neurosciences 26(12): 671-675.

Baer, Ruth A., Emily L. B. Lykins and Jessica R. Peters, 2012. "Mindfulness and Self-Compassion as Predictors of Psychological Wellbeing in Long-Term Meditators and Matched Non-Meditators." The Journal of Positive Psychology 7(3): 230-238.

Bærentsen, Klaus B., Hans Stødkilde-Jørgensen, Bo Sommerlund, Tue Hartmann, Johannes Damsgaard-Madsen, Mark Fosnæs and Anders C. Green, 2010. "An Investigation of Brain Processes Supporting Meditation." Cognitive Processing 11(1): 57-84.

Baker, Alexzandria C., 2016. "Sacred Kink: Finding Psychological Meaning at the Intersection of BDSM and Spiritual Experience." Sexual and Relationship Therapy 31(1): 1-14.

Barbas, Helen, 2000. "Connections Underlying the Synthesis of Cognition, Memory, and Emotion in Primate Prefrontal Cortices." Brain Research Bulletin 52(5): 319-330.

Barker, Steven A., Ethan H. McIlhenny and Rick Strassman, 2012. "A Critical Review of Reports of Endogenous Psychedelic N, N-Dimethyltryptamines in Humans: 1955–2010." Drug Testing and Analysis 4(7-8): 617-635.

Barley, Nigel, 1995. Dancing on the Grave. London: John Murray.

Barlow, H. B. and J. D. Mollon, 1982. The Senses. Cambridge, UK: Cambridge University Press.

Barkow, Jerome, Leda Cosmides and John Tooby (eds), 1992. The Adapted Mind: Evolutionary Psychology and the Generation of Culture. Oxford: Oxford University Press.

Barnes, P. M., B. Bloom and R. Nahin, 2008. "Complementary and Alternative Medicine Use among Adults and Children: United States, 2007." CDC National Health Statistics Report #12.

Barnhofer, Thorsten et al., 2007. "Effects of Meditation on Frontal ⊠-Asymmetry in Previously Suicidal Individuals." Neuroreport 18(7): 709-712.

Baron-Cohen, Simon, 1997. Mindblindness: An Essay on Autism and Theory of Mind. Cambridge, MA: MIT Press.

Barraza, J. and P. J. Zak, 2009. "Empathy towards Strangers Triggers Oxytocin Release and Subsequent Generosity." Annals of the New York Academy of Science. 2009(1167): 182–189.

Barrett, Deirdre, 1992. "Fantasizers and Dissociaters: Data on Two Distinct Subgroups of Deep Trance Subjects." Psychological Reports 71(3): 1011-1014.

Barrett, Deirdre (ed), 1996. Trauma and Dreams. Cambridge, MA: Harvard University Press.

Barth, F., 1975. Ritual and Knowledge Among the Baktaman of New Guinea. New Haven: Yale University Press.

Bartlett, F. C., 1932. Remembering: A Study in Experimental and Social Psychology. Cambridge, UK: Cambridge University Press.

Barušs, I., 2003. Alterations of Consciousness. Washington, D.C.: American Psychological Association.

Bateson, G., 1980. Mind and Nature: A Necessary Unity. New York: Bantam Books.

Battaglia, D., 1990. On the Bones of the Serpent: Person, Memory, and Morality in Sabarl Island Society. Chicago: University of Chicago Press.

Battaglia, D. (ed.), 1995. Rhetorics of Self-Making. Berkeley, CA: University of California Press.

Bauernfeind, Amy L., Alexandra A. de Sousa, Tanvi Avasthi, Seth D. Dobson, Mary Ann Raghanti, Albert H. Lewandowski, Karl Zilles et al., 2013. "A Volumetric Comparison of the Insular Cortex and Its Subregions in Primates." Journal of Human Evolution 64(4): 263-279.

Bayne, Tim. "Closing the Gap? Some Questions for Neurophenomenology." Phenomenology and the Cognitive Sciences 3(4): 349-364.

Beck, A. T. and B. A. Alford, 2009. Depression: Causes and Treatment (2nd ed.). Philadelphia: University of Pennsylvania Press.

Beck, F., and J. C. Eccles, 1992. "Quantum Aspects of Consciousness and the Role of Consciousness." Proceedings of the National Academy of Sciences 89: 11357.

Becker, Ernest, 1971. The Birth and Death of Meaning: An Interdisciplinary Perspective on the Problem of Man (Second Edition). New York: Free Press.

Becker, Ernest, 1973. The Denial of Death. New York: Free Press.

Becker, Ernest, 1975. The Escape from Evil. New York: Free Press.

Behr, John, 2000. Asceticism and Anthropology in Irenaeus and Clement. London: Oxford University Press.

Behrmann, M., 2000. The Mind's Eye Mapped Onto the Brain's Matter. Current Directions in Psychological Science 9: 50–54.

Bekoff, M., 2002. Minding Animals: Awareness, Emotions and Heart. Oxford: Oxford University Press.

Belanti, John, Mahendra Perera and Karuppiah Jagadheesan, 2008. "Phenomenology of Near-death Experiences: A Cross-cultural Perspective." Transcultural Psychiatry 45(1): 121-133.

Bellah, R. N., 2008. Tokugawa Religion. New York: Simon and Schuster.

Ben-Āmôş, D. and L. Weissberg (eds.), 1999. Cultural Memory and the Construction of Identity. Detroit, MI: Wayne State University Press.

Bentov, I., 1977. Stalking the Wild Pendulum. New York: E. P. Dutton.

Bera, Manasi, Atin Kumar Barik and Tushar Kanti Bera, 2017. "Role of Yoga in Psychological Correlates of Learning Ability in School Children." Yoga Mimamsa 49(1): 13-16.

Berkovich-Ohana, Aviva et al., 2015. "Repetitive Speech Elicits Widespread Deactivation in the Human Cortex: The "Mantra" Effect?." Brain and Behavior 5(7): 1-13.

Berlin, Heather A., 2011. "The Neural Basis of the Dynamic Unconscious." Neuropsychoanalysis 13(1): 5-31.

Bermúdez, J. L., A. J. Marcel and N. Eilan (eds.), 1998. The Body and the Self. Cambridge, NA: MIT Press.

Beyer, S., 1973. The Cult of Tara. Berkeley, CA: University of California Press.

Bharati, Agehananda, 1961. The Ochre Robe. Seattle, WA: University of Washington Press.

Bharati, Agehananda, 1975. The Tantric Tradition. New York: Samuel Weiser.

Bien, Christian G. et al., 2000. "Localizing Value of Epileptic Visual Auras." Brain 123(2): 244-253.

Bierman, Dick J. and Dean I. Radin, 1997. "Anomalous Anticipatory Response on Randomized Future Conditions." Perceptual and Motor Skills 84 (2): 689–690.

Bierman, Dick J. and H. Steven Scholte, 2002. "A fMRI Brain Imaging Study of Presentiment." unpublished manuscript.

Biersack, A., 2011a. "The Sun and the Shakers, Again: Enga, Ipili, and Somaip Perspectives on the Cult of Ain, Part One." Oceania 81 (2): 113.

Biersack, A., 2011b. "The Sun and the Shakers, Again: Enga, Ipili, and Somaip Perspectives on the Cult of Ain, Part Two." Oceania 81 (3): 225-243.

Biesele, Megan and Nancy Howell, 1981. "'The Old People Give You Life': Aging among !Kung Hunter-Gatherers." in Other Ways of Growing Old: Anthropological Perspectives, Pamela T. Amoss and Stevan Harrell, editors. Stanford, CA: Stanford University Press, pp. 77-99.

Biro, Dora, Tatyana Humle, Kathelijne Koops, Claudia Sousa, Misato Hayashi, and Tetsuro Matsuzawa, 2010. "Chimpanzee Mothers at Bossou, Guinea Carry the Mummified Remains of their Dead Infants." Current Biology 20: R351–R352.

Bischof, Marco and Emilio Del Giudice, 2013. "Communication and the Emergence of Collective Behavior in Living Organisms: A Quantum Approach." Molecular Biology International 2013.

Blanke, O., T. Landis, L. Spinelli and M. Seeck, 2004. "Out-of-Body Experience and Autoscopy of Neurological Origin." Brain 127(2): 243-258.

Blanke, O. et al., 2005. "Linking Out-Of-Body Experience and Self Processing to Mental Own-Body Imagery at the Temporoparietal Junction." The Journal of Neuroscience 25(3): 550-557.

Block, Maurice, 1977. "The Past and the Present in the Present." Man 12(2): 278-292.

Block, Maurice and J. Parry, 1982. "Introduction: Death and the Regeneration of Life." In Death and the Regeneration of Life, ed. by M. Block and J. Parry. Cambridge: Cambridge University Press, pp. 1-44.

Block, Ned, 1995. "On a Confusion about a Function of Consciousness." Behavioral and Brain Sciences 18: 227–287.

Bloom, Sandra L., 2010. "Terror Management Theory." Retrieved from http://sanctuaryweb.com/Portals/0/2010%20PDFs%20NEW/2010%20Bloom%20Terror%20Management%20Theory.pdf [accessed on September 28, 2017].

Blumer, D. and D. F. Benson, 1975. "Personality Changes with Frontal and Temporal Lobe Lesions." Psychiatric Aspects of Neurologic Disease 1: 151-170.

Boddy, J., 1994. "Spirit Possession Revisited: Beyond Instrumentality." Annual Review of Anthropology 23: 407-434.

Bodhi, B., 1999. The Noble Eightfold Path. From the Access to Insight Website. Retrieved on 21 March 2014 from: http://www.accesstoinsight.org/lib/authors/bodhi/waytoend.html.

Bogen, J. E., 1998. "Locating the Subjectivity Pump: The Thalamic Intralaminar Nuclei." In Toward a Science of Consciousness II: The 1996 Tucson Discussions and Debates, ed. by S. Hameroff et al. Cambridge, MA: MIT Press, pp. 237–246.

Bohm, David, 1980. Wholeness and the Implicate Order. Boston: Routledge and Kegan Paul.

Boly, Melanie, Anil K. Seth, Melanie Wilke, Paul Ingmundson, Bernard Baars, Steven Laureys, David B. Edelman and Naotsugu Tsuchiya, 2013. "Consciousness in Humans and Non-Human Animals: Recent Advances and Future Directions." Frontiers in Psychology 4. http://journal.frontiersin.org/article/10.3389/fpsyg.2013.00625/full (accessed July 24, 2017)

Bond, George D., 1980. "Theravada Buddhism's Meditations on Death and the Symbolism of Initiatory Death." History of Religions 19(3): 237–258.

Bondeson, Jan, 2001. Buried Alive: The Terrifying History of Our Most Primal Fear. New York: Norton.

Boring, E. G., 1953. A History of Introspection." Psychological Bulletin 50: 169–189.

Botvinick, M. et al., 2005. "Viewing Facial Expressions of Pain Engages Cortical Areas Involved in the Direct Experience of Pain." Neuroimage 25: 315–319.

Bourdieu, P., 1977. Outline of a Theory of Practice (translated by R. Nice). Cambridge: Cambridge University Press.

Bourguignon, Erica, 1973. Religion, Altered States of Consciousness, and Social Change. Columbus, Ohio: Ohio State University Press.

Bourguignon, Erica, 1976. Possession. San Francisco: Chandler and Sharp.

Bourguignon, Erica, 1989. "Multiple Personality, Possession Trance, and the Psychic Unity Of Mankind." Ethos 17(3): 371-384.

Bourguignon, E. and T. I. Evascu, 1977. "Altered States of Consciousness Within a General Evolutionary Perspective: A Holocultural Analysis." Behavior Science Research 12: 197-216.

Braboszcz, C., S. Hahusseau and A. Delorme, 2010. Meditation and Neuroscience: From Basic Research to Clinical Practice. In Handbook of Integrative Clinical Psychology, Psychiatry, and Behavioral Medicine: Perspectives, Practices, and Research, ed. by R. A. Carlstedt. New York: Springer, pp. 1910-1929.

Bradley, Sean, 2010. "The Pineal Gland's Biochemical Function in the Fighting and Meditative Arts: Exemplified in Korean Sinmoo Hapkido." Journal of Asian Martial Arts 19(2): 22-34.

Brady, Ivan A. (ed.), 1991. Anthropological Poetics. Savage, MD: Rowman & Littlefield.

Brady, Ivan A., 2005. "Poetics for a Planet." Handbook of Qualitative Research. London: Sage.

Brady, Ivan A., 2008. "Ethnopoetics." In Sage Encyclopedia of Qualitative Research Methods, ed. by L. M. Given. Thousand Oaks, CA: Sage, pp. 296-298.

Brainard, F. Samuel, 1996. "Defining 'Mystical Experience'." Journal of the American Academy of Religion 64(2): 359-393.

Brainard, F. Samuel, 2000. Reality and Mystical Experience. Pittsburg, PA: Penn State University Press.

Brandmeyer, Tracy, Arnaud Delorme and Helané Wahbeh, 2019. "The Neuroscience of Meditation: Classification, Phenomenology, Correlates, and Mechanisms." In Progress in Brain Research 244: 1-29.

Branham, R. Bracht and Marie-Odile Goulet-Cazé (eds.), 2000. The Cynics: The Cynic Movement in Antiquity and Its Legacy. Berkeley, CA: University of California Press.

Braud, William G., 2002. "Thoughts on the Ineffability of the Mystical Experience." The International Journal for the Psychology of Religion 12(3): 141-160.

Brefczynski-Lewis, J.A., A. Lutz, H. S. Schaefer, D. B. Levinson and R. J. Davidson, 2007. Neural Correlates of Attentional Expertise in Long-Term Meditation Practitioners. Proceedings of the National Academy of Sciences USA 104: 11483–11488.

Brewer, Judson A. et al., 2011. "Meditation Experience Is Associated with Differences in Default Mode Network Activity and Connectivity." Proceedings of the National Academy of Sciences USA 108(50): 20254-20259.

Briggs, J. L., 1970. Never in Anger: Portrait of an Eskimo Family. Cambridge, MA: Harvard University Press.

Brock, H. B., 2000. "Yellow Crocodiles and Bush Spirits: Timpaus Islanders' Conceptualization of Ethereal Phenomena." Ethos 28: 3-19.

Brockelman, P., 1985. Time and Self: Phenomenological Explorations. New York: Crossroad.

Brook, Michael and David S. Kosson, 2013. "Impaired Cognitive Empathy in Criminal Psychopathy: Evidence from a Laboratory Measure of Empathic Accuracy." Journal of Abnormal Psychology 122(1): 156.

Brown, D., 1986. "The Stages of Meditation in Cross-Cultural Perspective." In Transformations of Consciousness: Conventional and Contemplative Perspectives on Development, ed. by K. Wilber, J. Engler and D. Brown. Boston, MA: Shambhala.

Brown, Stephanie L., R. Michael Brown and Louis A. Penner (eds.), 2011. Moving Beyond Self-Interest: Perspectives from Evolutionary Biology, Neuroscience, and the Social Sciences. Oxford: Oxford University Press.

Brunner, C., 1986. Anima as Fate. Dallas, TX: Spring Publications. (Originally published 1963)

Bryant, Edwin F., 2009. The Yoga Sūtras of Patañjali. New York: North Point Press.

Bruce, Robert D., 1975. Lacandon Dream Symbolism: Dream Symbolism and Interpretation among the Lacandon Maya of Chiapas, Mexico. Perugino, Mexico: Ediciones Euroamericanas Klaus Thiele.

Bruce, S., 2002. God is Dead: Secularization in the West. Oxford, UK: Blackwell.

Bucke, Richard Maurice, 2009[1961]. Cosmic Consciousness: A Study in the Evolution of the Human Mind. New York: Courier Corporation, 2009.

Buckner, R. L. and C. D. Carroll, 2007. "Self-Projection and the Brain." Trends in Cognitive Sciences 11(2): 49-57.

Buddha, G., 1997. The Udana: Inspired Utterances of the Buddha (translated from the Pali by John D. Ireland). Kandy, Sri Lanka: Buddhist Publication Society.

Buddhaghosa, B., 1976. The Path of Purification (Visuddhimagga), Volumes I and II. Berkeley: Shambhala.

Bulkeley, Kelly, 2008. Dreaming in the World's Religions. New York: New York University Press.

Bunge, S. A., K. N. Ochsner, J. E. Desmond, G. H. Glover and J. D. E. Gabrieli, 2001. "Prefrontal Regions Involved in Keeping Information In and Out of Mind." Brain 124: 2074-2086.

Burckhardt, Titus, 1967. Alchemy: Science of the Cosmos, Science of the Soul, trans. by William Stoddart. Baltimore: Penguin.

Burns, Tom and Charles D. Laughlin, 1979. "Ritual and Social Power." In The Spectrum of Ritual, ed. by E. G. d'Aquili, C. D. Laughlin and J. McManus. New York: Columbia University Press, 249-279.

Bush, Mirabai (ed.), 2011. Contemplation Nation: How Ancient Practices are Changing the Way We Live. Kalamazoo, MI: Fetzer Institute.

Buss, David M., 2004. Evolutionary Psychology: The New Science of the Mind. Boston: Pearson.

Butler, Jesse, 2013. Rethinking Introspection: A Pluralist Approach to the First-Person Perspective. New York: Springer.

Butler, N., 2004. "Marabouts and Magic (West Africa)." In Shamanism: An Encyclopedia of World Beliefs, Practices, and Culture, ed. by M. N. Walter and E. J. Neumann Fridman. Santa Barbara, CA: ABC-Clio, pp. 930-934.

Butterworth, G. and L. Grover, 1988. "The Origins of Referential Communication in Human Infancy." In Thought Without Language ed. by L. Weiskrantz. Oxford, England: Clarendon Press.

Cacioppo, J.T., P. S. Visser and C. L. Pickett, 2005. Social Neuroscience: People Thinking about Thinking People. Cambridge, MA: MIT Press.

Cahn, B. R. and J. Polich, 2006. "Meditation States and Traits: EEG, ERP and Neuroimaging Studies." Psychological Bulletin 132: 180–211.

Cahn, B. R. and John Polich, 2009. "Meditation (Vipassana) and the P3a Event-Related Brain Potential." International Journal of Psychophysiology 72(1): 51-60.

Cairns, D., 1976. Conversations with Husserl and Fink. The Hague: Martinus Nijhoff.

Caldwell, D. K. and M. C. Caldwell, 1972. The World of the Bottlenosed Dolphin. Philadelphia: Lippincott.

Calitoiu, Dragos, B. John Oommen and Doron Nussbaum, 2012. "Large-Scale Neuro-Modeling for Understanding and Explaining Some Brain-Related Chaotic Behavior." Simulation 88(11): 1316-1337.

Callebaut, Werner, and Rik Pinxten (eds.), 2012. Evolutionary Epistemology: A Multiparadigm Program. Vol. 190. New York: Springer Science & Business Media.

Callen, Kenneth E., 1983. "Auto-Hypnosis in Long Distance Runners." American Journal of Clinical Hypnosis 26(1): 30-36.

Campagno, L., M. Dando and S. Fowler, 2005. Princeton Field Guides: Sharks of the World. Princeton, New Jersey: Princeton University Press.

Campbell, R. L. and P. S. Staniford,1978. "Transpersonal Anthropology." Phoenix: The Journal of Transpersonal Anthropology 2(1): 28 40.

Cannon, Walter B., 1942. "'Voodoo' Death." American Anthropologist 44: 169-181.

Cardeña, Etzel, Dietrich Lehmann, Peter Jönsson, Devin Terhune and P. Faber, 2007. "The Neurophenomenology of Hypnosis." In Proceedings of the 50th Annual Convention of the Parapsychological Association, pp. 17-30.

Cardeña, Etzel, Marjolein Van Duijl, Lupita Weiner and Devin Terhune, 2010. "Possession/Trance Phenomena." In Dissociation and the dissociative disorders: DSM-V and beyond, ed. by Paul F. Dell and John A. O'Neil. New York: Routledge, pp. 171-181.

Cardeña, Etzel, S. J. Lynn, and S. Krippner (eds.), 2000. Varieties of Anomalous Experience: Examining the Scientific Evidence. Washington, DC: American Psychological Association.

Carlisle, C., 2006. "Becoming and Un-Becoming: The Theory and Practice of Anatta." Contemporary Buddhism 7(1): 75-89.

Cardoso. R., R. de Souza, L. Camano and J. R. Leite, 2007. "Prefrontal Cortex in Meditation." NeuroQuantology 5: 233-240.

Carlisle, C., 2006. "Becoming and Un-Becoming: The Theory and Practice of Anatta." Contemporary Buddhism 7(1): 75-89.

Carpenter, G. A. and S. Grossberg, 2003. "Adaptive Resonance Theory." In The Handbook of Brain Theory and Neural Networks (second edition), ed. by M. A. Arbib. Cambridge, MA: MIT Press, pp. 87-90.

Carpenter, G. A., S. Grossberg and D. B. Rosen, 1991. "Fuzzy ART: Fast Stable Learning and Categorization of Analog Patterns by an Adaptive Resonance System." Neural Networks 4(6): 759-771.

Carr, Christopher, 1993. "Death and Near-Death: A Comparison of Tibetan and Euro-American Experiences." Journal of Transpersonal Psychology 25(1): 59-110.

Carsten, Janet, 1995. "The Substance of Kinship and the Heat of the Hearth: Feeding, Personhood, and Relatedness among Malays in Pulau Langkawi." American Ethnologist 22(2): 223-241.

Carvalko, Joseph R., 2013. "Law and Policy in an Era of Cyborg-Assisted-Life 1: The Implications of Interfacing In-The-Body Technologies to the Outer World 2." In Technology and Society (ISTAS), the IEEE International Symposium, pp. 204-215.

Cassian, John, 2015. The Conferences of Desert Fathers. London: Aeterna Press.

Cassirer, Ernst, 1957. The Philosophy of Symbolic Forms. Vol. 3: The Phenomenology of Knowledge. New Haven, CT: Yale University Press.

Cavalieri, P. and P. Singer, 1993. The Great Ape Project: Equality beyond Humanity. St. Martin's Press: New York.

Cawte, John, 1985. "Psychoactive Substances of the South Seas: Betel, Kava and Pituri." Australian and New Zealand Journal of Psychiatry 19 (1): 83-87.

Chalmers, David J., 1995. "Explaining Consciousness: The Hard Problem." Journal of Consciousness Studies 2: 200–219.

Chalmers, David J., 1996. "Facing Up to the Hard Problem of Consciousness." Toward a Science of Consciousness: The First Tucson Discussions and Debates, ed. by S. R. Hameroff, A. W. Kaszniak and A. Scott. New York: Bradford, pp. 5-28.

Chang, Garma C. C., 1991[1963]. Teachings of Tibetan Yoga. Secaueus, New Jersey: The Citadel Press.

Chang, Garma C. C., 1986. The Six Yogas of Naropa and Teachings on Mahamudra. Boulder, CO: Snow Lion.

Chang, Garma C. C., 1991[1963]. Teachings of Tibetan Yoga. Secaueus, New Jersey: The Citadel Press.

Changeux, J-P., 1985. Neuronal Man: The Biology of Mind. Oxford, UK: Oxford University Press.

Chaudhuri, Haridas, 1972. "The Philosophy and Yoga of Sri Aurobindo." Philosophy East and West 22(1): 5-14.

Chauhan, B. C., 2015. "A New Paradigm of Science." International Journal of Recent Scientific Research 6(3): 2912-2918.

Chavan, D. V., 2007. "Vipassana: the Buddha's Tool to Probe Mind and Body." Progress in Brain Research 168: 247-253.

Cheney, Dorothy L. and Robert M. Seyfarth, 2007. Baboon Metaphysics: The Evolution of a Social Mind. Chicago: University of Chicago Press.

Chidester, David, 2003. "Primitive Texts, Savage Contexts: Contextualizing the Study of Religion in Colonial Situations." Method and Theory in the Study of Religion 15(3): 272-283.

Chiesa, Alberto, Raffaella Calati and Alessandro Serretti, 2011. "Does Mindfulness Training Improve Cognitive Abilities? A Systematic Review of Neuropsychological Findings." Clinical Psychology Review 31(3): 449-464.

Chiesa, Alberto and Alessandro Serretti, 2009. "Mindfulness-Based Stress Reduction for Stress Management in Healthy People: A Review and Meta-Analysis." The Journal of Alternative and Complementary Medicine 15(5): 593-600.

Child, Louise, 2016. Tantric Buddhism and Altered States of Consciousness: Durkheim, Emotional Energy and Visions of the Consort. New York: Routledge.

Chinen, A. B., 1985. "Fairy-Tales and Transpersonal Development in Later Life." Journal of Transpersonal Psychology 17(2): 99-122.

Chodorow, Joan, 2006. "Active Imagination." In The Handbook of Jungian Psychology, ed. by Renos K. Papadopoulos. London: Routledge, pp. 215-243.

Churchland, P. S., 2013. Touching a Nerve: The Self as Brain. New York: Norton.

Cicero, Marcus Tullius, 1997[45 BCE]. The Nature of the Gods. Amherst, NY: Prometheus Books.

Clark, Elizabeth A, 1998. "Holy Women, Holy Words: Early Christain Women, Social History, and the ' Linguistic Turn'." Journal of Early Christian Studies 6(3): 413-430.

Clayton, N. S., T. J. Bussey and A. Dickinson, 2003. Can Animals Recall the Past and Plan for the Future? Nature Reviews Neuroscience 4(8): 685-691.

Cleary, Thomas, 1998. The Sutra of Hui-Neng, Grand Master of Zen: With Hui-neng's Commentary on the Diamond Sutra. Boulder, CO: Shambhala Publications.

Clegg, Joshua (ed.), 2013. Self-Observation in the Social Science. New Jersey: Transaction.

Cohen, A. P., 1994. Self-Consciousness: An Alternative Anthropology of Identity. London: Routledge.

Cole, A. L. and J. G. Knowles, 2001. Lives in Context: The Art of Life History Research. New York: AltaMira Press.

Cole, Ardra L. and J. Gary Knowles (eds.), 2001. Lives in Context: The Art of Life History Research. New York: Rowman Altamira.

Cole, Michael, 1996. "Interacting Minds in a Life-Span Perspective: A Cultural-Historical Approach To Culture and Cognitive Development." Interactive Minds: Life-Span Perspectives on the Social Foundation of Cognition, ed. by Paul Baltes. Cambridge: Cambridge University Press, pp. 59-87.

Collett, Lora-Jean and David Lester, 1969. "The Fear of Death and the Fear of Dying." Journal of Psychology 72: 179-181.

Collins, A., 1994. Fatherson: A Self Psychology of the Archetypal Masculine. Wilmette, IL: Chiron.

Collins, S., 1982. Selfless Persons: Imagery and Thought in Theravāda Buddhism. Cambridge: Cambridge University Press.

Conze, Edward, 1999. "Buddhaghosa on the Recollection of Death." In The Ways of Religion: An Introduction to the Major Traditions (third edition), ed. By Roger Eastman. Oxford: Oxford University Press, pp. 105-109.

Corballis, M. C., 2011. The Recursive Mind: The Origins of Human Language, Thought and Civilization. Princeton, NJ: Princeton University Press.

Corbin, H., 1969. Alone with the Alone: Creative Imagination in the Sufism of Ibn 'Arabi. Princeton, NJ: Princeton University Press.

Cosmides, L. and J. Tooby, 1995. "From Function to Structure: The Role of Evolutionary Biology and Computational Theories in Cognitive Neuroscience." In The Cognitive Neurosciences, ed. by M. S. Gazzaniga. Cambridge, MA: MIT Press.

Cotterill, R. M. J., 2001. "Evolution, Cognition and Consciousness." Journal of Consciousness Studies 8(2): 3–17.

Count, E.W., 1973. Being and Becoming Human. New York: Van Nostrand Reinhold.

Craig, P. Erik, 1987. The Realness of Dreams." in Richard A. Russo (ed), Dreams Are Wiser Than Men. Berkeley, CA: North Atlantic Books, pp. 34-57.

Crapanzano, Vincent, 1973. The ⬛amadsha: A Study in Moroccan Ethnopsychiatry. Berkeley, CA: University of California Press, 1973.

Crick, F. and C. Koch, 1998. Consciousness and Neuroscience. Cerebral Cortex 8: 97–107.

Crist, Eileen, 2002[1985]. "The Inner Life of Earthworms: Darwin's Argument and Its Implications." The Cognitive Animal: Empirical and Theoretical Perspectives on Animal

Cognition, ed. by Marc Bekoff, Colin Allen, and Gordon M. Burghardt. Cambridge, MA: MIT Press, pp 3.

Croiset, Rev. John, 2007. The Devotion to the Sacred Heart of Jesus: How to Practice the Sacred Heart Devotion. Charlotte, NC: TAN Books.

Csikskentmihalyi, M., 1975. Beyond Boredom and Anxiety. San Francisco: Jossey Bass.

Csikszentmihalyi, Mihaly, 2008. Flow: The Psychology of Optimal Experience. New York: Harper.

Csordas, T. J., 1994. The Sacred Self: A Cultural Phenomenology of Charismatic Healing. Berkeley, CA: University of California Press.

Curie, Marie, 2012[1923]. Pierre Curie. New York: Dover.

Czaplicka, Marie Antoinette, 1914. Aboriginal Siberia: A Study in Social Anthropology. Oxford: Oxford University Press.

Csikszentmihalyi, M. and I. S. Csikszentmihalyi, 1988. Optimal Experience: Psychological Studies of Flow in Consciousness. Cambridge: Cambridge University Press.

Dainton, Barry, 2006. Stream of Consciousness: Unity and Continuity in Conscious Experience. New York: Taylor & Francis.

Damasio, A. R., 1985. "The Frontal Lobes." In Clinical Neuropsychology (2nd ed.), K. Heilman and E. Valenstein. New York: Oxford University Press, pp. 339-375.

Damasio, A. R., 1994. Descartes' Error: Emotion, Reason and the Human Brain. New York: Avon Books.

Damasio, A. R., 1999. The Feeling of What Happens: Body and Emotion in the Making of Consciousness. New York: Harcourt.

Damasio, A. R., 2003. "The Person Within." Nature 423(6937): 227.

Damasio, A. R., 2010. Self Comes to Mind: Constructing the Conscious Brain. New York: Pantheon.

Daniels, M., 2002. "The Transpersonal Self: 2. Comparing Seven Psychological Theories." Transpersonal Psychology Review 6(2): 4-21.

D'Aquili, Eugene G., 1975. The Influence of Jung on the Work of Claude Levi-Strauss. Journal of the History of the Behavioral Sciences 11(1): 41-48.

D'Aquili, Eugene G., 1982. "Senses of Reality in Science and Religion: A Neuroepistemological Perspective." Zygon 17 (4): 361-384.

D'Aquili, Eugene G., Charles D. Laughlin and John McManus, 1979. The Spectrum of Ritual. New York: Columbia University Press.

D'Aquili, Eugene G., Charles D. Laughlin and John McManus, 1993. "Mature Contemplation." Zygon 28(2): 133-176.

D'Aquili, Eugene G. and Andrew B. Newberg, 1993. "Religious and Mystical States: A Neuropsychological Model." Zygon 28: 177-200.

D'Aquili, Eugene G. and Andrew B. Newberg, 1998. "The Neuropsychological Basis of Religions, or Why God Won't Go Away." Zygon 33: 187-201.

D'Aquili, Eugene G. and Andrew B. Newberg, 1999. The Mystical Mind: Probing the Biology of Religious Experience. Minneapolis: Fortress Press.

D'Aquili, Eugene G. and Andrew B. Newberg, 2000. "The Neuropsychology of Aesthetic, Spiritual, and Mystical States." Zygon 35: 39-51.

D'Argembeau, A. et al., 2007. "Distinct Regions of the Medial Prefrontal Cortex Are Associated with Self-Referential Processing and Perspective Taking." Journal of Cognitive Neuroscience 19(6): 935-944.

David-Neel, Alexandra, 1971. Magic and Mystery in Tibet (originally in French, Paris 1929). New York: Dover Publications, New York.

Davidson, J. M., 1976. "The Physiology of Meditation and Mystical States of Consciousness." Perspectives in Biology and Medicine 19: 345-379.

Davidson, Richard J., 2003. "Alterations in Brain and Immune Function Produced by Mindfulness Meditation." Psychosomatic Medicine 65: 564–570.

Davidson, Richard J., D. J. Goleman and G. E. Schwartz, 1976. "Attentional and Affective Concomitants of Meditation: A Cross Sectional Study." Journal of Abnormal Psychology 85: 235-238.

Davidson, Richard J. and Antoine Lutz, 2008. "Buddha's Brain: Neuroplasticity and Meditation [In the Spotlight]." IEEE Signal Processing Magazine 25(1): 176-174.

Davis-Floyd, Robbie E. and Charles D. Laughlin, 2016. Power of Ritual. Brisbane, Australia: Daily Grail.

Deacon, T. W., 1997. The Symbolic Species: The Co-Evolution of Language and the Brain. New York: Norton.

Decety, Jean and T. Chaminade, 2003. "When the Self Represents the Other: A New Cognitive Neuroscience View on Psychological Identification." Consciousness and Cognition 12(4): 577-596.

Decety, Jean and William Ickles (eds.), 2009. The Social Neuroscience of Empathy. Cambridge, MA: MIT Press.

Decety, Jean and P. L. Jackson, 2004. "The Functional Architecture of Human Empathy". Behavioral and Cognitive Neuroscience Reviews 3(2): 71–100.

Decety, Jean and J. A. Sommerville, 2003. "Shared Representations Between Self and Other: A Social Cognitive Neuroscience View." Trends in Cognitive Sciences 7(12): 527-533.

DeCicco, Teresa L. and Mirella L. Stroink, 2007. "A Third Model of Self-Construal: The Metapersonal Self." Transpersonal Studies 26flahood: 86-104.

Decker, Ronald, 2013. The Esoteric Tarot: Ancient Sources Rediscovered in Hermeticism and Cabalah. Wheaton, IL: Quest Books.

DeGrazia, David, 2009. "Self-Awareness in Animals." The Philosophy of Animal Minds, ed. by Robert W. Lurz. Cambridge: Cambridge University Press, 2009, pp. 201-217.

DeGrasse Tyson, Neil and Donald Goldsmith, 2004. Origins: Fourteen Billion Years of Cosmic Evolution. New York: Norton.

Dehaene, Stanislas, 2014. Consciousness and the Brain: Deciphering how the Brain Codes Our Thoughts. New York: Viking.

Deikman, Arthur J., 1966. "De-Automatization and the Mystical Experience." Psychiatry 29: 324-338.

Deikman, Arthur J., 1982. The Observing Self: Mysticism and Psychotherapy. New York: Beacon Press.

Dell, Mary Lynn, 1993. "Brain, Symbol, and Experience: A Psychiatric and Theological Dialogue." Zygon 28(2): 217-230.

Del Monte, Michael M., 1996. "Meditation in the Christian Tradition." In Comparative and Psychological Study on Meditation, ed. by Y. Haruki, Y. Ishii and M. Suzuki. Netherlands: Eburon, pp. 121-130.

De Munck, Victor C. (ed.), 1998. Romantic Love and Sexual Behavior: Perspectives from the Social Sciences. Westport, CT: Praeger.

Desbordes, Gaëlle et al., 2012. "Effects of Mindful-Attention and Compassion Meditation Training on Amygdala Response to Emotional Stimuli in an Ordinary, Non-Meditative State." Frontiers in Human Neuroscience 6(292): 1-15.

Desbordes, Gaëlle, and Lobsang Tenzin Negi, 2013. "A New Era for Mind Studies: Training Investigators in Both Scientific and Contemplative Methods of Inquiry."

Frontiers in Human Neuroscience 7: 741.

Deshmukh, V. D., 2006. "Neuroscience of Meditation." TSW Holistic Health and Medicine 1: 275–289.

Desjarlais, Robert, 1992. Body and Emotion: The Aesthetics of Illness and Healing in the Nepal Himalayas. Philadelphia: University of Pennsylvania Press.

Desjarlais, Robert and C. Jason Throop, 2011. "Phenomenological Approaches in Anthropology." Annual Review of Anthropology 40: 87-102.

Deutsch, D., 1985. "Quantum Theory, the Church-Turing Principle and the Universal Quantum Computer." Proceedings of the Royal Society of London A 400: 97-117.

Deutsch, D., 1992. "Quantum Computation." Physics World 5(6): 57-61.

Devereux, Paul, 2008. The Long Trip: A Prehistory of Psychedelia. Brisbane, Australia: Daily Grail.

DeWaal, F. B., 2001. The Ape and the Sushi Master: Cultural Reflections of a Primatologist. Basic Books: Boulder, CO.

DeWaal, F. B., 2008. "Putting the Altruism Back into Altruism: The Evolution of Empathy." Annual Review of Psychology 59: 279–300.

Diamond, S., 1986. "Preface." In A Special Issue of Poetry and Anthropology, ed. by S. Diamond. Dialectical Anthropology 11(2-4): 131-132.

Dietrich, A., 2003. "Functional Neuroanatomy of Altered States of Consciousness: The Transient Hypofrontality Hypothesis." Consciousness and Cognition 12: 131-156.

Dietrich, A. (2007). Introduction to Consciousness: Neuroscience, Cognitive Science, and Philosophy. New York: Palgrave Macmillan.

Dilley, R. M., 1992. "Dreams, Inspiration and Craftwork among Tukolor Weavers." In Dreaming, Religion and Society in Africa), ed. by M. C. Jedrej and R. Shaw. Leiden, The Netherlands: E.J. Brill, pp. 71-85.

Dittrick, Howard, 1948. "Devices to Prevent Premature Burial." Journal of the History of Medicine and Allied Sciences 3(1): 161-171.

Dobkin de Rios, M., 1984. Hallucinogens: Cross Cultural Perspectives. Albuquerque, N.M.: University of New Mexico Press.

Dobkin de Rios, M. and Michael Winkelman (eds.), 1989. Shamanism and Altered States of Consciousness. Special issue of the Journal of Psychoactive Drugs 21(1).

Dornhege, Guido (ed.), 2007. Toward Brain-Computer Interfacing. Cambridge, MA: MIT press.

Domínguez Duque, Juan F., 2012. "Neuroanthropology and the Dialectical Imperative." Anthropological Theory 12(1): 5-27.

Domínguez Duque, Juan F., Robert Turner, E. Douglas Lewis, and Gary Egan, 2009. "Neuroanthropology: a Humanistic Science for the Study of the Culture–Brain Nexus." Social Cognitive and Affective Neuroscience 5(2-3): 138-147.

Donald, Merlin, 1995. "The Neurobiology of Human Consciousness: An Evolutionary Approach." Neuropsychologia 33(9):1087-1102.

Donald, Merlin, 2003. A Mind So Rare: The Evolution of Human Consciousness. New York: Norton.

Dornan, Jennifer, 2004. "Beyond Belief: Religious Experience, Ritual, and Cultural Neurophenomenology in the Interpretation of Past Religious Systems." Cambridge Archaeological Journal 14(1): 25-36.

Dorsey, George Amos, 1905. The Ponca Sun Dance. Vol. 7, no. 2. Field Columbian Museum.

Douglas, Mary, 1966. Purity and Danger. New York: Praeger.

Douglas-Hamilton, Iain, 1972. On the Ecology and Behaviour of the African Elephant: The Elephants of Lake Manyara. D.Phil. dissertation, Oxford University.

Douglas-Hamilton, Iain, Shivani Bhalla, George Wittemyer and Fritz Vollrath, 2006. "Behavioural Reactions of Elephants Towards a Dying and Deceased Matriarch." Applied Animal Behaviour Science 100: 87–102.

Dudzinski, K. M., et al., 2003. "Behavioral Observations of Adult and Sub-Adult Dolphins towards Two Dead Bottlenose Dolphins (One Female and One Male)." Aquatic Mammals 29(1): 108-116.

Duesbury, Evelyn M., 2016. A Dream-Guided Meditation Model and the Personalized Method for Interpreting Dreams. New York: Routledge.

Dunbar, Robin L. M., 2002. "The Social Brain Hypothesis." In Foundations in Social Neuroscience, ed. by J. Cacioppo. Cambridge, MA: The MIT Press, pp. 69-87.

Dunbar, Robin I. M., 2003. "The Social Brain: Mind, Language, and Society in Evolutionary Perspective." Annual Review of Anthropology 32(1): 163-181.

Dunbar, Robin I. M., C. Gamble and J. A. Gowlett, 2010. Social Brain, Distributed Mind. Oxford: Oxford University Press.

Dunbar, Robin I. M. and Susanne Shultz, 2007. "Evolution in the Social Brain." Science 317(5843): 1344-1347.

Duncan, John et al., 2000. "A Neural Basis for General Intelligence." Science 289(5478): 457-460.

Durkheim, Émile, 1995 [1912]. The Elementary Forms of Religious Life, translation Karen E, Fields. New York: The Free Press.

Earhart, H. B., 2004. Japanese Religion: Unity and Diversity (4th ed.). Belmont, CA: Wadsworth/Thomson.

Earle, J. B. B., 1981. "Cerebral Laterality and Meditation: A Review of the Literature." The Journal of Transpersonal Psychology 13: 155-173.

Earle, J. B. B., 1984. Cerebral Laterality and Meditation: A Review of the Literature. In Meditation: Classic and Contemporary Perspectives, ed. by D. H. Shapiro and R. N. Walsh. New Brunswick, NJ: Aldine, pp. 396-414.

Eddy, Matthew Daniel, Seymour H. Mauskopf and William Royall Newman (eds.), 2014. Chemical Knowledge in the Early Modern World. Chicago: University of Chicago Press.

Edelman, David B., Bernard J. Baars and Anil K. Seth, 2005. "Identifying Hallmarks of Consciousness in Non-Mammalian Species." Consciousness and Cognition 14(1): 169-187.

Edge, Hoyt, 1996. "Possession in Two Balinese Trance Ceremonies." Anthropology of Consciousness 7(4): 1-8.

Edinger, Edward F., 1995. The Mysterium Lectures: A Journey through C.G. Jung's Mysterium Coniunctionis. Toronto: Inner City Books.

Egan, Harvey D., 1991. An Anthology of Christian Mysticism. Collegeville, MN: Liturgical Press.

Eggan, Dorothy, 1966. "Hopi Dreams in Cultural Perspective." In The Dream and Human Societies, ed. by G.E. von Grunebaum and R. Caillois. Berkeley: University of California Press, pp. 237-265.

Eisenberg, Ronald L., 2004. The JPS Guide to Jewish Traditions. Philadelphia, PA: The Jewish Publication Society.

Ekman, Paul, 1980. The Face of Man: Expressions of Universal Emotions in a New Guinea village. New York: Garland STPM Press.

Eliade, Mircea, 1964. Shamanism: Archaic Techniques of Ecstasy. Princeton, N.J.: Princeton University Press.

Eliade, Mircea, 1965. Rites and Symbols of Initiation: The Mysteries of Birth and Rebirth, (trans.) W. R. Trask. New York: Harper Torchbooks.

Eliade, Mircea, 1967. From Primitives to Zen: A Thematic Sourcebook on the History of Religions. New York: Harper and Row.

Eliade, Mircea, 1994. The Forge and the Crucible. Albany, NY: State University of New York Press.

Elkholy, Ramsey, 2016. Being and Becoming: Embodiment and Experience Among the Orang Rimba of Sumatra. New York: Berghahn Books.

Ellmann, Richard and Charles Feidelson (eds.), 1965. The Modern Tradition: Backgrounds of Modern Literature. New York: Oxford University Press.

Emboden, William A., 1978. "The Sacred Narcotic Lily of the Nile: Nymphaea caerulea." Economic Botany 32(4): 395-407.

Emerick, E. J., 2000. "Death and the Corpse: An Analysis of the Treatment of Death and Dead Bodies in Contemporary American Society." Anthropology of Consciousness 11(1-2): 34-48.

Engström, Maria, Johan Pihlsgård, Peter Lundberg and Birgitta Söderfeldt, 2010. "Functional Magnetic Resonance Imaging of Hippocampal Activation During Silent Mantra Meditation." The Journal of Alternative and Complementary Medicine 16(12): 1253-1258.

Engström, Maria and Birgitta Söderfeldt, 2010. "Brain Activation during Compassion Meditation: A Case Study." The Journal of Alternative and Complementary Medicine 16(5): 597-599.

Erchak, G. M., 1992. The Anthropology of Self and Behavior. New Brunswick, NJ: Rutgers University Press.

Eskildsen, Stephen, 1998. Asceticism in Early Taoist Religion. Albany, NY: SUNY Press.

Evans Wentz, W. Y., 1958. Tibetan Yoga and Secret Doctrines. Oxford: Oxford University Press.

Evans-Wentz, W. Y., 1960. The Tibetan Book of the Dead. New York: Galaxy.

Fábián, T. K., 2012. Mind-Body Connections: Pathways of Psychosomatic Coupling Under Meditation and Other Altered States of Consciousness. New York: Nova Science.

Falcone, Jessica M., 2010. "A Meditation on Meditation: The Horizons of Meditative Thinking in Tibetan Monasticism and American Anthropology." Michigan Discussions in Anthropology 18(1): 402-441.

Fallon, James, 2013. The Psychopath Inside: A Neuroscientist's Personal Journey into the Dark Side of the Brain. New York: Penguin.

Farella, J. R., 1984. The Main Stalk: A Synthesis of Navajo Philosophy. Tucson, AR: University of Arizona Press.

Farley, B. P., 1998. "Anxious Conformity: Anxiety and the Sociocentric-Oriented Self in a Tlaxcalan Community." Ethos 26(3): 271-294.

Fashing, Peter J., Nga Nguyen, Tyler S. Barry, C. Barret Goodale, Ryan J. Burke, Sorrel CZ Jones, Jeffrey T. Kerby, Laura M. Lee, Niina O. Nurmi and Vivek V. Venkataraman, 2011. "Death Among Geladas (Theropithecus gelada): A Broader Perspective on Mummified Infants and Primate Thanatology." American Journal of Primatology 73(5): 405-409.

Fecteau, S., A. Pascual-Leone and H. Théoret, 2008. "Psychopathy and the Mirror Neuron System: Preliminary Findings from a Non-Psychiatric Sample." Psychiatry Research 160(2):137-144.

Federman, A., 2011. What Buddhism Taught Cognitive Science About Self, Mind and Brain. Enrahonar: quaderns de filosofia 47: 39-62.

Feifel, H., 1990. "Psychology and Death: Meaningful Rediscovery." American Psychologist 45: 537–543.

Feinberg, T. E. and J. P. Keenan, 2005a. "Where in the Brain Is the Self?" Consciousness and Cognition 14(4): 661-678.

Feinberg, T. E. and J. P. Keenan, 2005b. The Lost Self: Pathologies of the Brain and Identity. New York, NY: Oxford University Press.

Fell, J., N. Axmacher, and S. Haupt, 2010. "From Alpha to Gamma: Electrophysiological Correlates of Meditation-Related States of Consciousness." Medical Hypotheses 75: 218–224.

Fenwick, Peter, Stephen Galliano, Mary Anne Coate, Vicky Rippere and Diana Brown, 1985. "'Psychic Sensitivity', Mystical Experience, Head Injury and Brain Pathology." Psychology and Psychotherapy: Theory, Research and Practice 58(1): 35-44.

Fernandez, Silvia, Emanuele Castano and Indramani Singh, 2010. "Managing Death in the Burning Grounds of Varanasi, India: A Terror Management Investigation." Journal of Cross-Cultural Psychology 41(2) 182–194.

Ferrone, Vincenzo, 2015. The Enlightenment: History of an Idea. Princeton, NJ: Princeton University Press.

Feyerabend, Paul, 2010. Against Method: Outline of an Anarchistic Theory of Knowledge (4th edition). New York: Verso.

Field, T. M., 1985. "Neonatal Perception of People: Maturation and Individual Differences." In Social Perception in Infants, ed. by T. M. Field and N. A. Fox. Norwood, NJ: Ablex Publishing.

Filmer-Lorch, A., 2012. Inside Meditation: In Search of the Unchanging Nature Within. Leicester, UK: Troubador Publishing.

Fink, E., 1981. "The Problem of the Phenomenology of Edmund Husserl." In Apriori and World, ed. by W. McKenna, R.M. Harlan and L.E. Winters. The Hague: Martinus Nijhoff.

Fink, E., 1995. Sixth Cartesian Meditation: The Idea of a Transcendental Theory of Method. Bloomington: Indiana University Press.

Finn, Richard, 2009. Asceticism in the Graeco-Roman World. Cambridge: Cambridge University Press.

Fischer, Kurt W. and Catherine Ayoub, 1994. "Affective Splitting and Dissociation in Normal and Maltreated Children: Developmental Pathways for Self in Relationships." Disorders and Dysfunctions of the Self, ed. by Dante Cicchetti and Sheree L. Toth. Rochester, NY: University of Rochester Press, pp. 149-222.

Fischer, Roland, 1971. "A Cartography of the Ecstatic and Meditative States." Science 174(4012): 897-904.

Fisher, Helen E., Arthur Aron, Debra Mashek, Haifang Li and Lucy L. Brown, 2002. "Defining the Brain Systems of Lust, Romantic Attraction, and Attachment." Archives of Sexual Behavior 31(5): 413-419.

Fisher, Helen E., Arthur Aron and Lucy L. Brown, 2006. "Romantic Love: A Mammalian Brain System for Mate Choice." Philosophical Transactions of the Royal Society of London B: Biological Sciences 361(1476): 2173-2186.

Fiske, Susan T. and Shelley E. Taylor, 2013. Social Cognition: From Brains to Culture. New York: Sage.

Fitch, W. Tecumseh, 2006. "The Biology and Evolution of Music: A Comparative Perspective." Cognition 100(1): 173-215.

Fitch, W. Tecumseh, 2010. The Evolution of Language. Cambridge: Cambridge University Press.

Fitzgerald, Michael Oren (ed.), 1991. Yellowtail, Crow Medicine Man and Sun Dance Chief: An Autobiography. Norman, OK: University of Oklahoma Press.

Flanagan, O., 2011. The Bodhisattva's Brain. Cambridge, MA: The MIT Press.

Flood, Gavin D., 1993a. Mapping Invisible Worlds. Edinburgh: Edinburgh University Press.

Flood, Gavin D., 1993b. "Introduction." In Mapping Invisible Worlds, ed. by Gavin D. Flood. Edinburgh: Edinburgh University Press, pp. 1-5.

Flood, Gavin D., 1996. An Introduction to Hinduism. Cambridge: Cambridge University Press.

Flor-Henry, Pierre, Yakov Shapiro and Corine Sombrun, 2017. "Brain Changes during a Shamanic Trance: Altered Modes of Consciousness, Hemispheric Laterality, and Systemic Psychobiology." Cogent Psychology 4(1): 1313522.

Føllesdal, Dagfinn, 1978. "Brentano and Husserl on Intentional Objects and Perception." Grazer Philosophische Studien 5: 83-94.

Føllesdal, Dagfinn, 1990. "Noema and Meaning in Husserl." Philosophy and Phenomenological Research 50: 263-271.

Forman, Robert K. C. (ed.), 1997. The Problem of Pure Consciousness. Oxford University Press, 1997.

Forman, Robert K. C. (ed.), 1998. The Innate Capacity: Mysticism, Psychology, and Philosophy. Oxford: Oxford University Press.

Forman, Robert K. C., 1999. Mysticism, Mind, Consciousness. Albany, NY: SUNY Press.

Fox, Kieran C. R. et al., 2014. "Is Meditation Associated with Altered Brain Structure? A Systematic Review and Meta-Analysis of Morphometric Neuroimaging in Meditation Practitioners." Neuroscience and Biobehavioral Reviews 43: 48-73.

Fracchia, Charles A., 1979. Living Together Alone: The New American Monasticism. New York: Harper and Row.

Franco, Eli., 2009. Meditation and Metaphysics: On their Mutual Relationship in South Asian Buddhism. Vol. 64. Verlag der Österreichischen Akademie der Wissenschaften.

Frazer, J. G., 1966[1933]. The Fear of the Dead in Primitive Religion. New York: Biblo and Tannen.

Frede, Dorothea, 2012. "The Endoxon Mystique: What Endoxa Are and What They Are Not." Oxford Studies in Ancient Philosophy 43: 185-215.

Freeman, Father Laurence, 2017. "A Christian Mantra Meditation Instruction." http://www.meditationplex.com/christian-meditation/simple-christian-meditation-instruction-laurence-freeman/ (retrieved August 20, 2017).

Freud, Sigmund, 2005[1915]. The Unconscious. New York: Penguin.

Freze, Michael, 1993. Voices, Visions, and Apparitions. Huntington, IN: OSV Publishing.

Friedlander, Shems and Nezih Uzel, 1992. Rumi and the Whirling Dervishes: Being an Account of the Sufi Order Known as the Mevlevis and Its Founder the Poet and Mystic Mevlana Jalaluddin Rumi. New York: Parabola Books.

Friedman, H. L., 2013. "Transpersonal Self-Expansiveness as a Scientific Construct." In The Wiley-Blackwell Handbook of Transpersonal Psychology, ed. by H. L. Friedman. New York: Wiley, p. 203.

Friedrich, Paul, 1991. "Polytropy." In Beyond Metaphor: The Theory of Tropes in Anthropology, ed. by J. W. Fernandez. Stanford, CA: Stanford University Press, pp. 17-55.

Frith, Christopher D. and Uta Frith, 2005. "Theory of Mind." Current Biology 15(17): R644-R645.

Frith, Christopher D. et al., 2016. "Willed Action and the Prefrontal Cortex in Man." Discovering the Social Mind: Selected Works of Christopher D. Frith, ed. by C. D. Frith. Washington, DC: Psychology Press, p. 109.

Full, G. E., H. Walach and M. Trautwein, 2013. "Meditation-Induced Changes in Perception: An Interview Study with Expert Meditators (Sotapannas) in Burma." Mindfulness 4(1): 55-63.

Funke, Gerhard, 1987. Phenomenology: Metaphysics or Method? Athens, OH: Ohio University Press.

Furst, Peter, 1976. Hallucinogens and Culture. San Francisco: Chandler and Sharp.

Fuster, Joaquin M., 2003. Cortex and Mind: Unifying Cognition. Oxford, UK: Oxford University Press.

Fuster, Joaquin M., 2015. The Prefrontal Cortex (5th edition). Academic Press, 2015.

Gaffin, Dennis, 1995. "The Production of Emotion and Social Control: Taunting, Anger, and the Rukka in the Faeroe Islands." Ethos 23(2): 149-172.

Gaffin, Dennis, 2013. Running with the Fairies: Towards a Transpersonal Anthropology of Religion. Cambridge: Cambridge Scholars Publishing.

Gallagher, H. L. and C. D. Frith, 2003. Functional Imaging of "Theory of Mind." Trends in Cognitive Science 7(2): 77- 83.

Gallagher, Shaun and Jesper Brøsted Sørensen, 2006. "Experimenting with Phenomenology." Consciousness and Cognition 15(1): 119-134.

Gallese, V., 2005. "Embodied Simulation: From Neurons to Phenomenal Experience." Phenomenology and the Cognitive Sciences 4: 23–48.

Gallese, V., M. Morris, M. N. Eagle and P. Migone, 2007. "Intentional Attunement: Mirror Neurons and the Neural Underpinnings of Interpersonal Relations." Journal of the American Psychoanalytic Association 55: 131-176.

Gardiner, John, 2012. "Insights into Plant Consciousness from Neuroscience, Physics and Mathematics: A Role for Quasicrystals?" Plant Signaling and Behavior 7(9): 1049-1055.

Gardiner, John, Robyn Overall and Jan Marc, 2010. "The Fractal Nature of the Brain: EEG Data Suggests That the Brain Functions as a 'Quantum Computer' in 5-8 Dimensions." NeuroQuantology 8(2).

Garfield, Patricia L., 1988. Women's Bodies, Women's Dreams. New York: Ballantine Books.

Garland, E. L. et al., 2010. "Mindfulness Training Modifies Cognitive, Affective, and Physiological Mechanisms Implicated in Alcohol Dependence: Results of a Randomized Controlled Pilot Trial." Journal of Psychoactive Drugs 42(2): 177-192.

Garro, L. C., 2007. "Effort After Meaning in Everyday Life." In A Companion to Psychological Anthropology: Modernity and Psychocultural Change, ed. by C. Casey and R. B. Edgerton. Oxford: Blackwell, pp. 48-71.

Gazzaniga, Michael S., 1985. The Social Brain: Discovering the Networks of the Mind. New York: Basic Books.

Gazzaniga, Michael S., 1998. The Mind's Past. Berkeley: University of California Press, 1998.

Gazzaniga, Michael S., 2002. "Brain and Conscious Experience." In Foundations in Social Neuroscience, ed. by John T. Cacioppo. MIT Press, pp. 203-214.

Geary, D. C., 2005. The Origin of Mind: Evolution of Brain, Cognition and General Intelligence. Washington, DC: American Psychological Association.

Geertz, Clifford, 1983. Local Knowledge. New York: Basic Books.

Geertz, Clifford, 1984. "From the Natives' Point of View: On the Nature of Anthropological Understanding." In Culture Theory, ed. by R. A. Shweder and R. A. Levine. Cambridge: Cambridge University Press, pp. 123-136.

Gell, Alfred, 1992. The Anthropology of Time. Oxford: Berg.

Gellhorn, E., 1967. Principles of Autonomic-Somatic Integration. Minneapolis: University of Minnesota Press.

Gellhorn, E., 1970. "The Emotions and the Ergotropic and Trophotropic Systems: II. The Tuning of the Central Nervous System and its Psychological Implication." Psychologische Forschung 34: 67-94.

Gellhorn, E. and W. F. Kiely, 1972. "Mystical States of Consciousness: Neurophysiological and Clinical Aspects." Journal of Nervous and Mental Diseases 154: 399-405.

Gellhorn, E., and G. N. Loofbourrow, 1963. Emotions and Emotional Disorders. New York: Harper and Row.

George, Leonard, 1995. Alternative Realities: The Paranormal, the Mystic and the Transcendent in Human Experience. New York: Facts on File.

George, Marianne, 1988. "A Wosak Maraluon!": The Barok Pidik of Hidden Power, and the Ritual Imaging of Intent and Meaning. Doctoral Dissertation, University of Virginia.

George, Marianne, 1995. "Dreams, Reality, and the Desire and Intent of Dreamers as Experienced by a Fieldworker." Anthropology of Consciousness 6(3):17-33.

Germer, Christopher K. and Kristin D. Neff, 2013. "Self-Compassion in Clinical Practice." Journal of Clinical Psychology 69(8): 856-867.

Geurts, K. L., 2002. Culture and the Senses: Bodily Ways of Knowing in an African Community. Berkeley, CA: University of California Press.

Gho, Mesias and Francisco J. Varela, 1987. "A Quantitative Assessment of the Dependency of the Visual Temporal Frame upon the Cortical Rhythm." Journal de physiologie (Paris) 83(2): 95-101.

Ghysen, Alain, 2003. "The Origin and Evolution of the Nervous System." International Journal of Developmental Biology 47,(7-8): 555-562.

Gibson, J. J., 1979. The Ecological Approach to Visual Perception. Boston: Houghton Mifflin.

Gillespie, George, 1987. "Dream Light: Categories of Visual Experience During Lucid Dreaming." Lucidity Letter 6(1).

Gillespie, George, 1991. "Early Hindu Speculation about Dreams: Implications for Dream Yoga." In Dream Images: A Call to Mental Arms, ed. by Jayne Gackenbach and Anees A. Sheikh. Amityville, NY: Baywood, pp. 225-230.

Gillihan, S. J. and M. J. Farah, 2005a. "Is Self Special? A Critical Review of Evidence from Experimental Psychology and Cognitive Neuroscience." Psychological Bulletin 131(1): 76.

Gillihan, S. J. and M. J. Farah, 2005b. "The Cognitive Neuroscience of the Self: Insights from Functional Neuroimaging of the Normal Brain." In The Lost Self: Pathologies Of The Brain And Identity, ed. by T. E. Feinberg and J. P. Keenan. New York, NY: Oxford University Press, pp. 20-32.

Ginot, Efrat, 2015. The Neuropsychology of the Unconscious. New York: Norton.

Giorgi, Amedeo, 2007. "Concerning the Phenomenological Methods of Husserl and Heidegger and Their Application in Psychology." Collection du Cirp 1(1): 63-78.

Ginsburgh, Rabbi Yitzchak, 2006. What You Need to Know about Kabbalah. Jerusalem: Gal Einai Institute.

Glicksohn, Joseph and Aviva Berkovich Ohana, 2011. "From Trance to Transcendence: A Neurocognitive Approach." The Journal of Mind and Behavior 32(1): 49-62.

Globus, Gordon, 1987. Dream Life, Wake Life: The Human Condition Through Dreams. Albany, NY: State University of New York Press.

Globus, Gordon, 1998. "Self, Cognition, Qualia and World in Quantum Brain Dynamics." Journal of Consciousness Studies 5(1): 34-52.

Glueck, B. and C. Stroebel, 1975. "Biofeedback and Meditation in the Treatment of Psychiatric Illness." Comprehensive Psychiatry 16: 303-321.

Goddard, C., 1996. "The 'Social Emotions' of Malay (Bahasa melayu)." Ethos 24(3): 426-464.

Goldberg, E., 2009. The New Executive Brain: Frontal Lobes in a Complex World. Oxford, UK: Oxford University Press.

Goldberg, Ilan I., Michal Harel and Rafael Malach, 2006. "When the Brain Loses Its Self: Prefrontal Inactivation During Sensorimotor Processing." Neuron 50(2): 329-339.

Goleman, D. J., 1984. "The Buddha on Meditation and States of Consciousness." In Meditation: Classic and Contemporary Perspectives, ed. by D. H. Shapiro and R. N. Walsh. Chicago: Aldine Transaction, pp. 317-360.

Goleman, D. J., 1996. The Meditative Mind: The Varieties of Meditative Experience. New York, NY: Tarcher/Putnam.

Goleman, Daniel and Richard J. Davidson, 2017. Altered Traits: Science Reveals How Meditation Changes Your Mind, Brain, and Body. New York: Penguin.

Goodenough, Ward H., 1971. Culture, Language, and Society. Reading, MA: Addison-Wesley.

Gordon, Susan A., 2014. Neurophenomenology and Its Applications to Psychology. New York: Springer.

Gould, Stephen J., 1991. "Exaptation: A Crucial Tool for an Evolutionary Psychology." Journal of Social Issues 47: 43-65.

Gould, Stephen J., 2013. "Multimodal Introspection Theory." In Self-Observation in the Social Sciences, ed. by Joshua Clegg. New Jersey: Transaction, pp. 121-146.

Goulet, Jean-Guy, 1987. "Ways of Knowing: Towards a Narrative Ethnography of Experiences among the Dene Tha." Journal of Anthropological Research 50(2): 113-139.

Goulet, Jean-Guy, 1998. Ways of Knowing: Experience, Knowledge, and Power Among the Dene Tha. Lincoln, NE: University of Nebraska Press.

Goulet, Jean-Guy and Bruce Granville Miller, 2007. Extraordinary Anthropology: Transformations in the Field. Lincoln, NE: University of Nebraska Press.

Govinda, Lama A., 1960. Foundations of Tibetan Mysticism. London: Century.

Gow, Peter, 2000. "Helpless: The Affective Preconditions of Piro Social Life." In The Anthropology of Love and Anger: The Aesthetics of Conviviality in Native Amazonia, ed. by Joanna Overing and Alan Passes. Washington, DC: Psychology Press, pp. 46-63.

Grant, Joshua A. et al., 2010. "Cortical Thickness and Pain Sensitivity in Zen Meditators." Emotion 10(1): 43–53.

Graziano, Michael S. A., 2013. Consciousness and the Social Brain. Oxford: Oxford University Press.

Gray, J. A., 1982. The Neuropsychology of Anxiety. Oxford: Oxford University Press.

Green, Celia, 1968. Lucid Dreams. Oxford: Institute of Psychophysical Research.

Green, Elmer and Alyce Green, 1977. Beyond Biofeedback. Toronto, ON: Delacorte.

Greenwood, Michael, 2006. "Acupuncture and the Chakras." Medical Acupuncture 17(3): 27-32.

Gregor, T., 1977. Mehinaku: The Drama of Daily Life in a Brazilian Indian Village. Chicago: University of Chicago Press.

Greguric, Ivana 2014. "Ethical Issues of Human Enhancement Technologies: Cyborg Technology as the Extension of Human Biology." Journal of Information, Communication and Ethics in Society 12(2): 133-148.

Grevenstein, Dennis and Matthias Bluemke, 2016. "Who's Afraid of Death and Terrorists? Investigating Moderating Effects of Sense of Coherence, Mindfulness, Neuroticism, and Meaning in Life on Mortality Salience." Journal of Articles in Support of the Null Hypothesis 13(1): 25-36.

Griffin, D. R., 1989. "Introduction." In Archetypal Process: Self and Divine in Whitehead, Jung and Hillman, ed. by D. R. Griffin. Evanston, IL: Northeastern University Press, pp. 1-76.

Griffin-Pierce, T., 1992. Earth Is My Mother, Sky Is My Father: Space, Time, and Astronomy in Navajo Sandpainting. Albuquerque, NM: University of New Mexico Press.

Grimes, Ronald L,. 2003. "Ritual Theory and the Environment." The Sociological Review 51 (s2): 31-45.

Groenewegen, Henk J. and Harry BM Uylings, 2000. "The Prefrontal Cortex and the Integration of Sensory, Limbic and Autonomic Information." Progress in Brain Research 126: 3-28.

Groisman, Alberto and A. B. Sell, 1996. "Healing Power: Neurophenomenology, Culture, and Therapy of Santo Daime." Yearbook of Cross-Cultural Medicine and Psychotherapy 4: 279-87.

Grossberg, S., 2012. "Adaptive Resonance Theory: How a Brain Learns to Consciously Attend, Learn, and Recognize a Changing World." Neural Networks 37: 1-47.

Grossman, Paul, 2010. Mindfulness for Psychologists: Paying Kind Attention to the Perceptible. Mindfulness 1:87–97.

Groth-Marnat, Gary and Roger Summers, 1998. "Altered Beliefs, Attitudes, and Behaviors Following Near-Death Experiences." Journal of Humanistic Psychology 38(3): 110-125.

Gruzelier, J. H., 2002. "A Review of the Impact of Hypnosis, Relaxation, Guided Imagery and Individual Differences on Aspects of Immunity and Health." Stress 5(2): 147-163.

Gu, Q. and Fritz A. Popp, 1993. "Biophoton Physics: Potential Measure of Organizational Order." in Biological Effects of Light (ed. by Ernst G. Jung). Walter de Gruyter.

Guerra-Doce, Elisa, 2015. "Psychoactive Substances in Prehistoric Times: Examining the Archaeological Evidence." Time and Mind 8(1): 91-112.

Gunaratana, B. H., 1988. The Jhānas in Theravada Buddhist Meditation. Kandy, Sri Lanka: Buddhist Publication Society.

Gunaratana, B. H., 2002. Mindfulness in Plain English. Boston: Wisdom Publications.

Gusnard, D. A., E. Akbudak, G. L. Shulman and M. E. Raichle, 2001. "Medial Prefrontal Cortex and Self-Referential Mental Activity: Relation to a Default Mode of Brain Function." Proceedings of the National Academy of Sciences 98(7): 4259-4264.

Hageman, Joan J., et al., 2009. "The neurobiology of trance and mediumship in Brazil." In Mysterious Minds: The Neurobiology of Psychics, Mediums, and Other Extraordinary People, ed. by Krippner, Stanley and Harris L. Friedman. New York: Praeger, pp. 85-111.

Hageman, Joan H., Stanley Krippner and Ian Wickramasekera, 2008. "Sympathetic Reactivity During Meditation." Subtle Energies & Energy Medicine Journal Archives 19(2): 23-48.

Hageman, Joan H., Stanley Krippner and Ian Wickramasekera, 2011. "Across Cultural Boundaries: Psychophysiological Responses, Absorption, and Dissociation Comparison between Brazilian Spiritists and Advanced Meditators." NeuroQuantology 9(1): 5-21.

Hagens, Bethe and S. Lansky, 2012. "Personal Report: Significance of Community in an Ayahuasca Jungle Dieta." Anthropology of Consciousness 23(1): 103–109.

Hakuin, E., 2010. Wild Ivy: The Spiritual Autobiography of Zen Master Hakuin. Boulder, CO: Shambhala Publications.

Hall, Calvin S., 1953. The Meaning of Dreams. New York: Harper.

Hallowell, A. Irving, 1955. Culture and Experience. Philadelphia: University of Pennsylvania Press.

Hallowell, A. I., 2002[1960]. Ojibwa Ontology, Behavior, and World View. Readings in Indigenous Religions, 22, pp. 17-49.

Halloy, Arnaud, 2015. "Pierre Smith's Mind Traps: The Origin and Ramifications of a Theory of Ritual Efficacy." Anthropological Theory 15(3): 358-374.

Halloy, Arnaud, 2016. "Full Participation and Ethnographic Reflexivity: An Afro-Brazilian Case Study." Journal for the Study of Religious Experience 2(1): 7-24.

Herambourg, Peter, 1960. St. John Eudes a Spiritual Portrait. New York: Newman Press.

Hanna, Fred J., 1993a. "Rigorous Intuition: Consciousness, Being, and the Phenomenological Method." Journal of Transpersonal Psychology 25(2): 181-197.

Hanna, Fred J., 1993b. "The Transpersonal Consequences of Husserl's Phenomenological Method." The Humanistic Psychologist 21(1): 41-57.

Hanna, Fred J., 1995. "Husserl on the Teachings of the Buddha." The Humanistic Psychologist 23(3): 365-372.

Hannah, Barbara, 2015[1981]. Encounters with the Soul: Active Imagination as Developed by C. G. Jung. Ashville, NC: Chiron.

Hanna, Robert and Evan Thompson, 2003. "Neurophenomenology and the Spontaneity of Consciousness." Canadian Journal of Philosophy 33(sup 1): 133-162.

Hanson, Rick, 2009. Buddha's Brain: The Practical Neuroscience of Happiness, Love and Wisdom. Oakland, CA: New Harbinger.

Harding, M. Esther, 1963. Psychic Energy: Its Source and Its Transformation, Foreword by C.G. Jung. Princeton, NJ: Princeton University Press.

Harner, Michael J., 1990[1980]. The Way of the Shaman. New York: HarperOne.

Harner, Michael J. 2010. "A Core Shamanic Theory of Dreams." Shamanism 23: 2-4.

Harris, G. G., 1978. Casting Out Anger: Religion among the Taita of Kenya. Cambridge: Cambridge University Press.

Hartmann, Ernest, 2011. The Nature and Functions of Dreaming. Oxford: Oxford University Press.

Haruki, Y., Y. Ishii and M. Suzuki (eds.), 1996. Comparative and Psychological Study on Meditation. Netherlands: Eburon.

Harvell, Lindsey A. and Gwendelyn S. Nisbett (eds.), 2016. Denying Death: An Interdisciplinary Approach to Terror Management Theory. Washington, D.C.: Psychology Press.

Harvey, P., 1995. The Selfless Mind: Personality, Consciousness and Nirvana in Early Buddhism. London: RoutledgeCurzon.

Hasenkamp, Wendy and Lawrence W. Barsalou, 2012. "Effects of Meditation Experience on Functional Connectivity of Distributed Brain Networks." Frontiers in Human Neuroscience 6: 1-14.

Hashi, Hisaki, 2016. "The Significance of "Mushin": The Essential Mind of Zen Buddhist Philosophy for Humans in a Contemporary World." Asian Studies 4(1): 97-112.

Heatherton, T. F. et al., 2006. "Medial Prefrontal Activity Differentiates Self from Close Others." Social Cognitive and Affective Neuroscience 1(1): 18-25.

Heelas, P., 1981a. Introduction: Indigenous psychologies. In P. Heelas & A. Lock (Eds.), Indigenous psychologies: The anthropology of the self (3-18). New York: Academic Press.

Heelas, P. (1981b). "The Model: Anthropology and Indigenous Psychologies." In Indigenous Psychologies: The Anthropology of the Self, ed. by P. Heelas and A. Lock. New York: Academic Press, pp. 39-63.

Heelas, P. and A. Lock (eds.), 1981. Indigenous Psychologies: The anthropology of the Self. New York: Academic Press.

Heidegger, Martin, 1996[1953]. Being and Time (trans. by Joan Stambaugh). Albany: State University of New York Press.

Heine, S. J., D. R. Lehman, H. R. Markus and S. Kitayama, 1999. "Is There a Universal Need for Positive Self-Regard?" Psychological Review 106(4): 766.

Heine, Steven and Dale S. Wright (eds.), 2000. The Kōan: Texts and Contexts in Zen Buddhism. New York: Oxford University Press.

Heinze, R-I., 1993. Shamanistic States of Consciousness: Access to Different Realities. In Shamans and Cultures, ed. by M. Hoppál and K. D. Howard. Budapest: Akadémiai Kiadó, pp. 169-178.

Held, Klaus, 2003. "Husserl's Phenomenological Method." In The New Husserl: A Critical Reader, ed. by D. Welton. Bloomington: Indiana University Press, pp. 3-31.

Hensch, Takao K., 2005. "Critical Period Plasticity in Local Cortical Circuits." Nature Reviews Neuroscience 6(11): 877-888.

Herdt, G. H., 1982. "Sambia Nosebleeding Rites and Male Proximity to Women." Ethos 10(3): 189-231.

Herr, Barbara, 1981. "The Expressive Character of Fijian Dream and Nightmare Experiences." Ethos 9(4): 331-352.

Herrero, Jose L., Simon Khuvis, Erin Yeagle, Moran Cerf and Ashesh D. Mehta, 2018. "Breathing Above the Brain Stem: Volitional Control and Attentional Modulation in Humans." Journal of Neurophysiology 119(1): 145-159.

Hess, W. R., 1925. On the Relations between Psychic and Vegetative Functions. Zurich: Schabe.

Hillman, Deborah J., 1987. "Dream Work and Field Work: Linking Cultural Anthropology and the Current Dream Work Movement." In Variety of Dream Experience, ed. by M. Ullman and C. Limmer. New York: Continuum, pp. 65-89.

Hillman, James, 1989. "The Poetic Basis of Mind." In A Blue Fire: Selected Writings by James Hillman, ed. by T. Moore. New York: Harper & Row, pp. 15-35.

Ho, Mae Wan, Fritz Albert Popp and Ulrich Warnke (1994) Bioelectrodynamics and Biocommunication. London: World Scientific.

Ho, Pao-Shen, 2014. "Plotinus' Mystical Teaching of Henosis: An Interpretation in the Light of the Metaphysics of the One." Unpublished doctoral dissertation, Institute for Christian Philosophy, Catholic Theological Faculty, Leopold-Franzens-University Innsbruck.

Ho, Pao-Shen, 2016. "Plotinus' and Dionysius' Negative Theologies: Comparative Analysis and Contemporary Interpretation." Sino-Christian Studies 22: 7-40.

Hobson, J. A., 1994. The Chemistry of Conscious States: Toward a Unified Model of the Brain and the Mind. New York: Back Bay.

Hobson, J. A., 2002. Dreaming: An Introduction to the Science of Sleep. Oxford, UK: Oxford University Press.

Hoelter, J. W. and J. A. Hoelter, 1978. "The Relationship Between Fear of Death and Anxiety." The Journal of Psychology 99(2): 225-226.

Hoffer, Eric, 2002[1951]. The True Believer: Thoughts on the Nature of Mass Movements. New York: Harper Perennial Modern Classics.

Hoffmann, E., J. M. Keppel-Hesselink and Y. M. da Silveira Barbosa, 2001. "Effects of a Psychedelic, Tropical Tea, Ayahuasca, on the Electroencephalographic (EEG) Activity of the Human Brain during a Shamanistic Ritual." Multidisciplinary Association for Psychedelic Studies (MAPS) Bulletin 11: 25-30.

Hofmann, Stefan G., Paul Grossman and Devon E. Hinton, 2011. "Loving-Kindness and Compassion Meditation: Potential for Psychological Interventions." Clinical Psychology Review 31(7): 1126-1132.

Holecek, Andrew, 2016. Dream Yoga: Illuminating Your Life through Lucid Dreaming and the Tibetan Yogas of Sleep. Louisville, CO: Sounds True.

Hollan, Douglas, 1992. "Cross-Cultural Differences in the Self." Journal of Anthropological Research 48(4): 283-300.

Holtkamp, M. B., 2012. Biology of the Archetype. New York: Bookbaby.

Hölzel Britta K. et al., 2007a. Differential Engagement of Anterior Cingulate and Adjacent Medial Frontal Cortex in Adept Meditators and Non-Meditators. Neuroscience Letters 421: 16–21.

Hölzel, Britta K. et al., 2007b. "Investigation of Mindfulness Meditation Practitioners with Voxel-Based Morphometry." Social Cognitive and Affective Neuroscience 3(1): 55-61.

Hölzel, Britta K. et al., 2011. "How Does Mindfulness Meditation Work? Proposing Mechanisms of Action from a Conceptual and Neural Perspective." Perspectives on Psychological Science 6(6): 537-559.

Homans, Peter, 2000a. Symbolic Loss: The Ambiguity of Mourning and Memory at Century's End. Charlottesville: University Press of Virginia.

Homans, Peter, 2000b. "Introduction: The Decline of Mourning Practices in Modern Western Societies: A Short Sketch." In Symbolic Loss: The Ambiguity of Mourning and Memory at Century's End, ed. by Peter Homans. Charlottesville: University Press of Virginia, pp 1-40.

Hongladarom, Soraj, 2002. "Cross-Cultural Epistemic Practices." Social Epistemology 16(1): 83-92.

Hood, B., 2012. The Self Illusion: How the Social Brain Creates Identity. Oxford: Oxford University Press.

Hood, Ralph, 2002. "The Mystical Self: Lost and Found." The International Journal for the Psychology of Religion 12: 1-14.

Hopcke, R. H., 1989. A Guided Tour of the Collected Works of C. G. Jung. Boston: Shambhala.

Horton, Robin, 1983. "Social Psychologies: African and Western." In Oedipus and Job in West African Religion, ed. by M. Fortes. Cambridge: Cambridge University Press. p. 82.

Hosaka, K, A. Matsumoto-Oda, M. Huffman and K. Kawanaka, 2000. "Reactions to Dead Bodies of Conspecifics by Wild Chimpanzees in the Mahale Mountains, Tanzania." Primate Research 1: 1–15.

Houben, Jan E. M., 2003. "The Soma-Haoma Problem." Electronic Journal of Vedic Studies 9(1a).

Hove, Michael J. et al., 2015. "Brain Network Reconfiguration and Perceptual Decoupling During an Absorptive State of Consciousness." Cerebral Cortex 26(7): 3116-3124.

Howes, D., 1991. The Varieties of Sensory Experience: A Sourcebook in the Anthropology of the Senses. Toronto, ON: University of Toronto Press.

Huang, Yanping, and Rajesh P. N. Rao, 2011. "Predictive Coding." Wiley Interdisciplinary Reviews: Cognitive Science 2(5): 580-593.

Huberman, B. A., 1995. "The Social Mind." In Origins of the Human Brain, ed. by J.-P. Changeux and J. Chavaillon. Oxford: Oxford University Press, pp. 250-261.

Hume, Lynn, 2002. Ancestral Power: The Dreaming, Consciousness, and Aboriginal Australians. Victoria: Melbourne University Press.

Hunt, Harry T., 1989. Multiplicity of Dreams: Memory, Imagination and Consciousness. New Haven, CT: Yale University Press.

Hurford, James R., Michael Studdert-Kennedy and Chris Knight (eds.), 1998. Approaches to the Evolution of Language: Social and Cognitive Bases. Cambridge: Cambridge University Press.

Hurlbert, R. T. and C. L. Heavey, 2001. "Telling What We Know: Describing Inner Experience." Trends in Cognitive Sciences 5: 400–403.

Husserl, Edmund, 1964[1905]. The Phenomenology of Internal Time Consciousness. Bloomington: Indiana University Press.

Husserl, Edmund, 1967. The Paris Lectures (translated with an introduction by Peter Koestenbaum). The Hague: Martinus Nijhoff.

Husserl, Edmund, 1969. Formal and Transcendental Logic. The Hague: Martinus Nijhoff.

Husserl, Edmund, 1970 [1900-01]. Logical Investigations (2 volumes), translated by J.N. Findley. New York: Humanities Press.

Husserl, Edmund, 1970 [1937]. The Crisis in European Sciences and Transcendental Phenomenology. Evanston: Northwestern University Press.

Husserl, Edmund, 1977[1931]. Cartesian Meditations: An Introduction to Phenomenology. The Hague: Martinus Nijhoff.

Husserl, Edmund, 1982 [1913]. Ideas: General Introduction to Pure Phenomenology. New York: The MacMillan Company.

Husserl, Edmund, 1989. Ideas Pertaining to a Pure Phenomenology and to a Phenomenological Philosophy. Book Two: Studies in the Phenomenology of Constitution. The Hague: Martinus Nijhoff.

Husserl, Edmund, 1997. Psychological and Transcendental Phenomenology and the Confrontation with Heidegger (1927-1931), translated by T. Sheehan and R. Palmer. Dordrecht: Kluwer .

Hutcherson, Cendri A., Emma M. Seppala and James J. Gross, 2008. "Loving-Kindness Meditation Increases Social Connectedness." Emotion 8(5): 720-724.

Huttenlocher, P. R., 2002. Neural Plasticity: The Effects of Environment on the Development of the Cerebral Cortex. Cambridge, MA: Harvard University Press.

Huxley, Aldous, 2004. The Perennial Philosophy (Harper Modern Classics 2004 ed.). New York: Harper and Row.

Hymes, Dell H., 2003. Now I know Only So Far: Essays in Ethnopoetics. Lincoln, NE: University of Nebraska Press.

Idel, Moshe, 1988. "Ramon Lull and Ecstatic Kabbalah: A Preliminary Observation." Journal of the Warburg and Courtauld Institutes 51: 170-174.

Idel, Moshe, 1990. Kabbalah: New Perspectives. New Haven, CT: Yale University Press.

Ihde, Don, 1977. Experimental Phenomenology. New York: Putnam.

Inglis, Brian, 1990. Trance: A Natural History of Altered States of Mind. London, Paladin.

Inkpin, Andrew, 2016. Disclosing the World: On the Phenomenology of Language. Cambridge, MA: MIT Press.

Insel, Thomas R., 2002. "Implications for the Neurobiology of Love." Altruism and Altruistic Love: Science, Philosophy, and Religion in Dialogue, ed. by Stephen G. Post et al.. Oxford: Oxford University Press, pp. 254-263.

Irrmischer, Mona, Simon J. Houtman, Huibert D. Mansvelder, Michael Tremmel, Ulrich Ott and Klaus Linkenkaer-Hansen, 2018. "Controlling the Temporal Structure of Brain Oscillations by Focused Attention Meditation." Human Brain Mapping 39(4): 1825-1838.

Irvine, William, 2008. A Guide to the Good Life: The Ancient Art of Stoic Joy. Oxford: Oxford University Press.

Irwin, Lee, 1994. "Dreams, Theory, and Culture: The Plains Vision Quest Paradigm." American Indian Quarterly 18(2): 229-245.

Jack, Anthony Ian and Andreas Roepstorff, 2002. "Introspection and Cognitive Brain Mapping: From Stimulus–Response to Script–Report." Trends in Cognitive Sciences 6(8): 333-339.

Jack, Anthony Ian and T. Shallice, 2001. "Introspective Physicalism as an Approach to the Science of Consciousness." Cognition 79: 161–96.

Jackson, P. L., A. N. Meltzoff and J. Decety, 2005. "How Do We Perceive the Pain of Others: A Window into the Neural Processes Involved in Empathy." NeuroImage 24: 771–779.

Jackson, Michael, ed., 1996. Things as They Are: New Directions in Phenomenological Anthropology. Washington, D. C.: Georgetown University Press.

Jahn, Robert G. and Brenda J. Dunne. 1987. Margins of Reality: The Role of Consciousness in the Physical World. New York: Harcourt Brace Jovanovich.

James, William. 1902 [1982]. The Varieties of Religious Experience. New York: Penguin Classics.

James, William, 1976 [1912]. Essays in Radical Empiricism. Cambridge, MA: Harvard University Press.

Jankowiak, W. R. and E. F. Fischer, 1992. A Cross-Cultural Perspective on Romantic Love. Ethnology 31: 149-155.

Jarvis, Erich D., 2004. "Learned Birdsong and the Neurobiology of Human Language." Annals of the New York Academy of Sciences 1016: 749.

Jay, Mike, 1999. Blue Tide: The Search for Soma. Cambridge, MA: Autonomedia.

Jenkins, A. C. and J. P. Mitchell, 2011. Medial Prefrontal Cortex Subserves Diverse Forms of Self-Reflection. Social Neuroscience 6: 211–218.

Jennings, Mary, 2016. Greetings from Utopia Park: Surviving a Transcendent Childhood. New York: Harper.

Jeremy, Sister Mary, 1962. Scholars and Mystics. New York: H. Regnery Company.

Jerison, H. J., 1973. Evolution of the Brain and Intelligence. New York: Academic Press.

Jerison, H. J., 2007. "Evolution of the Frontal Lobes." In The Human Frontal Lobes: Functions and Disorders, ed. by B. L. Miller & J. L. Cummings. New York: Guilford, pp. 107-120.

Jha, A. P., J. Krompinger and M. J. Baime, 2007. "Mindfulness Training Modifies Subsystems of Attention." Cognitive, Affective, and Behavioral Neuroscience 7(2): 109-119.

Jiang, Haiteng, Bin He, Xiaoli Guo, Xu Wang, Menglin Guo, Zhuo Wang, Ting Xue et al., 2020. "Brain–Heart Interactions Underlying Traditional Tibetan Buddhist Meditation." Cerebral Cortex 30(2): 439-450.

Jibu, M, K. H. Pribram and K. Yasue, 1996. "From Conscious Experience to Memory Storage and Retrieval: The Role of Quantum Brain Dynamics and Boson Condensation of Evanescent Photons," International Journal of Modern Physics B 10(13-14): 1735–1754.

Johansson, R. E. A., 1969. The Psychology of Nirvana: A Comparative Study of the Natural Goal of Buddhism and the Aims of Modern Western Psychology. Garden City, NY: Doubleday.

Johnson, M. H., 2005. Developmental Cognitive Neuroscience: An Introduction (second edition). Oxford: Blackwell.

Johnson, Robert H., 1986. Inner Work. San Francisco, CA: Harper.

Johnson, Willard L., 1982. Riding the Ox Home: A History of Meditation from Shamanism to Science. New York: Rider.

Johnston, William, 1978. The Inner Eye of Love: Mysticism and Religion. New York: Fordham University Press.

Johnston, William (ed.), 2012. The Cloud of Unknowing and The Book of Privy Counseling. New York: Image.

Joralemon, Donald, 1984. "The Role of Hallucinogenic Drugs and Sensory Stimuli in Peruvian Ritual Healing." Culture, Medicine and Psychiatry 8(4): 399-430.

Jordan, G., S. S. Deeb, J. M. Bosten and J. D. Mollon, 2010. The Dimensionality of Color Vision in Carriers of Anomalous Trichromacy. Journal of Vision 8(10): 1-19.

Jorgensen, Dan, 1980. "What's in a Name: The Meaning of Nothingness in Telefolmin." Ethos 8(4): 349-366.

Jorgensen, Joseph G., 1972. The Sun Dance Religion: Power for the Powerless. Chicago: University of Chicago Press.

Joseph, R., 1992. The Right Brain and the Unconscious. New York: Plenum.

Josipovic, Zoran, 2019. "Nondual Awareness: Consciousness-as-Such as Non-Representational Reflexivity." In Progress in Brain Research 244: 273-298.

Josipovic, Zoran, Ilan Dinstein, Jochen Weber and David J. Heeger, 2012. "Influence of Meditation on Anti-Correlated Networks in the Brain." Frontiers in Human Neuroscience 5: 183. https://doi.org/10.3389/fnhum.2011.00183 (retrieved on 11/14/17)

Jost, John T., Gráinne Fitzsimons and Aaron C. Kay, 2004. "The Ideological Animal." Handbook of Experimental Existential Psychology, ed. by Jeff Greenberg, Sander L. Koole and Tom Pyszczynski. New York: Guilford Press, pp. 263-83.

Jost, John T. and O. Hunyady, 2005. "Antecedents and Consequences of System-Justifying Ideologies." Current Directions in Psychological Science 14: 260–265.

Jost, John T., Alison Ledgerwood and Cutis D. Hardin, 2008. "Shared Reality, System Justification, and the Relational Basis of Ideological Beliefs." Social and Personality Psychology Compass 2: 171–186.

Jost, John T., Brian A. Nosek and Samuel D. Gosling, 2008. "Ideology: Its Resurgence in Social, Personality, and Political Psychology." Perspectives on Psychological Science 3(2): 126-136.

Jugrin, Daniel, 2015. "Negation and Mystical Union in Plotinus." Philobiblon 20(1): 94-108.

Jung, Carl G., 1955. The Symbolic Life. Princeton, NJ: Princeton University Press, (Collected Works No. 12).

Jung, Carl G., 1956 [1912]). Symbols of Transformation: An Analysis of the Prelude to a Case of Schizophrenia. London: Routledge and Kegan Paul (Collected Works No. 5).

Jung, Carl G., 1959 [1951]. Aion: Researches into the Phenomenology of the Self. Princeton, NJ: Princeton University Press (Collected Works No. 9).

Jung, Carl G., 1964. Man and His Symbols. Garden City, NY: Doubleday.

Jung, Carl G., 1965 [1961]. Memories, Dreams, Reflections. New York: Vintage Books.

Jung, Carl G., 1966. Two Essays on Analytical Psychology (2nd ed.). Princeton: Princeton University Press. (Originally published 1928)

Jung, Carl G., 1967. Alchemical Studies. Princeton, NJ: Princeton University Press, (Collected Works No. 10).

Jung, Carl G., 1968a. The Archetypes and the Collective Unconscious. Princeton, NJ: Princeton University Press, (Collected Works No. 9i).

Jung, Carl G., 1968b. Psychology and Alchemy. Princeton, NJ: Princeton University Press, (Collected Works No. 12).

Jung, Carl G., 1969a [1946]. "The Structure of the Psyche." in The Structure and Dynamics of the Psyche. Princeton, NJ: Princeton University Press, pp. 139-158 (Collected Works No. 8).

Jung, Carl G., 1969b. Mandala Symbolism. Princeton, N.J.: Princeton University Press.

Jung, Carl G., 1969c [1958]. "The Transcendent Function." in The Structure and Dynamics of the Psyche. Princeton, NJ: Princeton University Press, pp. 67-91 (Collected Works No. 8).

Jung, Carl G., 1969d. The Structure and Dynamics of the Psyche. Princeton, NJ: Princeton University Press, (Collected Works No. 8).

Jung, Carl G., 1969e. "On the Nature of Psyche." In The Structure and Dynamics of the Psyche, trans. by R. F. C. Hull. Princeton, NJ: Princeton University Press, (Collected Works No. 8).

Jung, Carl G., 1970. Mysterium Coniunctionis: An Inquiry into the Separation and Synthesis of Psychic Opposites in Alchemy. Princeton, NJ: Princeton University Press (Collected Works No. 14). (Originally published 1955/1956)

Jung, Carl G., 1971. Psychological Types. Princeton, N.J.: Princeton University Press (Collected Works No. 6).

Jung, Carl G., 1973. Experimental Researches. Princeton, NJ: Princeton University Press, (Collected Works No. 2).

Jung, Carl G., 1976. The Symbolic Life. Collected Works. Vol. 13. Princeton, NJ: Princeton University Press.

Jung, Carl G., 1991. "Psychology of the Unconscious: A Study of the Transformations and Symbolism of the Libido." Bollingen Series XX. (Collected Works 7).

Jung, Carl G., 1997a. Jung on Active Imagination (edited by Joan Chodorow). Princeton, NJ: Princeton University Press.

Jung, Carl G., 1997b. Visions: Notes on the Seminar Given in 1930-1934 by C. G. Jung. Princeton, NJ: Princeton University Press. (Originally published 1930-1934)

Jung, Carl G., 2009. The Red Book: Liber Novus. New York: Norton.

Kaelber, Lutz F., 1998. Schools of Asceticism: Ideology and Organization in Medieval Religious Communities. University Park, PA: Pennsylvania State University Press.

Kagan, Jerome, 2013. The Human Spark: The Science of Human Development. New York: Basic Books.

Kagawa-Singer, Marjorie, 1995. "Diverse Cultural Beliefs and Practices About Death and Dying in the Elderly." Gerontology and Geriatrics Education 15(1): 101-116.

Kakar, S., 1982. Shamans, Mystics and Doctors: A Psychological Inquiry into India and Its Healing Traditions. Boston: Beacon Press.

Kakumanu, Ratna Jyothi, Ajay Kumar Nair, Arun Sasidharan, John P. John, Seema Mehrotra, Ravindra Panth and Bindu M. Kutty, 2019. "State-Trait Influences of Vipassana Meditation Practice on P3 EEG Dynamics." Progress in Brain Research 244: 115-136.

Kalsched, Donald, 1996. The Inner World of Trauma: Archetypal Defenses of the Personal Spirit. New York: Routledge.

Kang, Do-Hyung, Hang Joon Jo, Wi Hoon Jung, Sun Hyung Kim, Ye-Ha Jung, Chi-Hoon Choi, Ul Soon Lee, Seung Chan An, Joon Hwan Jang and Jun Soo Kwon, 2012. "The Effect of Meditation on Brain Structure: Cortical Thickness Mapping and Diffusion Tensor Imaging." Social Cognitive and Affective Neuroscience 8(1): 27-33.

Kaplan, Aryeh, 1995. Meditation and Kabbalah. New York: Jason Aronson.

Karna, Bishal, 2013. "Contemplative Studies in Context." MA thesis, Georgia State University. http://scholarworks.gsu.edu/rs_theses/39

Kastenbaum, Robert J., 2006. Death, Society, and the Human Experience (9th Edition). Boston, MA: Allyn & Bacon.

Katz, Richard, 1976. "Education for Transcendence: !Kia-Healing with the Kalahari !Kung." In Kalahari Hunter-Gatherers, ed. by R. B. Lee & I. Devore. Cambridge, MA: Harvard University Press, pp. 281-301.

Katz, Richard, 1982. Boiling Energy: Community Healing among the Kalahari !Kung. Cambridge, MA: Harvard University Press.

Katz, Richard, Megan Biesele, and Verna St. Denis, 1997. Healing Makes Our Hearts Happy: Spirituality and Cultural Transformation among the Kalahari Ju|'Hoansi. Rochester, VT: Inner Traditions/Bear & Co.

Katz, Steven T. (ed.), 1978a. Mysticism and Philosophical Analysis. Oxford: Oxford University Press.

Katz, Steven T., 1978b. "Language, Epistemology, and Mysticism." In Mysticism and Philosophical Analysis, ed. By Steven T. Katz. Oxford: Oxford University Press, pp. 22-74.

Keating, Daniel P., R. M. Lerner and L. Steinberg, 2004. "Cognitive and Brain Development." Handbook of Adolescent Psychology (2nd edition), ed. by Richard M. Lerner and Laurence Steinber. New York: Wiley, pp. 45-84.

Keating. T., 1994. Invitation to Love: The Way of Christian Contemplation. New York: Continuum.

Keating. T., 2002. Foundations for Centering Prayer and the Christian Contemplative Lift. New York: Continuum.

Keeney, Bradford and Hillary Keeney, 2013. "Reentry into First Creation: A Contextual Frame for the Ju/'Hoan Bushman Performance of Puberty Rites, Storytelling, and Healing Dance." Journal of Anthropological Research 69(1): 65-86.

Keesing, R. M., 1984. "Rethinking 'Mana.'" Journal of Anthropological Research 40(1): 137-156.

Keith, K. D., 2011. "Ethnocentrism: Seeing the World from Where We Stand." In Cross-Cultural Psychology: Contemporary Themes and Perspectives, ed. by K. D. Keith. London, UK: Wiley-Blackwell, pp. 20-33.

Kerényi, Karl, 1959. "Asklepios: Archetypal Image of the Physician's Existence." Archetypal Images of Greek Religion, ed. by Carl Kerényi. Princeton, NJ: Princeton University Press.

Kernberg, Otto F., 1970. "Factors in the Psychoanalytic Treatment of Narcissistic Personalities." Journal of the American psychoanalytic Association 18(1): 51-85.

Kesebir, Pelin, 2014. "A Quiet Ego Quiets Death Anxiety: Humility as an Existential Anxiety Buffer." Journal of Personality and Social Psychology 106(4): 610-623.

Keysers, Christian and Luciano Fadiga (eds.), 2017. The Mirror Neuron System: A Special Issue of Social Neuroscience. Washington, D. C.: Psychology Press.

Khema, Sister A., 1994. "All of Us." From the Access to Insight Website. Retreived on 21 March 2014 from http://www.accesstoinsight.org/lib/authors/khema/allofus.html#ch12.

Kierulff, S. and S. Krippner, 2004. Becoming Psychic: Spiritual Lessons for Focusing Your Hidden Abilities. Franklin Lakes, NJ: New Page Books.

Kilborne, Benjamin, 1992. "On Classifying Dreams." in Barbara Tedlock (ed), Dreaming: Anthropological and Psychological Interpretations. Cambridge: Cambridge University Press, pp. 171-193.

Killingsworth, Matthew A. and Daniel T. Gilbert. "A Wandering Mind Is an Unhappy Mind." Science 330(6006): 932-932.

Kilner, James M. and R. N. Lemon, 2013. "What We Know Currently About Mirror Neurons." Current Biology 23(23): R1057-R1062.

Kilner, Walter J., 1911. The Human Atmosphere, or the Aura Made Visible by the Aid of Chemical Screens, reprinted as The Human Aura. New York: Citadel Press, 1965.

Kim, Ji-Woong et al., 2009. "Compassionate Attitude Towards Others' Suffering Activates the Mesolimbic Neural System." Neuropsychologia 47(10): 2073-2081.

King, Barbara J., 2013. How Animals Grieve Chicago: University of Chicago Press.

Kirmayer, Laurence J., and Gail Guthrie Valaskakis, eds., 2009. Healing Traditions: The Mental Health of Aboriginal Peoples in Canada. Vancouver, BC: UBC Press.

Kirtsoglou, Elisabeth, 2010. "Dreaming the Self: A Unified Approach towards Dreams, Subjectivity and the Radical Imagination." History and Anthropology 21(3):321–335.

Kitayama, S., S. Duffy and Y. Uchida, 2010. "Self as Cultural Mode of Being." In Handbook of Cultural Psychology, ed. by S. Kitayama and D. Cohen. New York: Guilford, pp. 136-174.

Kitayama, S. and J. Park, 2010. "Cultural Neuroscience of the Self: Understanding the Social Grounding of the Brain." Social Cognitive and Affective Neuroscience 5(2-3): 111-129.

Kjaer, Troels W. et al., 2002. "Increased Dopamine Tone during Meditation-Induced Change of Consciousness." Cognitive Brain Research 13(2): 255-259.

Kluckhohn, Clyde E. and Henry A. Murray, 1948. Personality in Nature, Society, and Culture. New York: Knopf.

Knysh, Alexander, 2000. Islamic Mysticism: A Short History. Leiden: Brill.

Koch, C., 2004. The Quest for Consciousness: A Neurobiological Approach. Englewood, CO: Roberts.

Kockelmans, J. J., 1967. Phenomenology: The Philosophy of Edmund Husserl. Garden City, New York: Doubleday.

Koepping, Klaus-Peter, 1983. Adolf Bastian and the Psychic Unity of Mankind: The Foundations of Anthropology in Nineteenth Century Germany. St. Lucia: University of Queensland Press.

Kolawole, Mosaku S. and Ajenifuja Ko Olusegun, 2008. "The Reliability and Validity of Revised Collett–Lester Fear of Death Scale (Version 3) in a Nigerian Population." Omega 57(2): 195-205.

Komjathy, Louis, 2018. Introducing Contemplative Studies. Oxford: Wiley.

Kooriyama, Takanori, 2009. "The Death of a Newborn Chimpanzee at Mahale: Reactions of Its Mother and Other Individuals to the Body." Pan African News 16: 19-21.

Kornblith, Hilary, 1985. "Ever Since Descartes." The Monist 68(2): 264-276.

Kornfield, Jack, 2009. A Path with Heart: A Guide through the Perils and Promises of Spiritual Life. New York: Bantam.

Kornhauser, William, 1959. The Politics of Mass Society. New York: Free Press.

Kortooms, Toine, 2002. Phenomenology of Time: Edmund Husserl's Analysis of Time-Consciousness. Dortrecht: Kluwer.

Kosko, B., 1993. Fuzzy Thinking: The New Science of Fuzzy Logic. New York: Hyperion.

Kosslyn S. M., G. Ganis and W. L. Thompson, 2001. "Neural Foundations of Imagery." Nature Reviews Neuroscience 2(9): 635–642.

Kracke, Waud H., 2006. "To Dream, Perchance to Cure: Dreaming and Shamanism in a Brazilian Indigenous Society." Social Analysis 50(2): 106-120.

Kragh, Helge, 2012. "Preludes to Dark Energy: Zero-Point Energy and Vacuum Speculations." Archive For History Of Exact Sciences 66(3): 199-240.

Krippner, Stanley, 1994. "Waking Life, Dream Life, and the Construction of Reality." Anthropology of Consciousness 5(3):17-23.

Krippner, Stanley, 1997a. "The Varieties of Dissociative Experience." In Broken Images, Broken Selves: Dissociative Narratives in Clinical Practice, ed. by S. Krippner and S. M. Powers. Washington, DC: Brunner/ Mazel, pp. 336-362.

Krippner, Stanley, 1997b. "The Role Played by Mandalas in Navajo and Tibetan Rituals." Anthropology of Consciousness 8(1): 22-31.

Krippner, Stanley, 2000. "The Epistemology and Technologies of Shamanic States of Consciousness." Journal for Consciousness Studies 7(11–12): 93–118.

Krippner, Stanley, 2002. "Conflicting Perspectives on Shamans and Shamanism: Points and Counterpoints." American Psychologist 57(11): 962.

Krippner, Stanley, 2008. "Learning from the Spirits: Candomblé, Umbanda, and Kardecismo in Recife, Brazil." Anthropology of Consciousness 19(1): 1-32.

Krippner, Stanley and Allan Combs, 2002. "The Neurophenomenology of Shamanism." ReVision 24(3): 46-49.

Krishna, G., 1970. Kundalini: The Evolutionary Energy in Man. Boulder, Co.: Shambhala.

Kruger, Justin and David Dunning, 1999. "Unskilled and Unaware of It: How Difficulties in Recognizing One's Own Incompetence Lead to Inflated Self-Assessments". Journal of Personality and Social Psychology 77 (6): 1121–1134.

Kuiken, Don and Shelley Sikora, 1993. "The Impact of Dreams on Waking Thoughts and Feelings." in Allan Moffitt, Milton Kramer and Robert Hoffman (eds), The Function of Dreaming. Albany, NY: State University of New York Press, pp. 419-476.

Kulshrestha, Asim, 2012. "Impact of Self Study and Meditation on Death Anxiety." ACADEMICIA: An International Multidisciplinary Research Journal 2(9): 80-85.

Kunzendorf, Robert G., 2007. "'Symbolic' Images in Dreams and Daydreams." in Deirdre Barrett and Patrick McNamara (eds), Cultural and Theoretical Perspectives, Volume 3 of The New Science of Dreaming. Westport CT: Praeger, pp. 155-170.

Kurth, Florian, Allan MacKenzie-Graham, Arthur W. Toga and Eileen Luders, 2014. "Shifting Brain Asymmetry: The Link between Meditation and Structural Lateralization." Social Cognitive and Affective Neuroscience 10(1): 55-61.

Kwee, Maurits G. T., 1996. "Travelling in the Footsteps of Hotai." In Comparative and Psychological Study on Meditation, ed. by Y. Haruki, Y. Ishii and M. Suzuki. Netherlands: Eburon, pp. 131-160.

LaBerge, S., L. Levitan and W. C. Dement, 1986. "Lucid Dreaming: Physiological Correlates of Consciousness during REM Sleep." Journal of Mind and Behavior 7: 251-258.

Lagercrantz, Hugo, 2016. Infant Brain Development: Formation of the Mind and the Emergence of Consciousness. New York: Springer.

Lagrou, S. M., 2000. "Homesickness and the Cashinahua Self: A Reflection on the Embodied Condition of Relatedness." In The Anthropology of Love and Anger: The Aesthetics of Conviviality in Native Amazonia, ed. by J. Overing and A. Passes. London: Routledge, pp. 152-169.

Lahood, Gregg, 2007. "One Hundred Years of Sacred Science: Participation and Hybridity in Transpersonal Anthropology." ReVision 29(3): 37-49.

Lakoff, George, 1991. "Metaphor and War: The Metaphor System Used to Justify War in the Gulf." Peace Research 23: 25-32.

Lakoff, George, 1997. "How Unconscious Metaphorical Thought Shapes Dreams." Cognitive Science and the Unconscious, ed. by D. J. Stein. Vancouver: American Psychiatric Publishing, pp. 89-120.

Lakoff, George, 2014. "Mapping the Brain's Metaphor Circuitry: Metaphorical Thought in Everyday Reason." Frontiers in Human Neuroscience 8: 1-14.

Landgrebe, L., 1973. "The Phenomenological Concept of Experience." Philosophy and Phenomenological Research 34 (1): 1-13.

Landgrebe, L., 1981. The Philosophy of Edmund Husserl. Ithaca, New York; Cornell University Press.

Langland-Hassan, Peter, 2015. "Introspective Misidentification." Philosophical Studies 172(7): 1737-1758.

Laria, A., 1998. "Dissociative Experiences among Cuban Spiritist Mediums and Mental Health Patients." Unpublished doctoral dissertation, University of Massachusetts, Boston.

Larrabee, Alary Jeanne, 1973. "Husserl on Sensation: Notes on the Theory of Hyle." The New Scholasticism 47(2): 179-203.

Larrabee, M. J., 1981. "The One and the Many: Yogācāra Buddhism and Husserl." Philosophy East and West 32(1): 3-15.

Laughlin, Charles D., 1985. "On the Spirit of the Gift." Anthropologica 27 (1 2): 137-159.

Laughlin, Charles D., 1988. "The Prefrontosensorial Polarity Principle: Toward a Neurophenomenology of Intentionality." Biology Forum 81(2): 243-260.

Laughlin, Charles D., 1989. "Transpersonal Anthropology: Some Methodological Issues." Western Canadian Anthropologist 5: 29-60.

Laughlin, Charles D., 1990a. "At Play in the Fields of the Lord: The Role of Metanoia in the Development of Consciousness." Play and Culture 3(3):173-192.

Laughlin, Charles D., 1990b. "Womb=Woman=World: Gender and Transcendence in Tibetan Tantric Buddhism." Pre and Perinatal Psychology Journal 5(2): 147 165.

Laughlin, Charles D., 1991. "Pre- and Perinatal Brain Development and Enculturation: A Biogenetic Structural Approach." Human Nature 2(3): 171-213.

Laughlin, Charles D., 1992. "Time, Intentionality, and a Neurophenomenology of the Dot." Anthropology of Consciousness 3(3 & 4): 14-27.

Laughlin, Charles D., 1993. "Fuzziness and Phenomenology in Ethnological Research: Insights from Fuzzy Set Theory." Journal of Anthropological Research 49: 17-37.

Laughlin, Charles D., 1994a. "Psychic Energy and Transpersonal Experience: A Biogenetic Structural Account of the Tibetan Dumo Practice." In Being Changed by Cross-Cultural Encounters, ed. by D. E. Young and J.-G. Goulet. Peterborough, Ontario: Broadview Press, pp. 99-134.

Laughlin, Charles D., 1994b. "Transpersonal Anthropology, Then and Now." Transpersonal Review 1(1): 7-10.

Laughlin, Charles D., 1996. "Archetypes, Neurognosis and the Quantum Sea." Journal of Scientific Exploration 10(3): 375-400.

Laughlin, Charles D., 1997a. "The Nature of Intuition: A Neuropsychological Approach." in Intuition: The Inside Story, ed. by Robbie E. Davis-Floyd and P. Sven Arvidson. New York: Routledge, Pp. 19-37.

Laughlin, Charles D., 1997b. "The Evolution of Cyborg Consciousness." Anthropology of Consciousness 8(4): 144 159.

Laughlin, Charles D., 1997c. "The Cycle of Meaning: Some Methodological Implications of Biogenetic Structural Theory." In Anthropology of Religion: Handbook of Theory and Method, ed. by S. Glazier. Westport, CT: Greenwood Press, pp. 471-488.

Laughlin, Charles D., 2000. "The Cyborg, the Ideology Chip and the Guru Program: The Implications of Cyborg Technologies for the Development of Human Consciousness." Foresight 2(3): 291-312.

Laughlin, Charles D., 2001. "Mandalas, Nixies, Goddesses, and Succubi: A Transpersonal Anthropologist Looks at the Anima." International Journal of Transpersonal Studies 20: 33-52.

Laughlin, Charles D., 2011. Communing with the Gods: Consciousness, Culture and the Dreaming Brain. Brisbane, Australia: Daily Grail.

Laughlin, Charles D., 2012. "Transpersonal Anthropology: What Is It and What Are the Problems Doing It?" In Paranthropology: Anthropological Approaches to the Paranormal, ed. by J. Hunter. Bristol, UK: Paranthropology, pp. 69-98.

Laughlin, Charles D., 2013a. "Justice: A Neuroanthropological Account." In Springer Handbook of Neuroethics, ed. by Neil Levy and Jens Clausen. New York: Springer, pp. 299-321.

Laughlin, Charles D., 2013b. "The Ethno-Epistemology of Transpersonal Experience: The View from Transpersonal Anthropology." International Journal of Transpersonal Studies 32(1): 43-50.

Laughlin, Charles D., n.d. "Ethnoneurology Project Report.: https:/sites.google.com/site/biogeneticstructuralism/home/ethnoneurology-project.

Laughlin, Charles D. and Elizabeth R. Allgeier, 1979. An Ethnography of the So of Northeastern Uganda. New Haven, CT: HRAF Press.

Laughlin, Charles D. and Eugene, G. d'Aquili, 1974. Biogenetic Structuralism. New York: Columbia University Press.

Laughlin, Charles D. and J. H. N. Loubser, 2010. "Neurognosis: The Development of Neural Models, and the Study of the Ancient Mind." Time and Mind 3(2): 135-158.

Laughlin, Charles D. and John McManus, 1995. "The Relevance of the Radical Empiricism of William James to the Anthropology of Consciousness." Anthropology of Consciousness 6(3): 34-46.

Laughlin, Charles D., John McManus and Eugene G. d'Aquili, 1990. Brain, Symbol and Experience: Toward a Neurophenomenology of Consciousness. New York: Columbia University Press.

Laughlin, Charles D., John McManus, and Eugene G. d'Aquili, 1993. "Mature Contemplation." Zygon 28: 133-176.

Laughlin, Charles D., John McManus, Robert A. Rubinstein and Jon Shearer, 1986. "The Ritual Transformation of Experience." In Studies in Symbolic Interaction, ed. by N. K. Dengin. Greenwich, CT: JAI Press, pp. 107-136.

Laughlin, Charles D., John McManus and Jon Shearer, 1983. "Dreams, Trance and Visions: What a Transpersonal Anthropology Might Look Like." Phoenix: The Journal of Transpersonal Anthropology 7(1/2): 141-159.

Laughlin, Charles D., John McManus and Jon Shearer, 1993. "Transpersonal Anthropology." In Paths Beyond Ego: The Transpersonal Vision, ed. by R. Walsh and F. Vaughan. Los Angeles, CA: Tarcher, pp. 190-195.

Laughlin, Charles D., John McManus and Christopher D. Stephens, 1981. "A Model of Brain and Symbol." Semiotica 33(3/4): 211-236.

Laughlin, Charles D., John McManus and Mark Webber, 1984. "Neurognosis, Individuation, and Tibetan Arising Yoga Practice." Phoenix: The Journal of Transpersonal Anthropology 8: 91-106.

Laughlin, Charles D. and Adam Rock, 2013. "Neurophenomenology: Enhancing the Experimental and Cross-Cultural Study of Brain and Experience." In Wiley-Blackwell Handbook of Transpersonal Psychology. ed. by H. Friedman and G. Hartelius. Chichester, West Sussex, UK: Wiley-Blackwell, pp. 261-280.

Laughlin, Charles D. and Adam Rock, 2014. "What Can We Learn from Shamans' Dreaming? A Cross-Cultural Exploration." Dreaming 24(4): 233-252.

Laughlin, Charles D. and Melanie Takahashi, 2020. "Mystical Love: The Universal Solvent." Anthropology of Consciousness 31(1): 5-62.

Laughlin, Charles D. and C. Jason Throop, 1999. "Emotion: A View from Biogenetic Structuralism." in A.L. Hinton (ed), Biocultural Approaches to the Emotions. Cambridge: Cambridge University Press, pp. 329-363.

Laughlin, Charles D. and C. Jason Throop, 2001. "Imagination and Reality: On the Relations Between Myth, Consciousness, and the Quantum Sea." Zygon 36(4): 709 736.

Laughlin, Charles D. and C. Jason Throop, 2003. "Experience, Culture, and Reality: The Significance of Fisher Information for Understanding the Relationship Between Alternative States of Consciousness and the Structures of Reality." International Journal of Transpersonal Studies 22: 7-26.

Laughlin, Charles D. and C. Jason Throop, 2006. Cultural Neurophenomenology: Integrating Experience, Culture and Reality through Fisher Information. Journal Culture & Psychology 12(3): 305-337.

Laughlin, Charles D. and C. Jason Throop, 2008. "Continuity, Causation and Cyclicity: A Cultural Neurophenomenology of Time-Consciousness." Time and Mind 1: 159-186.

Laughlin, Charles D. and C. Jason Throop, 2009. "Husserlian Meditations and Anthropological Reflections: Toward a Cultural Neurophenomenology of Experience and Reality." Anthropology of Consciousness 20(2): 130-170.

Laughlin, Charles D. and Vincenza A. Tiberia, 2012. "Archetypes: Toward a Jungian Anthropology of Consciousness." Anthropology of Consciousness 23(2): 127-157.

Laurienti, Paul J., Mark T. Wallace, Joseph A. Maldjian, Christina M. Susi, Barry E. Stein and Jonathan H. Burdette, 2003. "Cross-Modal Sensory Processing In the Anterior Cingulate and Medial Prefrontal Cortices." Human Brain Mapping 19(4): 213-223.

Lazar, Sara W. et al., 2000. "Functional Brain Mapping of the Relaxation Response and Meditation." Neuroreport 11(7): 1581-1585.

Lazar, Sara W. et al., 2005. "Meditation Experience is Associated with Increased Cortical Thickness." Neuroreport 16(17): 1893.

Leary, M. R. et al., 2007. "Self-Compassion and Reactions to Unpleasant Self-Relevant Events: The Implications of Treating Oneself Kindly." Journal of Personality and Social Psychology 92: 887–904.

Lebot, V, M. Merlin and L. Lindstrom, 1997. Kava: The Pacific Elixir: The Definitive Guide to Its Ethnobotany, History, and Chemistry. Inner Traditions. Rochester, VT: Bear & Co.

Leder, Drew, 1990. The Absent Body. Chicago: The University of Chicago Press.

Lederman, Carol, 1988. "Wayward Winds: Malay Archetypes, and Theory of Personality in the Context of Shamanism." Social Science and Medicine 27(8): 799-810.

Lederman, Carol, 1991. Taming the Wind of Desire: Psychology, Medicine and Aesthetics in Malay Shamanistic Performance. Berkeley: University of California Press.

Ledi, S., 2007. The Manual of Light. The Manual of the Path to Higher Knowledge. Kandy: Buddhist Publication Society.

LeDoux, Joseph, 2003a. "The Emotional Brain, Fear, and the Amygdala." Cellular and Molecular Neurobiology 23(4-5): 727-738.

LeDoux, Joseph, 2003b. Synaptic Self: How Our Brains Become Who We Are. New York: Penguin.

LeDoux, Joseph, 2008. "Remembrance of Emotions Past." In The Jossey-Bass Reader on the Brain and Learning, ed. by K. Fischer and M. H. Immordino-Yang. San Francisco: Jossey-Bass, pp. 151–179.

Lee, Tatia M. C. et al., 2012. "Distinct Neural Activity Associated with Focused-Attention Meditation and Loving-Kindness Meditation." PLoS One 7(8): e40054. [Retrieved August 25, 2017: http://journals.plos.org/plosone/article/file?id=10.1371/journal.pone.0040054&type=printable]

Lehmann, Dietrich et al., 2001. "Brain Sources of EEG Gamma Frequency during Volitionally Meditation-Induced, Altered States of Consciousness, and Experience of the Self." Psychiatry Research: Neuroimaging 108(2): 111-121.

Leinweber, Marcus, et al., 2017. "A Sensorimotor Circuit in Mouse Cortex for Visual Flow Predictions." Neuron 95(6): 1420-1432.

Lehrer, P. 2003. "Applied Psychophysiology: Beyond the Boundaries of Biofeedback." Applied Psychophysiology and Biofeedback 28 (4): 291-304.

Lende, Daniel H. and Greg Downey, 2012. The Encultured Brain: An Introduction to Neuroanthropology. Cambridge, MA: MIT Press.

Lerner, Richard M. and Laurence Steinberg, 2004. Handbook of Adolescent Psychology (second edition). New York: Wiley.

Lester, David, 1990. "The Collett-Lester Fear of Death Scale: The Original Version and a Revision." Death Studies 14(5): 451-468.

Leung, M-K. et al., 2013. "Increased Gray-Matter Volume in the Right Angular and Posterior Parahippocampal Gyri in Loving-Kindness Meditators." Social Cognitive and Affective Neuroscience 8: 34-39.

Levine, P. A., 2010. In an Unspoken Voice: How the Body Releases Trauma and Restores Goodness. Berkeley, CA: North Atlantic Books.

Levi-Strauss, Claude, 1971. Totemism. New York: Beacon.

Levy, J. E., R. Neutra and D. Parker, 1987. Hand Trembling, Frenzy Witchcraft, and Moth Madness: A Study of Navajo Seizure Disorders. Tucson, AZ: University of Arizona Press.

Levy-Bruhl, Lucein, 1966[1923]. Primitive Mentality. Boston: Beacon Press.

Lewis, E. Douglas, Robert Turner and Gary F. Egan, 2009. "The Brain in Culture and Culture in the Brain: A Review of Core Issues in Neuroanthropology." Progress in Brain Research 178: 43-64.

Lewis, P. W., 2000. "Towards a Pentecostal Epistemology: The Role of Experience in Pentecostal Hermeneutics." The Spirit and Church 2 (1): 95-125.

Lewis, T. H., 1972. "The Oglala (Teton Dakota) Sun Dance: Vicissitudes of Its Structures and Functions." Plains Anthropologist 17(55): 44-49.

Lewis-Fernández, Roberto, Alfonso Martínez-Taboas, Vedat Sar, Sapana Patel, and Adeline Boatin, 2007. "The Cross-Cultural Assessment of Dissociation." In Cross-Cultural Assessment of Psychological Trauma and PTSD, edited by Wilson, John P. and Catherine C. So-Kum Tang. pp. 279-317. Boston: Springer.

Lewis-Williams, J. D., 1992. "Ethnographic Evidence Relating to 'Trance' and 'Shamans' among Northern and Southern Bushmen." The South African Archaeological Bulletin 47: 56-60.

Lewis-Williams, J. D., 1997. "Harnessing the Brain: Vision and Shamanism in Upper Paleolithic Western Europe." Beyond Art: Pleistocene Image and Symbol 23: 321-342.

Lewis-Williams, J. D., 2002. The Mind in the Cave: Consciousness and the Origins of Art. London, UK: Themes and Hudson.

Lewis-Williams, J. D. and T. A. Dowson, 1988. The Signs of All Times: Entoptic Phenomena in Upper Paleolithic Art. Current Anthropology 29: 201-245.

Lex, Barbara W., 1979. "The Neurobiology of Ritual Trance." In The Spectrum of Ritual, ed. by Eugene G. d'Aquili, Charles D. Laughlin and John McManus. New York: Columbia University Press, pp. 117-151.

Libet, Benjamin, 1994. "A Testable Field Theory of Mind-Brain Interaction." Journal of Consciousness Studies 1(1): 119-126.

Lifton, R. J., 1971. "Protean Man." Archives of General Psychology 24(4): 298-304.

Lifton, R. J., 1999. The Protean Self: Human Resilience in an Age of Fragmentation. Chicago: University of Chicago Press.

Lincoln, J. S., 1935. The Dream in Primitive Culture. London: Cresset.

Linden, Stanton J., 2003. The Alchemy Reader: From Hermes Trismegistus to Isaac Newton. Cambridge: Cambridge University Press.

Lindholm, C., 2007. Culture and Identity: The History, Theory, and Practice of Psychological Anthropology. Oxford: Oneworld Publications.

Locke, Ralph G. and Edward F. Kelly, 1985. "A Preliminary Model for the Cross-Cultural Analysis of Altered States of Consciousness." Ethos 13(1): 3-55.

Lockwood, Michael, 1989. Mind, Brain and the Quantum. Oxford: Basil Blackwell.

Londoño-Sulkin, C. D., 2000. "'Though It Comes as Evil, I Embrace It as Good': Social Sensitivities and the Transformation of Malignant Agency among the Muiname." In The Anthropology of Love and Anger: The Aesthetics of Conviviality in Native Amazonia, ed. by J. Overing and A. Passes. London: Routledge, 170-186.

Longair, Malcolm S., 2006. The Cosmic Century: A History of Astrophysics and Cosmology. Cambridge University Press, 2006.

Long, Anthony A., 1996. "Stoic Psychology and the Elucidation of Language." In Knowledge Through Signs: Ancient Semiotic Theories and Practices, ed. by Elizabeth Asmis. Belgium: Brepols Publishers, pp. 109-131.

Lowe, Scott and David Lane, 1996. DA: The Strange Case of Franklin Jones. Walnut, CA: Mt. San Antonio.

Lowen, Alexander, 1976. Bioenergetics." New York: Penguin.

Lowenstein, Tom, 2003. Dawning of Clear Light: A Western Approach to Tibetan Dark Retreat Meditation. Newburyport, MA: Hampton Roads Publishing.

Lowie, Robert Harry, 1915. "The Sun Dance of the Crow Indians." Anthropological Papers of the American Museum of Natural History 16(1).

Loewenstein, Werner, 2013. Physics in Mind: A Quantum View of the Brain. New York: Basic Books.

Lou, Hans C., Markus Nowak and Troels W. Kjaer, 2005. "The Mental Self." Progress in Brain Research 150: 197-594.

Luders, Eileen, 2014. "Exploring Age-Related Brain Degeneration in Meditation Practitioners." Annals of the New York Academy of Sciences 1307(1): 82-88.

Luders, Eileen, Kristi Clark, Katherine L. Narr and Arthur W. Toga, 2011. "Enhanced Brain Connectivity in Long-Term Meditation Practitioners." Neuroimage 57(4): 1308-1316.

Luders, Eileen et al., 2012. "The Unique Brain Anatomy of Meditation Practitioners: Alterations in Cortical Gyrification." Frontiers in Human Neuroscience 6 (2012).

Luders, Eileen, Arthur W. Toga, Natasha Lepore and Christian Gaser, 2009. "The Underlying Anatomical Correlates of Long-Term Meditation: Larger Hippocampal and Frontal Volumes of Gray Matter." Neuroimage 45(3): 672-678.

Luke, David P. and Marios Kittenis, 2005. "A Preliminary Survey of Paranormal Experiences with Psychoactive Drugs." The Journal of Parapsychology 69(2): 305.

Luhrmann, T. M., H. Nusbaum and R. Thisted, 2010. "The Absorption Hypothesis: Learning To Hear God in Evangelical Christianity." American Anthropologist 112(1): 66-78.

Lutz, Antoine, 2007. "Neurophenomenology and the Study of Self-Consciousness." Consciousness and Cognition 16(3): 765-767.

Lutz, Antoine, John D. Dunne and Richard J. Davidson, 2007. "Meditation and the Neuroscience of Consciousness." Cambridge Handbook of Consciousness, ed. by

Philip David Zelazo, Morris Moscovitch and Evan Thompson. Cambridge: Cambridge University Press, pp. 499-555.

Lutz, Antoine, Julie Brefczynski-Lewis, Tom Johnstone and Richard J. Davidson, 2008. "Regulation of the Neural Circuitry of Emotion by Compassion Meditation: Effects of Meditative Expertise." PloS One 3(3): e1897.

Lutz, Antoine, Heleen A. Slagter, John D. Dunne and Richard J. Davidson, 2008. "Attention Regulation and Monitoring in Meditation." Trends in Cognitive Sciences 12(4): 163-169.

Lyons, W., 1986. The Disappearance of Introspection. Cambridge: Bradford.

MacDonald, Cynthia, 1989. Mind-Body Identity Theories. London: Routledge.

MacDonald, George F., 1984. Symbols of Wealth in Tsimshian Art and Myth. In The Tsimshian and Their Neighbors of the North Pacific Coast, ed. by J. Miller and C. M. Easton. Seattle: University of Washington Press, pp. 89-105.

MacDonald, George F., John Cove, Charles D. Laughlin and John McManus, 1989. "Mirrors, Portals and Multiple Realities." Zygon 24(1): 39-64.

Machchhar, Chintan K., Dharav C. Koticha and Mohammed Abdullah Mohammed Aysan 2014. "Brain Machine Interface." International Journal of Advanced Research in IT and Engineering 3(4): 1-9.

MacLean, K. A. et al., 2010. "Intensive Meditation Training Improves Perceptual Discrimination and Sustained Attention." Psychological Science 21(6): 829-839.

Macmillan, M. B., 2000. An Odd Kind of Fame: Stories of Phineas Gage. Cambridge, MA: MIT Press.

Macrae, C. N. et al., 2004. "Medial Prefrontal Activity Predicts Memory for Self." Cerebral Cortex 14(6): 647-654.

Mac Suibhne, S., 2009. "'Wrestle to Be the Man Philosophy Wished to Make You': Marcus Aurelius, Reflective Practitioner." Reflective Practice 10(4): 429–436.

Mageo, J. M., 1995. "The Reconfiguring Self." American Anthropologist 97(2): 282-296.

Mageo, J. M., 1998. Theorizing Self in Samoa: Emotions, Genders, and Sexualities. Ann Arbor: University of Michigan Press.

Mageo, J. M., 2001a. "Introduction." In Cultural Memory: Reconfiguring History and Identity in the Postcolonial Pacific, ed. by J. M. Mageo. Honolulu: University of Hawaii Press, pp. 1-10.

Mageo, J. M., 2001b. "On Memory Genres: Tendencies in Cultural Remembering." In Cultural Memory: Reconfiguring History and Identity in the Postcolonial Pacific, ed. by J. M. Mageo. Honolulu: University of Hawaii Press, pp. 11-33.

Mageo, J. M., (ed.), 2002a. Power and the Self. Cambridge: Cambridge University Press.

Mageo, J. M., 2002b. "Self Model and Sexual Agency." In Power and the Self, ed. by J. M. Mageo. Cambridge: Cambridge University Press, pp. 141-174.

Mageo, J. M. (ed.), 2003. Dreaming and the Self: New Perspectives on Subjectivity, Identity, and Amotion. Albany, NY: State University of New York Press.

Mahāsi Sayādaw, 1978. The Progress of Insight: A Treatise on Buddhist Satipatthana Meditation. Kandy, Sri Lanka: Buddhist Publication Society.

Maidenbaum, A., 1998. "Dreams and Other Aspects of Jungian Psychology." In Current Theories of Psychoanalysis, ed. by R. Langs. New York: International Universities Press, pp. 227-254.

Main, John, 2011. Word into Silence: A Manual for Christian Meditation. New York: Canterbury Press.

Main, Roderick, 2006. "Religion." In The Handbook of Jungian Psychology, ed. by Renos K. Papadopoulos. London: Routledge, pp. 298-323.

Majid, Asifa and Nicole Kruspe, 2018. "Hunter-Gatherer Olfaction Is Special." Current Biology 28: 409–413.

Manjunath, N. K. and Shirley Telles, 2004. "Spatial and Verbal Memory Test Scores Following Yoga and Fine Arts Camps for School Children." Indian Journal Physiology and Pharmacology 48(3): 353-356.

Mann, Steve and Hal Niedzviecki, 2001. Cyborg: Digital Destiny and Human Possibility in the Age of the Wearable Computer. New York: Doubleday.

Manna, A. et al., 2010. "Neural Correlates of Focused Attention and Cognitive Monitoring in Meditation." Brain Research Bulletin 82(1): 46-56.

Mara, C., T. L. DeCicco and M. L. Stroink, 2010. "An Investigation of the Relationships among Self-Construal, Emotional Intelligence, and Well-Being." International Journal of Transpersonal Studies 29(1): 1-11.

Marcuse, Herbert, 2013[1964]. One-Dimensional Man: Studies in the Ideology of Advanced Industrial Society. New York: Routledge.

Markus, H. R. and S. Kitayama, 1991a. "Cultural Variation in the Self-Concept." In The Self: Interdisciplinary Approaches, ed. by J. Strauss and G. R. Goethals. Berlin: Springer-Verlag, pp. 18-48.

Markus, H. R. and S. Kitayama, 1991b. "Culture and the Self: Implications for Cognition, Emotion, and Motivation." Psychological Review 98(2): 224.

Markus, H. R. and S. Kitayama, 2003. "Culture, Self, and the Reality of the Social." Psychological Inquiry 14(3-4): 277-283.

Marlan, Stanton, 2006. "Alchemy." In The Handbook of Jungian Psychology, ed. by Renos K. Papadopoulos. New York: Routledge, pp. 263-295.

Marshall, Lorna, 1969. "The Medicine Dance of the ⊠Kung Bushmen." Africa: Journal of the International African Institute 39(4): 347-381.

Marchand, William R., 2012. "Mindfulness-Based Stress Reduction, Mindfulness-Based Cognitive Therapy, and Zen Meditation for Depression, Anxiety, Pain, and Psychological Distress." Journal of Psychiatric Practice 18(4): 233-252.

Mazrui, Ali Al⊠Amin, 1967. Towards a Pax Africana: A Study of Ideology and Ambition. Chicago: University of Chicago Press.

Merrill, W., 1992. "The Rarámuri Stereotype of Dreams." In Dreaming: Anthropological and Psychological Interpretations, ed. by B. Tedlock. Cambridge: Cambridge University Press, pp. 194-219.

Marstaller, Lars, 2009. "Towards a Whiteheadian neurophenomenology." Concrescence: The Australasian Journal of Process Thought 10: 57-66.

Martelli, Matteo, 2014. The Four Books of Pseudo-Democritus. London: Routledge.

Martin-Ordas, G., D. Haun, F. Colmenares and J. Call, 2010. Keeping Track of Time: Evidence for Episodic-Like Memory in Great Apes. Animal Cognition 13: 331–340.

Mathers, Dale, Melvin E. Miller and Osamu Ando (eds.), 2009. Self and No-Self: Continuing the Dialogue Between Buddhism and Psychotherapy. London: Routledge.

Matsuzawa, Tetsuro, 1997. "The Death of an Infant Chimpanzee at Bossou, Guinea." Pan Africa News 4(1): 4-6.

Matt, Daniel C., 2005. "Kabbalah and Contemporary Cosmology: Discovering the Resonances." In Science, Religion, and the Human Experience, ed. by James D. Proctor. Oxford: Oxford University Press, pp. 129-142.

Matt, Daniel C., 2009. The Essential Kabbalah: The Heart of Jewish Mysticism. New York: HarperOne.

Matthews, W., 1994. Navajo Legends. Salt Lake City, Utah: University of Utah Press. (Originally published 1897)

Maturana, H. R. and F. J. Varela, 1980. Autopoiesis and Cognition. Dordrecht, Holland: D. Reidel.

Maturana, H. R. and F. J. Varela, 1987. The Tree of Knowledge: The Biological Roots of Human Understanding. Boston: New Science Library.

Metzinger, T., 2009. The Ego Tunnel: The Science of the Mind and the Myth of the Self. New York: Basic Books.

Mauss, Marcel, 1969 [1924]. The Gift. London: Cohen and West.

McClelland, J.L. and D.E. Rumelhart (eds), 1986. Parallel Distributed Processing, Vol 2: Psychological and Biological Models. Cambridge, MA: MIT Press.

McClenon, James, 1997. "Shamanic Healing, Human Evolution, and the Origin of Religion." Journal for the Scientific Study of Religion 36(3): 345-354.

McComb, D. M., T. C. Tricas and S. M. Kajiura, 2009. "Enhanced Visual Fields in Hammerhead Sharks." The Journal of Experimental Biology 212: 4010-4018.

McComb, K., L. Baker and C. J. Moss, 2005. "African Elephants Show High Levels of Interest in the Skulls and Ivory of Their Own Species." Biology Letters doi:10.1098/rsbl.2005.0400 Published online.

McCrae, Robert R. and Paul T. Costa, 2003. Personality in Adulthood: A Five-Factor Theory Perspective. New York: Guilford Press.

MacGinn, Bernard, 2006. The Essential Writings of Christian Mysticism. New York: Modern Library.

McGuire, W. and R. F. C. Hull, 1977. C. G. Jung Speaks: Interviews and Encounters. Princeton, NJ: Princeton University Press.

McKenna, Terrance, 1992. Food of the Gods: The Search for the Original Tree of Knowledge. New York: Bantam.

McKenna, Terrance and Dennis McKenna, 1975. The Invisible Landscape. New York: Seabury Press.

McMahan, David and Erik Braun (eds.), 2017. Meditation, Buddhism, and Science. Oxford University Press.

McNeill, David, 2005. Gesture and Thought. Chicago: University of Chicago Press.

McNeley, James K., 1981. Holy Wind in Navajo Philosophy. Tucson: University of Arizona Press.

Meggitt, M. J., 1962. Dream Interpretation among the Mae Enga of New Guinea. Southwestern Journal of Anthropology, 18(3): 216-229.

Meggitt, M. J., 1973. The sun and the shakers: A millenarian cult and its transformation in the new guinea highlands. Oceania, 44(2), pp.109-126.

Meier, C. A., 1995. Personality: The Individuation Process in Light of C. G. Jung's Typology. Einsiedeln, Switzerland: Daimon.

Meier, C. A., 2009. Healing Dream and Ritual: Ancient Incubation and Modern Psychotherapy. Einsiedeln, Switzerland: Daimon.

Meldman, Louis William, 1990. Mystical Sex: Love, Ecstacy, and the Mystical Experience. New York: Harbinger House.

Menzel, Emil W., 1963. "The Effects of Cumulative Experience on Responses to Novel Objects in Young Isolation Reared Chimpanzees." Behavior 21: 1-12.

Menzel, Emil W., 1966. "Responsiveness to Objects in Free Ranging Japanese monkeys." Behavior 26: 130-150.

Menzel, Emil W., 1967. "Naturalistic and Experimental Research on Primates." Human Development 10: 170-186.

Menzel, Emil W., 1972. "Protocultural Aspects of Chimpanzee's Responsiveness to Novel Objects." Folia Primatologica 17: 161-170.

Meredith, Martin, 2001. Elephant Destiny: Biography of an Endangered Species in Africa. New York: Public Affairs.

Merkur, Dan, 1993. Gnosis: An Esoteric Tradition of Mystical Visions and Unions. Albany, NY: State University of New York Press.

Merleau-Ponty, Maurice, 1962. Phenomenology of Perception. London: Routledge and Kegan Paul.

Merleau-Ponty, Maurice, 1968. The Visible and the Invisible. Evanston, IL: Northwestern University Press.

Merrell-Wolff, F., 1973. The Philosophy of Consciousness Without an Object. New York: The Julian Press.

Merton, Thomas, 2008. Choosing to Love the World: On Contemplation. Boulder, CO: Sounds True Books.

Mesquita, Batja, Lisa Feldman Barrett and Eliot R. Smith (eds.), 2010. The Mind in Context. New York: Guilford Press.

Metzinger, T., 2009. The Ego Tunnel: The Science of the Mind and the Myth of the Self. New York: Basic Books.

Metzner, Ralph, 1998. "Hallucinogenic Drugs and Plants in Psychotherapy and Shamanism." Journal of Psychoactive Drugs 30(4): 333-341.

Milán, E. G. et al., 2012. "Auras in Mysticism and Synaesthesia: A Comparison." Consciousness and Cognition 21(1): 258-268.

Miller, G. A., E. H. Galanter and K. H. Pribram, 1960. Plans and the Structure of Behavior. New York: Holt, Rinehart and Winston.

Miller, I., 1984. Husserl, Perception, and Temporal Awareness. Cambridge: MIT Press.

Miller, Jeffrey C., 2004. The Transcendent Function: Jung's Model of Psychological Growth through Dialogue with the Unconscious. Albany, NY: SUNY Press.

Miller, Jonathan Scott, 2009. "Are Mystical Experiences Evidence for the Existence of a Transcendent Reality? Evaluating Eugene d'Aquili and Andrew Newberg's Argument for Absolute Unitary Being." Florida Philosophical Review 9(1): 40-55.

Miller, John P., 2013. The Contemplative Practitioner: Meditation in Education and the Workplace. Toronto, ON: University of Toronto Press.

Miller, Lisa et al., 2018. "Neural Correlates of Personalized Spiritual Experiences." Cerebral Cortex 29 May issue. https://doi-org.ezproxy1.lib.asu.edu/10.1093/cercor/bhy102 (retrieved on 6/20/2018).

Milonni, P. W., 1994. The Quantum Vacuum: An Introduction to Quantum Electrodynamics. Boston: Academic Press.

Mindell, A., 1982. Dreambody: The Body's Role in Revealing the Self. Santa Monica, CA: SIGO Press.

Mishra, Lakshmi-Chandra, Betsy B. Singh and Simon Dagenais, 2001. "Ayurveda: A Historical Perspective and Principles of the Traditional Healthcare System in India." Alternative Therapies in Health and Medicine 7(2): 36-42.

Mitchell, J. P., M. R. Banaji and C. N. Macrae, 2005. "The Link Between Social Cognition and Self-Referential Thought in the Medial Prefrontal Cortex." Journal of Cognitive Neuroscience 17: 1306-1315.

Mithen, S., 2003. After the Ice: A Global Human History 20,000–5,000 BC. Cambridge. MA: Harvard University Press.

Modesto, Ruby and Guy Mount, 1980. Not for Innocent Ears: Spiritual Traditions of a Desert Cahuilla Medicine Woman. Angeles Oaks, CA: Sweetlight.

Moeran, B., 2007. "Marketing Scents and the Anthropology of Smell." Social Anthropology 15(2): 153–168.

Moga, Margaret M., 2017. "Exceptional Experiences of Healers: A Survey of Healing Touch Practitioners and Students." Journal of Exceptional Experiences and Psychology 5(1): 24-34.

Mograbi, Gabriel José Corrêa, 2011. "Meditation and the Brain: Attention, Control and Emotion." Mens Sana Monographs 9(1): 276–283.

Mohanty, J. N., 1972. "Phenomenology and Existentialism: Encounter with Indian Philosophy." International Philosophical Quarterly 12(4): 485-511.

Molenberghs, P, R. Cunnington and J. Mattingley, 2009. "Is the Mirror Neuron System Involved in Imitation? A Short Review and Meta-Analysis." Neuroscience and Biobehavioral Reviews 33(1): 975–980.

Money, M., 2000. "Shamanism and Complementary Therapy." Complementary Therapies in Nursing and Midwifery 6: 207–212.

Mookerjee, A., 1982. Kundalini: The Arousal of the Inner Energy. New York: Destiny Books.

Moran, Dermot, 2000. Introduction to Phenomenology. New York: Routledge.

Morinis, Alan, 1985. "The Ritual Experience: Pain and the Transformation of Consciousness in Ordeals of Initiation." Ethos 13(2): 150-174.

Morris, B., 1994. Anthropology of the Self: The Individual in Cultural Perspective. London: Pluto.

Moss, Cynthia, 2000. Elephant Memories: Thirteen Years in the Life of an Elephant Family. Chicago: University of Chicago Press.

Mothersill, Carmel, et al., 2014. "Transmission of Signals from Rats Receiving High Doses of Microbeam Radiation to Cage Mates: An Inter-Mammal Bystander Effect." Dose-Response 12(1): 72-92.

Motoyama, H. and R. Brown (1978) Science and the Evolution of Consciousness. Brookline, Mass.: Autumn Press.

Moulinet, Inès, Edelweiss Touron and Gaël Chételat, 2018. "Meditation and Ageing: Potential Impact on Well-Being, Cognition and Brain Integrity of Older Adults." Revue de neuropsychologie 10(4): 304-312.

Mpofu, E., 1994. "Exploring the Self-Concept in an African Culture." The Journal of Genetic Psychology 155(3): 341-354.

Murdock, George Peter, 1945. "The Common Denominator of Culture." In The Science of Man in the World Crisis, ed. by Ralph Linton. New York: Columbia University Press.

Murdock, George Peter, 1980. Theories of Illness: A World Survey. Pittsburgh, PA: University of Pittsburgh Press.

Murphy, Gardner, 1947. Personality: A Biosocial Approach to Origins and Structure. New York: Harper.

Murphy, K. and C. Jason Throop (eds.), 2010.Toward an Anthropology of the Will. Stanford University Press.

Murphy, M. and S. Donovan, 1999. The Physical and Psychological Effects of Meditation: A Review of Contemporary Research with a Comprehensive Bibliography 1931-1996. Sausalito, CA: Institute of Noetic Sciences.

Murray, L. and C. Trevarthen, 1985. "Emotional Regulation of Interactions Between Two-Month-Olds and Their Mothers." In Social Perception In Infants, ed. by T. M. Field and N. A. Fox. Norwood, NJ: Ablex, pp. 25-52.

Nahm, Oliver, 2017. Dealing with Death: A Search for Cross-Cultural and Time-Transcending Similarities. Vol. 14. LIT Verlag Münster.

Nair, Prashant, 2013. "Brain–Machine Interface." Proceedings of the National Academy of Sciences 110(46): 18343.

Nakamichi, Masayuki, Naoki Koyama and Alison Jolly, 1996. "Maternal Responses To Dead and Dying Infants In Wild Troops Of Ring-Tailed Lemurs At the Berenty Reserve, Madagascar." International Journal of Primatology 17(4): 505-523.

Namgyal Rimpoche, Venerable, 1981. The Womb of Form: Pith Instructions in the Six Yogas of Naropa. Ottawa: Crystal Word Publications.

Nanda, Serena, 1999. Gender Diversity: Cross-cultural Variations. Long Grove, IL: Waveland Press.

Neal, Arthur G. and Sara F. Collas, 2013. Intimacy and Alienation: Forms of Estrangement in Female/Male Relationships. New York: Routledge.

Neff, Kristin D., 2003. "Self-Compassion: An Alternative Conceptualization of a Healthy Attitude toward Oneself." Self and Identity 2: 85–101.

Neff, Kristin D., 2011. Self-Compassion. New York, NY: Harper Collins.

Neff, Kristin D. and Oliver Davidson, 2016. "Self-Compassion: Embracing Suffering with Kindness." In Mindfulness in Positive Psychology: The Science of Meditation and Wellbeing, ed. by Itai Ivtzan and Tim Lomas. London: Routledge, pp. 37-50.

Neihardt, John G., 1961. Black Elk Speaks: The Life Story of a Holy Man of the Oglala Sioux. New York: Bison Books.

Neisser, U., 1993. "The Self Perceived." In The Perceived Self: Ecological and Interpersonal Sources of Self-Knowledge, ed. by U. Neisser. Cambridge: Cambridge University Press, pp. 3-21.

Neto, Félix, Etienne Mullet, Jean-Claude Deschamps, José Barros, Rosario Benvindo, Leôncio Camino, Anne Falconi, Victor Kagibanga and Maria Machado, 2000. "Cross-Cultural Variations in Attitudes toward Love." Journal of Cross-Cultural Psychology 31(5): 626-635.

Newberg, Andrew and Eugene G. D'Aquili, 1994. "The Near-Death Experience as Archetype: A Model for "Prepared" Neurocognitive Processes." Anthropology of Consciousness 5(4): 1-15.

Newberg, Andrew and Eugene G. d'Aquili, 2008. Why God Won't Go Away: Brain Science and the Biology of Belief. New York: Ballantine Books.

Newberg, Andrew B. and Jeremy Iversen, 2003. "The Neural Basis of the Complex Mental Task of Meditation: Neurotransmitter and Neurochemical Considerations." Medical Hypotheses 61(2): 282-291.

Newberg, Andrew B. et al., 2003. Cerebral Blood Flow during Meditative Prayer: Preliminary Findings and Methodological Issues. Perceptual and Motor Skills 97: 625-630.

Newberg, Andrew B. et al., 2010. "Meditation Effects on Cognitive Function and Cerebral Blood Flow in Subjects with Memory Loss: A Preliminary Study." Journal of Alzheimer's Disease 20(2): 517-526.

Newell, W. H., 1947. "The Kava Ceremony in Tonga." The Journal of the Polynesian Society 56 (4): 364-417.

Nichols, David E., 2018. "N, N-Dimethyltryptamine and the Pineal Gland: Separating Fact from Myth." Journal of Psychopharmacology 32(1): 30–36.

Nicholson, P. T., 2009. Meditation and Light Visions: A Neurological Analysis. Boulder, CO: CreateSpace Publishing.

Noll, R., 1985. "Mental Imagery Cultivation as a Cultural Phenomenon: The Role of Visions in Shamanism." Current Anthropology 26(4): 443-461.

Nolte, David D. "The Tangled Tale of Phase Space." Physics today 63(4): 33-38.

Northoff, G. et al., 2006. Self-Referential Processing in Our Brain—A Meta-Analysis of Imaging Studies on the Self. Neuroimage 31(1): 440-457.

Nunez, Paul L., 2010. Brain, Mind, and the Structure of Reality. New York: Oxford University Press.

Nyanaponika Mahatera, 1998. Abhidhamma Studies. Boston, MA: Wisdom Publications.

Nyberg, Lars, Alice S. N. Kim, Reza Habib, Brian Levine and Endel Tulving, 2010. "Consciousness of Subjective Time in the Brain." Proceedings of the National Academy of Sciences 107(51): 22356-22359.

Nydahl, L. O., 1990. Ngondro: The Four Foundational Practices of Tibetan Buddhism. Nevada City, CA: Blue Dolphin Publishing.

Obeyesekere, G., 1981. Medusa's Hair: An Essay on Personal Symbols and Religious Experience. Chicago: University of Chicago Press.

Obrist, Barbara, 2003. "Visualization in Medieval Alchemy." Hyle: International Journal for Philosophy of Chemistry 9: 131-70.

O'Connell, Mark 2017. "To Be a Machine: Adventures among Cyborgs, Utopians, Hackers, and the Futurists Solving the Modest Problem of Death." New York: Doubleday.

Odajnyk, V. W., 2011. Gathering the Light: A Jungian View of Meditation. New York: Fisher King.

Odorisio, David M., 2014. "The Alchemical Heart: A Jungian Approach to the Heart Center in the Upaniṣads and in Eastern Christian Prayer." International Journal of Transpersonal Studies 33(1): 27-38.

Ohnuki-Tierney, Emiko, 1973. "The Shamanism of the Ainu of the Northwest Coast of Southern Sakhalin." Ethnology 12(1): 15-29.

Olivelle, Patrick, 1993. The Āśrama System: The History and Hermeneutics of a Religious Institution. Oxford: Oxford University Press.

Olson, Ingrid R., Alan Plotzker and Youssef Ezzyat, 2007. "The Enigmatic Temporal Pole: A Review of Findings on Social and Emotional Processing." Brain 130(7): 1718-1731.

Ong, Walter J., 1991. The Shifting Sensorium. In The Varieties of Sensory Experience. David Howes, ed. Toronto: University of Toronto Press, pp. 47-60.

Oord, Thomas Jay, 2010. Defining Love: A Philosophical, Scientific, and Theological Engagement. Ada, MI: Brazos Press.

Oohashi, T. et al., 2002. "Electroencephalographic Measurement of Possession Trance in the Field." Clinical Neurophysiology 113: 435–445.

Ortiz, A., 1972. "Ritual Drama and the Pueblo Worldview." In New Perspectives on the Pueblos, ed. by A. Ortiz. Albuquerque: University of New Mexico Press, pp. 135-161.

Osaka, Naoyuki (ed.), 2003. Neural Basis of Consciousness. Amsterdam: Benjamins.

Oschman, James L. and Maurie D. Pressman, 2014. "An Anatomical, Biochemical, Biophysical and Quantum Basis for the Unconscious Mind." International Journal of Transpersonal Studies 33(1): 77-96.

Osvath, Mathias and Helena Osvath, 2008. "Chimpanzee (Pan troglodytes) and Orangutan (Pongo abelii) forethought: Self-Control and Pre-Experience in the Face of Future Tool Use." Animal Cognition 11(4): 661-674.

Ott, Ulrich, 2007. States of Absorption: In Search of Neurobiological Foundations. In Hypnosis and Consciousness States: The Cognitive-Neuroscience Perspective, ed. by G. A. Jamieson. New York: Oxford University Press, pp. 257–270.

Ott, Ulrich, 2013. "Time Experience during Mystical States." The Evolution of Time in Science, Anthropology, Theology, ed. by A. Nicolaidis and W. Achtner. London: Bentham Science Publishers, pp. 104-116.

Otto, Rudolf, 1923. The Idea of the Holy: An Inquiry into the Non-rational Factor in the Idea of the Divine and Its Relation to the Rational. London: Oxford University Press.

Overing, J. and A. Passes, 2002a. "Introduction: Conviviality and the Opening Up of Amazonian Anthropology." In The Anthropology of Love and Anger: The Aesthetics of Conviviality in Native Amazonia, ed. by J. Overing and A. Passes. London: Routledge, pp. 1-30.

Overing, J. and A. Passes (eds.), 2002b. The Anthropology of Love and Anger: The Aesthetics of Conviviality in Native Amazonia. London: Routledge.

Ozturk, Ozge, Shakila Shayan, Ulf Liszkowski and Asifa Majid, 2013. "Language is Not Necessary for Color Categories." Developmental Science 16(1): 111-115.

Pace-Schott, E. F., 2007. The Frontal Lobes and Dreaming. In Biological Aspects, Volume 1: The New Science of Dreaming, ed. by D. Barrett and P. McNamara. Westport CT: Praeger, pp. 115-154.

Pace-Schott, E. F., 2011. The Neurobiology of Dreaming. In Principles and Practice of Sleep Medicine (4th ed.), ed. by M. H. Kryger, T. Roth and W. C. Dement. Philadelphia: Elsevier, pp. 563-575.

Pagano, R.R. and S. Warrenburg, 1983. "Meditation: In Search of a Unique Effect." In Consciousness and Self Regulation, Vol. 3, ed. R.J. Davidson, G.E. Schwartz and D. Shapiro. New York: Plenum.

Pagel, J. F., 2008. The Limits of Dream: A Scientific Exploration of the Mind/Brain Interface. Amsterdam: Elsevier.

Palgi, Phyllis and Henry Abramovitch, 1984. "Death: A Cross-Cultural Perspective." Annual Review of Anthropology 13: 385-417.

Paper, Jordan D., 2004. The Mystic Experience: A Descriptive and Comparative Analysis. Albany, NY: State University of New York Press.

Pappas, J. D. and H. L. Friedman, 2012. "The Importance of Replication: Comparing the Self-Expansiveness Level Form Transpersonal Scale with an Alternate Graphical Measure." The Humanistic Psychologist 40(4): 364-379.

Paravahera Vajiranana Mahathera, 1987. Buddhist Meditation in Theory and Practice: A General Exposition According to the Pali Canon of the Theravada School. Kuala Lumpur, Malaysia: Buddhist Missionary Society.

Park, Oksoon et al., 2016. "The Effect of Insight Based Death Meditation on Death Anxiety and Qualify of Life." International Journal of Existential Psychology and Psychotherapy 6(1): 10.

Parker, Stephen, 2019. "Training Attention for Conscious Non-REM Sleep: The Yogic Practice of Yoga-Nidrā and Its Implications for Neuroscience Research." In Progress in Brain Research 244: 255-272.

Parker, Sue Taylor, Robert W. Mitchell and Maria L. Boccia (eds.), 2006. Self-Awareness in Animals and Humans: Developmental Perspectives. Cambridge: Cambridge University Press.

Parkes, Colin Murray, Pittu Laungani and Bill Young (Eds.), 1997a. Death and Bereavement across Cultures. London: Routledge.

Parkes, Colin Murray, Pittu Laungani and Bill Young, 1997b. "Introduction." In Death and Bereavement across Cultures, ed. by Colin Murray Parkes, Pittu Laungani and Bill Young. London: Routledge, pp. 3-9.

Parman, Susan, 1979. "An Evolutionary Theory of Dreaming and Play," In Forms of Play of Native North Americans, ed. by Edward Norbeck and Claire R. Farrer. New York: West Publishing Co., pp. 17-34.

Parra, Alejandro, 2013. "Cognitive and Emotional Empathy in Relation to Five Paranormal/Anomalous Experiences." North American Journal of Psychology 15(3): 405-412.

Pastor, Maria et al., 2004. "The Functional Neuroanatomy of Temporal Discrimination." Journal of Neuroscience 24(10): 2585-2591.

Pearson, J. L., 2002. Shamanism and the Ancient Mind: A Cognitive Approach to Archaeology. New York: Altamira.

Penfield, Wilder, 2015. Mystery of the Mind: A Critical Study of Consciousness and the Human Brain. Princeton, NJ: Princeton University Press.

Penrose, Roger, 1989. The Emperor's New Mind. Oxford: Oxford University Press.

Perreira, Todd LeRoy, 2010. "'Die before you die:' Death Meditation as Spiritual Technology of the Self in Islam and Buddhism." Muslim World 100: 247-267.

Peters, Larry G., 1989. "Shamanism: Phenomenology of a Spiritual Discipline." The Journal of Transpersonal Psychology 21(2): 115.

Peters, Larry G., 1994. "Rites of Passage and the Borderline Syndrome: Perspectives in Transpersonal Anthropology." Anthropology of Consciousness 5(1): 1-15.

Peters, Larry G., 2004. Trance, Initiation and Psychotherapy in Nepalese Shamanism: Essays on Tamang and Tibetan Shamanism. New Delhi: Nirala.

Peters, Larry G. and Douglas Price-Williams, 1980. "Towards an Experiential Analysis of Shamanism." American Ethnologist 7(3): 397-418.

Petersen, G., 1995. "The Complexity of Power, the Subtlety of Kava." Canberra Anthropology 18 (1-2): 34-60.

Philippi, C. L., J. S. Feinstein, S. S. Khalsa, A. Damasio, D. Tranel, G. Landini et al., 2012. "Preserved Self-Awareness following Extensive Bilateral Brain Damage to the Insula, Anterior Cingulate, and Medial Prefrontal Cortices." PLoS ONE 7(8): e38413. (accessed July 12, 2017 from https://doi.org/10.1371/journal.pone.0038413)

Piaget, Jean, 1977. The Development of Thought. New York: The Viking Press.

Piaget, Jean, 1980. Adaptation and Intelligence. Chicago: University of Chicago Press.

Piet, Jacob and Esben Hougaard, 2011. "The Effect of Mindfulness-Based Cognitive Therapy for Prevention of Relapse in Recurrent Major Depressive Disorder: A Systematic Review and Meta-Analysis." Clinical Psychology Review 31(6): 1032-1040.

Pinker, Steven, 2003. The Blank Slate: The Modern Denial of Human Nature. New York: Penguin.

Pinxten, Rik, 1976. "Epistemic Universals: A Contribution to Cognitive Anthropology." in Universalism Versus Relativism in Language and Thought, R. Pinxten (ed.). The Hague: Mouton, pp.117-175.

Pitts-Taylor, Victoria, 2010. "The Plastic Brain: Neoliberalism and the Neuronal Self." Health 14(6): 635-652.

Plotinus, 1992. The Enneads (LP Classic Reprint Series). Osseo, MN: Larson Publications.

Pockett, Susan, 2000. The Nature of Consciousness: A Hypothesis. Lincoln NE: iUniverse. com, (accessed from https://cdn.auckland.ac.nz/assets/psych/about/our-people/documents/sue-pockett/TheNatureofConsciousnessAHypothesis.pdf, June 30, 2017).

Pockett, Susan, 2012. "The Electromagnetic Field Theory of Consciousness: A Testable Hypothesis about the Characteristics of Conscious As Opposed To Non-Conscious Fields." Journal of Consciousness Studies 19(11-12): 191-223.

Poirier, S., 1990. Flexibilite structurelle et creativite onirique chez les groupes aborigines du desert Occidental australien. Unpublished Ph.D. dissertation, Laval University, Quebec, Canada.

Poole, Joyce, 1996. Coming of Age with Elephants: A Memoir. Hyperion Press: New York.

Popp, Fritz-Albert. 1998. "Biophotons and Their Regulatory Role in Cells." Frontier Perspectives 7(2):13-22.

Popp, Fritz-Albert and Lev V. Beloussov (eds), 2013. Integrative Biophysics: Biophotonics. New York: Springer Science & Business Media.

Popper, Karl R. and John C. Eccles, 1977. The Self and Its Brain. New York: Springer International.

Posner, M. I., 2004. Cognitive Neuroscience of Attention. New York: Guilford.

Posner M. I. and S. E. Peterson, 1990. "The Attention System of the Human Brain." Annual Review of Neuroscience 13: 25–42.

Post, Stephen G., 2002. "The Tradition of Agape." In Altruism and Altruistic Love: Science, Philosophy, and Religion in Dialogue, ed. by Stephen G. Post, Lynn G. Underwood, Jeffrey P. Schloss and William B. Hurlbut. Oxford: Oxford University Press, pp. 51-64.

Prabhavananda, Swami, 1979. The spiritual heritage of India. Garden City, NJ: Doubleday.

Premack, D. and G. Woodruff, 1978. "Does the Chimpanzee Have a Theory of Mind?" The Behavioral and Brain Sciences 4: 515–526.

Preston, S. D. and F. B. de Waal, 2002. "Empathy: Its Ultimate and Proximate Bases." Behavioral Brain Sciences 25(1): 1–71.

Pribram, Karl H., 1971. Languages of the Brain: Experimental Paradoxes and Principles in Neuropsychology. Englewood Cliffs, NJ: Prentice-Hall.

Price-Williams, D. and D. J. Hughes, 1994. "Shamanism and Altered States of Consciousness." Anthropology of Consciousness 5(2): 1-15.

Prigatano, G. P., 1991. "Disturbances of Self-Awareness of Deficit After Traumatic Brain Imagery." In Awareness of Deficit After Brain Injury: Clinical and Theoretical Issues, ed. by G. P. Prigatano and D. L. Schacter. Oxford: Oxford University Press, pp. 111-126.

Prince, D. (ed.), 1968. Trance and Possession States. Proceedings of the D. M. Burke Memorial Society, March, 1966. Montreal: Electra Publications

Purcell, S., A. Moffitt and R. Hoffman, 1993. "Waking, Dreaming, and Self-Regulation." In The Functions of Dreaming, ed. by A. Moffitt, M. Kramer and R. Hoffman. Albany, NY: State University of New York Press, pp. 197-260.

Purves, Dale, 1990. Body and Brain: A Trophic Theory of Neural Connections. Cambridge, MA: Harvard University Press.

Purves, Dale, 2010. Brains: How They Seem to Work. Upper Saddle River, NJ: Pearson Education.

Puthoff, Harold E., 1987. "Ground State of Hydrogen as a Zero-Point-Fluctuation-Determined State." Physical Review D 35(10): 3266-3269.

Puthoff, Harold E., 1989. "Source of Vacuum Electromagnetic Zero-Point Energy." Physical Review A 40.

Puthoff, Harold E., 1990. "Everything for Nothing." New Scientist, July 28 issue, pp. 52-55.

Puthoff, Harold E., Russell Targ and Edwin C. May, 1981. "Experimental Psi Research: Implication for Physics." in The Role of Consciousness in the Physical World, ed. by Robert G. Jahn. Washington, D.C.: American Association for the Advancement of Science, pp. 37-86.

Pyszczynski, Tom, Jeff Greenberg, and Sheldon Solomon, 1999. "A Dual-Process Model of Defense Against Conscious and Unconscious Death-Related Thoughts: An Extension of Terror Management Theory." Psychological Review 106(4): 835-845.

Pyszczynski, Tom, Sheldon Solomon and Jeff Greenberg, 2003. In the Wake of 9/11: The Psychology of Terror. Washington, D. C.: American Psychological Association.

Pyszczynski, T. et al., 2006. "On the Unique Psychological Import of the Human Awareness of Mortality: Theme and Variations." Psychological Inquiry 17(4): 328-356.

Quigley, Christine, 1996. The Corpse: A History. Jefferson, NC: McFarland.

Radha, Swami Sivananda, 1994. Realities of the Dreaming Mind. Boulder, CO: Shambala.

Radin, Dean, 1997. The Conscious Universe: The Scientific Truth of Psychic Phenomena. New York: Harper.

Radin, Dean, 2006. Entangled Minds: Extrasensory Experiences in a Quantum Reality. New York: Paraview.

Radin, Dean I., Cassandra Vieten, Leena Michel, and Arnaud Delorme, 2011. "Electrocortical Activity Prior to Unpredictable Stimuli in Meditators and Nonmeditators." Explore: The Journal of Science and Healing 7(5): 286-299.

Radin, Dean et al. 2012. "Consciousness and the Double-Slit Interference Pattern: Six Experiments." Physics Essays 25(2): 157-171.

Radin, Dean, Leena Michel, James Johnston, and Arnaud Delorme, 2013. "Psychophysical Interactions with a Double-Slit Interference Pattern." Physics Essays 26(4): 553-566.

Raffone, Antonino and Narayanan Srinivasan, 2010. "The Exploration of Meditation in the Neuroscience of Attention and Consciousness." Cognitive Processing 11(1): 1-7.

Raffone, Antonino, Laura Marzetti, Cosimo Del Gratta, Mauro Gianni Perrucci, Gian Luca Romani and Vittorio Pizzella, 2019. "Toward a Brain Theory of Meditation." In Progress in Brain Research 244: 207-232.

Rahula, W., 1974. What the Buddha Taught: Revised and Expanded Edition with Texts from Suttas and Dhammapada. New York: Grove Press.

Raichle, M. E., et al., 2001. "A Default Mode of Brain Function." Proceedings National Academy of Sciences USA 98: 676–682.

Rakic, P. A., 1995. "A Small Step for a Cell, a Giant Step for Mankind: A Hypothesis of Neocortical Expansion During Evolution." Trends in Neuroscience 18: 383-388.

Ramachandran, V. S., 2004. A Brief Tour of Human Consciousness: From Impostor Poodles to Purple Numbers. Honolulu, HI: Pi Press.

Ramachandran, V. S., 2012. "Self Awareness: The Last Frontier." Edge Foundation web essay. (www. edge. org/ 3rd_ culture/ rama08/ rama08_ index. html Retrieved April 16, 2012).

Ramachandran, V. S. and S. Blakeslee, 1999. Phantoms in the Brain: Probing the Mysteries of the Human Mind. New York: William Morrow.

Rand, Ayn, 1957. Atlas Shrugged. New York: Dutton.

Rapaport, David, 1951. "Toward a Theory of Thinking." In Organization and Pathology of Thought, ed. by David Rapaport. New York: Columbia University Press, pp. 689–730.

Rapaport, David, 1967. "States of Consciousness: A Psychopathological and Psychodynamic View." In The Collected Papers of David Rapaport, ed. by M. M. Gill. New York: Basic Books, pp. 385–405.

Rappaport, Roy A., 1999. Ritual and Religion in the Making of Humanity. Cambridge, UK: Cambridge University Press.

Reddy, Michael J., 1979. "The Conduit Metaphor: A case of frame conflict in our language about language." in Metaphor and Thought, ed. by A.Ortony. Cambridge: Cambridge University Press, pp. 284–310.

Reichard, G. A., 1950. Navaho Religion: A Study of Symbolism. Princeton, NJ: Princeton University Press.

Reichel-Dolmatoff, Gerardo, 1949-1950. "Los Kogi: Una tribu de la Sierra Nevada de Santa Marta, Columbia (Vol. 1)." Revista 4: 1-319.

Reichel-Dolmatoff, Gerardo, 1976. "Training for the Priesthood among the Kogi of Columbia." In Enculturation in Latin America: An Anthology, ed. by J. Wilbert. Los Angeles, CA: University of California Press, pp. 265-288.

Reichel-Dolmatoff, Gerardo, 1981. "Brain and Mind in Desana Shamanism." Journal of Latin American Lore 7(1): 73-98.

Reimann, Michael W. et al., 2017. "Cliques of Neurons Bound into Cavities Provide a Missing Link between Structure and Function." Frontiers in Computational Neuroscience 11: 48.

Rendu, W. et al., 2014. "Evidence Supporting an Intentional Neanderthal Burial at La Chapelle-Aux-Saints." Proceedings of the National Academy of Sciences 111(1): 81–86.

Revonsuo, Antti, 2000. "The Reinterpretation of Dreams: An Evolutionary Hypothesis of the Function of Dreaming." Behavioral and Brain Sciences 23:793-1121.

Revonsuo, Antti, 2006. Inner Presence: Consciousness as a Biological Phenomenon. Cambridge, MA: MIT Press.

Rhine, L.E., 1969. "Case Study Review." Journal of Parapsychology 33: 228–66

Riba, J. et al., 2006. "Increased Frontal and Paralimbic Activation Following Ayahuasca, the Pan-Amazonian Inebriant." Psychopharmacology 186: 93–98.

Richards, William A., 2015. Sacred Knowledge: Psychedelics and Religious Experiences. New York: Columbia University.

Ricoeur, Paul, 1962. "The Hermeneutics of Symbols and Philosophical Reflection." International Philosophical Quarterly 2: 191-218.

Ricoeur, Paul, 1968. "Structure, Word, Event." Philosophy Today 12(2-4): 114-129.

Ridington, R. and T. Ridington, 1970. "The Inner Eye of Shamanism and Totemism." History of Religions 10: 49-61.

Rill, B. R., 2011. Shugendō: Cultivating Spiritual Power and Health in Contemporary Japan. Unpublished Doctoral Dissertation, College of Arts and Sciences, Florida State University.

Rilling, J. K. T. R. Insel, 1999. "The Primate Neocortex in Comparative Perspective Using Magnetic Resonance Imaging." Journal of Human Evolution 37: 191-223.

Rivers, W. H. R,, 1918. "Dreams and Primitive Culture." The Bulletin of the John Rylands Library 4(3-4): 5-28.

Rivers, W. H. R,, 1923. Conflict and Dream. New York: Harcourt Brace.

Roberts, A. C., T. W. Robbins and L. Weiskrantz, 1998. The Prefrontal Cortex: Executive and Cognitive Functions. Oxford, UK: Oxford University Press.

Robbins, Michael, 2012. The Primordial Mind in Health and Illness: A Cross-Cultural Perspective. New York: Routledge.

Robbins, Thomas and Susan J. Palmer, 1997. Millennium, Messiahs, and Mayhem: Contemporary Apocalyptic Movements. New York: Routledge.

Roberts, Bernadette, 1993. The Experience of No-Self: A Contemplative Journey. Albany, NY: State University of New York Press.

Rochat, M. J., E. Serra, L. Fadiga and V. Gallese, 2008. :The Evolution of Social Cognition: Goal Familiarity Shapes Monkeys' Action Understanding." Current Biology 18: 227–232.

Rock, Adam J. and Stanley Krippner, 2011. Demystifying Shamans and Their World: An Interdisciplinary Study. Exeter, UK: Imprint Academic.

Rockwell, W. Teed, 2005. Neither Brain nor Ghost: A Nondualist Alternative to the Mind-Brain Identity Theory. Cambridge, MA: MIT Press.

Rodd, Robin, 2002. "Märipa teui: A Radical Empiricist Approach to Piaroa Shamanic Training and Initiation." Antropológica 96: 53-82.

Rodd, Robin, 2006. "Piaroa Sorcery and the Navigation of Negative Affect: To Be Aware, To Turn Away." Anthropology of Consciousness 17(1): 35-64.

Rodd, Robin and A. Sumabila, 2011. "Yopo, Ethnicity and Social Change: A Comparative Analysis of Piaroa and Cuiva Yopo Use." Journal of Psychoactive Drugs 43: 36-45.

Rogers, T. B., N. A. Kuiper and W. S. Kirker, 1977. "Self-Reference and the Encoding of Personal Information." Journal of Personality and Social Psychology 35: 677–88.

Rogers, Timothy T. and James L. McClelland, 2014. "Parallel Distributed Processing At 25: Further Explorations in the Microstructure of Cognition." Cognitive Science 38(6): 1024-1077.

Rolls, E. T., 1998. "The Orbitofrontal Cortex." In The Prefrontal Cortex: Executive and Cognitive Functions, ed. by A. C. Roberts, T. W. Robbins and L. Weiskrantz. Oxford, UK: Oxford University Press, pp. 67-86.

Rosch, E., 1977. "Human Categorization." Studies in Cross-Cultural Psychology 1: 1-49.

Rosch, E., 1978. "Principles of Categorization." In Cognition and Categorization, ed. by E. Rosch and B. B. Lloyd. Hillsdale, NJ: Erlbaum, pp. 27-48.

Rosch, E. et al., 1976. "Basic Objects in Natural Categories." Cognitive Psychology 8: 382-439.

Rosenberg, Larry, 1994. "Shining the Light of Death on Life: Maranasati Meditation (Part II)." Insight (fall issue): 23-26.

Rosenberg, Larry, 2001. Living in the Light of Death: On The Art of Being Truly Alive. Boulder, CO: Shambhala Publications.

Rossano, Matt J., 2007. "Did Meditating Make Us Human?" Cambridge Archaeological Journal 17(1): 47-58.

Rossano, Matt J., 2012. "The Essential Role of Ritual in the Transmission and Reinforcement of Social Norms." Psychological Bulletin 138(3): 529.

Rotenberg, Vadim S., 2004. "The Peculiarity of the Right-Hemisphere Function in Depression: Solving the Paradoxes." Progress in Neuro-Psychopharmacology and Biological Psychiatry 28(1): 1-13.

Roth, Harold D., 2006. "Contemplative Studies: Prospects for a New Field." Teachers College Record 108(9): 1787-1815.

Roth, Harold D., 2014. "A Pedagogy for the New Field of Contemplative Studies." In Contemplative Approaches to Learning and Inquiry Across Disciplines, ed. by Olen Gunnlaugson, Edward W. Sarath, Charles Scott and Heesoon Bai. Albany, NY: SUNY Press, pp. 97-118.

Royce, A. P., 2011. Becoming an Ancestor: The Isthmus Zapotec Way of Death. Albany, NY: State University of New York Press.

Rubia, Katya, 2009. "The Neurobiology of Meditation and Its Clinical Effectiveness in Psychiatric Disorders." Biological Psychology 82(1): 1-11.

Ruck, C. A. P., J. Bigwood, D. Staples, J. Ott, and R. G. Wasson, 1979. "Entheogens." Journal of Psychoactive Drugs 11(1-2): 145-146.

Rudgley, R., 1993. Essential Substances: A Cultural History of Intoxicants in Society. New York: Kodansha.

Rudrauf, David, Antoine Lutz, Diego Cosmelli, Jean-Philippe Lachaux and Michel Le Van Quyen, 2003. "From Autopoiesis To Neurophenomenology: Francisco Varela's Exploration of the Biophysics of Being." Biological Research 36(1): 27-65.

Runehov, Anne L C., 2007 Sacred or Neural?: The Potential of Neuroscience To Explain Religious Experience. Göttingen, Germany: Vandenhoeck & Ruprecht.

Rush, John (ed.), 2013. Entheogens and the Development of Culture: The Anthropology and Neurobiology of Ecstatic Experience. Berkeley, CA: North Atlantic Books.

Ryback, David, 1988. Dreams That Came True: Their Psychic and Transforming Powers. New York: Bantam Doubleday.

Sade, Donald S., 2012. "Natural History of the Self." In Bones, Genetics, and Behavior of Rhesus Macaques: Developments in Primatology: Progress and Prospects, ed. by Q. Wang. New York: Springer, pp. 263-297.

Sade, Donald S., M. Altmann, J. Loy, G. Hausfater and J. A. Breuggeman, 1988. "Sociometrics of Macaca mulatta: ii. Decoupling Centrality and Dominance in Rhesus Monkey Social Networks." American Journal of Physical Anthropology 77: 409-425.

Sadler, William A., 1969. Existence and Love: A New Approach in Existential Phenomenology. New York: Scribner's.

Salzberg, Sharon, 1995. Loving-Kindness: The Revolutionary Art of Happiness. Boston: Shambhala.

Sanes, Dan H., Thomas A. Reh, and William A. Harris, 2011. Development of the Nervous System. New York: Academic Press.

Saniotis, Arthur, 2001. "Mystical Styles of Expression among North Indian Faqir: Nara as a Manifestation of Hukm." The Australian Journal of Anthropology 12(3): 355-366.

Saniotis, Arthur, 2004. "Tales of Mastery: Spirit Familiar in Sufis' Religious Imagination." Ethos 32(3): 397-411.

Saniotis, Arthur, 2008. "Enchanted Landscapes: Sensuous Awareness as Mystical Practice Among Sufis in North India." The Australian Journal of Anthropology 19(1): 17-26.

Saniotis, Arthur, 2009. "Evolving Brain: Neuroanthropology, Emergence, and Cognitive Frontiers." NeuroQuantology 7(3): 482-490.

Saniotis, Arthur, 2012. "Attaining the Mystical Body: Indian Sufi Ascetic Practices." The Australian Journal of Anthropology 23(1): 65-83.

Saniotis, Arthur, and Maciej Henneberg, 2011. "Future Evolution of the Human Brain." Journal of Futures Studies 16(1): 1-18.

Sannella, Lee, 1987. The Kundalini Experience: Psychosis or Transcendence? Lower Lake, CA: Integral Publishing.

Saradananda, Swami, 1978. Sri Ramakrishna the Great Master, Vols. I and II. Madras, Sri Ramakrishna Math.

Sato, W. and S. Aoki, 2006. "Right Hemisphere Dominance in Processing Unconscious Emotion." Brain and Cognition 62: 261-266.

Saxe, R., J. M. Moran, J. Scholz and J. Gabrieli, 2006. "Overlapping and Non-Overlapping Brain Regions for Theory of Mind and Self Reflection in Individual Subjects." Social Cognitive and Affective Neuroscience 1(3): 229-234.

Scaer, Robert, 2014. The Body Bears the Burden: Trauma, Dissociation, and Disease (third edition). New York: Routledge.

Scharfstein, B. A., 1973). Mystical Experience. New York: Bobbs-Merrill.

Scherer, Klaus R. and Harald G. Wallbott, 1994. "Evidence for Universality and Cultural Variation of Differential Emotion Response Patterning." Journal of Personality and Social Psychology 66(2): 310-328.

Schimmel, Annemarie, 1975. Mystical Dimensions of Islam. University of North Carolina Press.

Schmitt, R., 1959. "Husserl's Transcendental-Phenomenological Reduction." Philosophy and Phenomenological Research 20(2): 238-245

Schmitz, T. W., T. N. Kawahara-Baccus and S. C. Johnson, 2004. "Metacognitive Evaluation, Self-Relevance, and the Right Prefrontal Cortex." Neuroimage 22(2): 941-947.

Schneider, Susan and Max Velmans, 2008. "Introduction." In The Blackwell Companion to Consciousness, ed. By Max Velmans and Susan Schneider. New York: Wiley, pp. 1-6.

Schoenemann, P. T., M. J. Sheehan and L. D. Glotzer, 2005. "Prefrontal White Matter Volume Is Disproportionately Larger in Humans Than in Other Primates." Nature Neuroscience 8: 242-252.

Schore, Allan N., 2000. "Attachment and the Regulation of the Right Brain." Attachment and Human Development 2: 23-47.

Schore, Allan N., 2003. Affect Regulation and the Repair of the Self. New York: W.W. Norton.

Schore, Allan N., 2008. "Paradigm shift: The Right Brain and the Relational Unconscious." Psychologist-Psychoanalyst 28: 20-26.

Schultes, R. E., A. Hofmann and C. Rätsch, 1998. Plants of the Gods: Their Sacred, Healing, and Hallucinogenic Powers. Rochester, VT: Healing Arts.

Schurr, Theodore G., 1995. "Aboriginal Siberian use of Amanita muscaria in Shamanistic Practices: Neuropharmacological Effects of Fungal Alkaloids Ingested During Trance Induction, and the Cultural Patterning of Visionary Experience." Curare 18(1): 31-65.

Schussler, G. C. and J. Orlando, 1978. "Fasting Decreases Triiodothyronine Receptor Capacity." Science 199: 686 688.

Schwab, Ivan R., 2012. Evolution's Witness: How Eyes Evolved. Oxford: Oxford University Press.

Schwartz, Carl E., Christopher I. Wright, Lisa M. Shin, Jerome Kagan, and Scott L. Rauch, 2003. "Inhibited and Uninhibited Infants 'Grown Up': Adult Amygdalar Response to Novelty." Science 300(5627): 1952-1953.

Schwarz, M. T., 1997. Molding in the Image of Changing Woman: Navajo Views on the Human Body and Personhood. Tucson: University of Arizona Press.

Schwartz-Salant, N., 1998. The Mystery of Human Relationship: Alchemy and the Transformation of the Self. London: Routledge.

Scudder, Vida Dutton, 1912. Socialism and Character. New York: Houghton Mifflin.

Searle, John R., 1993. "The Problem of Consciousness." in Experimental and Theoretical Studies of Consciousness, ed. by G. R. Brock and J. Marsh. Chichester: John Wiley & Sons, pp. 61–80.

Sears, Sharon and Sue Kraus, 2009. "I Think Therefore I Om: Cognitive Distortions and Coping Style as Mediators for the Effects of Mindfulness Meditation on Anxiety, Positive and Negative Affect, and Hope." Journal of Clinical Psychology 65(6): 561-573.

Seeger, A., 1981. Nature and Society in Central Brazil: The Suyà Indians of Mato Grosso. Cambridge: Harvard University Press.

Segarra-Echebarría, Rafael, Marta Crego-Meda, Aníbal Arrillaga-Trueba and Margarita Sáenz-Herrero, 2015. "Paraphilic Disorders: Sexual Sadist and Masochistic Disorders."

In Psychopathology in Women, ed. by Margarita Sáenz-Herrero. New York:Springer International Publishing, pp. 237-265.

Seligman, Rebecca, 2005. "From Affliction to Affirmation: Narrative Transformation and the Therapeutics of Candomblé Mediumship." Transcultural Psychiatry 42(2): 272-294.

Seligman, Rebecca, 2010. "The Unmaking and Making of Self: Embodied Suffering and Mind–Body Healing in Brazilian Candomblé." Ethos 38(3): 297-320.

Seligman, Rebecca, 2014. Possessing Spirits and Healing Selves: Embodiment and Transformation in an Afro-Brazilian Religion. New York: Palgrave Macmillan.

Selye, Hans, 1956. The Stress of Life. New York: McGraw-Hill.

Selye, Hans, 1974. Stress Without Distress. Toronto: McClelland and Stewart.

Seth, Anil, 2017. "How Your Brain Hallucinates Your Conscious Reality." TED Talk, https://www.ted.com/talks/anil_seth_how_your_brain_hallucinates_your_conscious_reality

Seth, Anil K., Bernard J. Baars and David B. Edelman, 2005. "Criteria for Consciousness in Humans and Other Mammals." Consciousness and Cognition 14(1): 119-139.

Seth, Anil K., Keisuke Suzuki and Hugo D. Critchley, 2011. "An Interoceptive Predictive Coding Model of Conscious Presence." Frontiers in Psychology 2. https://doi.org/10.3389/fpsyg.2011.00395 (accessed July 24, 2017)

Shankman, Richard, 2008. The Experience of Samadhi: An In-Depth Exploration of Buddhist Meditation. Boulder: Shambhala Publications.

Shapiro, D. H., 1984. "Overview: Clinical and Physiological Comparison of Meditation with Other Self-Control Strategies. In Meditation: Classic And Contemporary Perspectives, ed. by D. H. Shapiro and R. N. Walsh. Piscataway, NJ: Aldine Transaction, pp. 5-12.

Shapiro, D. H. and R. N. Walsh, eds., 1984. Meditation: Classic and Contemporary Perspectives. New York: Aldine.

Shapiro, S. L. et al., 2006. "Mechanisms of Mindfulness." Journal of Clinical Psychology 62(3): 373-386.

Sharp, Patricia E., 2014. "Meditation-Induced Bliss Viewed as Release from Conditioned Neural (Thought) Patterns That Block Reward Signals in the Brain Pleasure Center." Religion, Brain & Behavior 4(3): 202-229.

Shear, J., 2006. The Experience of Meditation: Experts Introduce the Major Traditions. St. Paul, MN: Paragon.

Sheikh, A. A. and Katharina S. Sheikh, 2003. "Death Imagery: Confronting Death Brings Us to the Threshold of Life." Healing Images: The Role of Imagination in Health, ed. by A. A. Sheikh. New York: Baywood, pp. 471-488.

Shen, Yang-Qian, Hui-Xia Zhou, Xiao Chen, Francisco Xavier Castellanos and Chao-Gan Yan, 2020. "Meditation Effect in Changing Functional Integrations Across Large-Scale Brain Networks: Preliminary Evidence From a Meta-Analysis of Seed-Based Functional Connectivity." Journal of Pacific Rim Psychology 14: 1-14.

Shields, D., 1978. "A Cross-Cultural Study of Out-Of-The-Body Experiences, Waking, and Sleeping." Journal of the Society for Psychical Research 49: 697-741.

Shirley, Robert W. and A. Kimball Romney, 1962. "Love Magic and Socialization Anxiety: A Cross-Cultural Study." American Anthropologist 64(5): 1028-1031.

Shirokogoroff, Sergei Mikhailovich, 1935. Psychomental Complex of the Tungus. London: Routledge and Kegan Paul.

Shobitha, M. and J. L. Agarwal, 2013. "Electroencephalographic Pattern and Galvanic Skin Resistance Levels During Short Duration of "AUM" Mantra Chanting." International Journal of Physiology 1(1): 68.

Shore, Bradd, 1988. Culture in Mind: Cognition, Culture, and the Problem of Meaning. Oxford: Oxford University Press.

Short, Baron et al., 2010. "Regional Brain Activation during Meditation Shows Time and Practice Effects: An Exploratory FMRI Study." Evidence-Based Complementary and Alternative Medicine 7(1): 121-127.

Sibatani, Atuhiro, 1987. "On Structuralist Biology." Biology Forum 80(4): 558-564.

Simmer-Brown, Judith and Fran Grace (eds), 2011. Meditation and the Classroom: Contemplative Pedagogy for Religious Studies. Albany, NY: SUNY Press, 2011.

Singer, June, 1994. Boundaries of the Soul: The Practice of Jung's Psychology. New York, NY: Anchor.

Singer, Margaret and Janja Lalich, 1995. Cults in Our Midst: The Hidden Menace in Our Everyday Lives. San Francisco: Jossey-Bass.

Singer, Tania et al., 2004. "Empathy for Pain Involves the Affective but Not Sensory Components of Pain." Science 303(5661): 1157-1162.

Singer, Tania and Olga M. Klimecki, 2014. "Empathy and Compassion." Current Biology 24(18): R875-R878.

Singh, Yogesh and Anjana Talwar, 2012. "Immediate and Long-Term Effects of Meditation on Acute Stress Reactivity, Cognitive Functions, and Intelligence." Alternative Therapies in Health and Medicine 18(6): 46-53.

Smith, Pierre, 1984. Le 'Mystère' et ses masques chez les Bedik. L'Homme 24(3–4): 5–33.

Smith, R., 2010. Stepping Out of Self-Deception: The Buddha's Liberating Teaching of No-Self. Boston: Shambhala.

Snyder, T. J. and J. Gackenback, 1991. "Vestibular Involvement in the Neurocognition of Lucid Dreaming." In Dream Images: A Call to Mental Arms, ed. by J. Gackenbach and A. A. Sheikh. Amityville, NY: Baywood, pp. 55-78.

Snyder, S. and T. Rasumussen, 2009. Practicing the Jhānas: Traditional Concentration Meditation as Presented by the Venerable Pa Auk Sayadaw. Boulder, CO: Shambhala.

Snyder, Timothy, 2017. On Tyranny: Twenty Lessons from the Twentieth Century. New York: Tim Duggan Books.

Solé-Leris, A., 1986. Tranquility and Insight: An Introduction to the Oldest Form of Buddhist Meditation. Boulder, CO: Shambhala.

Sood, Amit and David T. Jones, 2013. "On Mind Wandering, Attention, Brain Networks, and Meditation." EXPLORE: The Journal of Science and Healing 9(3): 136-141.

Spiro, Melvin E., 1993. "Is the Western Conception of the Self 'Peculiar' within the Context of the World Cultures?" Ethos 21(2): 107-153.

Sporns, Olaf, 2010. Networks of the Brain. Cambridge, MA: MIT Press.

Srinivasan, Mandyam V., 2010. "Honey Bees as a Model for Vision, Perception, and Cognition." Annual Review of Entomology 55: 267-284.

Stace, W. T., 1960. Mysticism and Philosophy. New York: Lippincott.

Staniford, Philip S., 1977. "Inside Out: Anthropological." Phoenix: New Directions in the Study of Man 1(1): 36-46.

Stapp, Henry, 2009. Mind, Matter and Quantum Physics (3rd edition). New York: Springer.

Steadman, Lyle B. and Craig T. Palmer, 1994. "Visiting Dead Ancestors: Shamans as Interpreters of Religious Traditions." Zygon 29(2): 173-189.

Stein, Alexandra 2016. Terror, Love and Brainwashing: Attachment in Cults and Totalitarian Systems. New York: Routledge.

Sternberg, Esther M., 2002. "Walter B. Cannon and "'Voodoo Death'": A Perspective from 60 Years On." American Journal of Public Health 92(10): 1564-1566.

Steinberg, W., 1993. Masculinity: Identity, Conflict, and Transformation. Boston: Shambhala.

Stevens. Anthony, 1982. Archetypes: A Natural History of the Self. New York: William Morrow.

Stiles, J. et al., 2012. Neural Plasticity and Cognitive Development: Insights from Children with Perinatal Brain Injury. Oxford, UK: Oxford University Press.

Stoller, P., 1989. The Taste of Ethnographic Things: The Senses in Anthropology. Philadelphia, PA: University of Pennsylvania Press.

Strassman, Rick, 2000. DMT: The Spirit Molecule: A Doctor's Revolutionary Research into the Biology of Near-Death and Mystical Experiences. New York: Simon and Schuster.

Suzuki, Daisetz T., 1959. Zen and Japanese Culture. New York: MJF Books.

Suzuki, Shunryū, 1970. Zen Mind, Beginner's Mind. New York: Weatherhill.

Swan, Wendy, 2007. C. G. Jung and Active Imagination: A Case Study of Tina Keller. Saarbrücken, Germany: VDM Verlag Dr. Müller.

Swain, James E. et al., 2012. "Parenting and Beyond: Common Neurocircuits Underlying Parental and Altruistic Caregiving." Parenting 12(2-3): 115-123.

Singer, Margaret Thaler and Janja Lalich, 1995. Cults in Our Midst. New York: Jossey-Bass.

Singer, Tania et al., 2004. "Empathy for Pain Involves the Affective but Not Sensory Components of Pain." Science 303(5661): 1157-1162.

Smith, R., 2010. Stepping Out of Self-Deception: The Buddha's Liberating Teaching of No-Self. Boston: Shambhala.

Sökefeld, M., 1999. "Debating Self, Identity, and Culture in Anthropology." Current Anthropology 40(4): 417-448.

Spiro, M. E., 1993. "Is the Western Conception of the Self 'Peculiar' within the Context of the World Cultures?" Ethos 21(2): 107-153.

Stevens, A., 1982. Archetypes: A Natural History of the Self. New York: William Morrow.

Stewart, Fiona Anne, Alexander Kenneth Piel and Robert C. O'Malley, 2012. "Responses of Chimpanzees to a Recently Dead Community Member at Gombe National Park, Tanzania." American Journal of Primatology 74:1–7.

Stickgold, Robert and Erin J. Wamsley, 2011. "Why We Dream." In Principles and Practice of Sleep Medicine, 4th edition, ed. by M. H. Kryger, T. Roth and W.C. Dement. Philadelphia: Elsevier, pp. 628-637.

Stierli, J., 1957. Heart and Savior. Freiberg, Germany: Herder and Herder.

St John, Graham, 2018. "The Breakthrough Experience: DMT Hyperspace and its Liminal Aesthetics." Anthropology of Consciousness 29(1): 57-76.

Stromberg, P. G., 1985. "The Impression Point: Synthesis of Symbol and Self." Ethos 13(1): 56-74.

Stuss, D. T., 1991. "Disturbance of Self-Awareness after Frontal System Damage." In Awareness of Deficit after Brain Injury: Clinical and Theoretical Issues, ed. by G. P. Prigatano and D. L. Schacter. Oxford: Oxford University Press, pp. 63-83.

Srinivasan, M.V., 2010. "Honey Bees as a Model for Vision, Perception, and Cognition." Annual Review of Entomology 55: 267-284.

Sumegi, Angela, 2008. Dreamworlds of Shamanism and Tibetan Buddhism. Albany: State University of New York Press.

Szpunar, K. K., J. M. Watson and K. B. McDermott, 2007. Neural Substrates of Envisioning the Future. Proceedings of the National Academy of Sciences (USA) 104: 642–647.

Takahashi, Melanie, 2018. "The Business of Meditation and the Expectation of 'Results': Kundalini Rising in a Culture of Instant Gratification." In Meditation: Practices, Techniques and Health Benefits, Lucia Brewer, ed. Pp 79-104. New York: Nova Science Publishers.

Takahashi, I. et al., 2005. "Changes in EEG and Autonomic Nervous System Activity during Meditation and Their Association with Personality Traits." International Journal of Psychophysiology 55: 199-207.

Takahashi, Melanie and T. Olaveson, 2003. "Music, Dance and Raving Bodies: Raving as Spirituality in the Central Canadian Rave Scene." Journal of Ritual Studies,17(2): 72-96.

Tang, Yi-Yuan, Britta K. Hölzel and Michael I. Posner, 2015. "The Neuroscience of Mindfulness Meditation." Nature Reviews. Neuroscience 16(4): 213–225.

Tart, Charles T., 1972. "States of Consciousness and State-Specific Sciences." Science 176: 1203-210.

Tart, Charles T., 1998. "Investigating Altered States of Consciousness on Their Own Terms: A Proposal for the Creation of State-Specific Sciences. Ciencia e Cultura, Journal of the Brazilian Association for the Advancement of Science 50(2/3): 103-116.

Tart, Charles T., 2001. Mind Science: Meditation Training for Practical People. Novato, CA: Wisdom.

Taylor, Eugene, 1994. Radical Empiricism and the Conduct of Research. In New Metaphysical Foundations of Modern Science, ed. By E. A. Burtt. Sausalito, CA: Institute of Noetic Sciences.

Taylor, Eugene, 1996. William James on Consciousness Beyond the Margin. Princeton, NJ: Princeton University Press.

Taylor, Eugene, 1999. "Introduction." In The Physical and Psychological Effects of Meditation: A Review of Contemporary Research with a Comprehensive Bibliography 1931-1996, ed. by M. Murphy and S. Donovan. Sausalito, CA: Institute of Noetic Sciences, pp. 1-32.

Taylor, Véronique A. et al., 2012. "Impact of Meditation Training on the Default Mode Network during a Restful State." Social Cognitive and Affective Neuroscience 8(1): 4-14.

Tebb, William and Edward Perry Vollum, 1905. Premature Burial and How It May Be Prevented: With Special Reference to Trance, Catalepsy, and Other Forms of Suspended Animation. London: Swan, Sonnenschein.

Tedlock, Barbara, 1999. "Sharing and Interpreting Dreams in Amerindian Nations." In Dream Cultures: Explorations in the Comparative History of Dreaming, ed. by David Shulman and Guy G. Stroumsa. New York: Oxford University Press, pp. 87-103.

Tedlock, Dennis, 1999. "Poetry and Ethnography: A Dialogical Approach." Anthropology and Humanism 24(2): 155-167.

Teleki, G., 1973. "Group Response to the Accidental Death of a Chimpanzee in Gombe National Park, Tanzania. " Folia Primatologica 20(2-3): 81-94.

Tellegen, Auke et al., 1988. Personality Similarity in Twins Reared Apart and Together. Journal of Personality and Social Psychology 54: 1031–1039.

Tellegen, Auke and Gilbert Atkinson, 1974. "Openness to Absorbing and Self-Altering Experiences ("Absorption"), A Trait Related To Hypnotic Susceptibility." Journal of Abnormal Psychology 83, no. 3 (1974): 268.

TenHouten, Warren D., 1993. "Dual Symbolic Classification, the Primary Emotions, and Mandala Symbolism." Anthropology of Consciousness 4(4): 10-16.

TenHouten, Warren D., 2005. Time and Society. Albany, NY: State University of New York Press.

Teper, Rimma and Michael Inzlicht, 2012. "Meditation, Mindfulness and Executive Control: The Importance of Emotional Acceptance and Brain-Based Performance Monitoring." Social Cognitive and Affective Neuroscience 8(1): 85-92.

Thanissaro, B., 1997. "One Tool Among Many: The Place of Vipassana in Buddhist Practice." From The Access to Insight Website. Retrieved on 21 March 2014 from: http://www.accesstoinsight.org/lib/authors/thanissaro/onetool.html.

Thanissaro, B., 1999. "No-Self or Not-Self?" In Noble Strategy: Essays on the Buddhist Path, ed. by B. Thanissaro. Valley Center, CA: Dhammayut Order, pp. 71-74.

Thanissaro, B., 2004. "Alagaddupama Sutta: The Water-Snake Simile." From the Access to Insight Website. Retrieved on 21 March 2014 from: http://www.accesstoinsight.org/tipitaka/mn/mn.022.than.html.

Thanissaro, B., 2012a. "Into the Stream: A Study Guide on the First Stage of Awakening (Part 1: The Way to Stream-Entry). From The Access to Insight Website. Retrieved on 21 March 2014 from: http://www.accesstoinsight.org/lib/study/into_the_stream.html.

Thanissaro B., 2012b. Into the Stream: A Study Guide on the First Stage of Awakening (Part 2: Stream-Entry and After). From The Access to Insight Website. Retrieved on 21 March 2014 from: http://www.accesstoinsight.org/lib/study/into_the_stream.html.

Thoman, E. B., 1979. Origins of the Infant's Social Responsiveness. New York: Wiley.

Thomas, K., 2005. Crow Is My Boss: The Oral Life History of a Tanacross Athabaskan Elder. Tulsa, OK: University of Oklahoma Press.

Thomas, William Isaac and Dorothy Swaine Thomas, 1928. "The Methodology of Behavior Study." In The Child in America: Behavior Problems and Programs, ed. by William I. Thomas and Dorothy S. Thomas. New York: Knopf, pp. 553-576.

Thompson, Evan, Antoine Lutz and Diego Cosmelli, 2005. "Neurophenomenology: An Introduction for Neurophilosophers." In Cognition and the Brain: The Philosophy and Neuroscience Movement, ed. by A. Brook and K. Akins. Cambridge: Cambridge University Press, pp. 40–97.

Thompson, Evan, Adrian Palacios and Francisco J. Varela, 1992. "Ways of Coloring: Comparative Color Vision as a Case Study for Cognitive Science." Behavioral and Brain Sciences 15(1): 56-74.

Thompson, Evan and Francisco J. Varela, 2001. "Radical Embodiment: Neural Dynamics and Consciousness." Trends in Cognitive Sciences 5(10): 418-425.

Throop, C. Jason, 2000. "Shifting from a Constructivist to an Experiential Approach to the Anthropology of Self and Emotion." Journal of Consciousness Studies 7(3): 27-52.

Throop, C. Jason, 2002. "Experience, Coherence, and Culture: The Significance of Dilthey's Descriptive Psychology for the Anthropology of Consciousness." Anthropology of Consciousness 13: 2-26.

Throop, C. Jason, 2003. "On Crafting a Cultural Mind: A Comparative Assessment of Some Recent Theories of 'Internalization' in Psychological Anthropology." Transcultural Psychiatry 40(1): 109-139.

Throop, C. Jason, 2010. Suffering and Sentiment: Exploring the Vicissitudes of Experience and Pain in Yap. Berkeley, CA: University of California Press.

Throop, C. Jason and Charles D. Laughlin, 2007. "Anthropology of Consciousness." In Cambridge Handbook of Consciousness, ed. by P. D. Zelazo, M. Moscovitch and E. Thompson. New York: Cambridge University Press, pp. 631-669.

Throop, C. Jason and Charles D. Laughlin, 2002. "Ritual, Collective Effervescence and the Categories: Toward a Neo Durkheimian Model of the Nature of Human Consciousness, Feeling and Understanding." Journal of Ritual Studies 16(1): 40 63.

Thrush, D. C., 1973. "Congenital Insensitivity to Pain." Brain 96(2): 369-386.

Thurman, Robert (trans.), 1994. The Tibetan Book of the Dead. London: Aquarian Press.

Tiberia, Vincenza A. and Charles D. Laughlin, 2016. "Dream Incubation: The Roles of Instinct and Archetype in Ritual." Journal of Human Sciences (Kuwait) 28: 458-486.

Tickell, G., 1869. The Life of Blessed Margaret Mary With Some Account of the Devotion to the Sacred Heart. London: Burns, Oates and Co.

Tillich, Paul, 1952. The Courage To Be. New Haven: Yale University Press.

Tomás-Sábado, Joaquín, Joaquín T. Limonero and Ahmed M. Abdel-Khalek, 2007. "Spanish Adaptation of the Collett-Lester Fear of Death Scale." Death Studies 31: 249–260.

Tomer, Raju, Alexandru S. Denes, Kristin Tessmar-Raible and Detlev Arendt, 2010. "Profiling by Image Registration Reveals Common Origin of Annelid Mushroom Bodies and Vertebrate Pallium." Cell 142(5): 800-809.

Tononi, G. and G. M. Edelman, 1998. "Consciousness and Complexity." Science 282: 1846–1851.

Tooby, J. and L. Cosmides, 1995. "Mapping the Evolved Functional Organization of Mind and Brain." In The Cognitive Neurosciences, ed. by M. S. Gazzaniga. Cambridge, MA: MIT Press.

Townsend, J. B., 2004. "Core Shamanism and Neo-Shamanism." In Shamanism: An Encyclopedia of World Beliefs, Practices, and Culture, ed. by M. N. Walter and E. J. Neumann Fridman. Santa Barbara, ABC-Clio, pp. 49-57.

Trakhtenberg, Ephraim C., 2008. "The Effects of Guided Imagery on the Immune System: A Critical Review." International Journal of Neuroscience 118(6): 839-855.

Trevarthen, C., 1995. "The Child's Need to Learn a Culture. Children and Society 9: 5–19.

Trevathan, W. R., 1987. Human Birth: An Evolutionary Perspective. New York: Aldine de Gruyter.

Trungpa, Chögyam, 2002. Cutting Through Spiritual Materialism. Boulder, CO: Shambhala Publications.

Trungpa, Chogyam and Francesca Fremantle, 2000. The Tibetan Book of The Dead: The Great Liberation Through Hearing in the Bardo. Boulder, CO: Shambhala Publications.

Tulving, Endel, 2002. "Chronesthesia: Conscious awareness of subjective time." In Principles of frontal lobe function, Donald T. Stuss and Robert T. Knight (Eds.). New York: Oxford University Press, pp. 311-325.

Turner, Edith, 1996. The Hands Feel It: Healing and Spirit Presence among a Northern Alaskan People. DeCalb, IL: Northern Illinois University Press.

Turner, Edith, 2011. Experiencing Ritual: A New Interpretation of African Healing. Philadelphia: University of Pennsylvania Press.

Turner, Victor, 1967. The Forest of Symbols. Ithaca: Cornell University Press.

Turner, Victor. 1969. The Ritual Process: Structure and Anti-Structure. Chicago: Aldine.

Turner, V., 1979. Process, Performance and Pilgrimage. New Delhi: Concept Publishing House.

Turner, Victor, 1985. On the Edge of the Bush: Anthropology as Experience. Tucson, AZ: University of Arizona Press.

Turner, Victor, 1992. Blazing the Trail: Way Marks in the Exploration of Symbols. Tucson, AZ: University of Arizona Press.

Turner, Victor and E. M. Bruner, 1986. The Anthropology of Experience. Urbana, Ill: University of Illinois Press.

Tuzin, Donald F., 1975. "The Breath of a Ghost: Dreams and the Fear of the Dead." Ethos 3:555-578.

Ucho, P. J., 1977. Form in Indigenous Art: Schematization in the Art of Aboriginal Australia and Prehistoric Europe. Canberra, Australia: Australian Institute of Aboriginal Studies.

Ucho, P. J. and A. Rosenfeld, 1967. Paleolithic Cave Art. London: Weidenfeld.

Uddin, L. Q. et al., 2005. "Self-Face Recognition Activates a Frontoparietal 'Mirror' Network in the Right Hemisphere: An Event-Related fMRI Study." Neuroimage 25(3): 926-935.

Ulanov, A. and B. Ulanov, 1994. Transforming Sexuality: The Archetypal World of Anima and Animus. Boston: Shambhala.

Ulrich, Martin, Johannes Keller and Georg Grön. 2016. "Neural Signatures of Experimentally Induced Flow Experiences Identified in a Typical fMRI Block Design with BOLD Imaging." Social Cognitive and Affective Neuroscience 11(3): 496-507.

Underhill, E., 1955. Mysticism: A Study in the Nature and Development of Man's Spiritual Consciousness. New York: Meridian.

Vaitl, Dieter, Niels Birbaumer, John Gruzelier, Graham A. Jamieson, Boris Kotchoubey, Andrea Kübler, Ute Strehl et al., 2013. "Psychobiology of Altered States of Consciousness." Psychological Bulletin 131(1): 98–127.

Valantasis, Richard, 2008. The Making of the Self: Ancient and Modern Asceticism. Cambridge: James Clarke.

Vallely, Anne, 2002. Guardians of the Transcendent: An Ethnography of a Jain Ascetic Community. Toronto: University of Toronto Press.

Valli, Katja and Antti Revonsuo, 2007. "Evolutionary Psychological Approaches to Dream Content." in Deirdre Barrett and Patrick McNamara (eds), Cultural and Theoretical Perspectives, Volume 3 of The New Science of Dreaming. Westport CT: Praeger, pp. 95-116.

Van de Port, Mattijs, 2005. "Circling Around the Really Real: Spirit Possession Ceremonies and the Search for Authenticity in Bahian Candomblé." Ethos 33(2): 149-179.

Van Gennep, A. L., 1960 [1909]. The Rite of Passage. Chicago: University of Chicago Press.

Van Tonder, Gert J., Michael J. Lyons and Yoshimichi Ejima, 2002. "Perception Psychology: Visual Structure of a Japanese Zen Garden." Nature 419 (6905): 359–360.

Van Wolputte, S., 2004. "Hang on to Your Self: Of Bodies, Embodiment, and Selves." Annual Review of Anthropology, pp. 251-269.

Varela, Francisco J., 1979. Principles of Biological Autonomy. New York: North Holland.

Varela, Francisco J., 1996. Neurophenomenology: A Methodological Remedy for the Hard Problem. Journal of Consciousness Studies 3: 330-49.

Varela, Francisco J., 1999. "Present-Time Consciousness." Journal of Consciousness Studies 6(2-3): 111-140.

Varela, F. J. and J. Shear, 1999. The View from Within: First-Person Approaches to the Study of Consciousness. Bowling Green, OH: Imprint Academic.

Varela, Francisco J., Evan Thompson and Eleanor Rosch, 1991. The Embodied Mind: Cognitive Science and Human Experience. Cambridge, MA: MIT Press.

Vásquez, Manuel, 2011. "Expanding the Conversation on Emplaced Religion." In More Than Belief: A Materialist Theory of Religion, ed. by Manuel A. Vasquez. New York: Oxford University Press, pp. 261-290.

Venkatesh, S., T. R. Raju, Yogini Shivani, G. Tompkins and B. L. Meti, 1997. "A Study of Structure of Phenomenology of Consciousness in Meditative and Non-Meditative States." Indian Journal of Physiology and Pharmacology 41: 149-153.

Verman, Mark, 1996. The History and Varieties of Jewish Meditation. Northvale, NJ: J. Aronson.

Verman, Mark and D. H. Shapiro, 1996. "Jewish Medication: Context and Content, Historical Background, Types, and Purpose." In Comparative and Psychological Study of Meditation, ed. by Y. Haruki, Y. Ishii and M. Suzuki. The Netherlands: Eburon, pp. 95-120.

Verny, Thomas R., 1981. The Secret Life of the Unborn Child. New York: Summit Books.

Verny, Thomas R. and P. Weintraub, 2002. Pre-Parenting: Nurture Your Child from Conception. New York: Simon and Schuster.

Vestergaard-Poulsen, P. et al., 2009. "Long-Term Meditation Is Associated with Increased Gray Matter Density in the Brain Stem." Neuroreport 20(2): 170-174.

Vidmar, John, 2014. Catholic Church Through the Ages: A History (Second Edition). New York: Paulist Press.

Vitebsky, Piers, 1995. The Shaman: Voyages of the Soul from the Arctic to the Amazon (London: Duncan Baird; Boston: Little Brown 1995; reprinted in 2001 as 'Shamanism' by University of Oklahoma Press.

Vivekananda, Swami, 1956. Raja-Yoga (1982 edition). New York: Ramakrishna-Vivekananda Center.

Voget, Fred W., 1984. The Shoshoni-Crow Sun Dance. Norman, OK: University of Oklahoma Press.

von Franz, Marie-Louise, 1980. Alchemy: An introduction to the Symbolism and the Psychology. Toronto: Inner City Books.

von Franz, Marie-Louise, 1997[1979]. Alchemical Active Imagination (revised edition). Boston: Shambhala.

Wagner, R., 1967. The Curse of Souw: Principles of Daribi Clan Formation and Alliance. Chicago: University of Chicago Press.

Walker, Evan Harris, 1973. "Application of the Quantum Theory of Consciousness to the Problem of Psi Phenomena." in Research in Parapsychology, 1972: Abstracts and Papers from the Fifteenth Annual Convention of the Parapsychological Association, Edinburgh, Scotland, September 3 5, 1972, Ed. by W.G. Roll, R.L. Morris and J.D. Morris. Metuchen, NJ: Scarecrow Press. pp. 51 53.

Walker, Evan Harris, 1975. "Foundations of Paraphysical and Parapsychological Phenomena." in Laura Oteri (ed), Quantum Physics and Parapsychology. New York: Parapsychology Foundation, pp. 1-53.

Walker, J. R., 2012. The Sun Dance and Other Ceremonies of the Oglala Division of the Teton Dakota. Charleston, SC: Nabu Press.

Wallace, B. Allan, 2006. The Attention Revolution: Unlocking the Power of the Focused Mind. Somerville, MA: Wisdom Publications.

Wallace, B. Allan, 2007. Contemplative Science: Where Buddhism and Neuroscience Converge. New York: Columbia University Press.

Wallace, B. Allan, 2009. Mind in the Balance: Meditation in Science, Buddhism, and Christianity. New York: Columbia University Press.

Wallace, B. Allan, 2011. Meditations of a Buddhist Skeptic: A Manifesto for the Mind Sciences and Contemplative Practice, New York: Columbia University Press.

Wallace, Anthony F. C., 1966. Religion: An Anthropological View. New York: Random House.

Wallace, Anthony F. C., 1969. The Death and Rebirth of the Seneca. New York: Random House.

Wallace, Ron, 1993a. "Cognitive Mapping and Algorithmic Complexity: Is there a Role for Quantum Processes in the Evolution of Human Consciousness?" Behavioral and Brain Sciences 16(3): 614-615.

Wallace, Ron, 1993b. "The Algorithmic Animal: Complexity, Quantum Mechanics, and the Evolution of Consciousness." Social Neuroscience Bulletin 6(2): 25-26.

Walsh, Roger, 1990. The Spirit of Shamanism. New York: Tarcher.

Walsh, Roger, 1994. "The Making of a Shaman: Calling, Training, and Culmination." Journal of Humanistic Psychology 34(3): 7-30.

Walsh, Roger, 2007. The World of Shamanism: New Views of an Ancient Tradition. Woodbury, MN: Llewellyn.

Walsh, Roger and Shauna L. Shapiro, 2006. "The Meeting of Meditative Disciplines and Western Psychology: A Mutually Enriching Dialogue." American Psychologist 61(3): 227-239.

Wang, Danny J. J. et al., 2011. "Cerebral Blood Flow Changes Associated with Different Meditation Practices and Perceived Depth of Meditation." Psychiatry Research: Neuroimaging 191(1): 60-67.

Wang ch'ug Dorje, 1978. The Mahamudra: Eliminating the Darkness of Ignorance. Dharamsala, India: Library of Tibetan Works and Archives.

Ward, Benedicta, 1975. The Sayings of the Desert Fathers: The Alphabetical Collection, Part 1. London: A. R. Mowbray.

Ward, Colleen, 1984. "Thaipusam in Malaysia: A Psycho-Anthropological Analysis of Ritual Trance, Ceremonial Possession and Self-Mortification Practices." Ethos 12(4): 307-334.

Ware, Kallistos, 2000. The Inner Kingdom. Crestwood, NY: St Vladimir's Seminary Press.

Wasson, R. Gordon, Stella Kramrisch, Jonathan Ott and Carl A.P. Ruck, 1986. Persephone's Quest: Entheogens and the Origins of Religion. New Haven: Yale University Press.

Warrior, Valerie M., 2006. Roman Religion. Cambridge: Cambridge University Press.

Watson, Richard A., 2014. Solipsism: The Ultimate Empirical Theory of Human Existence. South Bend, IN: St. Augustine's Press.

Weiner, J. F., 2001. Tree Leaf Talk: A Heideggerian Anthropology. Oxford: Berg.

Weinberg, I., 2000. "The Prisoners of Despair: Right Hemisphere Deficiency and Suicide." Neuroscience and Biobehavioral Reviews 24(8): 799-815.

Weiskrantz, Lawrence (ed.), 1988. Thought Without Language. Oxford: Clarendon Press.

Wells, Martin John, 2013. Octopus: physiology and Behaviour of an Advanced Invertebrate. New York: Springer.

Werner, G., 2011. Consciousness Viewed in the Framework of Brain Phase Space Dynamics, Criticality, and the Renormalization Group. Quantitative Biology, (q-bio) eprint arXiv:1103.2366.

West, M. A., 1990. The Psychology of Meditation. Oxford, UK: Oxford University Press.

West, Melissa Gayle, 2011. Exploring the Labyrinth: A Guide for Healing and Spiritual Growth. Danvers, MA: Harmony.

Wexler, B. E., 2006. Brain and Culture: Neurobiology, Ideology, and Social Change. Cambridge, MA: The MIT Press.

Wheeler, M. A., D. T. Stuss and E. Tulving, 1997. "Toward a Theory of Episodic Memory: The Frontal Lobes and Autonoetic Consciousness." Psychological Bulletin 121(3): 331.

Whetstine, Leslie M., 2008. "The History of the Definition(s) of Death: From the 18th Century to the 20th Century." In David W. Crippen (Ed.), End-of-Life Communication in the ICU: A Global Perspective (pp. 65-78). New York: Springer.

Whitehead, Charles, 2004. "Everything I Believe Might Be a Delusion. Whoa! Tucson 2004: Ten years on, and are we any nearer to a Science of Consciousness?." Journal of Consciousness Studies 11(12): 68-88.

Whitehead, Charles, 2010a. "Cultural Distortions of Self- and Reality-Perception." Journal of Consciousness Studies 17, no. 7-1 (2010): 95-118.

Whitehead, Charles, 2010b. "The Culture Ready Brain." Social Cognitive and Affective Neuroscience 5(2-3): 168-179.

Whitehead, Charles, 2012. "Why the Behavioural Sciences Need the Concept of the Culture-Ready Brain." Anthropological Theory 12(1): 43-71.

Whitehead, Charles, 2016. "Health, Development, and the Culture-Ready Brain." The Oxford Handbook of Cultural Neuroscience. Oxford: Oxford University Press, p. 57.

Whiteman, Joseph Hilary Michael, 1961. The Mystical Life: An Outline of its Nature and Teachings from the Evidence of Direct Experience. London: Faber and Faber.

Whitley, D. S., 2004. "Archaeology of Shamanism. In M. N. Walter & E. J. Neumann Fridman (Eds.), Shamanism: An encyclopedia of world beliefs, practices, and culture (pp. 16-21). Santa Barbara, ABC-Clio.

Whittaker, E., 1992. "The Birth of the Anthropological Self and Its Career." Ethos 20(2): 191-219.

Wilber, Ken, 1996. The Atman Project: A Transpersonal View of Human Development. Wheaton, IL: Quest Books.

Wilber, Ken, 1998. The Essential Ken Wilber. Boulder, CO: Shambhala.

Wilber, Ken, 2005[1983]. A Sociable God: Toward a New Understanding of Religion. Boulder, CO: Shambhala.

Wilhelm, R., 1962. The Secret of the Golden Flower: A Chinese Book of Life. New York: Harcourt Brace Jovanovich.

Wilkinson, M., 2006. Coming into Mind: The Mind-Brain Relationship: A Jungian Clinical Perspective. New York: Routledge.

Williams, D., 2012. The Trickster Brain: Neuroscience, Evolution, and Narrative. Lanham, MD: Lexington.

Williams, J. Mark G. et al., 2014. "Mindfulness-Based Cognitive Therapy for Preventing Relapse in Recurrent Depression: A Randomized Dismantling Trial." Journal of Consulting and Clinical Psychology 82(2): 275-286.

Wilson, James Q., 1997. The Moral Sense (reprint edition). New York: Free Press.

Wilson, Timothy D., 2003. "Knowing When to Ask: Introspection and the Adaptive Unconscious." Journal of Consciousness Studies 10(9-10): 131-140.

Wilson, Timothy D., 2004. Strangers to Ourselves. Cambridge, MA: Harvard University Press.

Wimbush, Vincent L. and Richard Valantasis (eds.), 1998a. Asceticism. Oxford: Oxford University Press.

Wimbush, Vincent L. and Richard Valantasis, 1998b. "Introduction." In Asceticism, ed. by Vincent L. Wimbush and Richard Valantasis. Oxford: Oxford University Press, pp. xix-xxxiii.

Wink, P. and J. Scott, 2005. "Does Religiousness Buffer Against the Fear of Death and Dying in Late Adulthood? Findings from a Longitudinal Study." Journal of Gerontology 60B: 207-214.

Winkelman, Michael J., 1986. "Trance States: A Theoretical Model and Cross-Cultural Analysis." Ethos 14(2): 174-203.

Winkelman, Michael J., 1996. "Shamanism and Consciousness: Metaphorical, Political and Neurophenomenological Perspectives." Transcultural Psychiatric Research Review 33:69-80.

Winkelman, Michael J., 2004. "Shamanism as the Original Neurotheology." Zygon 39(1): 193-217.

Winkelman, Michael J., 2005. "Drug Tourism or Spiritual Healing? Ayahuasca Seekers in Amazonia." Journal of Psychoactive Drugs 37: 109-218.

Winkelman, M., 2013. "The Integrative Mode of Consciousness: Evolutionary Origins of Ecstasy." Ekstasen: Kontexte–Formen–Wirkungen, ed. by T. Passie, W. Belschner, and E. Petrow. Würzburg: Ergon-Verlag GmbH. Pp. 67-83.

Winkelman, Michael J., 2010. Shamanism: A Biopsychosocial Paradigm of Consciousness and Healing (second edition). Santa Barbara, CA: Praeger.

Winkelman, Michael J., 2013. "Altered Consciousness and Drugs in Human Evolution." In Entheogens and the Development of Culture: The Anthropology and Neurobiology of Ecstatic Experience, ed. by John Rush. Berkeley, CA: North Atlantic Books, pp. 23-50.

Winkelman, M., and J. R. Baker, 2015. Supernatural as Natural: A Biocultural Approach to Religion. London: Routledge.

Wittmann, Marc, 2011. "Moments in Time." Frontiers in Integrative Neuroscience 5.

Wittmann, Marc, 2015. "Modulations of the Experience of Self and Time." Consciousness and Cognition 38: 172-181.

Woodroffe, J., 1974. The Serpent Power (orig. pub. 1919). New York: Dover.

Wrangham, Richard W., W. C. McGrew, Frans B. M. Dewaal and Paul G. Heltne (Eds.), 1994. Chimpanzee Cultures. Cambridge, MA: Harvard University Press.

Wright, Peggy Ann, 1989. "The Nature of the Shamanic State of Consciousness: A Review." Journal of Psychoactive Drugs 21(1): 25-33.

Wright, Robin M., 1992. "Guardians of the Cosmos: Baniwa Shamans and Prophets, Part II." History of Religions 32(2): 126-145.

Wyman, L. C., 1936. "Navaho Diagnosticians." American Anthropologist 38: 236-246.

Wynne, A., 2009. The Origin of Buddhist Meditation. New York: Routledge.

Yellowtail, Thomas and Michael Oren Fitzgerald, 1994. Yellowtail, Crow Medicine Man and Sun Dance Chief: An Autobiography. Tulsa: University of Oklahoma Press.

Young, A. W. and Ned Block, 1996. "Consciousness." In Unsolved Mysteries of the Mind: Tutorial Essays in Cognition, ed. by V. Bruce. New York: Lawrence Erlbaum, pp. 149–179.

Young, David E., 1994. "Visitors in the Night: A Creative Energy Model of Spontaneous Visions." In Being Changed by Cross-Cultural Encounters, ed. by David E. Young and Jean-Guy Goulet. Peterborough, Ontario: Broadview Press, pp. 166-194.

Young, David E. and Jean-Guy Goulet (eds.), 1994. Being Changed by Cross-Cultural Encounters. Peterborough, Ontario: Broadview Press.

Young J. Z., 1971. The Anatomy of the Nervous System of Octopus vulgaris. Oxford: Claredon Press.

Young, Larry J. and Zuoxin Wang, 2004. "The Neurobiology of Pair Bonding". Nature Neuroscience 7(10): 1048–1054.

Yu, Xinjun et al., 2011. "Activation of the Anterior Prefrontal Cortex and Serotonergic System Is Associated with Improvements in Mood and EEG Changes Induced by Zen Meditation Practice in Novices." International Journal of Psychophysiology 80(2): 103-111.

Zaehner, Robert Charles, 1961. Mysticism, Sacred and Profane: An Inquiry into Some Varieties of Praeternatural Experience. Oxford: Oxford University Press.

Zagano, Phyllis (ed.), 2013. Mysticism and the Spiritual Quest: A Crosscultural Anthology. New York: Paulist Press.

Zeidan, Fadel et al., 2011. "Brain Mechanisms Supporting the Modulation of Pain by Mindfulness Meditation." Journal of Neuroscience 31(14): 5540-5548.

Zeller, A. C., 1991. "The Grieving Process in Non-Human Primates." In Coping With the Final Tragedy, ed. by David R. Counts and Dorothy A. Counts. Amityville, NY: Baywood Press, pp 5-6.

Zeranska-Kominek, Slawomira, 1998. "The Concept of Journey (Yol) in Turkmen Music Tradition." Ethnomusicology 42(2): 265-282.

Zeyrek, Eiliek Yuce and David Lester, 2008. "Cronbach Alpha Reliability and Concurrent Validity of the Collett-Lester Fear of Death Scale in a Turkish Sample." Psychological Reports 102: 706-708.

Zingrone, Nancy L., Carlos S. Alvarado and Natasha Agee, 2009. "Psychological Correlates of Aura Vision: Psychic Experiences, Dissociation, Absorption, and Synaesthesia-Like Experiences." Australian Journal of Clinical & Experimental Hypnosis 37(2): 131–168.

Zubek, John Peter, 1969. Sensory deprivation: Fifteen years of research. Appleton-Century-Crofts and Fleschner Publishing Company.

Zullo, Letizia and Binyamin Hochner, 2011. "A New Perspective on the Organization of an Invertebrate Brain." Communicative and Integrative Biology 4(1): 26-29.

Index

CPSIA information can be obtained
at www.ICGtesting.com
Printed in the USA
LVHW042111220723
753132LV00007B/105